New Product Development:
A Reader

New Product Development:
A Reader

Edited by
Susan Hart

The Dryden Press
Harcourt Brace & Company Limited
London   Fort Worth   New York   Orlando
Philadelphia   San Diego   Toronto   Sydney   Tokyo

The Dryden Press
24/28 Oval Road,
London NW1 7DX

A catalogue record for this book is available from the British Library
ISBN 0–03–099009–2

Typeset by Fakenham Photosetting
Printed in Great Britain at WBC Book Manufacturers, Bridgend, Mid Glamorgan

Contents

Introduction and Overview

Susan Hart

ORIGINS AND DEFINITIONS

The subject of new product development (NPD) is recognized as being vital to the economic success of companies and nations alike. New product development is the process by which companies survive in the long term. Innovation may refer to successful developments, to products and services or to the process of manufacturing and delivery. Analyses of industries abound, showing that industrial decline and success relate to the number of product innovations and/or process innovations. The world shipbuilding industry, for example, is characterized by a decline in the number of product innovations by British companies and a rise in product innovations by Japan, Germany, Norway and Sweden from the beginnings of the industry in the early nineteenth century to the latter half of the twentieth century. Concurrently, the British share of the market has declined from producing around 80% in 1890 to less than 4% in 1974, while by 1969 Japan's share had risen to 40% and by 1970 Germany's share had risen to 20% and Sweden's share had risen to 8% (Ughanwa and Baker, 1989). The trend continues with countries like Spain, Brazil, Korea and Portugal developing their shipbuilding industries by both product and process innovation. Patterns similar to this can be seen in other areas of manufacturing including machine tools, agricultural machinery, passenger cars, bicycles and motorcycles, to name but a few. A comprehensive study of five industries (mechanical engineering, electronics, motor vehicles, chemicals and textiles) in the UK, the US, Germany and Japan, found that since the early 1970s, British industries have invested less in the research, design and development of new products (Cox and Kriegbaum, 1989). For companies, and, by extension, national economies, innovation is fundamental to long-term survival, growth and success. Because of its importance and the elusive nature of its success, there is a plethora of research and conceptual articles written on the subject. The subject of innovation is a sub-topic of a great many disciplines as well as becoming increasingly recognized as a topic in its own right with the establishment of the *Journal of Product Innovation Management*. Figure 1 displays the range of disciplines which focus on new product development.

This is not to suggest that these disciplines are the only ones with a potential contribution to make in the process of developing new products. Indeed, as can be seen from Part

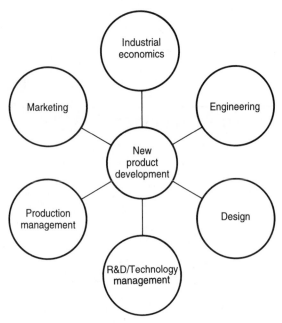

Figure 1. Disciplines in New Product Development.

VII, the number of 'functions' involved in developing new products is large. Functions, representing the disciplines shown in Figure 1, are joined by finance, purchasing and third parties such as customers and suppliers. Not surprisingly, the disciplines outlined in Figure 1 have each developed paradigms and vocabularies, which allow them to communicate issues of importance in new product development to their academic and industrial peers. While this is inevitable in the academic world, where individuals' work survives or perishes depending on peer review, it is also unfortunate on three counts. First, it engenders a certain amount of repetition of ideas and theories, as each discipline further researches NPD from within its own platforms and paradigms, without incorporating parallel (and in some cases identical) theories from other cognate areas. Second, terminology proliferates in a confusing manner, as the same *basic* concepts are given different names and titles in different disciplines. (Even more confusing is the tendency to 'invent' differences in concepts in trying to preserve the terminology prevailing in one's preferred approach.) Third, and perhaps most important, barriers to communication across disciplines are reinforced by dint of a lack of common language in a subject which deals with an endeavour which requires an inter-disciplinary approach if it is to succeed. Thus researchers, perhaps unwittingly, are contributing to the very 'tribalism' that their own research shows to be incongruous with successful new product development. This collection incorporates research from a variety of journals representing several of the necessary disciplines: engineering management, R&D management, marketing, management science, technology management and the more general 'business' journals. It should be said, however, that the spheres of R&D management, technology management and design, in particular, make up a rich source of knowledge to which the student of new product development should refer often.

The material chosen for this reader has been selected to provide a flavour of the range of subjects that fall within the broader remit of 'new product development'. Some, like Crawford (1980) (Reading 5), Cooper (1984) (Reading 6) or Utterback (1971) are milestones in NPD research, while others, although less commonly cited, are nonetheless important contributions to a rich and complex subject area. A majority of articles is based on empirical research, across a range of commercial settings, both consumer and industrial. Inevitably, some 'classic' studies, such as Project SAPPHO carried out at the Science Policy Research Unit at Sussex University have been omitted. The importance of this particular study is such, however, that frequent reference to it is made in several articles included in the present volume.

Brief perusal of the contents page will show that the articles refer to 'product development', 'product innovation', 'innovation' and 'design'. This terminology reflects the broad range of disciplines which give rise to research into the steps, mechanisms and organization necessary for bringing successful new products on to the market. While there are real nuances of difference among these terms, which are briefly outlined below, the basic concerns that fall within the domain of each are remarkably similar: at their core, they are concerned with a managerial process whereby creativity, market knowledge and technical expertise are woven together to produce goods and services that will serve market requirements.

In attempting to present an overview of the various terms used, it is alluring to think of a continuum related to the concept of newness, where terms related to 'innovation' are seen as dealing with a phenomenon delivering more 'newness' than 'development'. This continuum might be represented as in Figure 2.

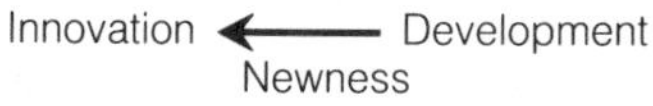

Innovation ◄——— Development
Newness

Figure 2. The Newness Continuum.

This could be made more sophisticated by adding other descriptors, such as 'technological' or 'product' as shown in Figure 3. The underlying premise of such a representation would be that a 'technological innovation' would describe a new (to the world) technology that had been successfully translated into an application which met the criterion of market success. Similarly, a 'technological development' would, under this representation, describe the further development of a technological application, already in existence. A 'product innovation' would therefore describe a new (to the world) product, not necessarily using new (to the world) technology, while a product development would describe further development of a product already in existence.

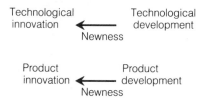

Technological   Technological
innovation ◄———   development
            Newness

Product   Product
innovation ◄———   development
           Newness

Figure 3. Adaptations of the Newness Continuum.

Such a classification, however, is fraught with difficulty, on a number of counts. First is the question of overlap. Is a 'technological development' the same as a product 'innovation' under this classification? For example, the Timex Corporation have been working on developing miniature electro-luminescence technology which is incorporated into their Indiglo Night-Light Watches; clearly, a case of technological development, resulting also in a 'product innovation'. A second problem is that this continuum ignores the market perspective. Although a technological innovation or development may be 'new' in technological terms, the application and the need served might be quite familiar to the market place, and in that sense be far from 'new'. For example, electro-luminescence in watches fulfils the need previously, but dangerously met, by radium in the 1930s. Third, the continuum does not encompass the transfer of technology from one industry to another. Thus, laser technology, developed initially for military application, has been transferred to several industries, including consumer electronics and medical equipment.

These issues of newness are further considered in the introduction to Part II, where the amount of 'newness', both technological and market, are forwarded as the core dimensions setting the direction of a company's new product programmes. In fact, when looking in detail at the readings, it can be seen that many authors use the terms almost interchangeably. For example, in the initial phases of the Stanford 'Innovation' Project, the focus of research was on 158 'new products' in the electronics industry. In this study, the electronics industry was chosen because of its production of new 'and often revolutionary' products (Maidique and Zirger, 1984) (Reading 2). So, by locating the study in a high-technology industry, the terms 'innovation' and 'new product development' are used interchangeably. Cooper's Project NewProd, which started in the 1970s and continues today, generally uses the term 'new product development', but identifies itself with the methodology used by Project SAPPHO, where a comparison of successful and unsuccessful *innovations* was made. In their seminal article on teams in *new product development*, Takeuchi and Nonaka (1986) focused on products which were 'breakthroughs', again showing an overlap in concepts and terminology. Crawford (1980) (Reading 5) developed the 'Charter for Product *Innovation*' by studying 125 American firms *new product* planning.

These examples, then, suggest that the terms are used interchangeably at a generic level and that the context of study provides the specific relationship between the terms and newness. However, there is much debate on these definitions, a good survey of which can be found in Tushman and Nadler (1986) (Reading 26). A second definitional distinction relates to *product* and *process* innovation. Product innovation (or development) relates to changes to the products and services themselves. As we have discussed, these changes may be minor or radical. Process innovation, which might also be minor or radical, relates to the way in which products and services are manufactured or delivered. The two kinds of innovation are often juxtaposed in terms of their relevance throughout a product's or industry's life cycle, as shown in Figure 4.

Product innovation is more important in the early stages, as competitors constantly redevelop innovations to win market share based on customer preference. In the late maturity and decline stages, the competitive focus shifts to process innovation, to reflect the need for efficiency and low-cost manufacture. These ideas and their limitations are given greater attention in Tushman and Nadler (1986) (Reading 26).

A final definitional issue is that of what constitutes a product. This question is much

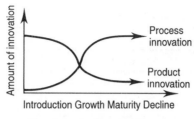

Figure 4. Product and Process Innovation.

considered in marketing literature where a number of classifications have been forwarded. These can be reviewed in articles such as Shostack (1977) and Levitt (1981). Of particular interest to the current collection is the distinction between physical products and services. While this 'distinction' can be viewed as a continuum, as for example, in Shostack's seminal article cited above, for our purposes, the concern is with the strategies, tasks and organization involved in developing new services. Historically, most of the research into new product development has been focused on manufactured products. While most textbooks on the subject do refer to the development of products and services, the reality of the detail of the contents is that the paradigms examined are largely those referring to manufactured products. Recently, however, increased attention being paid to the marketing of services has been mirrored by research into new service development. Part of this volume, therefore, is devoted to new service development (Part VI).

STRUCTURE OF THE READER

The articles chosen for the current volume are those that relate to the various stages in the NPD process as outlined by Booz, Allen and Hamilton's study (1982) and those which represent the important issues which have emerged from research in NPD.

Part I includes articles which represent a huge topic of research, namely, what factors distinguish new product success and failure. These studies (and many more to be found in each article's reference list) provide a prescriptive context for further parts of the book which have been selected to expand upon the key new product success factors.

Part II comprises articles that underline the importance of developing a strategy of NPD, and suggest ways of doing so. This section deals with the 'first' step in the NPD process.

Part III presents influential papers on NPD models, which discuss the NPD process in its totality.

Part IV focuses in greater detail on articles dealing with the early stages of the NPD process, once the NPD strategy has been defined, such as idea generation, screening of ideas and concept testing.

Part V presents articles which tackle issues of relevance in the later stages of the NPD process such as forecasting sales for new products, product testing and commercialization.

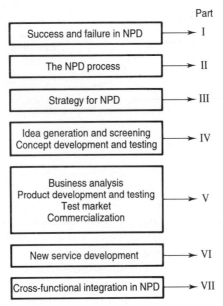

Figure 5. Key Issues in NPD Research.

Part VI departs from the organizing framework of the new product process and presents recent research articles on the development of new services.

Part VII focuses on the organizational dimension of NPD which have been given research attention, largely due to the fact that inter-disciplinary or cross-functional NPD processes seem to correlate frequently with higher levels of success in NPD.

Figure 5 presents this structure in a diagram for easy reference.

The readings are ordered numerically, irrespective of part. Each part is preceded by a short introduction to the main themes.

REFERENCES

Booz, Allen and Hamilton (1982) *New Products Management for the 1980's*, Booz, Allen and Hamilton, New York.

Cox and Kriegbaum (1989) *Innovation and Industrial Strength: A Study in the United Kingdom, West Germany, the United States and Japan*. Policy Studies Institute in Association with the Anglo-German Foundation, London.

Levitt, T. (1981) 'Marketing Intangible Products and Product Intangibles', *Harvard Business Review* **59** (3): 94–102.

Shostack, L. (1977) 'Breaking Free from Product Marketing', *Journal of Marketing*, **31** (April): 73–80.

Takeuchi, H. and Nonaka, I. (1986) The New Product Development Game, *Harvard Business Review*, Jan–Feb, 137–146.

Ughanwa, D. O. and Baker, M. J. (1989) *The Role of Design in International Competitiveness*, Routledge, London.

Utterback, J. M. (1971) 'The Process of Technological Innovation Within the Firm', *Academy of Management Journal* (March): 75–88.

Part I

Success and Failure in New Product Development

CONTENTS

Introduction to Part I

Susan Hart

The four opening readings of the volume are concerned with what characterizes success and failure in new product development (NPD). The first three give evidence of the wide range of research methodologies that can be employed to tackle this complex question, and are dealt with first. Reading 4, by Hart (1993) contrasts the various ways in which new product success might be measured. Cooper's article (Reading 1) is based on results from a mail survey. Maidique and Zirger's research (Reading 2) uses unstructured and structured questionnaires, backed up by case studies, while Johne and Snelson's field-work (Reading 3) was carried out by means of personal interviewing, using both structured and open-end questioning techniques. Their collective results are remarkably similar, especially given the difference in methodologies and their separation, both geographical and in time. Cooper's sample of companies were located in Ontario and Quebec; Maidique and Zirger's respondents were participants at the Stanford-AEA Executive Institute, while Johne and Snelson compared British and American companies approaches to NPD. The success factors common to all three relate to understanding user needs, and proficient marketing. Themes common to at least two are top management support and efficiency in the development process. The latter is perhaps the precursor of the important factor of speed in NPD, which has been highlighted more recently by Gupta and Wilemon (1990), Crawford (1992) and Vessey (1992). Interestingly, only Cooper's work *categorically* identifies 'product uniqueness and superiority' as a critical success factor in NPD. This factor was, in fact, the single most important dimension leading to new product success. In subsequent studies, this result has been confirmed (refs by Cooper). However, it is a composite dimension, comprising of innovativeness, reliability, quality and the extent to which customer needs are better met than by competing products. In reaching Maidique and Zirger's summary of critical success factors, we do not see 'product uniqueness'. Indeed, the location of the study within the electronics industry was assumed to imply automatic technical competence and thus its importance to the investigation was de-emphasized. Whether this assumption was valid is, however, a moot point. In looking, however, at the detail of their findings, factors such as 'better matched with user needs' product and 'products benefit-to-cost ratio' are given importance. Both these studies acknowledge that 'no single factor' can account for new product success or failure, and both try to consolidate the *really* critical success factors by appropriate techniques for data reduction. Their findings span numerous dimensions: the new products themselves, their synergy with current products' marketing conditions and the way in which the NPD process is carried out, for example. Johne and Snelson's study adapted the '7S framework' made famous by Peters and Waterman's *In Search of Excellence* (1982), to examine the process and management of NPD and compare successful and unsuccessful innovators. They did not therefore examine product-related variables, but rather the *inputs* to the development of new products. In this respect, the approach is much similar to that taken by the SAPPHO study (summaries in Maidique and Zirger) where organizational factors played a larger role. Like the SAPPHO study, Johne and Snelson found that successful innovators provide top management support for new product development and that efficiency of development is encouraged by cross-functional teams.

The work by Johne and Snelson differs from Cooper, Maidique and Zirger and SAPPHO, in two further respects. First, Johne and Snelson contrast the practices of successful and less successful innovators in developing 'new' new products as well as 'old' new products. This perspective is unique, in that it shows how, for example, the nature of objective setting for both types of development is different for more radical product development, objectives are broader than for less radical development. Although Maidique and Zirger collected information about the degree of innovativeness in the projects examined, they did not use this to analyse the data further. Second, Johne and Snelson compared the new product processes and management of successful and less successful product innovators—that is—taking a view of the companies *overall* performances in innovation. (In this paper they do not give details of how they measured successful and less successful innovators.) In the work of Cooper, Maidique and Zirger and SAPPHO, the level, or unit of analysis is not the overall company, but the specific development projects. In these studies, pairwise comparisons of successful and unsuccessful launches are made. The difference in approach has important implications for the interpretation of the results. The main reasons for investigating NPD success at the project level is that information about specific projects is readily identifiable, available and accessible, as long as the specific projects are not too historic. The individuals responsible can be identified, project objectives can be recalled, as well as details of the development process. Focusing on a whole organization's approach to its NPD process and management is bound to be fraught with the usual problems of locating reliable and valued personnel to interview and the inability to recall all the facts as opposed to a more 'average' picture of how NPD occurs, generally, within the firm. However, focusing on the comparison of the new product success and one new product failure is hardly indicative of the longer term ability a firm may or may not have to innovate.

A further issue differentiating the three papers is the way in which they deal with factors that might moderate the relationship between new product development activities and their outcome. Issues such as company size, industry maturity, competitive intensity and background and position of the respondent are likely to have an impact on the relationship between dependent and independent variables. This was handled very differently by the three papers.

The approach by Maidique and Zirger was the most meticulous, as they investigated the effect of several moderating factors on their emergent relationships, including: respondent position and experience, company size and industry category. Cooper included 'moderating' issues such as market competition, market size and market growth in his list of variables that formed the various independent factors that were then related to success. Johne and Snelson investigated 'newness', but otherwise confirmed their comparison to the US/UK dimension. They did not examine these moderating variables in an integrated fashion.

Finally, all papers measured success differently. Maidique and Zirger used the financial breakeven point to differentiate successes and failures; Cooper used the 'minimum acceptable profit' for this type of project, while Johne and Snelson, measuring success at the overall company level, used unspecified measures for assigning the status of successful and less successful innovator! The variety in measuring new product success presented by these three papers is representative of the bodies of literature dealing with new products. That such a variety exists, and largely without comment or criticism is, at best, surprising, given the impact that the measurement of new product access will have on the nature of its relationship with the independent variables. Indeed, if the theory of what differentiates new product success is to advance, then it would help to have agreement on at least the nature(s) and measurement(s) of the dependent variable. This issue is considered by the final paper in this part, by Hart. This paper reviews the various ways in which the dependent variable has been measured and begins to answer some of the ensuing questions by a small-scale empirical survey. The findings suggest that the somewhat indiscriminate use of a variety of measures of new product success cannot allow researchers to view the measures interchangeable, or as surrogates. By extension, then, factors associated with one success measure, for example, profit, may not be associated with another, for example, market share. The impact of this observation has yet to be taken on board by the majority of those studying new product success.

To conclude the introduction to Part I, it can be seen that a plenitude of factors are central to the outcome of new product development projects. In addition, the means of researching this phenomenon are varied. Finally, the factors commonly associated with new product success relate to the strategy for new products within the company, the process of developing new products and the organization of those charged with the responsibility of delivering these new products.

REFERENCES

Crawford, C. M. (1992) 'The Hidden Costs of Accelerated Product Development', *Journal of Innovation Management* **9**: 188–199.

Gupta, A. K. and Wilemon, D. L. (1990) 'Accelerating the Development of Technology Based New Products', *California Management Review* **32** (Winter): 24–45.

Peters, T. J. and Waterman, R. H. (1982) *In Search of Excellence: Lessons from America's Best Run Companies*, New York, Harper & Row.

Vessey, J. T. (1992) Time-to-market: Put Speed in Product Development, *Industrial Marketing Management* **21**, 151–158.

1

The Dimensions of Industrial New Product Success and Failure

R. G. Cooper

The high incidence of industrial new product failure has long been acknowledged (Booz, Allen and Hamilton, 1968). The call has been for a greater marketing orientation, more marketing research and improved marketing launch efforts as the route to stemming the tide of new product failures (Cooper, 1975; Crawford, 1977; Hatch, 1957; Hopkins and Bailey, 1971). However, surprisingly little has been done in the way of empirical research to probe the question of what makes a successful new product. In this article, we report the results of such an empirical study whose purpose was to identify the major factors which differentiate between successful and unsuccessful new industrial products.

Being able to 'predict a winner' in the new product game has been an elusive goal. A variety of tools and techniques have been provided to assist in screening new product ideas, including rating scale and checklist models to judge the overall suitability of the product idea to the company and concept test models to screen ideas for market acceptability (Wind, 1973). One of the problems with the rating scale or checklist approach is that neither the screening variables included nor their relative weightings, whether variable or fixed, have been empirically derived; they simply are based on subjective estimates (Shocker, Gensch and Simon, 1969). Thus, a major impetus for research into new product success/failure discriminators is the desire to provide an empirical base to new product screening models.

An equally important reason for investigating success versus failure is the potential for developing prescriptive guides for the new product process. Many of the variables which might separate the 'winners' from the 'losers' are within the control of the firm. A knowledge of what these variables are and their relative importance would lead to corrective action to improve the way the firm develops and launches new products.

WHAT SEPARATES THE 'WINNERS' FROM THE 'LOSERS'

Recent years have witnessed several research thrusts into industrial product innovation. The Booz, Allen and Hamilton (1968) studies in the mid 1960s provided an overview of

Reprinted with permission from *Journal of Marketing*, Vol. 43, Summer 1979, pp. 93–103 the field and highlighted many of the problems faced by product developers. Another research direction was the investigation of new product failures (Cooper, 1975; Davidson, 1976; Hopkins and Bailey, 1971; Lazo, 1965; NICB, 1964). The rationale for this research was that an understanding of one's past deficiencies is the first step to a prescriptive solution. Shortly after, a number of researchers began to probe case histories of new product successes with the goal of uncovering the key to success (Cooper, 1976; Globe, Levy and Schwartz, 1973; Marquis, 1969; Myers and Marquis, 1969; Roberts and Burke, 1974). Such research, typified by the Myers and Marquis studies, identified the need for a strong market orientation, even in the case of complex and moderate to high technology innovations.

More recent research has focused on comparing and contrasting new product successes and failures. Such research is based on the premise that only through a direct comparison of successes with failures will the variables that differentiate the two be identified. Project SAPPHO[1] in 1972 was the first of these success versus failure studies (Rothwell, 1972). The results of it, and several other European studies that followed, identified a number of key facets of product innovation—variables that described the process, venture, organization, industry and environment—which were related to successful new product outcomes (Gerstenfeld, 1976; Kulvik, 1977; Rothwell, 1974, 1976; Rothwell et al., 1974; Utterback et al., 1976).

These success/failure comparison studies, while the most fruitful in terms of useful and interesting results, have not been without their problems. There have been the usual methodological ailments which commonly plague any new research field. Operational definitions are often vague or inconsistent (for example, how does one define 'a new product success'?). Evidence of conceptual model building is rare; as a result, there appears little logic or consistency in the variables any particular researcher chooses to measure. Sample sizes are typically small; their method of selection is often suspect; the data analysis techniques are naive. Finally, from a North American and marketer's perspective, the studies lack some relevance. Virtually all of the research is set in a European context, while the researchers themselves are nonmarketing people (industrial economists, technologically-oriented researchers and so on). Hence the variables probed are not ones of greatest interest to marketers.

The current research was designed to overcome many of the problems that have beset previous work. First, a conceptual model was outlined, and from this model a set of variables was identified that were expected to impact on new product outcomes. Next, a substantial and randomly-selected sample—about 100 successes and 100 failures—was utilized. Data analysis techniques used were the multivariate ones familiar to marketers. Finally, the study was set in North America, and focused on variables of particular interest to the practicing marketers.[2]

THE RESEARCH

Previous research has uncovered a great diversity of variables which are related to new product outcomes. A sampling of these findings is provided in Table 1 where correlates of success versus failure are summarized.

A review of the many variables that were found to influence new product outcomes led to the development of a conceptual descriptive model (Cooper, 1975, 1979). This

Table 1. Recent findings from success versus failure investigations

Variables discriminating between success and failure	Research study[a]	Type of variable
Understanding user needs	1, 2, 3, 6	
Extensive customer-producer interfacing	1, 2, 3, 4, 6	
Efficient performance of development process		New product process
(few 'bugs'; fewer modifications; better planning etc.)	1, 2, 3, 6	
Sales forecasting carried out	1, 2, 6	
Strong selling (and marketing) effort	1, 2, 3, 6	
Product and/or price advantages	4, 7	Launch effort and
Strong promotional, user education effort	1	product offering
Fewer after sales problems	1, 2, 3, 4, 6	
No initial marketing difficulties	4	
Market pull (idea derived from market)	1, 2, 3, 4, 5, 6	
Technology push (for major successes)	5, 6, 7	Nature of venture
Good fit with company potentials, resources	3	
Close to current market (familiarity with market)	1, 3, 4	
Better internal and external communication	1, 2, 3, 4, 5, 6	
Better coordination of R&D, marketing, production	1, 2, 3, 6	Organizational
Product champion or top management support	1, 2, 4, 6	descriptors
Better planning and systematic approach to innovation	1, 3, 4, 5, 6	
Industry maturity (affects nature of venture)	4, 6	
Business cycle (influenced efforts)	5, 6	External: industry,
Government role (induced efforts)	4, 5	market, environment
Government support insignificant (except for major innovations)	1, 4, 6	

[a] 1: Rothwell (1972), Rothwell et al. (1974); 2: Rothwell (1974) (Hungarian SAPPHO); 3: Kulvik (1977); 4: Utterback et al. (1976); 5: Gerstenfeld (1976); 6: Rothwell (1976); 7: Davidson (1976).

communicative model lent structure to the research area by identifying as its elements the main blocks or groups of variables that impact on new product outcomes. Six blocks of particular interest to marketers were singled out for investigation in the current research. These include:

- *The commercial entity*: that with which the firm enters the marketplace. This block includes the attributes and advantages of the new product, its price, the nature of the launch efforts and the production or manufacturing effort underlying the launch. The commercial entity is the *result* of the new product process.
- *Information acquired*: the nature or quality of information acquired (or known) during the new product process. For example, whether the firm had accurate data on market potential, on buyer behavior, on production costs etc.
- *Proficiency of process activities*: how well certain activities were undertaken during the new product process (if at all), from idea generation to launch. For example, whether or not a detailed market study, pilot production or a test market were expertly undertaken, or undertaken at all.
- *Nature of the marketplace*: the characteristics of the new product's market. For example,

Table 2. Research propositions

New product success is expected to be positively related to:

1. Products which are superior, have a differential or economic advantage, or are unique relative to competing products 2. Products where the other elements of the commercial entity— selling, distribution, production etc.—are proficient	Commercial entity
3. Projects where considerable technical and market knowledge is acquired	Information acquired
4. Projects where the technical, marketing and evaluative (process) activities are proficiently undertaken	Proficiency of process activities
5. Products entering mass, large, growing, dynamic and uncompetitive markets, with a high but unsatisfied need for such products	Nature of marketplace
6. Projects where a high degree of resource compatibility exists between the needs of the project and the resource base of the firm	Resource base of firm
7. Familiar projects to the firm (do not involve new technologies, new markets etc.) 8. Market-derived projects (product idea came from the marketplace)	Nature of the project

In addition, other characteristics of the project—for example, whether a custom product or not; whether a true innovation or a 'me too' effort, etc.—were expected to impact on product outcomes, but in a moderating way.

degree and nature of competition, market-size and growth rate, and product life cycle characteristics.

- *Resource base of the firm*: the compatibility of the resource base of the firm with the requirements of the project; that is the 'company/product fit' in terms of a variety of resources, including R&D, production, distribution and sales force capabilities.
- *Nature of the project*: the characteristics of the new product project or venture. For example, the magnitude of the project, the level and complexity of the technology, the innovativeness of the product, the source of the idea.

The delineation of these blocks permitted the development of a list of 77 variables that were expected to be related to new product outcomes. The number of variables and the exploratory nature of the research precluded individual and detailed statements of hypotheses. Nonetheless, a set of general propositions was developed to indicate the expected impact that each major block of variables would have on product outcomes (Table 2). An overview of the 77 variables considered in the research is obtained from Table 3.

A mailed questionnaire was utilized to measure these variables for a large sample of new product successes and failures. A random sample of 177 firms was first selected from a government listing of active industrial product producers.[3]

Firms initially were contacted by telephone to solicit cooperation, identify the appropriate respondent and provide direction. Respondents within firms were selected to be 'functionally neutral' and have an overall knowledge of their firm's total new product efforts. (In smaller firms, the president or owner was typically the respondent; in larger firms, the division manager or corporate new product development officer provided the data.) A detailed questionnaire, which had been extensively pretested (to check clarity, operationality, etc.[4]), was mailed to each respondent. He was requested to select two

Table 3. Factors underlying new product projects

Factor name (% variance explained)[a]	Variables loading on factor	Type of variable	Variable loadings
1 Technical and production synergy and proficiency (28.8%)	Had compatible engineering skills for project	Firm resources	0.638
	Had compatible production resources for project	Firm resources	0.601
	Undertook preliminary technical assessment well	Activity	0.691
	Undertook product development well	Activity	0.642
	Undertook in-house prototype test well	Activity	0.639
	Undertook pilot production well	Activity	0.635
	Undertook production start-up well	Activity	0.687
	Knew product technology well	Info. acquired	0.669
	Knew product design well—no 'bugs'	Info. acquired	0.672
	Knew production process and technology	Info. acquired	0.794
	Production facilities well geared up	Comm. entity	0.719
2. Marketing knowledge and proficiency (11.7%)	Undertook preliminary market assessment well	Activity	0.470
	Undertook market study well	Activity	0.570
	Undertook test market well	Activity	0.421
	Undertook market launch well	Activity	0.451
	Understood customers' needs, wants	Info. acquired	0.583
	Understood buyer price sensitivity	Info. acquired	0.612
	Understood competitive situation	Info. acquired	0.616
	Understood buyer behavior	Info. acquired	0.761
	Understood/knew size of potential market	Info. acquired	0.740
	Were confident about success	Info. acquired	0.425
	Had a strong sales force launch effort	Comm. entity	0.408
	Sales force effort well targeted	Comm. entity	0.507
3. Newness to the firm (10.1%)	Potential customers were new to firm	Project	0.649
	Product class new to firm	Project	0.758
	Product use (need served) new to firm	Project	0.746
	Production process new to firm	Project	0.516
	Product technology new to firm	Project	0.514
	Distribution, sales force new to firm	Project	0.745
	Advertising, promotion new to firm	Project	0.750
	New competitors for the firm	Project	0.668
4. Product uniqueness/ superiority (9.0%)	Highly innovative product, new to market	Project	0.449
	Product had unique features for customer	Comm. entity	0.799
	Superior to competing products in meeting customer's needs	Comm. entity	0.832
	Product let customer reduce his costs	Comm. entity	0.410
	Product did unique task for customer	Comm. entity	0.564
	Product higher quality than competitor's	Comm. entity	0.691
5. Market competitiveness and customer satisfaction (6.7%)	Highly competitive market	Market	0.754
	Intense price competition in market	Market	0.765
	Many competitors in market	Market	0.797
	Customers satisfied with competitors' products	Market	0.402

Table 3. (*continued*)

Factor name (% variance explained)[a]	Variables loading on factor	Type of variable	Variable loadings
6. Marketing and managerial synergy (5.1%)	Had adequate financial resources	Firm resources	0.576
	Had necessary market research resources	Firm resources	0.677
	Had needed managerial skills	Firm resources	0.727
	Had compatible sales force/distribution resources	Firm resources	0.655
	Had adequate advertising skills	Firm resources	0.562
7. Product technical complexity and magnitude (4.4%)	A high technology product	Project	0.820
	A high per unit price—'big ticket' item	Project	0.623
	Mechanically, technically complex product	Project	0.875
8. Market need, growth and size (3.5%)	Customers had great need for product type	Market	0.558
	Market size (dollar volume) was large	Market	0.570
	High growth market	Market	0.634
9. Strength of marketing communications and launch effort (3.1%)	Had adequate advertising skills	Firm resources	0.464
	Had a strong sales force launch effort	Comm. entity	0.544
	Had a strong advert./promo launch effort	Comm. entity	0.762
	Advertising effort well targeted	Comm. entity	0.668
	Undertook market launch well	Activity	0.457
10. Product determinateness (2.8%)	Market determinateness (product clearly specified by marketplace)	Project	0.689
	Technical determinateness (technical solution clear at start)	Project	0.577
11. Production start-up proficiency (2.5%)	Production facilities geared up (for launch)	Comm. entity	0.422
	Production volume adequate to meet demand	Comm. entity	0.526
12. Product uniqueness (first to market) (2.2%)	Product did unique task for customer	Comm. entity	0.400
	Company first into market with product	Comm. entity	0.616
	Existence of potential demand only (no actual demand)	Market	0.586
13. Existence of a dominant competitor/ customers satisfied (2.1%)	Existence of a dominant competitor	Market	0.586
	Loyalty to competitors' products	Market	0.793
	Customers satisfied with competitors' products	Market	0.494

Table 3. (*continued*)

Factor name (% variance explained)[a]	Variables loading on factor	Type of variable	Variable loadings
14. Market dynamism (1.8%)	Frequent new product introductions in market	Market	0.441
	Users' needs change rapidly in market	Market	0.435
15. Relative price of product (1.7%)	Product let customer reduce costs	Comm. entity	−0.457
	Product priced higher than competing product	Comm. entity	0.608
16. Proficiency of precommercialization activities (1.6%)	Undertook initial idea screening well	Activity	0.401
	Undertook preliminary market assessment well	Activity	0.374
	Undertook preliminary technical assessment well	Activity	0.336
	Undertook market study well	Activity	0.284
	Undertook product development well	Activity	0.212
	Undertook financial analysis well	Activity	0.338
	Role of government in marketplace	Market	0.436
17. Product customness (1.6%)	Whether product was a custom product	Project	0.552
	Existence of a mass market	Market	−0.542
18. Source of idea/ investment magnitude (1.4%)	Relative magnitude of investment in project	Project	0.288
	Market-derived idea	Project	0.280

[a] After rotation add to 100%.

typical, recent new product projects: one a commercial success, the other a failure. Success and failure were defined from the point of view of the firm, and in terms of profitability (that is, the degree to which a product's profitability exceeded, or fell short of, the minimum acceptable profitability for this type of project or investment, regardless of the way the firm measured profitability). Because of selection errors which could result from difficulties in the use of this operational definition, managers were asked to select products which were clear-cut successes and failures.

The respondent then was asked to characterize each venture on each of the 77 variables that made up the six major blocks. Variables were measured by presenting a phrase or sentence, and requesting the manager to indicate whether the description applied to the project (agree/disagree, 0–10 scales).

The eventual sample numbered 102 successes and 93 failures (195 projects) from 103 firms, which represents an effective response rate of 69% after correction for inappropriate or nonexistent firms. A review of the industry categories and sizes of the responding firms revealed no evidence of a response bias.

RESULTS

Preliminary analysis revealed the need to collapse the many variables measured into a more useful and manageable subset (Cooper, 1979). The correlation matrix of the 77 characteristics measured for each new product project showed that the great majority were highly intercorrelated, often with correlation coefficients in excess of 0.50. This network of correlations suggested that the 77 variables could be explained by a handful of underlying dimensions.

The dimensions of new product projects

Eighteen dimensions or factors that describe new product projects were identified and labelled. Factor analysis[5] was utilized to reduce the 77 variables to their underlying factors.[6] All 18 factors had eigenvalues in excess of 1.0; 11 had eigenvalues greater than 2.0. The factors explained 71.3% of the variance in the original 77 variables, and thus appear to describe new product projects fairly well.

The 18 dimensions, in spite of their numbers, proved quite easy to label. In all but the last factor, variable loadings of at least several variables were strikingly high, mostly over 0.60. The factors are identified and labelled in Table 3, which summarizes the important factor loadings and provides an indication of the strength and clarity of the evolved factors. The factor analysis was validated using a split-half method: the structure of the factors—variables and loadings—was essentially the same for the two halves of the sample. A total of 19 and 20 factors were generated in the two factor analysis runs (eigenvalues $\geq$ 1.0), and 14 of the factors were virtually identical to each other (and the same as those in the full-sample run, Table 3).[7]

A review of this list of 18 underlying dimensions reveals that many of them are both familiar and intuitively obvious. The first two dimensions describe a *production/technical* orientation and a *market* orientation, which have been the topic of much discussion and research into product innovation (Kulvik, 1977; Rothwell, 1974). The current research supports the notion that both dimensions are important characteristics of product projects. Of particular interest is the fact that these two orientations are not mutually exclusive; the dimensions are independent of each other.[8] A project simultaneously can have both a strong market orientation *and* a strong technical/production orientation.

Three of the 18 factors identified describe the innovativeness of the venture:

- *newness to the firm*: a project which takes the firm into new markets, new technologies etc.
- *product uniqueness*: a product which is truly unique; firm is first into the market with type of product.
- *product uniqueness/superiority*: a product which has significant improvements over previous products making it unique and superior.

Previous literature has often referred to 'product innovativeness' as an important descriptor of new products (Davidson, 1976; Marquis, 1969; Rothwell, 1976). But on closer inspection, it appears that the term 'innovativeness' is perhaps too global; there are at least three dimensions of newness quite independent of each other.

A number of dimensions describe the nature of the product or project. These include (references are to previous work identifying similar variables):

- technical complexity and magnitude (Marquis, 1969; Myers and Marquis, 1969);
- product customness (Little, 1970);

- product determinateness (Globe, Levy and Schwartz, 1973; Roberts and Burke, 1974);
- relative price of product (Calantone and Cooper, 1977);
- source of idea/investment magnitude (Marquis, 1969; Myers and Marquis, 1969).

That these descriptors evolve in a study of product innovation is not surprising. Indeed all have been mentioned or alluded to in previous work, although not all in one single investigation.

Similarly, some of the market descriptors, namely:

- market need, growth and size (Globe, Levy and Schwartz, 1973; Marquis, 1969; Rubenstein et al., 1974, 1976);
- market dynamism (frequency of new introductions);
- market competitiveness (Cooper, 1975); and
- existence of a dominant competitor (Cooper, 1975).

are also the types of dimensions one might logically expect in a study of new product projects.

Finally, several factors describe the company and its proficiencies, particularly as they pertain to the new product under investigation. The first two—a market orientation and a production orientation—have already been mentioned, but here are others:

- marketing and managerial synergy (Kulvik, 1977);
- strength of marketing communications launch effort (Rothwell, 1972; Rothwell et al., 1974);
- proficiency of production start-up (Cooper, 1975);
- proficiency of precommercialization activities (Cooper, 1975).

The 18 dimensions identified help to clarify and simplify the set of variables that describe the new product situation. Instead of working with 77 or more interrelated project characteristics, the problem has been reduced to more manageable proportions: 18 independent dimensions. Not only were the dimensions readily identified and labeled from the results of the factor analysis, but they also appear to be valid. And most important, the dimensions make sense and have meaning to managers.

Success and failure

The next logical question concerns the relationship between success/failure and the underlying dimensions identified above. Linear discriminant analysis was utilized to relate group membership (success or failure) to the 18 factors in Table 3.[9] Factor scores were calculated for each of the 195 project cases and used as the variables in the discriminant analysis. A total of 11 of the 18 factors entered the discriminant solution, and appeared to differentiate between new product successes and failures. In order of inclusion, these were:

- introducing a unique but superior product;
- having market knowledge and marketing proficiency;

Table 4. Discriminant analysis results: determinants of new product success

Factor	Factor name[a]	Standardized function coefficients	Wilks'[b] Lambda	F To enter or remove
F4	Product uniqueness/superiority	0.527	0.859	31.66
F2	Market knowledge and marketing proficiency	0.465	0.730	33.95
F1	Technical/Production synergy and proficiency	0.325	0.680	14.13
F14	Market dynamism (frequency of new product introductions)	−0.264	0.644	10.65
F8	Market need, growth and size	0.271	0.610	10.49
F15	Relative price of product	−0.252	0.576	10.62
F6	Marketing and managerial synergy	0.193	0.557	6.49
F5	Marketing competitiveness and customer satisfaction	−0.186	0.540	5.88
F3	Newness to the firm	−0.170	0.526	4.93
F9	Strength of marketing communications and launch effort	0.137	0.517	3.24
F18	Source of idea/investment magnitude	0.114	0.510	2.27

Group
centroids: Successes: 0.666   ($N = 102$)
　　　　　Failures: −0.731   ($N = 93$)

[a] in order of inclusion in the discriminant solution.
[b] significant at the 0.001 level.

- having technical and production synergy and proficiency;
- avoiding dynamic markets with many new product introductions;
- being in a large, high need, growth market;
- avoiding introducing a high-priced product with no economic advantage;
- having a good 'product/company fit' with respect to managerial and marketing resources;
- avoiding a competitive market with satisfied customers;
- avoiding products 'new to the firm';
- having a strong marketing communications and launch effort;
- having a market-derived idea with considerable investment involved.

The coefficients of the discriminant functions are shown in Table 4 along with group centroids for the two groups, success and failure. The discriminant relationship is a particularly strong one, with 84.10% of the cases correctly classified. (The model had greater accuracy predicting successes than failures, with 89.2% of successes correctly classified.) The Wilks' Lambda criterion for the ability of the variables to discriminate was 0.51 with an associated F statistic of 15.95 (d.f. = 11; 183), significant at the 0.001 level.

The discriminant analysis results were validated using Montgomery's (1975) V_3 method for small samples. The limited sample size, the extremely high cost of collecting data, and the focus of the research (on description and explanation, not prediction) pointed to the use of a validation technique which tests for spurious results (as opposed to a hold-out sample validation). Observations were scrambled randomly into arbitrary groups, and then the performance of the discriminant analyses observed. The results of the five V_3 runs undertaken stand in sharp contrast to the original discriminant findings: correct classifications around 60%; F values in the low 2.0 to 3.0 range; Wilks' Lambdas equalling 0.90 to 0.95; and relatively few variables entering the solution. These V_3 validations confirm that the figure of 84% correctly classified in the original discriminant analysis is not spurious. The successful validation of the discriminant and factor analyses, the lack of a response bias in the sample, and the nature of the population (see footnote 2) suggest the results can be generalized to industrial product innovation in North America.

IMPLICATIONS TO NEW PRODUCT MANAGEMENT

The research provides a vital insight into the factors which separate the successes from the failures in industrial product innovation. The complex problem of new product outcomes has been greatly simplified by identifying 18 underlying dimensions that capture much of the new product situation.

The keys to success

The single most important dimension leading to new product success is *Product uniqueness and superiority*. Unique, superior products were typically highly innovative and new to the market (Table 3); incorporated unique features for the customer; met customers' needs better than competing products; allowed the customer to reduce costs or to do something previously impossible; and were of higher quality (tighter specifications, stronger, lasted longer, more reliable etc.) than competing products. That product uniqueness and superiority is such an important ingredient in new product success is so obvious and truistic that it tends to be overlooked. The product is the core or central strategy in most industrial new product ventures; and it is through the product that the firm must seek its differential advantage.

Market knowledge and marketing proficiency plays a critical role in new product outcomes. Projects which were strong on this dimension were those where the market-oriented activities were proficiently undertaken (market assessment, market studies, test market, market launch). The firm had a sound understanding of the important facets of the market: customers' needs and wants, price sensitivities, buyer behavior, market potential and competition. Finally, the sales force and distribution effort was strong and well-targeted at launch. The obvious point needs reinforcing: the commercial viability of a new product rests in the hands of its potential customers; and therefore a solid understanding of the marketplace together with an effective market launch effort is vital to new product success.

The third most important new product dimension which impacts on success/failure is a technical one, *technical and production synergy and proficiency*. Projects where such synergy and proficiency existed were undertaken in firms with a particularly strong and compatible technical engineering and production and resource base. The technical and production activities were carried out proficiently: preliminary technical assessment, product development, prototype testing, pilot production and production start-up. In addition, such firms had a thorough understanding of the product and design technology, and also the production process. That all of these technical and production facets are important to new product success has long been taken for granted. Perhaps the most noteworthy conclusion is that this technical dimension, although very important, does *not stand alone* as the most critical dimension to new product success, even in a study of industrial product innovation.

Three barriers to success

Another six dimensions are closely related to product outcomes, although not as strongly as the first three. Of these, three are considered to be barriers to success since they are negatively related. These are:

- having a high-priced product, relative to competition (with no economic advantage to the customer);
- being in a dynamic market (with many new product introductions);
- being in a competitive market, where customers are already well satisfied.

The high-priced product dimension and the competitive 'brick wall' factor have both been identified as barriers in studies of new product failure (Calantone and Cooper, 1977). The dynamic market dimension is somewhat surprising: one might expect that such markets are particularly receptive to new ideas; hence facilitating new introductions. But dynamic markets, characterized by many new product introductions, can become a quagmire of problems and hidden obstacles, and a breeding ground for competitive one-upmanship (Calantone and Cooper, 1977). Intense product competition results, often with deadly outcomes for the new product launched into the market.

Three facilitators

Three contributors to new product success are:

- marketing and managerial synergy;
- strength or marketing communications and launch effort;
- market need, growth and size.

All three describe the marketplace or the marketing function. That a strong marketing and managerial synergy is critical to success simply echoes the importance of a market orientation in product innovation. This synergy factor (people and skills) complements the more important determinant of success, market knowledge and marketing proficiency, which focuses on market information and activities.

The strength of the marketing communications and launch effort also is related to new product outcomes. Again the need for careful attention to the marketing function—sales force, advertising, promotion and distribution—as a part of the innovation process is reinforced.

The final dimension—being in a high need, high growth, large market—is an obvious and expected result. More surprising is the fact that large, high growth, high need markets do not play an even more pivotal role in new product successes than the research results suggest. One might speculate that such lucrative markets also are attractive to others, making success a competitive and up-hill battle; in contrast there may exist many smaller, apparently less lucrative markets which also offer unique opportunities for new products.

Weakly-related factors

Two additional dimensions appear related to new product outcomes, but in a somewhat weaker fashion. Newness to the firm is a dimension which was clearly identified in the factor analysis and is frequently cited as a proxy for synergy in the literature. Yet the factor entered the discriminant solution towards the end of the analysis, and in other analyses (correlation and multiple regression) did not stand out as a significant factor in product success. One must conclude that although newness is a familiar dimension, it is probably more useful as a moderating or classifying variable than as a direct predictor of outcomes.

Another weakly-related dimension, source of idea/investment magnitude, also yielded an unexpected result. Previous work by Marquis (1969) and Myers and Marquis (1969) showed that the majority of innovation successes were market-derived. The implication was that market-derived products are clearly more successful . The current research also revealed that successful products tended to be market-derived (mean of 7.19 on a 0–10 scale, 10 = market-derived). The problem is that *failure products are also largely market-derived* (7 out of 10), and that whether a product is market-derived or not—the source of the idea—simply does not differentiate all that well between success and failure.

Dimensions with no impact on success

Of particular interest is a review of the many strong dimensions that do not differentiate successes from failures.

- One hotly debated dimension is the 'first to market' factor. The current research found that although product uniqueness (first to market) is an important dimension describing new product projects (factor analysis results), it is *not* a determinant of success or failure. The results suggest that the advantages of being 'first in' are almost equally balanced by the many pitfalls and disadvantages.
- Another important dimension not related to success is the proficiency of the precommercialization activities (market assessment, technical assessment, detailed market study, product development, financial analysis). Note that the market activities did load heavily on other factors that were related to success. The message is that proficiently executing the 'front end' of the development process alone is not a condition for success. In contrast, the commercialization phase, or 'back end' of the process *was* found to be of particular importance.
- The intensity of competition was found to be a barrier to new product success (above); in contrast, the mere existence of a dominant competitor does not impact on product outcomes. Both dimensions are commonly lumped together in a global measure when a manager speaks of 'strong competition'. The conclusion is that these

are two quite independent dimensions; and that only intensity of competition is a barrier to success.

- Another factor that has no direct bearing on success/failure is the proficiency of production start-up. The two variables which load most heavily on this dimension, 'adequacy of production volume' and 'smoothness of start-up', are also highly loaded on another dimension that did impact on success: technical and production synergy and proficiency. The discriminating factor included production facilities *as well as* a number of other variables, such as technical and engineering proficiencies and synergies. Production capability alone is not the key variable, but must be considered in concert with other vital ingredients as a determinant of success.

Finally, several remaining factors simply describe the product or project, and *a priori* were not expected to impact directly on success/failure. These include:

- product technical complexity and magnitude (big ticket item);
- product determinateness (degree to which product was predetermined, i.e. market specifications, technical solution);
- product customness.

Such dimensions are likely to be of greater use as classifying or moderating variables, and not so much as determinants of product outcomes.

CONCLUSION

The secrets to success in industrial product innovation remain a mystery, for the problem is very complex. What this research has done is identify a set of underlying dimensions that can be used to characterize and perhaps cluster new product projects. This identification of the relative importance of each dimension as a determinant of success provides valuable inputs into the screening decision. Moreover, a knowledge of which dimensions are critical to success can be used to suggest needed improvements—which activities need attention, what information is critical, etc.—to individual firms' new product processes.

The research suffers from a number of limitations. A lack of descriptive model building, questions of reliability of the data (after the fact, scaled measures), and issues of predictability are some of the unresolved problems. Overriding all of these is the basic issue: is there really an answer to what makes a new product a success? Perhaps the problem is so complex, and each case so unique, that attempts to develop generalized solutions are in vain.

The research question—what makes a new product a success—is an important one, and so the search will continue. Future research will aim at the development of an empirically-based predictive screening model to improve the idea selection decision. Another research thrust will focus on the moderating impact of other variables: for example, are the determinants of success the *same* for high technology versus low technology areas, for big versus small firms etc.? Finally, future work should also bring together the type of model derived from this research (empirically derived, based on management opinion) with market concept test methods (Wind, 1973) to yield comprehensive new product screening models.

The message from the current research is gratifying to marketers. The critical role of a market orientation, marketing information, marketing communication, and marketing launch strategy was strongly demonstrated. Indeed a review of the nine factors closely linked to success shows that all but one directly or indirectly pertain to the marketing function or to the marketplace. The wisdom of the marketing concept, even for industrial, often high technology new products, prevails.

There are words of warning for marketers as well. The dominant position of product strategy as the central or core strategy in new industrial products was made clearer than ever. While marketing communications, promotion, sales force and launch strategies certainly were important, *product* stood out above all. Those marketers, often with consumer goods backgrounds, who believe in the preeminence of communication, promotion and sales force (at the expense of product), are on dangerous ground in the field of industrial product innovation. Similarly, while market dimensions did dominate the results, the need for a strong technical/production orientation to complement (rather than to detract from) a strong market orientation also was revealed. The research results provide both encouragement and warning to the technically-oriented and the market-oriented product developer.

NOTES

1. SAPPHO is an acronym for Scientific Activity Predictor from Patterns with Heuristic Origins.
2. Although the study was undertaken in Canada, the proximity and similarity with the United States both geographically and in terms of industry structure; nature of firms (many were MNCs); tariff structure; and market characteristics (albeit much smaller than United States) suggest that the research results are likely to be applicable in the United States.
3. Firms were located in Ontario and Quebec, Canada. The survey was conducted in the latter half of 1977.
4. Pretest respondents were personally interviewed following completion of the test questionnaires.
5. Varimax rotation. SPSS routine.
6. Although variables were not continuous, the fact that all scales were 11-point (0–10) with anchors at each end suggest that an interval scale assumption is not a bad one. Data appeared normally distributed along the scales.
7. Additionally, percent variance explained by each factor was almost identical at equal number of factors. For example, after 16 factors, 72.0% variance was explained in one half (94.2% after rotation) versus 74.0% in the other half (95.0% after rotation).
8. Factors are orthogonal (at right angles).
9. Stepwise discriminant analysis, SPSS routine; Wilks' method for selection of variables.

REFERENCES

Booz, Allen and Hamilton (1968) *Management Of New Products*, Booz, Allen and Hamilton, Inc., New York.

Calantone, R. J. and R. G. Cooper (1977) 'A Typology Of Industrial New Product Failure', in *Contemporary Marketing Thought*. Greenberg & Bellanger, eds., Chicago: American Marketing Association, 492–497.

Cooper, R. G. (1975) 'Why New Industrial Products Fail', *Industrial Marketing Management*, **4** (January): 315–326.

Cooper, R. G. (1976) 'Introducing Successful New Products', *MCB Monographs, European Journal of Marketing*, **10**, Bradford, England.

Cooper, R. G. (1979) 'Identifying Industrial New Product Success: Project New Prod', *Industrial Marketing Management*, **8** (May).

Crawford, C. M. (1977) 'Marketing Research And The New Product Failure Rate', *Journal of Marketing*, **41** (April): 51–61.

Davidson, H. J. (1976) 'Why Most New Consumer Brands Fail', *Harvard Business Review*, **54** (March–April), 117–122.

Gerstenfeld, A. (1976) 'A Study of Successful Projects, Unsuccessful Projects, and Projects in Process in West Germany', *IEEE Transactions On Engineering Management*, **23** (August), 116–123.

Globe, S., G. W. Levy and C. M. Schwartz (1973) 'Key Factors and Events in The Innovation Process', *Research Management*, **16** (July), 8–15.

Hatch, R. S. (1957) 'Product Failures Attributed Mainly to a Lack of Testing, Faulty Marketing', *Industrial Marketing*, **43** (February), 112–126.

Hopkins, D. S. and E. L. Bailey (1971) 'New Product Pressures', *The Conference Board Record*, **8** (June), 16–24.

Kulvik, H. (1977) *Factors Underlying The Success or Failure of New Products*, Helsinki: University of Technology, Report No. 29, Finland.

Lazo, H. (1965) 'Finding a Key to Success in New Product Failures', *Industrial Marketing*, **50** (November), 74–77.

Little, B. (1970) 'Characterizing The New Product For Better Evaluation and Planning', *Working Paper Series*, No. 21, University of Western Ontario, London, Canada (July).

Marquis, D. G. (1969) 'The Anatomy of Successful Innovations', *Innovation Magazine*, **1** (November), 28–37.

Montgomery, D. B. (1975) 'New Product Distribution: An Analysis of Supermarket Buyer Decisions', *Journal of Marketing Research*, **12** (August), 255–264.

Myers, S. and D. G. Marquis (1969) 'Successful Industrial Innovations', *National Science Foundation*. NSF 69–17.

National Industrial Conference Board (1964) 'Why New Products Fail', *The Conference Board Record*. New York: NICB.

Roberts, R. W. and J. E. Burke (1974) 'Six New Products—What Made Them Successful', *Research Management*, **16** (May), 21–24.

Rothwell, R. (1972) 'Factors For Success in Industrial Innovations', from *Project SAPPHO—A Comparative Study of Success And Failure in Industrial Innovation*. Brighton, Sussex: S.P.R.U.

Rothwell, R. (1974) 'The "Hungarian Sappho": Some Comments And Comparison', *Research Policy*, **3**, 30–38.

Rothwell, R. (1976) 'Innovation In Textile Machinery: Some Significant Factors In Success and Failure', *SPRO Occasional Paper Series*. No. 2, Brighton, Sussex, United Kingdom. (June).

Rothwell, R., C. Freeman, A. Horsley, V. T. P. Jervis, A. B. Robertson and J. Townsend (1974) 'SAPPHO Updated—Project Sappho Phase II', *Research Policy* **3**, 258–291.

Rubenstein, A. H., A. K. Chakrabarti and R. D. O'Keefe (1974 eds) 'Field Studies of The Technological Innovation Process', in *Progress in Assessing Technical Innovations* by H. R. Clauser, Technomic Publication, Westport, CT.

Rubenstein, A. H., W. E. Sounder and H. C. Young (1976) 'Factors Influencing Innovation Success at The Project Level', *Research Management*, **16** (May), 15–20.

Shocker, A. D., D. Gensch and L. S. Simon (1969), 'Toward The Improvement of New Product Search and Screening', *AMA Conference Proceedings* (Fall), 168–175.

Utterback, J. M., T. J. Allen, J. H. Holloman and M. H. Sirbu (1976) 'The Process Of Innovation in Five Industries in Europe and Japan', *IEEE Transactions on Engineering Management*, No. 1 (February), 3–9.

Wind, Y. (1973) 'A New Procedure For Concept Evaluation', *Journal of Marketing*, **37** (October), 2–11.

2

A Study of Success and Failure in Product Innovation: The Case of the US Electronics Industry

Modesto A. Maidique and Billie Jo Zirger

There is nothing more difficult to plan, more doubtful of success, nor more dangerous to manage than the creation of a new system. (Niccolo Machiavelli, *The Prince.*)

I. INTRODUCTION

Effective new product development is virtually synonymous with success in high-technology industries such as electronics, computers, aerospace, biotechnology, chemicals and pharmaceuticals. The fate of leaders and followers alike in these industries is determined by the performance, quality and timing of their new product offerings. For leaders, new products are the vehicles through which new markets are created and old ones revolutionized. For followers, new products provide an opportunity to set new standards in cost and quality and to make minor enhancements which may later result in considerable competitive advantage.

This constant redefinition of the rules of the game, a direct consequence of the swiftness of technological change, makes these high-technology industries fertile ground for the study of new product success. In this environment, today's technological marvel is tomorrow's obsolete product. No sooner is one product launched than a development team is working at an accelerated pace on the next generation, sometimes under a new corporate logo. This rapid technological change often leads to equally rapid growth when a product is found that results in a more economical, faster, or more reliable way to perform a new function or a combination of old functions.

For these reasons we chose the high-technology industries, and in particular the electronics industry as the starting point of our long-term study of success and failure in US industrial product and process innovation.[1] Few, if any, industries over the last half century have produced a greater stream of new, and often revolutionary, products than

Reprinted with permission from *IEEE Transactions on Engineering Management*, Vol. EM–31, No. 4, 1984, pp. 192–203
© 1984 IEEE

the electronics industry. The transistor, the integrated circuit, the microprocessor, colour television and personal computers are but five of the most remarkable examples.

In this paper we describe the methods employed in our research and the results obtained thus far, and briefly summarize the salient aspects of the open literature that led up to our project. The paper is divided into four sections. In the first section we review the prior literature on new product success and failure and highlight opportunities for extending previous research. In the second section we describe the Stanford Innovation Project and the methodology followed in this study. In the third section we describe our results. Finally, in the concluding section we summarize our progress, review its implications for subsequent research and present a conceptual model of the new product process.

II. RESEARCH ON NEW PRODUCT SUCCESS AND FAILURE

Early research on new product development consisted mainly of exploratory case studies (Morrison, 1966; Tushman and Moore, 1982; Sorenson 1971; Wise, 1966a, b; Baruch and Barbour 1971, 1972; Baruch and Kiser, 1973; Rosenbloom, 1976; and Maidique and Ince, 1979a, b). Such exploratory case studies have served as rich sources of hypotheses for subsequent exploration by means of larger samples and structured surveys.

From individual cases, research in the field moved to groups of cases (e.g. Schon, 1963; Booz, Allen and Hamilton, 1968; Maidique, 1980) and to large surveys. The landmark study of this latter type was Myers and Marquis' study of 567 innovations in 121 firms in five industries (railroad, railroad supplies, computer manufacturers and computer supplies, and housing suppliers) (Marquis, 1969; Myers and Marquis, 1969). The industries were selected to allow comparison of more and less technologically advanced products. According to Myers and Marquis, their sample was composed of innovations that were considered significantly important by the informants, usually technical people. The respondents 'almost always chose an innovation which had been commercially successful in terms of return on product sales or savings in production costs' (Myers and Marquis, 1969, p. 11).

The principal difficulty with this pioneering treatise stems from the sentence just quoted. Though Myers and Marquis' large sample cut across a variety of industries and firms, the innovations they studied were predominantly commercially successful innovations. The other set, those innovations that were not commercially successful, were not studied as a control group. A second important methodological problem results from the use of 'one or more technical people' as the principal informants (Myers and Marquis, 1969). Cooper, for instance, has argued that the most balanced view of a product's success and failure is one free of functional bias, that is, the view of the general manager (Cooper, 1979a, p. 95).

The next major advance in this field was the pioneering SAPPHO study (Rothwell *et al.*, 1974; Science Policy Research Unit, 1972) in the United Kingdom in 1974, which used a pairwise comparison methodology that facilitates differentiation between successful and unsuccessful policies and practices by contrasting successful and unsuccessful innovations. Since then the pairwise methodology has become the methodology of choice for contemporary researchers on product development.

This technique involves comparing the characteristics of two innovations, one failure and one success, to find areas of contrast and similarity. Using this methodology, the SAPPHO group studied 43 pairs of innovations in the instruments and chemicals industries and compared them along 122 different dimensions. Forty-one of the variables tested (34%) were found to produce statistically significant results. Those variables were then grouped into five general areas that discriminate between failure and success, the first two of which are generally supportive of Myers and Marquis' earlier findings, as follows:

(1) understanding of user needs;
(2) attention to marketing and publicity;
(3) efficiency of development;
(4) effective use of outside technology and external scientific communication;
(5) seniority and authority of responsible managers ((SAPPHO) Rothwell *et al.*, 1976).

The first two SAPPHO findings can be further categorized into 'market factors' while the last three can be viewed as 'organizational variables'. Their results balance earlier conclusions regarding the preeminence of market related factors with an emphasis on how the company organizes and manages its new product development process. Subsequent investigators have used the pairwise comparison methodology to reach conclusions broadly similar to the SAPPHO findings in other countries (Canada, West Germany, Japan, Finland and Hungary) and industrial settings, though usually with smaller scale data bases (Cooper, 1983). In the US, a study using this methodology has not yet been performed.

Rubenstein *et al.* (1976), however, analyzed 103 innovations in six firms in a study that included both successes and failures, and measured both technical and economic success, but used a very different methodology than the SAPPHO pairwise comparison approach. In this study, the characteristics of successful and unsuccessful innovation pairs were not statistically contrasted to identify significant differences, rather 'facilitators and barriers' to the innovation process were identified by interviewing the managers involved and obtaining their opinions. Notwithstanding these differences, Rubenstein *et al.*'s findings also coincided with SAPPHO in several major areas, such as the importance of market factors, communication and organizational commitment to the project.

In addition to the broad areas of agreement, the post-SAPPHO studies also brought new insights. Important additional variables, such as product characteristics, planning and environmental variables, have emerged as significant. For a more detailed review of these studies, the reader is referred to a recent critical review of the literature by Cooper (1983). See also, for a critique of the SAPPHO study, Mowery and Rosenberg (1979).

Of the pairwise studies that followed SAPPHO, Project NewProd was the most ambitious and employed the largest sample ($n = 195$; 93 failures, 102 successes). Almost 200 randomly selected Canadian industrial new products were evaluated along 77 different dimensions using a mailed survey (Cooper 1979a, b; 1980a, b). The overall results were divided into three general areas that were believed to be strongly correlated with new product success:

(1) having a unique or superior product in the eyes of the customer;
(2) having marketing knowledge and proficiency;

(3) having technical and production synergy and proficiency (Cooper, 1983, p. 4).

Although superficially similar, the results of SAPPHO and Project NewProd also reflect some major differences. For instance, the SAPPHO findings highlight organizational factors, such as seniority and authority of responsible managers and effective use of outside technology in addition to market factors, while largely ignoring the product itself. The results of Project NewProd emphasize product characteristics, in addition to the market and organizational variables. The word 'product', on the other hand, doesn't even appear in summaries of the SAPPHO work.

We believe this is, in part, the result of the different methodologies employed by the two groups. In the SAPPHO case, 43 pairs of innovations from different companies that competed for the same markets were examined by interviewing several informants in each firm. In the Project NewProd study, 93 pairs of innovations from individual firms were described via a mailed survey by a single respondent, usually the general manager. In both cases, however, individual successes and failures were paired and analyzed statistically. Thus in the SAPPHO study the *markets* were held constant for each pair, while in the NewProd study the *firms* were held constant. It is reasonable to expect that the SAPPHO project would be most revealing regarding the contrasts in the organizational and market approaches of the *successful firms*. On the other hand, one would anticipate that by holding the firm constant the NewProd study would tend to emphasize the characteristics of the *successful products* themselves.

III. THE STANFORD INNOVATION PROJECT: SCOPE AND METHODOLOGY

That different methodologies (as well as different settings) should give a somewhat different view of the proverbial elephant should not be surprising. Rubenstein *et al.* (1976), after reviewing the literature in the field, suspected that some of the dispersion in the results might be due to methodological differences (p. 20). This is not to say that ideally researchers would all use the same methodology. On the contrary, the use of complementing methodologies is essential to optimum triangulation. Utterback argues that useful research can be defined as research that helps to complete the picture developed by previous researchers (Alloway and Utterback, 1977).

With these thoughts in mind we organized the Stanford Innovation Project in 1982 to attempt to address certain gaps in the field of new product research and to test the impact of differences in research design on pairwise studies of innovation. Our study was conducted among firms in the electronics industry and was divided into three parts (Maidique, 1983). Each phase was conducted serially to provide progressive hypotheses refinement and validation. The second and third phases sampled subsets of the original 158 innovation data base, but utilized different research methodologies.

The first part of the study consisted of an open-ended survey (Survey I) which was administered to 120 participants of the Stanford-AEA Executive Institute held annually at Stanford University. Participants in this program were predominantly presidents, vice-presidents or senior functional managers of US electronics firms. Seventy-nine of the surveys were fully completed and used in the research data base. The second phase of the study was a detailed questionnaire consisting of 60 questions (Survey II), and 59 of the 79 Survey I participants completed this survey. The third phase consisted of in-depth case studies of 20 of the companies that collaborated in both Survey I and Survey II.

Survey I was an open-ended questionnaire which was divided into three parts: (1) respondent and firm demographics; (2) innovation selection and description; (3) factors of success or failure for the innovation pair. The first part of the survey requested general demographic data about the respondent and general financial statistics about the firm. The second section asked the respondent to select an innovation pair, one success and one failure, from within his firm, observing the following criteria:

(1) developed for the same or related markets;
(2) developed no more than five years apart;
(3) whose individual financial potential was expected to be significant for the firm or business unit;
(4) which was believed to be technically feasible.

Success and failure was differentiated by whether the innovation did or did not achieve financial breakeven (Figure 1). The third section of Survey I consisted of two open-ended questions which asked the respondent to identify factors which contributed to the success or failure of the innovation pair selected.

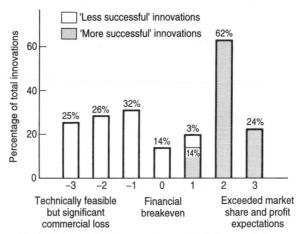

Figure 1. Distribution of Survey I Sample by Degree of Innovation's Success/Failure.

The second survey was structured similarly to the SAPPHO study and compared each of the 60 variables against the innovation pair chosen in Survey I. The respondents were asked to determine whether the variable influenced the success, failure, neither, or both innovations. The variables were a composite of proportions derived from three sources: (1) the Survey I responses; (2) previous research; (3) our own experience.

The third and last part of the study comprised in-depth case studies of 20 sites. The research was conducted by teams of two to three graduate assistants (see Acknowledgments). Each team visited its firm with three objectives: (1) to test the validity of the results obtained in Survey II by replicating the survey based on personal interviews; (2) to contrast and compare their results with the original survey; (3) to determine any additional factors which influenced product success or failure. The teams summarized their results in 25–30 page reports, which included summaries or transcripts of their interviews. In this phase of the study, 101 executives and technical personnel were interviewed during 148 hours of interviews and over 600 pages of interview notes were prepared.

Each phase of the research had a specific purpose. Survey I was an exploratory instrument which was used to determine which factors executives believed influenced new product success or failure. Collection of unstructured data was critical because the literature does not provide a comprehensive variable pool which is both specific to this industry and timely.

The purpose of Survey II was twofold. The primary goal was to identify those variables which had significant influence on product outcome, thereby reducing the variable data set. Since the variables tested were derived from studies of different industries, markets, firm locations, and time periods, it was anticipated all the factors would not be relevant. Survey II was also used to determine whether the significant variables were associated with either success or failure. Relative ranking of importance of the factors could be inferred from the data, but is not discussed due to the exploratory nature of this phase of the study.

The last phase of the study (the case studies) served to validate the earlier findings and to identify additional factors which may have been ignored due to the single respondent structure of Surveys I and II. Figure 2 illustrates the research format and flow. The results from this three-part exploratory study are the basis for our proposed model, which we plan to test in our subsequent research.

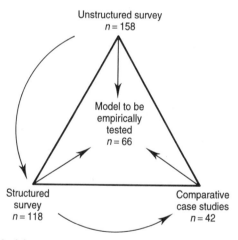

Figure 2. Triangulation Methodology.

IV. ANALYSIS AND RESULTS

A. Survey I

The empirical data derived from Survey I were used (1) to establish the basic demographics of the sample and, most importantly, (2) to provide unstructured exploratory data about the determinants of product success or failure which could be used as source material for designing Survey II. These unstructured responses were then categorized by type of comments into three general categories.

The demographics of the sample showed little variance from Survey I to Survey II. This result was to be expected since 75% of the respondents to Survey I participated in Survey II and examination of the backgrounds of those that did not participate did not reveal a significant bias. As Table 1 shows, analysis of the backgrounds of the participants in the second survey reveals little difference between the first and second surveys. This was the case for the remainder of the demographic data. About half of our informants were functional vice presidents, directors or managers, while another third were presidents or general managers. On the average, they had spent five years with their companies. The median business unit sampled had sales of $20 000 000, return on sales of 10%, and employed 200–300 people. Business unit size and employment and return on sales, however, varied considerably. Fifty-nine percent of the business units were under $30 000 000 in sales and almost a third (30%) were over $50 000 000 in sales.

Table 1. Position of respondents by survey

Respondent's position	Survey I (%)(n = 79)	Survey II (%) (n = 59)
President/CEO/general mgr	34	36
Vice president/functional mgr	51	51
Other	15	13

The products studied were roughly evenly split into instruments, computers and computer peripherals, electronic systems and other (electronic components, materials and services). The smaller sample of case studies, however, was split, half into instruments and the remaining half roughly equally divided into computers and electronic systems (Table 2). The overwhelming majority of the firms in both surveys were located on the West Coast and to minimize travel expenses *all* the case studies were done in collaboration with West Coast firms (Table 3).

Table 2. Product categories of innovations by survey

Product categories	Survey I (%) (n = 79)	Survey II (%) (n = 59)	Survey II validation (%) (n = 20)
Instruments	25	29	50
Computers	28	25	20
Systems	25	27	25
Other	22	19	5

The majority of the innovations surveyed were true innovations (new to the industry) that involved significant technical changes (Table 4 and Table 5). One-third were innovations that were based on products already existing in the marketplace (adopted). Approximately one-sixth of the products were viewed as radical technological breakthroughs by the respondents, while about a quarter were considered incremental

Table 3. Site distribution by survey

Location of firms	Survey I (%) (n = 79)	Survey II (%) (n = 59)	Survey II validation (%) (n = 20)
West Coast (CA, WA, OR)	78	78	100
Southwest (AR, CO, TX)	6	7	–
Northeast (MA, NY, NJ, PA)	10	10	–
North Central (MI, MN, IL, OH)	5	3	–
Other (Switzerland)	1	2	–

changes—the remainder were classified as significant technical changes. By our own assessment, however, very few, if any, of the products in the study could be classified as 'technological breakthroughs', that is, fundamental innovations such as jet aircraft, gene splicing and the transistor. The median successful innovation cost $500 000 to develop. The median for the less successful innovations, $400 000, was about 20% lower. About half of the innovations cost less than $500 000 to develop, while about 40% cost more than $1 000 000.

Table 4. Innovation type

Type of innovation	Survey I (%) (n = 78) Success	Failure	Survey II (%) (n = 58) Success	Failure	Survey II validation (%) (n = 20) Success	Failure
True (new to industry)	64	54	66	59	70	60
Adoption (existing in industry)	36	46	34	41	30	40

Table 5. Degree of technical change

Technological content of innovations	Survey I (%) (n = 78) Success	Failure	Survey II (%) (n = 58) Success	Failure	Survey II Validation (%) (n = 20) Success	Failure
Radical breakthrough	15	12	16	16	20	25
Significant technical change	57	44	56	41	60	45
Incremental change	28	44	28	43	20	30

The responses regarding factors which contributed to the success or failure of the innovation pair were classified under three broad categories: (1) environmental variables; (2) corporate skills and resources; (3) products and product strategy; and coded using the framework shown in Table 6. Each individual response was given a weight of one, even though some respondents listed more than one fact to explain the success (or failure) of the innovations they selected. When a statement was indefinite enough that it could be placed in two different categories, each category was assigned the value 0.5. In total, 284 individual success factors and 217 failure factors were coded using the

Table 6. Analysis of Survey I responses

	Success factors (% of total)	Failure factors (% of total)
I. Environment		
A. Market characteristics	14	13
1. Size	3	8
2. Growth rate	2	0
3. Newness	2	0
4. Difficulty of market development	7	5
B. Competition	5	6
1. Strength	2	3
2. Number	2	2
3. Timing	1	1
C. Government regulation	0	2
D. Economy	0	0
E. Other	1	1
Total:	20	22
II. Corporate skills and resources		
A. Marketing	18	18
1. Marketing proficiency	13	15
2. Resource commitment	2	1
3. Timing of entry	2	2
4. Customer funding of product	1	0
B. Research/development and engineering	6	16
1. Technological capability	2	5
2. Program management	4	9
3. Resource commitment	0	2
C. Manufacturing	4	3
1. Technological capability	3	3
2. Organization and management	1	0
3. Resource commitment	0	0
D. Functional and external coordination	4	3
1. Marketing/customer	3	3
2. Marketing/engineering	1	0
3. Engineering /manufacturing	0	0
E. Organizational commitment	1	1
1. Product champion	0	0
2. Management support	1	1
F. Corporate reputation	2	1
G. Other	1	2
Total:	36	45

framework. The percentages in Table 6 were calculated by using the aggregate comment totals as a base.

Two categories of variables stood out from the others; market and product variables. Together they accounted for well over half of the factors that our sample of managers believed are the principal determinants of both new product success and failure: product

Table 6. (*continued*)

	Success factors (% of total)	Failure factors (% of total)
III. Product and product strategy		
A. Product characteristics	33	18
1. Performance/uniqueness	6	8
2. Ease of use	2	3
3. Quality/reliability	4	1
4. Compatibility	2	1
5. Serviceability	0	1
6. Price (or cost)	5	2
7. Benefit to cost (value)	13	2
8. Overall design	1	0
B. Product strategy	9	4
1. Closeness to strengths	5	4
2. Synergy with other products	4	0
C. Protection	3	5
1. Patent	1	0
2. Technological lead	2	3
D. Other	0	2
Total:	45	27

Note : Columns do not total to 100% due to rounding.

characteristics (33%), marketing (18%), and market characteristics (14%) for the successes; and product characteristics (18%), marketing (18%), and market characteristics (13%) for the failures. Within these categories, two closely related individual variables, the product's benefit-to-cost ratio and the organizations's marketing proficiency accounted for one-quarter of the success factors. The reasons for failure, however, were more varied than the factors which facilitated success. The role of research development and engineering, for instance, was cited three times as often as a factor causing failure (16%) than as a success facilitator (6%).

These results are significant because of what managers chose to include as well as because of what they left out. Despite a litany of complaints by industrial executives regarding government interference and the pressures of the business cycle, these factors accounted for only 2% of the responses. Likewise, manufacturing, a focus of national attention in the mature industries, seems to play a secondary role in the success and failure in new electronic products. Patents, generally considered of great importance as a competitive weapon in the technology-based industries, appeared to be of little significance (only mentioned twice) though these results might have been significantly different in the chemical or pharmaceutical industries. In the electronics industry, having a technological lead seems to be far more important. The product champion hypothesis, an important variable in most research on new products, was mentioned by our executive respondents in only one of the almost 500 responses recorded.

Survey I served two purposes. First, it represents the first tangible results of our study. Secondly, it serves as a guide to identify and prioritize variables for our 60-question Survey II. Indeed, while it is tempting to assign priorities to the different variables listed in Table 6, based on the frequency with which they were mentioned, our view of this stage of the research is that its principal value is to improve the effectiveness and completeness of our subsequent structured surveys. We believe, however, that these results are representative of executives' general beliefs regarding product success and failure in the electronics industry.

B. Survey II

The results of the 60-question Survey II were analyzed using several statistical techniques. First, a cumulative binomial statistic was calculated for each variable. This binomial test was used to determine if the variable was a significant influencer on new product success or failure. This technique was also used in the SAPPHO study, which had a similar data format. The null hypothesis for this test stated that the likelihood of a success or failure response for each variable tested was equivalent. If the calculated binomial value (x) was less than 0.1, the null hypothesis was rejected, and we assumed that the variable did distinguish between success and failure.

The variables were then grouped according to the results of the cumulative binomial test into four categories. Thirty-seven of the original 60 variables were significant to the 10% (0.1) or better level.

Binomial value	Number of variables	Significance rating
$x < 1\%$	18	$+ + +/- - -$
$1\% \leq x \leq 5\%$	9	$+ +/- -$
$5\% < x \leq 10\%$	10	$+/-$
$x > 10\%$	23	(not significant)

The significance rating shown above was used in subsequent analyses and indicates level of binomial significance. The sign (+ or −) distinguishes whether the variable was correlated more with successes (+) or failures (−). The variables which differentiated between successes and failures were then intuitively grouped into the ten index variables shown in Table 7, roughly in accordance with the overall statistical significance of each grouping. If the variable correlated more with failures than successes, the inverse of it was assumed to relate to successes. Those variables which were tested but were not statistically significant are shown in Table 8.

In addition to the intuitive analysis just described, the Survey II variable set was also analyzed using a statistical cluster analysis routine. Although factor analysis is generally preferred for data reduction over clustering, it was not feasible due to the data format and limited sample size. The cluster analysis was conducted in order to provide a more systematic and rigorous grouping of variables. The cluster groups were then evaluated to determine if they supported our intuitive analysis. In addition, this analysis provided new insights about variable interrelationships.

The clustering was conducted using an SAS hierarchical variable clustering route (Varclus) with the 27 variables which were significant to better than 5%. Several iterations were done changing the number of clusters and the clustering algorithm. Since the data base size was limited (59 observations) the ten variables in the 5–10% significance range (see above), were not clustered in order to improve the ratio of data points to the number of variables. The cluster descriptions and groups are shown in Table 9.

The cluster results were broadly consistent with the earlier intuitive variable groups. Six of the index variables shown in Table 7 were confirmed by the cluster routine.

Successful innovations were:

Index variable number	Description
1	better matched with user needs;
2	planned more effectively and efficiently;
5	more efficiently developed;
6	more actively marketed and sold;
7	closer to the firm's areas of expertise;
8	introduced to the market earlier than competition.

In addition, we found that several of the intuitive index variables combined into single clusters, while others split into two clusters. For example, index variable 3, Table 7 (higher benefit to cost), was composed of variables which related to both the customer (value) and to the firm (profit margins). The cluster grouping procedure split this index variable into two separate clusters. On the other hand, product value (performance to cost ratio) merged with the user needs factor index variable. Thus understanding user needs effectively is both a function of determining the appropriate product features as well as designing the product within a realistic price range. A second factor also emerged from the original index variable 3 cluster, the contribution of the product to the firm.

The cluster groupings also noted a distinction between planning and coordination *within* the R&D organization and functional coordination such as marketing and manufacturing. Superior R&D execution in the product conceptualization and planning stages resulted in less redesign and reengineering effort. While superior R&D management is a subset of overall interfunctional product planning, management, and coordination, the cluster group analysis placed special importance on the R&D management link in the product development chain.

While the cluster results improved the sophistication of our analysis, our overall statistical results of Survey II, however, rest on at least two assailable methodological assumptions. The Survey II data was based on only one respondent per innovation pair, and, secondly, the respondents were a mixture of general managers and functional managers. To test the first assumption, we completed 20 in-depth comparative case studies for which we interviewed an average of five informants per site. To test the second, we contrasted the responses of the functional managers with those of the general management respondents. We then analyzed the interview data obtained from the site visits and contrasted it with the original Survey II data.

At each site where a case study had been done, the project staff independently filled out a Survey II form after the interviews were completed. The subset of these responses (the 'Survey II validation') was then analyzed using the same statistical techniques employed for Survey II and compared to the original results (see Table 10). Due to the considerably smaller sample (20 versus 59), it was expected that many of the variables for which statistical significance had been originally weak would now be lost in the noise,

Table 7. Summary of variables intuitively grouped by index variables (Survey II)

Successful innovations were:	S>F	F>S	Cumulative binomial	Significance rating
(1) Better matched with user needs				
Better matched to customer needs	40	4	8.53 E–09	+++
Developed by teams which more fully understood user needs	36	8	1.27 E–05	+++
Accepted more quickly by users	13	36	7.01 E–04	– – –
(2) Planned more effectively and efficiently				
Forecast more accurately (market)	38	5	1.25 E–07	+++
Developed with a clearer market strategy	35	10	1.24 E–04	+++
Formalized on paper sooner	32	13	3.30 E–03	+++
Developed with less variance between actual and budgeted expenses	16	30	2.70 E–02	– –
Expected initially to be more commercially successful	26	16	8.21 E–02	+
(3) Higher in benefit-to-cost				
Priced with higher profit margins	44	7	6.06 E–08	+++
Allowed greater pricing flexibility	43	9	1.02 E–06	+++
More significant with respect to benefit to cost ratio	30	13	6.86 E–03	+++
(4) Developed by better-coupled organizations				
Developed by better-coupled functional divisions	35	4	1.68 E–07	+++
(5) More efficiently developed				
Less plagued by after-sales problems	6	29	5.84 E–05	– – –
Developed with fewer personnel changes on the project team	7	21	6.27 E–03	– – –
Impacted by fewer changes during production	13	28	1.38 E–02	– –
Developed with a more experienced project team	26	13	2.66 E–02	++
Changed less after production commenced	18	29	7.19 E–02	–
Developed on a more compressed time schedule	24	15	9.98 E–02	+
(6) More actively marketed and sold				
More actively publicized and advertised	28	11	4.74 E–03	+++
Promoted by a larger sales force	21	7	6.27 E–03	+++
Coupled with a marketing effort to educate users	26	11	1.00 E–02	++
(7) Closer to the firm's areas of expertise				
Aided more by in-house basic research	19	6	7.32 E–03	+++
Required fewer new marketing channels	6	19	7.32 E–03	– – –
Closer to the main business area of firm	22	8	8.06 E–03	+++
More influenced by corporate reputation	20	9	3.07 E–02	++
Less dependent on existing products in the market	13	23	6.62 E–02	–
Required less diversification from traditional markets	8	16	7.58 E–02	–

but that those variables for which there had been strong (better than 1%) support originally would still be statistically significant for the smaller sample.

Over two-thirds of the 37 significant Survey II variables were again found to be

Table 7. (*continued*)

Successful innovations were:	S>F	F>S	Cumulative binomial	Significance rating
(8) Introduced to the market earlier than competition				
In the market longer before competing products introduced	30	14	1.13 E−02	++
First-to-market type products	27	12	1.19 E−02	++
More offensive innovations	29	17	5.19 E−02	+
Generally not second-to-market	13	23	6.62 E−02	−
(9) Supported more by management				
Supported more by senior management	24	7	1.66 E−03	+++
Potentially more impactful on the careers of the project team members	21	11	5.51 E−02	+
Developed with a more senior project leader	24	15	9.98 E−02	+
(10) Technically superior				
Closer to the state-of-the-art technology	24	12	3.26 E−02	++
More difficult for competition to copy	29	16	3.62 E−02	++
More radical with respect to world technology	26	16	8.21 E−02	+

S: number of successes; *F*: number of failures.

statistically significant, while over four-fifths of the variables that were originally significant to better than 1% were still significant to better than 5%. No new variable emerged with statistical significance of better than 5%. Analysis of the responses of the original Survey II informants for the subset of sites where the cases were done (Table 10, last column) indicated that the three <1% variables which the validation had not confirmed, while significant for the overall Survey II, were also *not* statistically significant to 5% or better in the *original* responses for the 20-site subset. Further analysis of the Survey II validation did not reveal any patterns of inconsistency that would make us suspect the validity of Survey II's findings. Qualitative analysis of the case studies themselves will be reported on separately.

The Survey II data set was also disaggregated by respondent background and position, business size, product category and type of innovation to contrast the response of different sets. Unfortunately, when sliced into subcategories the sample often became too small for statistical analysis to be consistently significant. For instance, as shown in Table 7 and Table 8, sample size (*n*) on any given question, though theoretically 59, was generally reduced to 30–45 for most question due to 'neither', 'both', or incomplete responses. When the sample is further disaggregated into various subsets, sample sizes often dropped a range of 10–15. Nonetheless, all the cuts noted above were made and analyzed.

Methodologically, the most important cut was the comparison of the responses based on informant position (general management versus functional managers). Ideally all of our respondents would be general managers who could be expected to have the most balanced and objective view of a new product's trajectory. For purposes of the comparison of general and functional managers' responses, the ten index variables shown in Table 7 were used as yardsticks. Statistical support for each set of propositions corresponding to each index variable was indicated on a scale of + to + + + (see Table 11).

Table 8. Variables with cumulative binomials greater than 10%

Variable description	S>F	F>S	Cumulative binomial
Successful innovations had a clearly identifiable product champion	16	9	1.15 E–01
Successful innovations had a higher technological content	27	18	1.16 E–01
Successful innovations were directed by an individual with more power and authority	19	12	1.41 E–01
Successful innovations used more technology outside the firm's areas of expertise	26	18	1.46 E–01
Successful innovations required more interaction with users in the development stage	24	17	1.74 E–01
Successful innovations required less adaptation by users	16	22	2.09 E–01
Successful innovations had more project reviews during development and commercialization	23	18	2.66 E–01
Successful innovations were developed by teams with higher education levels	14	10	2.71 E–01
Successful innovations were approved for development at less senior levels	4	7	2.74 E–01
Successful innovations had larger development teams	25	21	3.29 E–01
Successful innovations had a longer time period before competitors introduced competing products	15	18	3.64 E–01
Successful innovations utilized fewer external advisors	15	18	3.64 E–01
Successful innovations had greater expenditures for specialized tooling or equipment	24	21	3.83 E–01
Project teams of successful innovations interfaced more with external resource	17	15	4.30 E–01
Successful innovations were developed by teams with newer employees	18	16	4.32 E–01
Successful innovations depended more on technology developed externally	18	16	4.32 E–01
Successful innovations were less defensive products in the market	17	19	4.34 E–01
Successful innovations required less understanding of competitive environment	18	20	4.36 E–01
Successful innovations required a more technically oriented user	19	18	5.00 E–01
Successful innovations required more new production processes	12	11	5.00 E–01
Successful innovations were introduced in a less competitive environment	23	24	5.00 E–01
Successful innovations required less change in the firm's strategy	17	16	5.00 E–01
Successful innovations were directed more towards a market need versus a result of a technology opportunity	21	21	5.61 E–01

S: number of successes; F: number of failures.

This scale is only an approximate indicator, since variables of different statistical significance are mixed within each index variable, but it corresponds roughly to our original definition of the + to + + + range (see above).

Analysis of the results reveals only one category where the support for the index variable varied considerably: management support. Not surprisingly, functional

Table 9. Cluster analysis results

Successful innovations were:	R^2 with cluster	R^2 with next highest cluster
(1) Better matched with user needs and provided high value		
Better matched to customer needs	0.65	0.09
Developed by teams which more fully understood user needs	0.57	0.08
More significant with respect to benefit-to-cost ratio	0.40	0.09
Forecast more accurately (market)	0.55	0.07
(2) Well-planned and executed during development		
Supported more by senior management	0.45	0.14
Developed with less variance between actual and budgeted expenses	0.65	0.06
Impacted by less changes during production	0.48	0.10
Less plagued by after-sales problems	0.63	0.03
(3) Higher contribution products for the firm[a]		
Priced with higher profit margins	0.78	0.05
Allowed greater pricing flexibility	0.78	0.02
(4) Well-planned and coordinated between functions		
Developed with fewer personnel changes on the project team	0.34	0.03
Formalized on paper sooner	0.35	0.09
Developed by better-coupled functional divisions	0.53	0.03
Developed with a clearer market strategy	0.36	0.13
(5) Introduced to the market earlier than competition		
First-to-the-market type products	0.58	0.08
In the market longer before competing products introduced	0.54	0.16
Accepted more quickly by users	0.33	0.08
(6) More actively marketed and sold		
More actively publicized and advertised	0.44	0.11
Coupled with a marketing effort to educate users	0.53	0.06
Promoted by a larger sales force	0.50	0.10
Developed with a more experienced project team	0.32	0.03
(7) Closer to the firm and areas of expertise		
Closer to the main business area of firm	0.30	C.08
Closer to the state-of-the-art technology	0.47	0.04
Aided more by in-house basic research	0.43	0.09
More influenced by corporate reputation	0.35	0.05
More difficult for competition to copy	0.40	0.11

[a] One variable was dropped because the variable's correlation with its assigned cluster was approximately equal to the next highest cluster correlation.

managers, who often have to fight for resources for their projects, believe that management support of an innovation is very important (+ + +) to the success of a new product. General managers and presidents, who presumably do the resource allocation, do not feel this variable is nearly as important (+). Part of the increase in significance, however, is doubtlessly a function of the sample size. There were 34 functional managers

Table 10. Shift in statistical significance of the 37 significant variables from Survey II to Sur...,
II validation study

Statistical significance in Survey II			Statistical significance in Survey II validation			
<1%	1–5%	>5–10%	<1%	1–5%	>5–10%	>10%
18	—	—	12	3	—	3
—	9	—	1	3	2	3
—	—	10	—	5	1	4
18	9	10	13	11	3	10

Table 11. Response by participant's position and experiential background (Survey II)

	Respondent's position		Respondent's functional background	
	Gen. mgr ($n = 20$)	Funct. mgr ($n = 34$)	Eng./R&D ($n = 25$)	Mktg. ($n = 18$)
1. User needs	+++	+++	++	++
2. Planning	++	+++	+	++
3. Benefit/cost	++	+++	+	++
4. Internal coupling	+++	+++	++	++
5. Development efficiency	+	++	+	+
6. Timing advantage	+	+	0	++
7. Marketing resources	++	+	+	++
8. Expertise compatibility	+	++	++	+
9. Management support	+	+++	0	+
10. Technological superiority	+	+	0	+

Code : 0: very weak or no statistical significance; +: weak support; ++: moderate support; +++: strong support.

in the sample and only 20 general managers (or presidents). Indeed, in every case but one it was the functional managers that provided stronger statistical support for each of the index variables. For this reason, we do not consider minor differences, in the right (statistically speaking) direction, as significant. The exception (variable 7) bears closer examination. The general managers appear to place significantly greater emphasis on the role of marketing and sales, since despite their considerably smaller numbers they provided greater statistical confirmation for that index variable than the functional managers. Most importantly, however, functional managers and general managers alike, though they differ in emphasis as noted above, supported every one of the index variables.

When the data set was cut by the experiential background of the informants, however, many differences emerged. Marketing executives, relative to technical managers, placed greater emphasis on planning, value to the customer and timing of market entry. The technical people, on the other hand, placed greater relative importance on internal variables, such as staying close to existing company strengths and on coupling to other functions within the company. Since the sample of technical executives was greater and yet their responses were, on an aggregate basis, less significant statistically, their responses reflect a greater diversity in their perception of the factors that shape product success.

The survey responses were also subdivided by business unit size (under \$20 000 000 (n = 28) and over \$20 000 000 (n = 27)), and the data analyzed in the manner described above. Since the overall sample sizes were equal, variations based on sample size were a lesser consideration for this cut. Only one strong difference emerged from the comparison: closeness to existing strengths had more leverage towards success in the large business units than in the small ones. Two less significant differences also emerged: technological superiority and emphasis on marketing were more important success factors for the products of the smaller business units.

Comparison of the three industry subgroupings in the survey—instruments, computers and computer peripherals, and electronic systems—revealed no significant differences. This was in part to be expected, since all three industries are part of what is loosely called the electronics industry. Contrasts would have been much sharper if the sample had included a mix of chemical or pharmaceutical products, for instance. Secondly, when the sample was split into three principal groupings, sample size became so small (n = 10–15) that no index variable registered strong statistical support. The same factors impeded us from drawing useful conclusions, using these techniques, from the remainder of the statistical cuts. For the different types of innovations, the situation was further complicated because of the many different typologies that existed, e.g. successful incremental changes might have been paired with less successful incremental, significant or radical changes. We are, however, continuing our analysis of this data using other techniques.

V. CONCLUSIONS

There is, unfortunately, no single magical factor that can explain the bulk of our results. For those who would reduce new product success to one (or two) variables, there is no panacea to be found here. As Jewkes and his coauthors wrote in their classic study of invention, 'The path of innovation is always thorny ... there are no short cuts to success, no infallible formulae' (Jewkes, Sawers and Stillerman, 1969). Indeed, 37 of the 60 variables that we tested in Survey II (62%) were found to be statistically significant. Nonetheless, many of these variables are correlated. Some of our questions tested similar propositions. For instance, in one question we asked about the importance of being first to market, while in another we asked whether products that were second to market were more or less successful. The response to both questions supports the hypothesis that, at least, in the electronics industry, being first to market generally yields a competitive advantage.

Several methods were used to reduce the redundancy inherent in the data and to consolidate similar answers into groups. First, the 37 significant variables were intuitively aggregated into ten index variables listed in Table 7. Clusters were then developed using hierarchical cluster techniques. Seven clusters were identified and compared with the index variables developed with the intuitive analysis. In most cases, the mathematical clustering helped us confirm our original clusters, but some new relationships were also discovered.

Our next step was to integrate the results of Survey I, Survey II and the cluster analysis of Survey II in order to begin to conceptualize a model for testing in subsequent research. We defined eight general categories under which we have grouped the findings of Phase I of the Stanford Innovation Project. (These are essentially the seven clusters listed in Table 9, except that cluster 2 was further broken down into two factors.) New product success is likely to be greater under the following circumstances.

(1) The developing organization, through in-depth understanding of the customers and the marketplace, introduces a product with a high performance-to-cost ratio.
(2) The developing organization is proficient in marketing and commits a significant amount of its resources to selling and promoting the product.
(3) The product provides a high contribution margin to the firm.
(4) The R&D process is well planned and executed.
(5) The create, make and market functions are well interfaced and coordinated.
(6) The product is introduced into the market early.
(7) The markets and technologies of the new product benefit significantly from the existing strengths of the developing business unit.
(8) There is a high level of management support for the product from the development stage through its launch to the marketplace.

This list does not, *directly*, highlight the importance of technological capability. Indeed, since at their initiation the projects we studied were believed by management to be technologically feasible, the importance of technological superiority was attenuated while market factors were emphasized. On the other hand, by the time the vast majority of industrial development projects are given the go-ahead, management, though not always right, is generally convinced that the technology can be made to work. In these projects, the proper role of the development group is to efficiently configure the technology in a way that the product has high value (see item (1), above) for the customer. The product should be designed to achieve the customer's goals, not simply technological goals. Technological prowess would have come strongly to the foreground had we studied R&D projects or exploratory development projects for which technological feasibility was far from assured.

Comparison of our results to the SAPPHO and NewProd studies reveals broad areas of agreement and several major differences. For instance, there is clear agreement that no single factor but rather a combination of factors generally account for the success of an innovation. Secondly, all three studies concluded that a good understanding of the marketplace is essential for new product success. This finding, which has its roots in Myers and Marquis, is the most pervasive finding of recent new product studies (Cooper, 1983). The related finding, that considerable effort and skill must be employed in order to effectively communicate the characteristics of the new product offering to the marketplace was also a consistent theme.

Due in part, we believe, to their different methodologies, the remaining findings are not consistent among the three studies. Take, for instance, the properties of the product itself and its relationship to the existing product line. Both the NewProd and this study emphasize the importance of the characteristics of the product—its uniqueness, particularly its value. Product 'value' was measured by both the customer and the firm, respectively, through performance-to-cost ratios and contribution margins. The product, however, was not a major variable in the SAPPHO study. The characteristics of the marketplace were not found to be major variables by the SAPPHO or NewProd studies, or, for that matter, in our Survey II. Yet our open-ended Survey I results (Table 6) clearly suggest that the environment is an important determinant of new product success. Specifically, Survey II indicated that timing of market entry in order to take advantage of a favourable competitive environment was important. Synergy with present capabilities, while not an important factor in the SAPPHO study, was found to be highly significant in the NewProd study and in our surveys. Overall, while our study does not reject the SAPPHO findings in a US context, our conclusions, for both methodological and contextual reasons, are closer to those of Cooper's NewProd study. Indeed, our findings validate two of Cooper's implicit hypotheses: (1) that a US-based study, using similar methodology, could largely coincide with the results obtained from his representative sample of Canadian industrial products; (2) that a single informant study, if large scale, would yield results similar to that obtained with a smaller number of in-depth case studies.

One of the principal objectives of our study, however, was to begin to move beyond a list of key findings and to propose a model of the new product process that would incorporate our findings and those of others. Using our eight major conclusions as a guide, a preliminary model of the critical elements of new product process was developed. The model (Figure 3) is based on an interpretation of the new product process in the electronics industry as a change-producing activity which is characteristically blocked at every transfer point by the tendency to resist change (Lawrence, 1969; Schon, 1967). We believe our findings provide strong support of this view.

Four of the factors that our research has identified as the most influential facilitators of new product success—marketing and sales emphasis, customer interaction, R&D and overall internal planning and coordination—deal directly with overcoming internal and external organizational gaps. These gaps are geometrically represented in the model as physical separations between the functional elements of the product development process and the organization's customer base. Two forces play an important role in overcoming these natural gaps: management and, indirectly the product's anticipated contribution. Management support is essential to overcome the internal obstacles that arise when significant change is necessary to accommodate a new product. This is not to say that product champions, the focus of much prior research, are not important, especially for radical innovations (Maidique and Ince, 1979b; Schon, 1963; Maidique, 1980). However, for our sample, which was largely composed of incremental and significant innovations, their role was secondary compared to managerial sponsorship (Maidique, 1980). (See Table 7, significant variables.) The product's anticipated profitability (margin) can also be a potent force inducing key constituencies within the firm to release resources and thus overcome internal and external obstacles to the new product's success. Everyone loves a winner. When a product is perceived to have high profit potential, major barriers to its development often dissolve.

The model also has explicatory value. One of our principal findings was that product success is higher if the new product builds on present technological and market strengths. Entry into new markets or technologies generally requires the establishment of new customer–company connections, and, if new personnel are brought in, new patterns of coordination between the stages of the new product development process, or both. Thus the critical balance and coordination required in the new product development loop can be significantly disrupted by the organizational restructuring that entry into new markets and technologies generally requires. It is for these reasons that teams from the same organization which are entering a market closely related to their previous business have the best chance of succeeding in a new venture (Cooper and Bruno, 1977).

Finally, the importance of the character of the marketplace and its degree of connectedness to the firm is reflected in the rectangular plug in the upper part of Figure 3, which is drawn to emphasize what Barnard pointed out nearly half a century ago, that customers should be viewed as part of the social organization of the firm (Barnard, 1968). The model presented here represents our preliminary thoughts on how to integrate our findings. If it stimulates thought and criticism, it will have achieved its purpose.

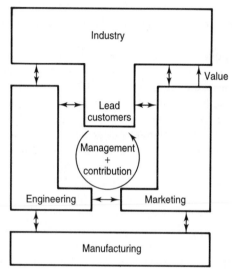

Figure 3. Model of Critical Elements of New Product Development Process.

Completion of this stage of our project has helped us to identify several deficiencies in our original survey instrument but also to ratify its general effectiveness. Secondly, the preliminary model described above has been developed. This conceptualization combined with the results of the original surveys and cases has allowed us to develop a new survey instrument designed to test several of the hypotheses inherent in our proposed model. In our subsequent research, the predictive power of our model will be tested in collaboration with the 1983 Stanford-AEA Executive Institute.

ACKNOWLEDGMENTS

This work was supported by the Department of Industrial Engineering and Engineering Management, Stanford University, and by the American Electronics Association through the Stanford-AEA Executive Institute. Portions of this paper were presented at the ORSA/TIMS Conference in Chicago in April 1983, and at the Worcester Polytechnic Institute Conference on the Management of Technological Innovation in Washington, DC, May 1983.

The authors wish to thank M. Booen, one of this project's original research assistants who contributed to the initial research design and did much of the early data analysis. The personal encouragement and support of Prof. W. Hausman and Prof. H. Riggs is gratefully acknowledged. W. Hausman, M. Horwitch and four anonymous reviewers made valuable comments on earlier drafts of this paper.

The authors also wish to express their appreciation to the following graduate and doctoral candidates, who assisted in preparation of the individual case studies: P. Achi, G. Ananthasubramanium, R. Angangco, C. Badger, B. Billerbeck, R. Cannon, D. Chinn, L. Christian, B. Connor, A. Dahlen, S. Demetrescu, B. Drobenko, R. Farros, H. Finger, H. G. Jagadish, L. Girault-Cuevas, R. Guior, T. Hardison, Y. Honda, J. Jover, C. Koo, T. Kuneida, S. Kurasaki, M. Lacayo, D. Lampaya, D. Ledakis, L. Lei, R. Ling, S. Makmuri, P. Matlock, C. Mungale, R. Ortiz, B. Raschle, R. Reis, B. Russ, E. Saenger, J. Sanghani, V. Sanvido, F. Sasselli, R. Simon, P. Stamats, R. Stauffer, L. Taruel, B. Walsh and F. Zustak.

NOTE

1. For purposes of this paper, the high-technology industries are defined as those which spend more than 3% of sales on R&D (research and development). Only five US industries meet this criterion: (1) chemicals and pharmaceuticals; (2) machinery (especially computers and office machines); (3) electrical equipment and communications; (4) professional and scientific instruments; and (5) aircraft and missiles. (*Source*: NSF, 1981.)

REFERENCES

Alloway, R. M. and Utterback, J. M. (1977) 'Strategies for research on management', Harvard Business School, Boston, MA:, Working Pap. 75–20, Dec.

Barnard, C. (1968) *The Functions of the Executive*. Cambridge, MA: Harvard Univ. Press.

Baruch, J. and Barbour, E. (1971) *Pilkington Float Glass (A)*. Boston, MA: Harvard Business Case Services, no. 9–672–069.

Baruch, J. and Barbour, E. (1972) *Pilkington Float Glass (B)*. Boston, MA: Harvard Business School Case Services, no. 9–673–042.

Baruch, J. and Kiser, D. (1973) *Advent Corporation (C)*. Boston, MA: Harvard Business School Case Services, no. 9–674–027.

Booz, Allen and Hamilton (1968) *Management of New Products*. New York: Booz, Allen and Hamilton.

Cooper, R. G. (1979a) 'The dimensions of industrial new product success and failure', *J. Marketing*, **43**(3), 93–103.

Cooper, R. G. (1979b) 'Identifying industrial new product success: Project NewProd', *Industrial Marketing Manag.*, **8**, 124–135.

Cooper, R. G. (1980a) 'Project NewProd: Factors in new product success', *Eur. J. Marketing*, **14**(5/6), 277–292.

Cooper, R. G. (1980b) 'Project NewProd: What makes a new product a winner?' Montreal, Canada: Quebec Industrial Innovation Centre.

Cooper, R. G. (1983) 'A process model for industrial new product development', *IEEE Trans. Eng. Manag.*, **EM-30**(1), 2–11.

Cooper, A. C. and Bruno, A. V. (1977) 'Success among high-technology firms', *Bus. Horizons*, **20** (2), 16–22.

Jewkes, J., Sawers, D., Stillerman, R. (1969) *The Sources of Invention*. New York: Norton, p. 227.

Lawrence, P. R. (1969) 'How to deal with resistance to change', *Harvard Bus. Rev.*, **47**(1), 4–12, 166–176.

Maidique, M. A. (Winter1980) 'Entrepreneurs, Champions and Technological Innovation', *Sloan Management Rev.*, **21**(2), 59–76.

Maidique, M. A. (1983) 'The Stanford innovation project: A comparative study of success and failure in high-technology product innovation', in *Proc. Conf. Management of Technological Innovation*, NSF and Worcester Polytechnic Institute, Washington, DC, May.

Maidique, M. and Ince, J. (1979) *Advent (E)*. Boston, MA: Harvard Business School Case Services, no. 9–680–102.

Maidique, M. and Ince, J. (1979) *Advent (F)*. Boston, MA: Harvard Business School Case Services, no. 9–680–103.

Marquis, D. G. (Nov. 1969) 'The Anatomy of Successful Innovations', *Innovation*, vol. **1**, pp. 28–37.

Morison, E. (1966) *Men, Machines and Modern Times*. Cambridge, MA: M.I.T. Press, ch. 2, pp. 17–44.

Mowery, D. and Rosenberg, N. (1979) 'The influence of market demand upon innovation: A critical review of some recent empirical studies', *Research Policy* **8**, pp. 101–153.

Myers, S. and Marquis, D. G. (1969) 'Successful industrial innovations', National Science Foundation, Rep. NSF 69–17.

NSF (1981) 'Science Resource Studies Highlights', Rep. NSF81–331, National Science Foundation, Dec. 31., p. 2.

Rosenbloom, R.S. (1976) *Advent Corporation (D)*. Boston, MA: Harvard Business School Case Services, no. 9–676–053.

Rothwell, R., Freeman, C., Horsley, A., Jervis, V. T. P., Robertson, A. B. and Townsend, J. (1974) 'SAPPHO updated—Project SAPPHO, Phase II', *Res. Policy* **3**, pp. 258–291.

Rothwell, R., Freeman, C., Horsley, A., Jervis, V. T. P., Robertson, A. B. and Townsend, J.(1976) 'SAPPHO updated—Project SAPPHO, Phase II', *Res. Policy* **3**, pp. 259–260.

Rubenstein, A. H., Chakrabarti, A. K., O'Keefe, R. D., Souder, W. E. and Young, H. C. (1976) 'Factors influencing innovation success at the project level', *Res. Manag.*, **19** (3), 15–20.

Science Policy Research Unit (1972) *Success and Failure in Industrial Innovation*. London, England: Center for the Study of Industrial Innovation, Univ. of Sussex.

Schon, D. A. (1963) 'Champions for radical new inventions', *Harvard Bus. Rev.*, **41**(2), 77–86.

Schon, Donald A. (1967) *Technology and Change*. New York: Dell.

Sorenson, R. Z. (1971) *Gould, Incorporated, Graphics Division*. Boston, MA: Harvard Business School Case Services, no. 9–571–071.

Tushman, M. and Moore, W. (1982) *Readings in the Management of Innovation*. New York: Pitman, pp. 84–96.

Wise, T. A. (1966a) 'IBM's $5,000,000,000 gamble', *Fortune*, **74** (4): 118–123, 224–228.

Wise, T. A. (1966b) 'The Rocky Road to the Marketplace', *Fortune*, **74** (5): 138–143, 199–212.

3

Successful Product Innovation in UK and US Firms

Axel Johne and Patricia Snelson

Product innovation is a potential strategic weapon for all businesses. Skilful product innovation is an urgent management task in markets experiencing rapid technological change—such as consumer electronics, biotechnology, information technology and financial services, to name some of the most obvious. However, while technology facilitates rapid product changes, it is rarely the sole cause of it. There is a long tradition of rapid product change in fashion-related industries, but there is nothing very high technology about fashion clothing or jewellery apart from a very considerable emphasis on new designs. Almost certainly, as has been asserted by Freeman (1982), the most common reason why established firms continue to change their products is fear of competitors who might offer more attractive alternatives.

Despite its undoubted importance, product innovation is not the sole contributor to profitable long-term business growth. Every element in a firm's value-added chain presents potential opportunities for increasing profits. Activities such as production, marketing, purchasing, distribution, advertising, promotion and pricing all offer scope for making better use of resources and therefore for beating competitors in new ways.

Of all the different types of innovation, product and marketing innovation present a particularly rich variety of competitive options. Product innovation is of undoubted importance for businesses which want to compete on the basis of quality and suitability of purpose. It is true that established businesses can fight a rearguard action in the face of more aggressive competitive product innovation by sticking with their old products and selling these to previously unexploited market niches to safeguard sales volume. Such rearguard action does, however, limit the scope for long-term growth. Margins in as yet unexploited market niches are unlikely to be high. More importantly, sticking with old products heightens the risk of failing to survive in the long run, because of likely lower aggregate levels of demand for outdated products no matter how efficiently these are produced. As emphasized by Foster (1986), the time will come for all businesses to update their products, and possibly even to develop completely new products, particularly when new technology makes this attractive. If businesses do not do this, they will in time be overtaken by competitors, either from inside their own industry or from outside.

Reprinted with permission from *European Journal of Marketing*, Vol. 24, No. 12, 1990, pp. 7–21

THE NEED FOR THE RESEARCH

There is a need for managers to learn more about the intricacies of product development. In recent years, the pace of product change has accelerated considerably in more
and more markets. It is only in a few basic extractive and commodity markets that
heightened competition in terms of product change is not yet evident. Often, the need for
product change has been forced on a sleepy domestic industry by foreign competition.
When domestic firms have failed to respond, they have been wiped out or very seriously
damaged, often in quite short periods, as has happened or is happening in both the UK
and US, in machine tools, in motorcycles, in radio and television, in motor vehicles and
in optical goods, including cameras. Hence, there is a growing need by manufacturing
firms, which now need to make more frequent changes to their products, for information
on how the required tasks can be managed efficiently.

For academic reasons, too, there is need for more research. Most academic writings in
the area have concentrated on specific sub-activities within the span of product development tasks. There have been studies into new product idea generation techniques; into
screening procedures and practices; into project management techniques; and into the
different ways in which newly developed products might best be launched. But only a
small number of academic researchers have considered all the elements involved in an
integrated way. The notable exceptions are: Booz, Allen and Hamilton (1982); Cooper
(1984a, b); Crawford (1980); Hopkins (1981); Rothwell (1977). However, none of these
studies adopted a specific inter-country perspective.

It was the specific purpose of the study reported here to look at the total span of
product development tasks in a sample of UK and US firms in a range of different
industry contexts. The investigation was funded by the Economic and Social Research
Council within a larger programme of research on the competitiveness of British industry. Without unduly anticipating the findings, we can state now that firms with little or
no experience of regular product development are faced with the following three important operational questions:

(1) What sort of product development strategies will work best?
(2) What sort of leadership is required of top management?
(3) What team skills are needed to get product developments completed quickly?

DESIGN OF THE FIELD STUDY

The original objectives of the investigation were to discover whether there are significant
differences in the way product innovation is managed (1) in different industries and (2)
in US- compared with UK-owned firms. The need for research into these two aspects
had been identified in earlier work by Johne (1984) in a study of product development
practices in one high-technology manufacturing industry—test and measurement
instrumentation—dominated at the time by US firms.

To meet the original research objectives, four important manufacturing industry
sectors were selected: electrical and electronic engineering, mechanical engineering,

chemicals and food. Within these broad sectors, it was decided to focus on large manufacturing firms because:

(1) these account for an important proportion of national economic output, exports and employment (Pratten, 1986);
(2) it is in large established firms that there is the greatest danger of getting locked into the *status quo* as far as the products being manufactured are concerned.

The actual choice of firms was biased towards the largest, as is explained below, meaning that the final sample included a selection of world-famous firms such as Du Pont, 3M, Grace, Pillsbury, Black & Decker, Dart & Kraft in the US, and ICI, Vickers, GEC, Plessey, Hawker-Siddeley and United Biscuits in the UK.

Questions were focused on how these large companies compete for business in the four industry sectors by considering their organizational and managerial approaches to specific markets, such as office computing, consumer white goods, earth moving equipment, machine tools, industrial rubber products and industrial plastics. The reason for focusing on specific markets in the industry sectors was deliberate: it is in these that businesses compete and where performance can be measured meaningfully.

For each market, two leading companies were selected—one UK-owned, the other US-owned. Selection was done on the basis of published market analyses and advice from government and employer federation personnel, both in the UK and in the US. The UK firms chosen were all *Times* 1000 companies; the US firms all *Fortune* 500 companies at the time the sample was drawn. While large companies were the subject of study, it is important to emphasize that our interest was in the parts of large companies which compete in certain selected markets. Because the relevant operating business belonging even to large world-famous companies can be quite small, in terms of the number of persons employed, a control was introduced whereby only business entities employing at least 200 persons were included in the final sample.

In each firm, initial contact was made by letter with the chief executive officer at the parent company head office, in order to identify the operating business responsible for competing in the selected market. An additional objective of this contact—which was followed up by telephoning the chief executive's office—was to obtain guidance on the appropriate managers to be interviewed in face-to-face meetings. This was, whenever possible, to include a senior person who was involved in determining the firm's product innovation strategy in the selected market, as well as a middle-level manager closely involved in particular product developments.

Bearing in mind the sensitive nature of the investigation, response from initially targeted companies for co-operation was favourable (the results were offered on a syndicated basis). A number of companies, particularly in the US, declined to co-operate for understandable reasons—a prime reason was, we suspect, fear of industrial espionage. When this occurred (and sometimes it occurred more than once in a particular market), substitutes were found from lists of reserve companies drawn up during the desk research stage.

The final selection of markets sampled is shown in Table 1. It will be noticed that certain important markets which one would expect to see represented within some of the industry sectors are missing. This was unavoidable: some markets proved difficult to access, others were difficult to match between UK and US firms. In total, 40 companies were investigated (20 UK and 20 US) in respect of how matched pairs compete in the markets shown.

Table 1. Markets sampled in the UK and US

• Mechanical engineering	• Electrical engineering
Mechanical handling	Test and measurement
Diesel engines	Office computing
Earth moving	Power hand tools
Machine tools	Telecommunications
Food processing	White goods
• Chemicals	• Food
Industrial plastics	Breakfast
Industrial rubber products	Dairy
Adhesives	Snack
Horticultural	Frozen
Industrial paint	Bread

It must be emphasized that the sample of businesses is not, and does not claim to be, representative of the population of firms in the UK and US. This is unavoidable, given the resources at our disposal. Our purpose was to illustrate successful and less successful product innovation practice in the UK and US—not to conduct a census aimed at revealing whether in aggregate there are more successful product innovators in the UK or US.

Because respondents were promised anonymity, it is not possible to name the actual businesses or divisions of the large firms from which data were obtained in personal interviews conducted in 1986 and 1987. Suffice it to say that the businesses which co-operated all belong to large well-known holding companies which are regarded as world players in the markets sampled.

RATIONALE FOR THE QUESTIONING METHOD

In order to discover managerial differences between the sample companies, use was made of the McKinsey 7Ss framework popularized by Peters and Waterman (1982). This framework has the advantage of parsimony: efficiency factors are encompassed under only seven headings which are meaningful to managers: strategy, shared values, style, structure, skills, staff, systems. They are described in Table 2.

While the 7Ss framework was developed originally to appraise the workings of a total organization, it can be applied with equal effectiveness to the analysis and understanding at the business unit level, that is to say, the level in the organization at which particular product developments are undertaken. Such developments will involve old and new products. Old product development is concerned with updating and improving existing lines and new product development is concerned with lines that are new to the manufacturing business. Table 3 shows how the 7Ss framework has been adapted for the purpose of examining specific product innovation activities.

Table 2. A framework for organizational analysis: the seven Ss

Strategy	The plan leading to the allocation of resources
Shared values	The goals shared by organizational members
Style	The cultural style of the organization
Structure	The characteristics of the organization chart
Skills	The distinctive capabilities of key personnel
Staff	The type of functional specialists employed
Systems	The nature of the proceduralized control processes

Source: based on Peters and Waterman (1982).

Table 3. Principal factors underlying efficient product development in the form of relevant questions

Strategy	Is there a product development strategy which defines the sort of old and new products to be developed and the resources to be released for this purpose?
Shared values	Is there a shared belief in the need to pursue product development for the purpose of growing the business?
Style	Does top management provide active support for those involved in key product development tasks, or is a 'divide and rule' management style practised in which individual functions are left to slog it out between themselves?
Structure	What types of formal organization structures are used to implement old and new product development tasks?
Skills	What specialist knowledge and techniques are applied for executing old and new product development tasks?
Staff	What types of functional specialists are there for executing old and new product development tasks?
Systems	What type of control and co-ordination mechanisms are used for executing old and new product development tasks?

Source: Adapted from Peters and Waterman (1982); Pascale and Athos (1982).

THE FINDINGS

Despite considerable efforts on our part to select the most active product innovators in the four industry sectors, we found that a number of well-known US firms display the same bad habits as some of their UK counterparts with respect to rejuvenating through organic product development. This is the case particularly with certain firms in what have traditionally been regarded as the lower-technology industry sectors. The issue has been highlighted by Senator Baucus, a co-founder of the congressional caucus on US competitiveness, in an interview with de Jonquieres and Kaletsky (1987):

There is a deep anxiety in our country that something is wrong. This is all new to us. We always assumed that our products were the best, that we were the envy of the world. Now we're losing jobs, we're buying all these products from Japan and we are being beaten. But we have seen the enemy and he is us.

The finding that managers in many US firms are faced with similar sorts of problems which confront managers of UK firms led us to focus on fundamental differences between businesses that rely on product innovation for growth, irrespective of nationality. An effective way of doing this is to compare businesses on the basis of whether or not they are successful at achieving high organic growth. For this purpose, we define a successful product innovator as a business which brings out a regular stream of updated and new products as quickly as is required by the competitive nature of the market in which it competes as a leader. Typically, these are business units within larger firms which are growing faster than their equivalents in other firms.

For the purpose of growing, successful product innovators engage in old product development as well as in new product development in order to achieve a balanced programme of rejuvenation. Typically, revenues from updated older cash-cow products are used to fund cash-hungry new product developments. On average, for the firms in our cross-industry sample, businesses categorized in Table 4 as successful obtain at least 50% of their current sales revenue from products updated in the last five years and at least 10% from completely new lines introduced in the last five years. It is this measure of performance which we have used to discriminate between businesses which are growing successfully through organic product innovation and those which are less successful using this route.

Table 4. Distribution of successful (+) and less successful (−) product innovators in the markets sampled

Mechanical engineering	UK	US	Electrical engineering	UK	US
Mechanical handling	−	−	Test and measurement	+	−
Diesel engines	−	+	Business computing	+	+
Earth moving	+	+	Power hand tools	−	+
Machine tools	−	−	Telecommunications	+	+
Food processing	+	−	White goods	−	−
Leading innovators	2/5	2/5		3/5	3/5

Chemicals	UK	US	Food	UK	US
Industrial plastics	+	+	Breakfast	−	−
Industrial rubber	−	−	Dairy	−	−
Adhesives	−	−	Snack	+	+
Horticultural	+	−	Frozen	+	+
Industrial paint	+	+	Bread	−	+
Leading innovators	3/5	2/5		2/5	3/5

Total successful product innovators in UK sample = 10/20
Total successful product innovators in US sample = 10/20

Note: the table shows the purposive sample used to illustrate successful and less successful product innovation practice in UK and US firms. It should not be used to infer that in aggregate US firms are no better or worse at managing product developments than UK firms. Because of a larger population of firms it is likely that there is far more successful management of product innovation in the US than in the UK.
Source: field study data.

Our criterion for a successful product innovator business is quite stiff. After all, the target figure for divisions of 3M—one of the world's most innovative firms by reputation—is to achieve 25% sales revenue from products newly introduced or reformulated within the last five years, i.e. both new and old product development. We consider, however, that in fast-changing markets any firm which has reached or exceeded our target figures for old and new product development will be making a truly determined effort to stay ahead in the competitive game. Indeed, as will be shown below, this is reflected in the way successful innovators manage product development, which is quite different from less successful firms.

For the purpose of explaining these differences use is made of the factors listed in Table 3. The seven factors fall into two groups. The first group of factors, *strategy, shared values, style, structure*, are top management responsibilities. Top management needs to:

(1) determine a product development strategy;
(2) engender a shared belief in the need to pursue a particular strategy;
(3) provide active support for those involved in key tasks;
(4) determine an appropriate formal organization structure for carrying out those tasks.

The second group of factors, *skills, staff, systems*, are the province of middle managers involved in detailed product development activities. At best, such managers engage in teamwork based on:

(5) appropriate skills;
(6) involving functional specialists of appropriate seniority;
(7) using appropriate control and co-ordinating mechanisms.

Tables 5 and 6 provide a summary of the findings. Table 5 summarizes the position in successful businesses. These are experienced at rejuvenating themselves through a balance of old and new product developments. In them, top management (in the form of the chief executive of both the holding company and of the business unit) involves itself fully in strategy determination. Product evolution and new product development are seen as important means for growing the business. Not only this, but top management provides active support for those undertaking actual development tasks. The form of this support is not meddlesome: specific tasks are delegated to relevant specialists but checked at regular intervals. In the case of important and expensive new product developments, top management involves itself especially closely in checking progress: there is no question of distancing itself from the consequences of key decisions.

As far as teamwork is concerned, successful businesses ensure that all important developments are headed by a team or project leader who is given a specific commission from top management which allows him/her to appeal right to the top in case of difficulties. The composition of teams differs between old and new product development. Teams for updating *existing* products are drawn from functions within the established organization. Indeed, in most successful firms, line managers are expected to institute product improvements as part of their normal duties. Sometimes, staff advisors, in the form of market research specialists, are also used. Progress is checked regularly, normally at monthly product development meetings chaired by top management. These regular meetings provide the tight control between periods of specialist activities during which teams are expected to use their initiative.

The format of teams charged with *new* product developments is different in successful innovator businesses. New product development teams are assembled to carry on their

Table 5. Summary characteristics of successful product innovators

| | For planning and executing | |
	Old product development	New product development
(1) Strategy	Top management determines explicit plans and budgets for development work	Top management sets broad objectives for organic growth
(2) Shared values	Top management fosters understanding of the need for product evolution	Top management fosters understanding of the need for really new products
(3) Style	Top management is supportive but does not meddle in development projects. Progress is checked regularly	Top management is intimately involved, often on a day-to-day basis
(4) Structure	Top management uses the existing organization which acknowledges the need to manage updates within a matrix of responsibilities	Top management uses new organizational forms, such as business teams, to nurture important developments outside the mainstream organization
(5) Skills	There is efficient product planning using sophisticated market analysis techniques	Techno-commercial idea generation, screening and testing in concept. Development work often based on new technology
(6) Staff	Existing line managers are used with some staff advice. When project leaders are appointed, they may be quite junior but receive a commission from top management	An intrapreneur is allowed to select his/her own team with whom rewards are shared. Failures are viewed as a learning experience
(7) Systems	Loose–tight using simultaneous or rugby approach. More tight than loose	Loose–tight using simultaneous or rugby approach. More loose than tight

Source: field study data.

work outside the established organization structure. Their task is seen as more than fulfilling a matrix requirement. The purpose of these teams is to build up a new business within the existing business: that is why they are headed by what Pinchot (1985) refers to as 'intrapreneurs'. Not surprisingly, such teams have high visibility within the organization. What differentiates them from the ill-fated experimental New Venture Divisions of the 1970s, described by Dunn (1977), is that top management has not provided them from inception with an open-ended commitment for continued existence. Under the intrapreneurial system, a team is disbanded if it fails to exploit a particular business proposition successfully, though the leader may start again with another team on another project if he/she can prepare a convincing business plan.

We found that teamwork activities are now increasingly being pursued in parallel, that is to say, across functions rather than only within individual functions as each function becomes primarily involved. It is this phenomenon which speeds developments in leading product innovators. This is important because a study reported by Reinertsen (1983) has shown that shipping a product six months late can cut life-cycle profits in consumer electronics by approximately one-third. More and more businesses are taking

Table 6. Summary characteristics of less successful innovators

| | For planning and executing | |
	Old product development	New product development
(1) Strategy	The product development strategy is not integrated within the corporate strategy: top management delegates responsibility for product development to the technical or marketing functions	Top management prefers to catch up not organically but by acquisition
(2) Shared values	Top management gives the responsibility for initiatives mainly to one function which then has to battle against the 'not-invented-here' syndrome	Top management accepts that the existing organization will feel threatened by any radical product developments which might undermine existing power bases
(3) Style	Top management either distances itself from or meddles in development projects	Top management involves itself directly only in acquisitions. Any organic new ventures are left to individuals prepared to take considerable personal risks
(4) Structure	Top management uses the existing formal structure supplemented with low-level staff specialists, such as NPD managers	Top management undertakes any radical developments right outside the existing formal structure, i.e. it is not organic NPD
(5) Skills	There is little or no explicit product planning. Sophisticated market analysis techniques are used rarely	There is only a very limited in-house base for the skills needed because these skills have never been nurtured
(6) Staff	Staff specialists battle it out with existing line managers. When teams are formed, they are led by a senior person	Great reliance on outside consultants, or in the case of an internal venture on 'godfathers'
(7) Systems	Loose or tight: 'over-the-wall' approach to teamwork	None

Source: field study data.

active steps to reduce development times—a common aim being to halve them. The simultaneous approach to development, referred to as the 'rugby approach' by Takeuchi and Nonaka (1986), involves specialists from different functions working together closely.

This new approach to teamwork is quite different from the old style relay, sequential or 'over-the-wall' approach which involves marketing, technical and other functional specialists one after the other as a project progresses through each and every stage. This is an aspect of managing where there is still a great deal to be learned. Not only are the formal work practices of team members important, but so also is the fostering of a team spirit. After all, effective teamwork encourages members to associate closely with projects. The resulting ownership will generate commitment among the different functional specialists, and this commitment will provide the momentum required to push through organizational barriers which will confront projects.

The situation in less successful product innovator businesses is different in nearly all respects. As can be seen in Table 6, a fundamental difference is in their strategic approach to product development. In these firms, the need for product evolution is often not fully recognized and therefore regarded as disrupting the smooth running of existing operations. Such businesses typically pursue an unbalanced approach to product development with internal efforts being directed almost exclusively at old product development. When top management does recognize the need for completely new products, it almost invariably finds that the intellectual and financial resources for this are lacking. Consequently, the only effective way open to pursue new developments is through acquiring a readymade new business. Not surprisingly, such a strategy for new product development tends to be not only very expensive but also very risky.

Because in less successful product innovator businesses the prime focus is on running the existing operation, staff specialists like new product development managers rather than line managers are sometimes used to stimulate product updating. These staffers do not usually enjoy high status, which means that they are unlikely, on their own, to be able to effect much change. When teams are formed in such businesses to explore opportunities for development work, a senior line manager is frequently appointed as leader, though not always by design, so that he/she can ensure that ongoing operations are not disrupted unduly. The team commonly lacks many of the needed skills because these have never been nurtured internally. Top management is likely to retain its distance and will not provide a positive lead. Control of progress is usually idiosyncratic; in some businesses, top management meddles needlessly, so hindering progress; in others, top management distances itself because of a fear of failure, in this way undermining important initiatives.

MAIN PRACTICAL IMPLICATIONS

The findings have highlighted areas of product innovation management where operational changes are likely to be needed in businesses which are not yet successful at rejuvenating themselves through organic product development. It is accepted that not all firms will aspire to this. But, as has already been stressed, more streamlined product development procedures are required in more and more industries, hence managements with little or no experience of regular product development will be wise to study successful practices closely. Not only this, but guidance will also be required on the sequence with which changes might best be made. It is to this practical issue that we turn next.

If a business now wants to become a more active product innovator, it is essential that top management, both in the holding company and in the operating business, think through the implications of the new strategy. These implications are likely to be considerable, both for top management, as well as for those in the operating unit. Becoming a leader in product innovation and remaining successful requires staff to believe in their products in the short and in the long run. All too often, top management and other staff believe only in yesterday's products, and have not taken steps to ensure that old products will remain competitive in the face of market and technological changes. Market change results most strikingly from new ways in offering products (transacting them as commodities or as enhanced products with or without additional customer support), as explained by Mathur (1986); product change, on the other hand, is made possible by the application of existing or new technology.

Commitment to tomorrow's business requires efficient updating of old products and the development of completely new product lines. New product lines are important because these will, in time, replace old lines. The new product lines will need to be based on existing technology until such time as new technology offers superior opportunities for growing the business. All this poses complicated strategic choices for top management. A timid choice will cause a business to stand still, and run the risk of being overtaken by competitors; an ambitious choice may over-extend a business. It is top management's responsibility to make the choice. It is also top management's responsibility to communicate the chosen strategy to the other managers who will be required to implement it by formulating appropriate sub-strategies for their co-workers, which will in turn also require explanation.

For the purpose of explaining the direction of needed changes, several companies we visited insist on monthly briefing meetings which are addressed both by top management and by managers responsible for achieving components of a particular business strategy. It is in this way that top management can infuse a sense of shared values, which, put in simple terms, means getting people to accept that they are doing something worthwhile in their work—not just for themselves, but for safeguarding and growing the business of which they are a part. We commend regular briefing sessions to top management because these will provide an opportunity for demonstrating to other staff that they are serious in their concern for the future of the business. In our opinion, such meetings provide the starting point for successful product innovation management, which then needs to be spiced with an appropriate supportive top management style to ensure the needed changes do happen.

Top management also has prime responsibility for deciding on appropriate organization structures. Formal organization structures are important. We have shown how new organization structures, in the form of intrapreneurial teams, can make things happen despite the existing organization. But these new organizational devices need to be selected with care. For old product development, the existing organization structure can be used, and established product managers can be given responsibility for product updating. For the development of new product lines, based on existing technology, temporary interfunctional teams are likely to be most effective, reporting both to top management and to the heads of established functions. For the development of completely new product lines, based on new technology, full-time business teams reporting direct to top management are being used increasingly, their use in Procter and Gamble having been illustrated by Smale (1985).

Different organizational devices will require appropriate staff and skills to effect the sort of developments aimed for. We observed in the span of businesses studied that input 'push' skills are necessary in businesses that are not yet leaders in product innovation. However, leaders put great emphasis on output skills. By output skills, we refer to their willingness to evaluate the consequences of alternative change strategies. Hence, in leader firms, the emphasis is on the total product proposition, whereas, in other firms, the emphasis is so often on unco-ordinated pushing for change by 'product champions', 'godfathers' or 'sponsors'.

The processes involved are demonstrated admirably in the operating systems in force. Such systems describe the way things get done, often despite the formal organization structure. Our findings point strongly in favour of loose–tight operating systems, where top management provides tightly defined strategic guidelines against which development progress can be checked. The tightly defined guidelines are then accompanied by loosely agreed parameters for working towards particular objectives. In this way, middle management can concentrate on giving of their best, without constantly being inter-rupted and interfered with by top management. Overall, operating systems are likely to be tighter for old product development and looser for new product development, but only once a business has built up expertise in sustaining organic growth through product innovation.

CONCLUSIONS AND THE NEED FOR FURTHER RESEARCH

Using the McKinsey 7Ss framework as an analytical guide, the results indicate import-ant differences in the way successful product developers in the UK and the US manage change. Differences have been highlighted at two levels of abstraction: first, from the level of the business as a whole, exemplified by the degree of top management support; second, from the level of the group of functional specialists involved in undertaking the required operational tasks. Both analytical perspectives are important. Top manage-ment must supply the vision and set the operating tone for a business. Middle manage-ment must then be allowed to follow through with the necessary specialist skills.

In many of the personal interviews, respondents stressed the overriding importance of top management leadership. We were supplied with much anecdotal evidence on how new chief executives have turned around what were sleepy cash-cow businesses into rejuvenated, growing and profitable ones. In all cases, support from the topmost level, that is to say, from the chief executive officer of the holding company was cited as being of critical importance. Frequently, we were able to verify these assertions by referring to recent annual reports. In all cases where there had been a recent turnaround, old-style managers had been removed to be replaced by fresh blood. Often, the fresh blood was infused from within; it came in the form of managers who had for years been frustrated by strategies and systems of management that did not utilize available resources to the full. Time and time again, we were told that many middle managers had for years been clear in their own minds as to the general direction needed to make better progress, and that when the time came they were very willing to help. Once movement was achieved, the turnaround was often fast—three years appears to be about the time needed to produce substantial results.

In addition to enlightened top management which strategically controls its business, efficient teamwork is needed to get product developments completed as quickly as possible. Successful product innovators make strenuous efforts to undertake the special-ist tasks simultaneously rather than sequentially. In several successful businesses, intra-preneurial teams are used to give added focus to particularly important developments.

It is interesting to note that less successful product innovators may also use intrapre-neurial teams. Such teams can serve as a mechanism to effect product change despite a prevailing attitude by top management which is hostile to more rapid or more radical product change. Burgelman (1984) refers to the efforts of such teams as 'autonomous strategic behavior' to differentiate them from efforts induced by strategies propounded by top management. The results of an intrapreneurial team in such a business will serve as a safety valve and may well come up with surprisingly successful individual results. However, this mechanism will not, in our opinion, be a match for the advantages which middle management team members enjoy in businesses where top management has thought through the implications of alternative growth strategies, has explained the reasons for selecting a preferred strategy, and is then openly supportive of efforts aimed at fulfilling it.

It has been asserted that successful businesses do little that is really new managerially, but what differentiates them from less successful firms is their ability to pursue business in a committed and disciplined way (Peters and Austin, 1985). We would not disagree with the spirit of this assertion. We do not, however, subscribe to the view that efficient product innovation is a matter of common sense. Our study has shed light on certain organizational and managerial aspects, but there are several other important aspects which urgently require additional work. Strategy formulation, that is to say the mix of old versus new product development in the face of changing technology, is an area which concerns all manufacturing businesses. Related to this is the role of intrapreneurial teams, popularized by Pinchot (1985), and of their little brothers, skunkworks, popularized by Peters and Waterman (1982). The question of the extent to which top management should countenance or rely on what Burgelman (1984) has termed 'autonomous strategic behavior' requires detailed investigation in different industry contexts. The advantages of simultaneous teamwork also require detailed study, because it is important for a business to know to what extent achieving greater speed in completing developments justifies the duplicated use of specialist resources.

If the need for further research along the lines outlined above is accepted—and it would surprise us if it were not, because it stems from problems highlighted by our respondents—then the question arises how such further research can be pursued best. In our view, there are likely to be considerable advantages in studying closely the practices of Japanese, West German and Swedish businesses which are successful in retaining and building on a position of success in particular world product markets. Indeed, we now believe that the greatest pay-off is likely to come from studying businesses which are the most successful at product innovation. The majority of these are likely to be found in the manufacture of exciting new electronic and chemical products. However, during the course of our study, we did come across several striking examples of businesses in quite unglamorous industry sectors which are now using organic product innovation very successfully as a means for achieving growth patterns that were previously thought unattainable. We also consider such firms to be very worthy of further study, because they serve as fine examples of how the future of not just a business, but also of the jobs within a business, can be safeguarded through skilful management.

ACKNOWLEDGEMENT

The managerial implications reported in this article are drawn from work funded by the Economic and Social Research Council under a programme of research into the competitiveness of British industry.

REFERENCES

Booz, Allen and Hamilton (1982) *New Products Management for the 1980s*, Booz, Allen and Hamilton Inc., New York.

Burgelman, R. A. (1984) 'Designs for Corporate Entrepreneurship in Established Firms', in Carroll, G. and Vogel, D. (eds), *Strategy and Organization—A West Coast Perspective*, Pitman, Boston, Mass.: 145–157.

Cooper, R. G. (1984a) 'How New Product Strategies Impact on Performance', *Journal of Product Innovation Management*, **1**(1): 5–18.

Cooper, R. G. (1984b) 'New Product Strategies: What Distinguishes the Top Performers?', *Journal of Product Innovation Management*, **1**(3): 151–164.

Crawford, C. M. (1980) 'Defining the Charter for Product Innovation', *Sloan Management Review*: (Fall): 3–12.

de Jonquieres, G. and Kaletsky, A. (1987) 'Can America Make It?: The Enemy Within', *Financial Times* (11 May): 24.

Dunn, D. T. (1977) 'The Rise and Fall of Ten Venture Groups', *Business Horizons* (October): 32–41.

Foster, R. N. (1986) *Innovation—The Attacker's Advantage*, Macmillan, London.

Freeman, C. (1982) *The Economics of Industrial Innovation*, Francis Pinter, London.

Hopkins, D. S. (1981) 'New Product Winners and Losers', *Research Management* (May): 12–17.

Johne, F. A. (1984) 'How Experienced Product Innovators Organize', *Journal of Product Innovation Management*, **1**(4): 210–233.

Mathur, S. S. (1986) 'Strategy: Framing Business Intentions', *Journal of General Management*, **12**(1): 77–97.

Pascale, R. T. and Athos, A. G. (1982) *The Art of Japanese Management*, Penguin, Harmondsworth, Middlesex.

Peters, T. J. and Austin, N. (1985) *A Passion for Excellence*, Collins, Glasgow.

Peters, T. J. and Waterman, R. H. (1982) *In Search of Excellence*, Harper & Row, New York.

Pinchot, G. (1985) *Intrapreneuring: Why You Don't Have to Leave the Corporation to Become an Entrepreneur*, Harper & Row, New York.

Pratten, C. (1986) 'The Importance of Giant Companies', *Lloyds Bank Review*, **159**, January: 33–48.

Reinertsen, D. G. (1983) 'Who Done It—The Search for New Product Killers', *Electronic Business*, **9**(8): 62–66.

Rothwell, R. (1977) 'The Characteristics of Successful Innovators and Technically Progressive Firms (with Some Comments on Innovation Research), *R & D Management*, **7**(3): 191–206.

Smale, J. (1985) 'Behind the Brands at P&G', *Harvard Business Review* (November–December): 79–90.

Takeuchi, H. and Nonaka, I. (1986) 'The New New Product Development Game', *Harvard Business Review* (January–February): 137–146.

4

Dimensions of Success in New Product Development: an Exploratory Investigation

Susan Hart

INTRODUCTION

The existence of a strong and positive relationship between a company's tendency to innovate and its continued market prosperity underpins the vast literature in new product development (NPD) and innovation. Much of the core of this literature deals with the search for what factors might be associated with success in NPD and innovation. This search continues in a variety of disciplines including marketing, management, economics, engineering, design and business policy. However prolific, scientific and insightful the various contributions have been, there is a notable lack of cohesion regarding its lynchpin, namely, the meaning of 'success' in new product development. Yet, if they seek to provide an understanding of what factors promote or inhibit success, it is vital that some attention be turned to how success might be described and, if appropriate, measured. Although there are always exceptions to the rule, much of the literature aimed at discovering what factors are associated with new product success have skilfully side-stepped the issue of what the essence of new product success is, and ignored the complex dynamics involved in profiling a successful new product (Service and Hart, 1989; Cooper, 1984; Walsh *et al.*, 1988; Johne and Snelson, 1988; Cooper and Kleinschmidt, 1987a; Cooper, 1979; Calantone and Cooper, 1981; Link, 1987; Rothwell *et al.*, 1974).

Clearly, the way in which NPD success is defined influences the findings which describe the factors contributing to NPD success! Some evidence for the effect which may be seen to occur when different definitions of success are applied, is to be found in the studies by Cooper (1984) and Nyström (1985). These studies examine the relationship between different types of strategy and different types of outcome. Cooper (1984) found a strong relationship between performance results and the product strategies elected by firms, showing that they can strive for different types of performance by employing different strategic thrusts. Nyström (1985) also found that different strategies relate to different NPD outcomes, whether technological, competitive or financial.

Unfortunately there is very little consensus amongst the major research studies on

Reprinted by permission of Harcourt Brace & Company, Limited from *Journal of Marketing Management*, Vol. 9, pp. 23–41 how best to define success: which dimensions of success to include and how to set about measuring these dimensions. In fact, commenting upon the vagueness and inconsistency of operational definitions in NPD research, Cooper (1979) makes specific reference to the ways in which success has been defined. This paper reviews the commonly-used measures of new product success and discusses their limitations, together with their overall contribution to our understanding of this complex subject. From this review, a number of research questions are drawn and answered using data from an empirical investigation of 69 companies.

WHAT IS SUCCESS IN NEW PRODUCT DEVELOPMENT?

There is a whole body of literature which deals with the *overall* competitive performance of companies and the alternative ways in which competitive performance can be gauged (Carroll, 1979; Saul, 1983; Frazier and Howell, 1983; Hooley and Lynch, 1985; Saunders and Wong, 1985; Doyle, 1985; Buckley *et al.*, 1988; Baker *et al.*, 1988; Baker and Hart, 1989; Saunders *et al.*, 1991). Although NPD performance is *one* aspect of a company's overall performance, often the underlying assumption of the positive relationship between NPD success and overall company success has meant that the latter is used by researchers to detect the former. The rich literature into areas of overall competitive success has provided a bountiful source of performance indicators to NPD researchers.

Studies into corporate performance have tended to use a variety of different measures of success, which can be classified into one of two groups: 'financial' and 'non-financial'. Researchers employ financial measures such as 'profit' (Saunders and Wong, 1985; Hooley and Lynch, 1985; ICC, 1987/88; Baker *et al.*, 1988), 'sales growth' (Baker *et al.*, 1988), 'turnover' (Frazier and Howell, 1983; ICC, 1989), 'return on investment' (Hooley and Lynch, 1985), 'return on capital employed' (Baker *et al.*, 1988), and 'inventory turnover' (Frazier and Howell, 1983) along with the softer, non-financial measures such as 'innovativeness' (Goldsmith and Clutterbuck, 1984), 'market standing' (Saunders and Wong, 1985; Hooley and Lynch, 1985), 'ethical standing', 'employee conditions', 'employment prospects', 'industrial relation', 'legal standing' and 'social responsibility' (Saul, 1983; Carroll, 1979). Further, studies of corporate performance measure success at different levels of analysis (e.g. national, industry, company and product), making the comparison of results from studies which use different levels of analysis difficult, as commented upon by Baker and Hart (1989), Buckley *et al.* (1988) and Frazier and Howell (1983). However, many of these measures have been used by researchers purporting to assess success in NPD. Studies of new product development success use both financial and non-financial indicators of success. The *financial* measures used can be grouped under a number of headings, which refer to the base of the measurement:

- profit;
- assets;
- sales;
- capital;
- equity.

These are listed more fully in Appendix 1 and are described in a previous paper (Hart and Craig, 1993). However, a number of criticisms of these financial measures can be identified.

Criticisms of financial measures

An over-riding complaint has been raised which suggests that success is not confined to financial issues. Added to this are a number of criticisms related to the way in which they have been operationalized by researchers. These are discussed below.

Success is defined as the achievement of something desired, planned or attempted. While financial return is one of the easily quantifiable industrial performance yardsticks, it is far from the only important one. New product 'failure' can result in other important by-products, organizational, technical and market developments (Maidique and Zirger, 1985).

Maidique and Zirger (1985) recognize the problem of employing a unidimensional financial measure of success, and the need to consider what may be thought of as the 'softer' measures. To illustrate this point, Maidique and Zirger (1985) give details of a company which, having developed a product based on a new technology, found it to be a failure when introduced into a new market. However, all was not lost, because the company gained valuable experience in the technology and the new market, allowing them to go on to introduce successfully new products to the market. This example shows that while the product could be viewed as a failure in financial terms, in technological as well as market development terms and in profit terms, it could be judged a success.

Closely associated with the notion of different types of success are strategy development and objective setting. It is suggested that the nature of objectives set should determine the way in which performance of the project or programme is measured. Therefore if, for example, the objective was 'to reduce competition in the market by the introduction of a low cost, new product', it would be highly inappropriate to measure performance of that product development in profit terms, since it is clearly not the intention to maximize profits, but rather to improve market share. However, apart from the rather hollow question, 'to what extent did the new product meet the objectives set for it?', few if any studies have attempted to define success in a non-financial manner. Furthermore, while non-financial success for new products may be desirable *per se*, it would be misleading to suggest that researchers and practitioners alike did not assume some positive relationship between non-financial and financial success. There may well be a time lag between the two, but non-financial success at the expense of financial success is an unviable long-term option.

The American study by Hayes and Abernathy (1980) recognizes the detrimental effect which *short term* financial measures of performance have had on US businesses. While American managers focus their attention on the short term, concerning themselves with quick return on investment, their more successful Japanese counterparts can be seen to focus on long term growth. The short-termism of financial measures of performance is further criticized by Aaker (1988) when considering suitable performance indicators in strategic market management:

... it is necessary to develop performance indicators that will reflect long-term viability and health ... (Aaker, 1988).

Another reason why it is desirable to apply measures which, as Aaker (1988) puts it, 'reflect long-term viability and health' is that there is no guarantee that success is going to last; success today does not guarantee success tomorrow. A prime example of this phenomenon was featured in an article in *Business Week* (1984) entitled 'Who's excellent now?', which reported on the downfall of no less than 14 of the companies held up as 'excellent companies' in Peters and Waterman's *In Search of Excellence* (1982) just two years before. Therefore, it is better to include non-financial measures which can indicate how the company will perform in the future, and not just the present. This line of argument is pursued by Buckley *et al.* (1988), who classify measures of competitiveness as those relating to competitive performance, potential and management process. Their conceptualization, while distilled from literature pertaining to overall company success, makes clear the dynamic nature of competitiveness. Such dynamism is also reflected at the 'product' or 'product development programme' levels.

Moving on to more specific criticisms of the way in which financial performance indicators have been operationalized by researchers, a number of points are salient. First, several studies have used measures of *overall* financial success as indicators of success in new product development (Peters and Waterman, 1982; Walsh *et al.* 1988; Cooper and Kleinschmidt, 1987a, b; Rothwell *et al.*, 1974). Such an approach ignores a host of factors which might account for good performance, only one of which might be the success of the new product development programme. Whether using indicators such as profits, asset-based, equity-based or sales-based measures, the possibility that these indicators might be influenced by other factors such as mergers, acquisitions or the purchase of buildings or land, is rarely discussed. However, it is worth re-emphasizing that the Peters and Waterman study was primarily aimed at investigating overall corporate performance and therefore it is not surprising that corporate level measures of success have been applied. The same cannot be said for Walsh *et al.* (1988), Cooper and Kleinschmidt (1987a) and Rothwell *et al.* (1974). It would be misleading to suggest that financial measures of success had been applied exclusively to measure *overall company* performance as a surrogate for new product performance. Despite the possible reluctance on the part of companies to divulge financial information for a specific new product or new products programme, several studies have based their assessments at either of these, more detailed, levels (Ayal and Raban, 1990; Hart and Service, 1988; Cooper and Kleinschmidt, 1987a; Maidique and Zirger, 1985; Nyström, 1985).

Second, whether financial measurement of performance takes place at the corporate level, the product development programme level, or the individual new product level, researchers may opt for one measure only. For example, sales growth has been used by Cooper (1984) and Hart and Service (1988), profits by Cooper (1979, 1980), Calantone and Cooper (1981), Nyström (1985) and Link (1987). Such an approach is flawed in that it ignores the relationship between sales and profits. It may well be an investment in innovation that decreases profits over the period of time of the study. Conversely, it may be a lack of investment in innovation that accounts for high profits at the time of the study. Looking at measures of sales growth, they are equally suspect because they can be affected by heavy promotion and/or price cutting, leading to the practice of 'buying' market share. While this practice is not, in itself, indicative of failure, since it may be initiated for strategic or non-financial reasons that are entirely commensurate with the company's overall direction, it would be misleading to suggest that sales growth was firm evidence of success in every case.

The third and final criticism of how measures of financial success have been operationalized relates to the frequent practice of using *indirect* and *relative* measures. Direct measures ask respondents to furnish *actual* performance figures, including 'average return on sales' (Peters and Waterman, 1982), 'the extent to which profits for the new product exceed the cost of the product development programme' (Cooper, 1984), 'profitability of the product over its life cycle' (Nyström, 1979), 'direct monetary gain' (Rothwell *et al.*, 1974), 'time to breakeven' (Cooper and Kleinschmidt, 1987a, b), and 'profit margin and profit growth' (Walsh *et al.*, 1988). Indirect measurement involves asking about whether or not breakeven was achieved, whether profits reached 'objectives set' or 'acceptable levels' (Cooper, 1979, 1980; Calantone and Cooper, 1981; Cooper and Kleinschmidt, 1987a, b; Link, 1987). These indirect measures rely on the memory, not to mention the veracity of the respondents, aspects which are rarely checked by survey research. The reasons forwarded for using indirect measures tend to relate to the problems in persuading respondents to part with what might be regarded as sensitive information, and which might lead to non-response or item non-response. This said, few studies, if any, have looked at the extent to which indirect measures do reflect direct measures. Knowledge of the nature of this relationship would allow future research to progress on a firmer base.

Similarly, relative measures such as 'sales relating to other recently introduced products', 'sales related to objectives', 'sales growth compared to the industry average' have been used (Cooper and Kleinschmidt, 1987a; Hart and Service, 1988). While these indicators allow a comparative perspective to emerge, there have been few checks, if any, on their reliability.

In response to the criticisms of uni-dimensional, financial measures, researchers have introduced 'softer', non-financial measures, which allow the researcher to cope with the possibility that there may be different types of success, e.g. organization, technological or market successes. The next section will discuss the different types of non-financial measures which NPD researchers have applied.

Non-financial measures

Non-financial measures of success can also be grouped under a number of headings:

- design;
- activity;
- market;
- technological;
- commercial.

Again, each of these is listed in fuller detail in Appendix 2, and has been discussed in an earlier paper (Hart and Craig, 1993). However, a number of criticisms are in order. First, of the list of non-financial measures that writers claim 'should' be used to assess the importance of NPD, few are empirically derived. Given that the objective set by the person responsible should be the guiding criterion (Baker, 1975), it is surprising that there is a dearth of information regarding how managers themselves would define success in terms other than financial. Attempts to measure 'technological innovativeness', involving the 'degree of novelty', 'the degree of patent protection' (Nyström, 1985) or whether the new product introduces a new category to the firm (Cooper and Kleinschmidt, 1987a, b), do not take the objectives of the new product developments into account. The same can be said for the market-based measures, which try to assess whether or not an NPD programme has 'opened up new markets for the firm'. An exception to these criticisms can be made for the design-based studies, as design was the primary focus for the studies, and, for the most part, for the companies involved in the studies (Walsh et al., 1988; Ughanwa and Baker, 1989).

The commercially-based measures suffer from a degree of vagueness. Specifically, Ayal and Raban (1990) ask respondents to make subjective evaluations as to whether the product was a failure or a success; Hise et al. (1989) relate product performance to the original expectations for the product. While each of these approaches is in keeping with the sentiments expressed by Baker (1975) above, the problem is that little reference is made to the nature of the guidance that was given on the dimensions against which performance should be assessed. While this may have been appropriate for the objectives of each individual study, it does not make for easy and meaningful aggregate comparisons in the NPD literature.

Activity-based measures split into those which determine the extent of product development activities within the company and those which determine the *proficiency* of these activities. Johne and Snelson (1988) apply an indirect, relative measurement, assessing 'the regularity of updated products in the relation to the competitive nature of the market'. This measurement is a surrogate for experience, in that those companies which regularly introduce new products have more experience and can be regarded as leading product innovators.

The measures which relate to the proficiency of activities include direct measures, 'the number of successful launches' (Hart and Service, 1988), and 'the rate of successes, failures and kills over a five year period' (Cooper, 1984) and indirect, relative measures, 'the success of the programme in relation to its objectives' and on 'a global rating' (Cooper, 1984). Gauging the extent and proficiency of product development activities allows an assessment of the innovativeness and success of companies' development programmes.

While these measures may be acceptable as ways to assess NPD performance, very little work has been carried out to establish the nature and extent of the link between the measures and the dimension they attempt to capture. Furthermore, in common with all the non-financial measures, their relationship with financial measures of success is a neglected issue in the literature. As stated previously, there is an assumption that some positive relationship does exist.

Taking both financial and non-financial measures together, it can be seen that, despite a number of conventions, there are still a number of un-researched assumptions underlying the measurement of the outcomes of NPD.

Firstly, the most commonly-used NPD financial measures tend to be overall company profit and sales growth. This said, often, it is *either* sales growth or profits which are used, thereby neglecting the dynamic relationship between sales and profits, especially when in relation to an activity like NPD which demands so much investment. Second, the decision to use overall company performance measures to assess NPD success in a company is intuitively appealing, but few researchers have, as yet, attempted to confirm, refute, or otherwise investigate the nature of any relationship between overall company measures of performance, and more direct measures of new product performance. Third, several studies have used indirect ways of assessing both sales and profits, by asking how respondents feel their company sales and profits compare to competitors or the industry in general. Seldom has any attempt been made to evaluate the accuracy of such an approach—largely because 'indirect' measures have been favoured, in order to boost response rates. Fourth, there have been many calls for the incorporation of non-financial measures in the battery of assessment techniques, on the ground that the nature of NPD achievement is multi-dimensional. However, to date, there have been virtually no attempts to examine the nature of non-financial achievement. In addition, little is known about the nature of the relationships which may exist between non-financial and financial achievement.

Given these shortcomings, which are apparent on an aggregate inspection of the literature, rather than within any one research study or article, the balance of this paper addresses the following questions:

(1) Can either sales or profit measures be used in cross-sectional mail surveys to give an accurate reflection of financial success?
(2) Can new product development success be measured accurately by using measures of *overall* financial success?
(3) Can indirect measures be used in place of direct measures of success?
(4) What are the main dimensions of success, both financial and non-financial, as defined by business people themselves?
(5) To what extent are non-financial success measures associated with financial success measures?

The next section describes the methods used to examine these questions.

METHODOLOGY

In order to address these issues, a short, four-page questionnaire was mailed to a cross-section of British manufacturing firms, to collect data regarding success in new product development. The mail survey was used in keeping with the majority of new product development success studies. Even where personal interviews have been employed, they have been of the structured variety (Johne and Snelson, 1988; Cooper and Klein-schmidt, 1987a).

Sample

A contact sample of 369 companies was drawn up, based on a previous study (Hart and Service, 1988). All of the contact sample were aware of the work of the authors, and had been supplied with summary copies of previous research. While this may have sensitized the contact sample unduly, resulting in bias, it was felt that the nature of the questions and the detailed financial information requested called for considerable goodwill on behalf of the respondents. The responses received are detailed in Table 1.

The total number of responses received was 87, which included 11 returns declining to divulge 'financial information' and seven returns which had very high levels of item non-response. The final, effective response sample was 69, a response rate of 18.7%. In order

Table 1. Sample characteristics

Industry category	No. of responses	%
FMCG	7	10
Industrial operating supplies	19	28
Consumer durables	11	16
Components	15	22
Capital equipment	17	24
Total	69	100

to determine the reasons behind such a low rate, a further 50 sample units were contacted by phone. Their reasons for non-response are detailed in Table 2.

Clearly, success measurement is a risky undertaking, and the reluctance and inability to part with financial data—particularly data not readily available in company reports—prompts researchers to find alternative ways to indicate 'success'.

Variables

The measures were derived from previous literature and are summarized in Table 3. As can be seen from Table 3, a variety of performance indicators were used, most of which are self-explanatory. However, the last set of indicators in Table 3 deserves greater explanation.

Eight characteristics of successful new products were derived from the literature and covered issues like technological achievement, competitive achievement, opening new markets, lowering product costs, gaining experience and increasing profits and sales. Respondents were asked to say to what extent they agreed or disagreed that each item was a characteristic of their major success stories. Further details of these are given in the analysis.

ANALYSIS

In order to address the questions raised by the literature, the analysis was approached in three stages. The first stage addressed research questions one to three, and is conceptualized in Figure 1. Analysis was done by means of simple correlation, and is summarized in Table 4.

There is no significant relationship between sales growth and average profits (although the direction is negative), or between sales growth and the percentage of turnover accounted for by new products, which is also negative. On the other hand, there is a weak, positive relationship between the percentage of turnover accounted for by new products and average profits. These findings tend to suggest that new product development in this sample is a 'replacement' rather than a 'growth' activity.

The indirect measures used show a significant positive correlation with sales growth, but a negative correlation with average profits, which in the case of 'sales compared to industry average' is significant. This lends weight to the argument that sales *and* profits measures are very different, and in cross-sectional studies are likely to yield opposite

Table 2. Reasons for non-response ($n = 50$)

Reasons	Number
Too busy	4
Financial information not to hand	11
Company policy discourages/disallows divulgence of financial information	19
Financial information not available at SBU level	13
Didn't get around to it	2
Original contact had left	1

Table 3. A classification of success measures used

	Company of new product 'level'	Financial or non-financial	Direct or indirect	Measure
Sales growth	Company	Financial	Direct	% growth (or decline for 5 yrs)
Average profits	Company	Financial	Direct	In £000s for 5-yr period
Sales growth vs industry average	Company	Financial	Indirect	5-point scale[a]
Sales growth vs five largest competitors	Company	Financial	Indirect	As above
% Turnover accounted for by products launched in last 5 years	New product	Financial	Direct	Percentage
No. of R&D projects	New product	Non-financial (activity)	Direct	Number in last 5 yrs
No. of new products launched	New product	Non-financial (activity)	Direct	As above
% successful launches	New product	Non-financial (activity)	Direct	As above
Characteristics of successful new products	New product	Non-financial (activity)	Indirect	8-item Likert-type scale

[a] 5 = much better, 1 = much worse.

views of how 'successful' a company is. However, the indirect measures of sales appear to give an indication of actual sales performance.

The second stage of the analysis concentrated on two separate issues: first, on the respondents' opinions of dimensions of success; second, on non-financial measures, which were based on 'activities', as derived from the literature.

In order to gauge respondents' opinions regarding the dimensions of new product success, the eight statements describing successful outcomes of new product developments were assessed using a five-point Likert-type scale. In order to reduce the data and determine the underlying dimensions of success as viewed by the respondents, principal components analysis was used. The statements, their means and the resultant dimensions are shown in Table 5.

The analysis resulted in three factors, which were determined on the basis of eigenvalues of greater than 1 and using the scree test.

Table 4. Interrelationships among financial measures

	Sales growth	Average profits	Industry average comparison	Five largest competitors comparison	% Turnover from products involved in last 5 years
Sales growth for 5 years	—				
Average profits for 5 years	$r = -0.07$	—			
Sales compared to industry average	$r = 0.24^b$	$r = -0.25^b$	—		
Sales compared to five largest competitors	$r = 0.25^b$	$r = 0.12$	$r = 0.83^a$	—	
% Turnover from products involved in last 5 years	$r = -0.03$	$r = 0.17^c$	$r = 0.00$	$r = 0.02$	—

[a] $p < 0.01$ (both tails).
[b] $p < 0.05$ (both tails).
[c] $p < 0.10$ (both tails).

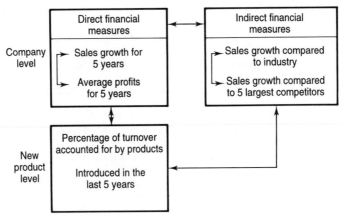

Figure 1. Financial Measures of Success.

Table 5. The dimensions of new product success

Statements	Factor 1	Factor 2	Factor 3
Our successful new products have:			
Beaten the competition technically	0.87	—	—
Been launched into new markets	—	0.50	—
Beaten the competition to market	0.52	—	0.57
Been technological breakthroughs	0.90	—	—
Generated profits in excess of costs	—	—	0.83
Beaten the competition on price	—	0.67	—
Met the objectives set	—	0.55	0.52
Resulted in reduced production costs	0.75	0.75	—
Eigenvalue	2.2	1.7	1.2
Percentage of variance explained	27.7	21.1	14.8

This solution explained 63.6% of the variance and featured strong individual loadings on each factor, enabling straightforward interpretation. The first factor comprises *beating competition technologically, beating the competition to market* and *technological breakthrough*. This factor seems to describe a success profile based on using a technological race with competitors. Factor 2 features strong loadings of *reduced production costs/beating the competition on price, meeting objectives* and *opening new markets*. The focus of the success dimension described by this factor appears to be cost reduction and price competitiveness. The final factor includes, *beating the competition to market, profit generation (ROI)* and *meeting objectives*. The success profile subsumed by this factor seems to be ROI, by being first to the market. It is extremely interesting to note that each dimension has a 'competitive' stance. The second battery of non-financial success indicators are activity-based, and include the number of new product projects undertaken in the last five years, number of new product launches in the last five years and the percentage of launches that were successful in the past five years. Table 6 shows the frequency distribution of these measures.

Table 6. Frequency of activity-based non-financial measures

Activity-based	Mean	Standard deviation
No. of R&D projects	22.6	28.6
No. of new product launches	13.4	20.6
% of successful launches	72%	27%

The third stage of the analysis involved examining the relationship between both sets of non-financial measures and the financial measures. Table 7 presents the results of the analysis, which was carried out by means of simple correlation.

Table 7. Correlation between financial and non-financial indicators of success

	Financial indicators of success				
	Overall company level				
	Direct measures		Indirect measures		
Non-financial success indicators	Sales growth	Average profits	Sales vs industry average	Sales vs five largest competitors	% of turnover accounted for by new products
Dimensions of success					
Technological competitiveness	−0.05	0.02	0.03	−0.01	−0.15
Cost and price competitiveness	−0.11	−0.27[c]	−0.02	−0.05	−0.07
First-to-market-good ROI	−0.08	0.00	−0.19	−0.31[b]	−0.05
Activity-based indicators					
No. of R&D projects	−0.15[c]	−0.12	−0.01	0.03	0.15[c]
No. of new products launched	−0.07	−0.13	−0.00	0.08	0.21[b]
% of successful launches	−0.40[a]	−0.23[c]	0.51[a]	0.40[a]	0.23[b]

[a] $p < 0.01$.
[b] $p < 0.05$.
[c] $p < 0.10$.

Looking at the three factors which describe non-financial measures of success shows that of the 15 possible correlations, only two are significant, which could be a chance result. However, looking at the activity-based indicators, where eight of the possible 15 correlations are significant, the results cannot be dismissed as spurious. The number of new product projects is weakly and negatively associated with sales growth, but positively associated with the percentage of turnover accounted for by new products. The number of new product launches is also positively associated with the percentage of turnover accounted for by new products. By far the most significant associations are found in relation to 'the percentage of successful launches' which is positively associated with sales growth, sales growth compared to the industry average and five largest competitors, and the percentage of turnover accounted for by new products. Given the interrelationships amongst the direct and indirect measures of sales growth, such a result is not too surprising. However, the 'percentage of successful new products' is negatively associated with 'average profits', perhaps reflecting the investment required to make new products successful.

Looking at these results pertaining to activity-based non-financial indicators it seems fair to say that, while new product-related activities can be detected by greater proportions of new products being marketed, it seems rash to suppose that any benefit could be detected measuring financial performance at the overall company level for the same period. This said, the results are far from conclusive, especially when related back to those in Table 4, where there is a positive (albeit weak) association between average profits and the percentage of turnover accounted for by new products.

SUMMARY AND DISCUSSION

In order to reflect on the meaning of the results, they are dealt with in this section by turning back to the five specific questions raised by the literature and providing the focus for the paper.

(1) Can either *sales* or *profit* be used in cross-sectional mail surveys to give an accurate reflection of financial success?

Our results show no significant relationship between sales growth and average profits over a five-year period. While an isolated finding such as this cannot claim to be reliable, it is interesting that neither a positive *nor* a negative relationship was confirmed. This reinforces the need for researchers to give careful consideration to the measures they choose to represent financial success. Clearly, sales and profits cannot be assumed to be 'alternative indicators', although judging by the nonchalance with which either appear to have been selected by past researchers, perhaps such an assumption has been at work.

(2) Can new product development success be measured accurately by using measures of *overall* financial success?

Our results are somewhat conflicting with regard to this question. Our only financial measure of success of new products was 'percentage of turnover accounted for by new products'. This measure showed a weak, positive relationship with 'average profits' only. Other measures of new product success were non-financial. Of these, 'percentage of launches that were successful' showed a positive association with both *direct* and *indirect* measures of overall sales growth, but a *negative* association with average profits. There is an apparent contradiction in these results, which is difficult to explain. The contradiction does serve to underline the complexity involved in the measurement of new product success. One such explanation may be that a higher percentage of successful launches may be the result of heavy investment which affects the average profits over the period in question. However, following this logic, one would assume that the higher the proportion of turnover accounted for by new products, the greater the investment, hence lower profits. However, this would only follow if the *number* of new products in the range was high. In some companies there may be a high proportion of turnover accounted for by relatively *few* new products, belying a direct relationship between this variable and low profits.

(3) Can indirect measures be used in place of direct measures of success?

The measures used in this study to examine this question were limited to sales growth, at the overall company level. The results suggest that asking an indirect, relative question about sales growth yields a picture consistent with a direct measurement. Furthermore, the experience of the authors in investigating low response rates suggests that indirect measures may well be more fruitful in accessing data.

(4) What are the dimensions of success, both financial and non-financial, as defined by business people themselves?

The dimensions of success identified by this study bear witness to the omnipresence of competitive thinking. The three dimensions all contained competitor-focused statements, with regard to technology, cost and price and time-to-market.

(5) To what extent are non-financial success measures associated with financial success measures?

Too few significant associations between the above-mentioned dimensions and measures of financial performance were observed to throw any insights into the existence, or lack of, such a relationship. On the other hand, the activity-based measures did show more significant associations. The amount of R&D projects is positively associated with the percentage of turnover accounted for by new products, but negatively associated with overall sales growth. This gives rise to speculation that companies with large numbers of product development projects may replace current turnover, rather than expand it. Similarly, the greater the number of launches, the more turnover is accounted for by new products. As previously mentioned, in dealing with question 2, the greater the percentage of successful launches, the higher is sales growth, and, as would be expected, the higher the proportion of turnover accounted for by new products. However, the association with average profit is negative, as discussed above.

In concluding this review of success measurement in new product development it is vital to note that future research must take cognisance of the responsibility it bears in making explicit and defending its chosen research methods. If research is to throw light on new product success, for the benefit of both the academic and business community, it must clearly show what types of product development strategies and processes will result in what *types* of success. Not only is success multi-dimensional, even *within* dimensions, the dynamic interrelationships are far from properly understood. This understanding will be crucial, particularly if recent initiatives such as the DTI's Innovation Unit are to have a meaningful bearing on future innovation policy.

ACKNOWLEDGEMENT

The author would like to thank Ms Angeline Craig for research assistance.

REFERENCES

Aaker, D. A. (1988) *Strategic Market Management*, Canada, John Wiley and Sons.

Ayal, I. and Raban, J. (1990) 'Developing Hi-Tech Industrial Products for World Markets', *IEEE Transactions on Engineering Management*, **37**, 89–101.

Baker, M. J. (1975) *Marketing New Industrial Products*, London, Macmillan.

Baker, M. J., Black, C. D. and Hart, S. J. (1988) 'The Competitiveness of British Industry: What Really Makes the Difference?', *European Journal of Marketing*, **22**: 70–85.

Baker, M. J. and Hart, S. J. (1989) *Marketing and Competitive Success*, Hemel Hempstead, Philip Allan.

Buckley, P. J., Pass, C. L. and Prescott, K. (1988) 'Measures of International Competitiveness: A Critical Survey', *Journal of Marketing Management*, **4**: 175–200.

Business Week (1984) 'Who's Excellent Now?' *Business Week*, November 5.

Calantone, R. J. and Cooper, R. G. (1981) 'New Product Scenarios: Prospects for Success', *Journal of Marketing*, **45**: 48–60.

Cannon, T. and Jackson, B. (1984) *Temporal and Organisational Factors in the Success Rates of Innovation*, Stirling, University of Stirling.

Carroll, A. B. (1979) 'A Three-Dimensional Conceptual Model of Corporate Performance', *Academy of Management Review*, **4**, 497–505.

Cooper, R. G. (1979) 'The Dimensions of Industrial New Product Success and Failure', *Journal of Marketing*, **43**: 93–103.

Cooper, R. G. (1980) 'How to Identify Potential New Product Innovation', *R&D Management*, **4**: 277–292.

Cooper, R. G. (1984) 'How new product strategies impact on performance', *Journal of Product Innovation Management*, **1**: 5–18.

Cooper, R. G. and Kleinschmidt, E. J. (1987a), 'What Makes a New Product a Winner: Success Factors at the Project Level', *R&D Management*, **17**, No. 3.

Cooper, R. G. and Kleinschmidt, E. J. (1987b) 'New products: What separates Winners from Losers?', *Journal of Product Innovation Management*, **4**(3): 169–184.

Craig, A. and Hart, S. J. (1992) 'Where to now in Product Development Research?', *European Journal of Marketing*, **26**: 3–49.

Doyle, P. (1985) 'Marketing and the Competitive Performance of British Industry: Areas for Research', *Journal of Marketing Management*, **1**: 87–98.

Frazier, G. L. and Howell, R. D. (1983) 'Business Definition and Performance', *Journal of Marketing*, **47**: 59–67.

Goldsmith, W. and Clutterbuck, D. (1984) *The Winning Streak, Britain's Top Companies Reveal their Formulas for Success*, London, Weidenfield and Nicolson.

Hart, S. J. and Service, L. M. (1988) 'The Effects of Managerial Attitudes to Design on Company Performance', *Journal of Marketing Management*, **4**: 217–229.

Hart, S. J. and Craig, A. (1993) 'Dimensions of Success in New Product Development'. In: *Perspectives in Marketing*, **3**. (ed.) Baker, M. J.

Hayes, R. and Abernathy, W. (1980) 'Managing our Way to Economic Decline', *Harvard Business Review*, July–August.

Hise, R. T., O'Neal, L., McNeal, U. and Parasuraman, A. (1989) 'The Effect of Product Design Activities on Commercial Success Levels of New Industrial Products', *Journal of Product Innovation Management*, **6**, 43–50.

Hooley, G. J. and Lynch, J. E. (1985) 'Marketing Lessons from the UK's High-Flying companies' *Journal of Marketing Management*, **1**: 65–74.

ICC (1987/88) *ICC Business Performance Analysis*, London, ICC Information Group.

Johne, A. F. and Snelson, P. (1988) 'Marketing's Role in Successful Product Development', *Journal of Marketing Management*, **3**: No. 3: 256–268.

Link, P. L. (1987) 'Keys to New Product Success and Failure', *Industrial Marketing Management*, **16**: 109–118.

Maidique, M. A. and Zirger, B. J. (1985) 'The New Product Learning Cycle', *Research Report Series, Innovation and Entrepreneurship Institute*. School of Business Administration, University of Miami, Coral Gables, FL (February).

Nyström, H. (1979) *Creativity and Innovation*, London, Wiley.

Nyström, H. (1985) 'Product Development Strategy: An Integration of Technology and Marketing', *Journal of Product Innovation Management*, **2**.

Pearce, F. T. (1966) *The Parameters of Research*, Lichfield, IMRA.

Peters, T. J. and Waterman, Jr, R. H. (1982) *In Search of Excellence, Lessons from America's Best-Run Companies*, London, Harper and Row.

Rothwell, R. (1972) *Factors for Success in Industrial Innovations. Project SAPPHO—A Comparative Study of Success and Failure in Industrial Innovation*, Science Policy Research Unit, University of Sussex, Brighton UK.

Rothwell, R. (1977) 'The Role of Technological Change in International Competitiveness: The Case of the Textile Machinery Industry', *Management Decision*, **15**, No. 6.

Rothwell, R., Freeman, C., Horsley, A., Jervis, V. T. P., Robertson, A. B. and Townsend, J. (1974) 'SAPPHO updated—project SAPPHO phase II', *Research Policy* **3**: 258–291.

Saul, P. (1983) 'New Ways of Measuring Company Performance', *Rydges*: 108–109.

Saunders, J. and Wong, V. (1985) 'Search of Excellence in the UK', *Journal of Marketing Management*, **1**: 119–137.

Saunders, J., Brown, M. and Laverick, S. (1991) 'The best of British: A Peer Evaluation of Britain's Leading Companies', *Marketing Education Group Proceedings of the 1991 Annual Conference*: 970–990.

Service, L. M. and Hart, S. J. (1989) 'The integrated approach to new product development: can management create the right climate?' *Proceedings of the 18th Conference of the European Marketing Academy*, April, Athens: 1178–1196.

Shipley, D., Edgett, S. and Forbes, G. (1991) 'New product Success Rates Among British and Japanese Companies', *EMAC 1991 Proceedings*.

Ughanwa, D. O. and Baker, M. J. (1989) *The Role of Design in International Competitiveness*, London, Routledge.

Voss, C. A. (1985) 'Determinants of Success in the Development of Applications Software', *Journal of Product Innovation Management*, **2**: 122–129.

Walsh, V., Roy, R. and Bruce, M. (1988) 'Competitive by Design', *Journal of Marketing Management*, **4**: No. 2.

APPENDIX 1. FINANCIAL MEASURES OF SUCCESS

Measure	Study
Profit-based Profitability, degree to which product's profitability fell short or exceeded firm's acceptable profitability level for this type of investment	Cooper (1979, 1980); Calantone and Cooper (1981); Cooper and Kleinschmidt (1987a, b); Link (1987)

Profits relative to other new products introduced in the last 5 years	Cooper and Kleinschmidt (1987a, b)
Meeting profit objectives	Cooper and Kleinschmidt (1987a, b)
Profits for new product minus the cost of the new product programme	Cooper (1984)
Profit margin	Walsh et al. (1988)
Profit growth	Walsh et al. (1988)
Financial success or failure, i.e. exceeded or fell short of acceptable profitability level	Cooper and Kleinschmidt (1987a)
Profitability of product over its life cycle	Nyström (1985)
Payback period (time to break even)	Cooper and Kleinschmidt (1987a, b)
Achievement of break even	Maidique and Zirger (1984)
Average return on sales	Peters and Waterman (1982)
Net direct monetary gain, accruing from the sale and/or licensing of the innovation and from the sale of technical, know-how generated through the innovation	Rothwell et al. (1974)
Importance of programme in generating profits for the company	Cooper (1984)

Asset-based

Asset growth	Peters and Waterman (1982); Walsh et al. (1988)

Sales-based

Turnover growth	Walsh et al. (1988)
Export sales	Walsh et al. (1988)
Percentage sales growth	Walsh et al. (1988)
Meeting sales objectives	Cooper and Kleinschmidt (1987a, b)
Sales relative to other new products introduced in the last 5 years	Cooper and Kleinschmidt (1987a, b)
Ratio of cumulative sales in the first 3 years on the market to the investment in R&D for the project	Ayal and Raban (1990)
Domestic market share, percentage share of domestic market 3 years after launch	Cooper and Kleinschmidt (1987a, b)
Foreign market share, percentage share of foreign markets 3 years after launch	Cooper and Kleinschmidt (1987a, b)
Diffusion coefficient, fitting installation data to classify diffusion equation	Voss (1985)
Market share in terms of the number of units sold and the average sales price per unit	Rothwell et al. (1974)
Importance of programme in generating sales for the company	Cooper (1984)
Percentage of company sales made up by new products introduced in the last 5 years	Cooper (1984); Hart and Service (1988)

Capital-based

Return on capital	Walsh et al. (1988)
Average return on capital	Peters and Waterman (1982)

Equity-based

Compound equity growth	Peters and Waterman (1982)

APPENDIX 2. NON-FINANCIAL MEASURES OF SUCCESS

Measure	Study
Design-based	
Number of design awards	Walsh *et al.* (1988)
Number of citations by Design Council	Walsh *et al.* (1988)
Competitors measure of their design reputation	Walsh *et al.* (1988)
Winning Queen's Award	Ughanwa and Baker (1989)
Activity-based	
(a) Extent of activities	
Regularity of updated and new products in relation to competitive nature of market	Johne and Snelson (1988)
(b) Proficiency of activities	
Number of launches resulting from new product development projects in last 5 years	Hart and Service (1988)
Percentage of successful launches from total number	Hart and Service (1988)
Success to which the new product met its performance objectives over the last 5 years	Cooper (1984)
Successfulness of programme relative to competitors	Cooper (1984)
Successfulness of programme—global rating	Cooper (1984)
Success, failure and 'kill' rates (percent) of products developed in the last 5 years	Cooper (1984)
Market-based	
Opportunity window on new markets, extent to which a new market for the firm was opened up by the new product	Cooper and Kleinschmidt (1987a, b)
Market potential, uniqueness or interchangeability of product from buyers point of view (greater uniqueness equals greater potential)	Nyström (1985)
Technologically-based	
Degree of novelty/uniqueness of technological solutions	Nyström (1985)
Degree of patent protection	Nyström (1985)
Time for development	Nyström (1985)
Company's 20-year record for innovation	Peters and Waterman (1982)
Opportunity on new categories, extent to which a new category of product was introduced to the firm by the new product	Cooper and Kleinschmidt (1987a, b)
Commercially-based	
Commercial success, successful if having been marketed it had sold beyond the initial installation for at least 1 year and not been withdrawn	Voss (1985)
Commercial success, i.e. the consensus as to whether the product met or did not meet original expectations on all important respects	Hise *et al.* (1989)
Success if survival for more than 4 years	Canon (1984)

| On the basis of subjective evaluations by management (1–6 scales, with 1 denoting abysmal failure and 6 resounding success) | Ayal and Raban (1990) |
| Success or failure by management assessment | Shipley *et al.* (1991) |

Strategically-based

Alignment with company strategy 'Company strategy' is a loose term which takes account of how well the innovation aligned with the overall planning of the company and any scientific, technical or other spin-off. In fact, anything other than direct monetary gain and market share	Rothwell *et al.* (1974)
Average return on equity	Peters and Waterman (1982)
Average 'market' to book ratio	Peters and Waterman (1982)

Part II

The Strategic Dimension of New Product Development

CONTENTS

Introduction to Part II

Susan Hart

New product development is a resource-hungry activity. In addition, it is high-risk, necessitating careful planning to ensure a sustainable return on investment. As the new product success articles in Part I have shown, the factors enhancing or inhibiting success are manifold, again implying analysis and planning of the process to determine its overall direction and purpose. Furthermore, its fundamental importance to the survival of companies links it inexplicably with the 'strategic problem', namely, the constant adaptation of the company with the demands of its changing environment.

The four articles in this part that deal with the strategy–new product development link are very different from one another, yet several of the issues covered are common to all of them: the need to build on existing synergies, the need to integrate marketing and R&D inputs, the need to adopt appropriate planning horizons and the need to avoid single or 'closed' product development. The approach taken by each is very different. Crawford (Reading 5) builds a picture of his 'Product Innovation Charter' on the basis of interviews and documentation studies of 125 companies, and is illustrated by reference to several examples. Cooper's work (Reading 6) reports, in detail, the analysis of 122 companies new product strategies and outcomes. Meyer and Utterback (Reading 7) illustrate their synthesis of the concepts of 'the product family' and 'core capability' with reference to a large company in the electronic imaging business, while Nyström's paper (Reading 8) applies a 'strategy framework', discussed below, to four Swedish pulp and paper companies. The contribution of each is briefly discussed below.

Crawford's 'Product Innovation Charter' developed in this 1980 paper has been reviewed and updated in the four editions of his book *New Product Management*. This early representation shows how it is derived from the application of strategic planning techniques to new product development. The Product Innovation Charter (PIC) is focused on each new product project and contains the following information: business arenas that the new product should target, goals and objectives of the new product activity, and the value of the new product activities to be undertaken, including R&D, manufacturing and marketing inputs, weaknesses to be avoided, the source of the innovation (internal/external to the company), degree of innovativeness and a host of 'special conditions'. Using numerous examples to illustrate the use of the PIC, Crawford argues that it helps to guide the cross-functional inputs to developing new products, and to guide those involved, thereby avoiding developments without direction.

Cooper's approach is once again one of providing empirical evidence upon which to base prescription for management. The article reports a study of the new product *strategies* and *outcomes* for 122 firms. He found that the outcomes for NPD activities could be grouped into three dimensions: the overall performance of the program (new products, meeting performance objectives etc.); the new product success rate (how many new products are 'killed' and how many are a commercial success); and finally, the impact of the program on the company (percentage of sales accounted for by new products etc.). Relating these performances profiled to the new product strategies employed by the firm, Cooper found that no strategy performs equally well on all three performance dimensions. This is interesting when related back to the discussion on measuring new product success by Hart, in Part I. Secondly, Cooper's research found that the most successful strategy overall combined a technologically aggressive, innovative stance with a solid market orientation. Thirdly, all the poorest performing firms tended not to have articulated strategies, were generally defensive and displayed neither a strong technological nor market orientation. Cooper's overall conclusion is that product innovation strategy is a cornerstone of corporate strategy.

Meyer and Utterback look at the question of new product strategies from the angle of core capabilities. In addition, they weave into their discussion the idea of 'the product family', arguing that consistently innovative firms tend to build on a solid base of core capabilities across several product families allowing them to benefit from synergies across product families, and also reducing lead lines in development. Based on intensive work with an electronic imaging company, the authors describe the process of defining product families, mapping product families over time, and assessing core capabilities, both between and within families, over time and in relation to key competitors.

They conclude that the one capability will decline if no development takes place as customer needs are constantly ending and that product families should be the key level of analysis and planning.

The final paper in this Part, by Nyström, picks up on an issue central to Cooper's finding, that companies need both marketing and technology strategies to deal effectively with product development. Based on an overview of a decade of research, this article develops and applies a framework of strategic analysis to encourage closer integration between technology and marketing. The key dimensions of the framework touch on several issues covered in Part I. In defining technology strategy, the dimensions of technology use and technology orientation are employed. Technology use is further defined as being isolated—where work on new products takes place within a well defined and established field of technology—or synergistic—where several technologies are combined in new product development. The technology orientation may be internal or external, that is, it comes from within the firm completely, or from outside the firm.

In defining marketing strategies, Nyström uses the product and customer foci of the company. The product focus encapsulates the options of product modifications or product diversifications, based on the closeness of NPD to current products. The customer focus may be on new or current customers (aggressive or defensive stances).

Using these definitions of new product strategy, Nyström posits that his research suggests that synergistic technology use and an external technology orientation contribute to an 'open' technology strategy. A focus on product diversification and new customers give evidence of an 'open' marketing strategy. He goes on to say that open strategies have greater potential in dynamic environments, while closed strategies are more suited to stable environments. There is, however, no discussion of which strategy is likely to exploit a firm's strengths and minimize its weaknesses.

Each of the articles in this part takes a different perspective on the strategic elements of new product development. Yet, Crawford's 'strategic planning' approach, Nyström's open and closed strategies and Meyer and Utterback's core capabilities all touch on the central issue of importance to NPD success: attaining the appropriate level of synergy and integration.

5

Defining the Charter for Product Innovation

C. Merle Crawford

Few businesses of any economic, social or political significance can be optimally managed today without strategic planning.[1] Perhaps the groups most appreciative of the advent of strategic planning are those engaged in producing new products. These groups, being multifunctional in nature, lack the organizational unity of purpose and direction enjoyed by, say, a typical sales force or factory. Informal planning styles have had a tendency to leave many of their multifunctional processes unplanned. Indeed, 'back-of-the-envelope' planning styles were the bane of new product developers until recent years.[2] There have been exceptions, of course. For instance, when the chief executive or operations officer has been *de facto* head of development (as was Land at Polaroid, Wilson at Xerox, Iacocca at Ford, and Sarnoff at RCA), sound processes have been possible without formal strategic planning. Other exceptions have included small firms or the really independent profit centres of such companies as 3M. In general, though, informal planning styles have been inadequate to guide new product development in a comprehensive way.

Today's strategic planning techniques enable any firm to give its product development function an integrated, goals-oriented character. The key element in accomplishing this orientation is a spin-off of the strategic planning process. It consists of a set of policies and objectives designed to guide new product development. This set of policies and objectives, which has not yet had a name, will here be called the *product innovation charter* (PIC). The purpose of this article is to report on a study of PICs and to describe the various dimensions these charters have assumed within companies.

THE STUDY

The research for this study was of two types. First, over 500 business press reports of companies' new product strategies were studied. Although most were quite incomplete, 71 reports were thought to yield enough detail for inclusion here.[3] Second, 54 field interviews were conducted between 1976 and 1979 by the author and various research assistants. Altogether, this research yielded partial charters for 125 firms. Characteristics of these firms are summarized in Table 1.

Reprinted from 'Defining the charter for product innovation' by C. Merle Crawford, *Sloan Management Review*, Fall 1980, pp. 3–12

Table 1. Firms in the sample[a]

	Number	Percentage
Markets		
Primarily industrial	57	45.6
Primarily consumer	68	54.4
Total	125	100.0
Size		
Large firms or closely integrated divisions of large firms	72	57.6
Medium, small, or independent divisions	53	42.4
Total	125	100.0
Output		
Products	116	92.8
Services	9	7.2
Total	125	100.0

[a] All are in the United States and are profit-making organizations.

Although all 125 firms included in this study are profit-making companies, many nonprofit organizations (e.g. state lotteries and business schools) have also reported on similar new service planning. However, these reports have not occurred with sufficient frequency to indicate solid patterns—perhaps because not enough nonprofit organizations have yet adopted overall strategic planning. Thus, nonprofit organizations were excluded from this study.

It should be noted that despite the increasing frequency and comprehensiveness of reports on companies' new product strategies, there is probably much information still undisclosed. Firms generally keep their new product strategies confidential, since they feel constrained from revealing too much to their competitors. Thus, published press reports—and to a lesser degree, field interviews—may be presumed to be incomplete or even deliberately misleading.

It should also be noted that the sample consists only of firms willing to discuss publicly the new product portion of their strategic planning. Because this sample, therefore, is not random, the discussion to follow may not necessarily reflect the current state of new product planning in American industry. However, it presents a composite outline of the PIC, based on what firms were willing to say they were doing. Its main purpose is to delineate the concept and content of PICs, rather than to quantify their use.

The most significant finding of this study is that one document can give comprehensive direction to *all* of a business unit's new product activities. In the past, a policy might only have cited a market to be served ('Babies are our business'), the organizational mode (P&G's brand system), or commitment to technical innovation (Corning, IBM). But now it appears that companies are pulling all of these elements together. Firms' policies include every strategy dimension deemed necessary to produce the particular flow of product innovation that will optimize profits.

The remainder of this article will discuss the various elements of PICs. Any such discussion meets with terminology problems. Some students of the subject prefer that the PIC be called 'policy' or 'program'. These terms are deliberately avoided here. The usage of 'charter' is intended to emphasize that the PIC carries a directional and activity mandate.

OUTLINE OF THE PIC

The PIC, which most larger firms and better-managed medium and smaller firms now use, contains the following sections.

A. The target business arenas that product innovation is to take the firm into or keep it in. These arenas are defined in four ways:[4]

(1) by product type (e.g. specialty chemicals or passenger cars);
(2) by end-user activity or function (e.g. data processing or food);
(3) by technology (e.g. fluidics or xerography);
(4) by intermediate or end-user customer group (e.g. service stations, state lotteries, younger men).

B. The goals or objectives of product innovation activities. These goals or objectives may be expressed in terms of:

(1) the quantitative results to be achieved by the product innovation. Examples include:

   (a) market share or position of leadership;[5]
   (b) sales volume (usually expressed in dollars and typically with growth goals); or
   (c) profit level (e.g. total dollars, ROI payback or percent on sales, considered on a short- or long-term basis).

(2) *Special qualitative goals or objectives* peculiar to the firm's unique situation. Examples are:

   (a) to create a sense of urgency or crisis;
   (b) to diversify;
   (c) to fill out a product line;
   (d) to maintain or seek an image;
   (e) to protect a position; or
   (f) to smooth out various irregularities.

C. The program of activities (policies) chosen to achieve the goals in Section B above. The program typically will discuss:

(1) *Strengths the program is to exploit.* These strengths are usually one or more of three types:

    (a) An R&D skill or capability (e.g. glass technology);
    (b) a manufacturing facility, process, skill, or material (e.g. food processing or wood chips); or
    (c) a marketing advantage (e.g. a strong sales force, an image or a trade franchise).

(2) *Weaknesses to avoid.* These weaknesses are usually of the same three types as noted above. For instance, a firm may wish to avoid investing in a particular R&D project, building a particular facility, or marketing to the government.

(3) *The source of the innovation.* The new product's points of differentiation can be developed in the following ways:

    (a) internally (by R&D, marketing etc.);
    (b) Externally (by licensing or by acquiring companies, products or processes); or
    (c) by a special combination of both, one variation of which is the joint venture.

(4) *The degree of innovativeness sought.* In terms of Ansoff and Stewart's paradigm, which was developed over ten years ago, the degrees of innovativeness sought by firms can be characterized as:[6]

    (a) *Inventive.* The firm seeks technological leadership *vis-à-vis* product packaging, positioning etc. It tries to be the 'first to market' with the product.
    (b) *Adaptive.* The firm chooses to wait and let others lead, then to quickly adapt or modify the product. By means of 'innovative imitation', it seeks to be 'second but best'.
    (c) *Economic.* The firm builds strength by producing what others have created, but by doing so more economically. It tries to be the low-cost producer, particularly in the early maturity phase of the life cycle.
    (d) *Innovative applications.* The firm utilizes established technology, but applies it creatively to new uses (e.g. adhesives or MOS technology).

(5) *Special conditions, restrictions, or mandates.* These conditions are highly situational, but not miscellaneous or casual. For example, special instructions to the innovation team may specify:

    (a) the product quality level—usually to protect or improve an image;
    (b) the level of risk that is acceptable;
    (c) seeking low-volume niches for 'quiet' intrusions;
    (d) serving only 'real' or 'genuine' needs;
    (e) the size or growth trends in markets being considered;
    (f) either specifically avoiding or confronting particular competitors;

(g) low-cost repeat-buying product categories;
(h) avoiding regulatory or social problems;
(i) patentability;
(j) keying to systems of products or of products and services; or
(k) avoiding systems of products.

A hypothetical example

Although many examples will be given later to illustrate these outline items, it is desirable to show how these ideas fit into a complete PIC. The power of the charter lies in its integration of otherwise isolated decisions. The following is a hypothetical PIC in highly abbreviated form.

XYZ Company PIC

The XYZ Company is committed to a program of innovation in specialty chemicals as utilized in the automobile and other metal-finishing businesses. Our goal is to become the market share leader in this market. We also intend to achieve at least 35% ROI from our program on a three-year payout basis. We seek recognition as the most technically competent company in metal finishing.

These goals will be achieved by building on our current R&D skills and by embellishing them as necessary. We will produce inhouse, with only emergency reliance on outside sources, new items that are technically superior to competitors' products. The Company is willing to invest funds as necessary to achieve these technical breakthroughs, even though 1980 and 1981 IATs may suffer. Care will be taken to establish patent-protected positions in these new developments and to increase the safety of customer company personnel.

The PIC versus scoring models of checklists

Several of the PIC items are similar to those found in many scoring models or checklists that are used to screen new product ideas. This similarity is not surprising, since scoring models should result directly from PICs. However, firms often rely upon scoring models in the absence of PICs. A typical checklist is the following one used by a chemical company:[7]

1. Do we have marketplace skills?
2. Is there patent protection?
3. Does it match our manufacturing capability?
4. Do we have the raw material?
5. Is the market large enough?

These are passive or reactive criteria: they do not stipulate positive direction. They clearly offer managers much less direction than would a PIC, which in contrast, charts a course. It says: 'Go this way, and do these things. They offer the best bet for optimizing profits from new products.'

COMPONENTS OF THE PIC

Target business arenas

Of the firms studied, about one-third defined their new product activity arenas in terms of products. Planning specialists have argued against this kind of definition, but apparently the practice has become highly institutionalized in such industries as cars, chemicals, banking services (albeit constrained by law), pharmaceuticals, women's wear, appliances, beer and tape labels. Some definitions that seemed to be keyed to products were actually based on activities (e.g. food, cosmetics and cutting tools), and have been so classified here.

The most common *nonproduct* definition, by far, was that of the end user's function or activity. Terms such as data processing, measuring electricity, preparing coal, controlling machine tools and law enforcement were typical.

Surprisingly, only about 10% of the firms said they used a definition based on technology. This low result, though, may be more a function of the firms' reluctance to disclose too many details to their competitors than of their actual strategies. Several of the firms' definitions, however, combined technology with function (e.g. electronic games, electromechanical devices for cardiovascular treatment, or xerography in education).

Equally surprising was the small number of firms who said they found a specific customer or customer orientation helpful. Actually, four of them were oriented to trade groups (e.g. beauty and barber shops and company-owned service stations), and two used unique groups (outdoor people and operators of state lotteries). One is no longer operative (Gerber's babies), and one is brand-new (Winchester's gun owners).

Goals to be achieved by the new products programme

It was apparent, particularly from the personal interviews, that managements differed on the question of how to state goals for the product innovation function. Their stated goals took several forms:

(1) The traditional *sales gap goal*. Closing the gap between planning objectives and an extension of current sales lines was often more a concept than a specific dollar target.
(2) Some expression of *profit*. This goal could be stated in many ways, though most often it was expressed as a gap concept.
(3) *A first-level surrogate for profit*. This goal was usually stated in terms of achieving some combination of 'large or growing markets' and a 'large or leading share'. Profit was then presumed to follow as a natural consequence. Loctite, Sarns (medical devices), Iroquois Brands, Keithley (measuring instruments), Jovan, Rucker, Stauffer, Texas Instruments and Gould are examples of firms that stated goals in this manner.

(4) *A second-level surrogate.* By far the most commonly stated goal was to exploit some company strength. The premise was that working from a strength should yield a good market share, which in turn should yield good profits. Firms using this approach actually avoided setting goals in the form of results or output.

(5) *Special situational goals.* There was no end to the variety of these goals, but common ones were:

- Urgency: some firms faced situations where new products were urgently essential—for example, to avoid a takeover.
- Diversification away from a high-risk or limiting situation: for example, Hoover Universal and Midland Adhesive both sought new products which would relieve them from dependence on the automobile.
- Offering a complete line: Frito-Lay, a large NYC bank, and Digital Equipment are examples of firms having this goal. NCR built its turnaround on this idea.
- Altering, holding or strengthening an image: Waterford Glass, Texas Instruments and Cincinnati Milacron, for example, stated such goals.
- Being defensive: often firms sought to protect a profitable market position or to add a seasonal pattern to complement existing ones. Hallmark had the latter goal.

Program of activities: strengths to exploit

Managements increasingly use the term 'technology' to mean any system or set of operations, skills or activities which constitutes a capability. For instance, Rockwell's engineering skill, a technology in the traditional sense, has been a strength that Rockwell clearly has planned to exploit. Similarly, GE's Carboloy Division has sought to exploit tungsten carbide technology; Hallmark, its creative processes and skills; Gelman, membrane filtration; Potlatch, high graphics; Rucker, oil well technology; Helena Rubenstein, the science of cosmetology; and Remington powdered metals technology. Most firms in the sample favoured the R&D technology. Those having no exploitable R&D technology often moved to acquire one. A chemical firm, a computer firm and a small bank, for instance, said they were doing so.

About a third of the companies cited manufacturing skills as exploitable strengths, and slightly fewer cited marketing capabilities. For example, Pillsbury has a strong supermarket franchise; a dental sundries firm has a strong sales force; and P&G has high-volume TV purchasing discounts. Tressler Oil owns a chain of service stations; Chelsea Milling has a unique franchise as a push-marketer on its line of Jiffy Mixes; and Standard Brands uses its Planters brand to seek a stronger position in snacks.

In sum, most of the firms in this study felt they had exploitable strengths of one sort of another. Assuming that the firms were somewhat reticent, owing to their reluctance to reveal too much to their competitors, it is entirely possible that their cleverest strategies remain undisclosed.

Weaknesses to avoid

Managements similarly were reluctant to discuss the weakness dimension, but examples were found. An engineering firm knew it had a weak marketing operation, so it listed 'no strong marketing required' as a key criterion. A bank decided it really had no exploitable creative skills, so it adopted a strategy of selecting new services from those introduced by other banks. Several firms that had acute dollar shortages stipulated a low R&D cost requirement.

Degree of innovation

New product strategists have recognized the importance of defining the degree of product innovativeness they wish to use. In this study 57 firms claimed to be invention-oriented, 68 adaptive, and 20 economic (low cost). Twenty-eight were in a unique situation: they could avoid the risks of invention by sticking to a known technology and seeking new applications for it. Loctite, the adhesive producer, was the classic example of a firm using the 'innovative applications' strategy. This strategy was also used by chemical firms such as Dow and by mineral firms such as Climax Molybdenum. Because data on slightly over half of the firms were taken from the business press, however, there may be some bias in the results: a firm is likely to find it more gratifying to discuss publicly its exciting policy of technical excellence than to comment on its commitment to be a low-cost imitator.

As the numbers indicate, most firms planned to follow more than one route. Inventiveness and adaptive innovation constituted the most typical combination. In terms of the new products that were actually developed and marketed, most firms ended up with at least two levels of innovativeness. Although there is a disparity here between the planned and actual strategies, it should be remembered that the charter reflected strategic intention; it is not meant to prevent the firm from exercising some flexibility. An indication that PICs are subject to change was that most of the firms referred to pasts or presents where commitments had been or would be different. Many Japanese firms (though not examined specifically in this study) had dramatized this point. They adopted economic strategies during the 1950s, progressed into adaptive strategies as resources permitted or as labour costs required, and now use inventive strategies, especially in markets where they have become volume leaders. Many United States firms probably had followed the same progression, though some that started out with inventive strategies either kept them (Hewlett-Packard) or gradually became adaptive (Sycor—computer peripherals). Of course, change caused by the *firm*'s life cycle should not be confused with the effect of a *product category* life cycle.

Source of innovation

Most of the firms studied decided to generate new products only internally; most of the others combined the internal and external routes. Personal discussions with managers revealed several alternative strategies regarding the source of innovation.

- *New products, but no innovation.* Betty Dain (women's clothing), most local banks, Tressler Oil, a food company and an auto parts firm all wanted products that were new to *them*, but which would have no innovative element. This approach related to the economic strategy of low-cost production or to that of serving the needs of a narrow captive market.

- *Innovative products developed totally inside.* This strategy called for a strong R&D program with no interest in outside sources. Some highly technical firms such as Hewlett-Packard used this approach, as did such consumer firms as Revlon and Pillsbury.
- *A general policy of seeking internal innovations, but with a willingness to take advantage of outside opportunities,* particularly licensing. Du Pont, Sybron and Upjohn followed this approach.
- *A policy of limited inside technical or marketing innovative skills, with principal reliance on outside sources.* A large technical machinery firm, having a small engineering department, mainly licensed developments found in Europe.

Special conditions, restrictions and mandates

Many special provisos came up in this investigation; the most common ones were related to some definition of product quality level. Only one company, a well-known, high-quality firm, actually indicated a desire for low quality in its new products. Its purpose was to tap the low end of its market. However, 26 others specifically said their Charters called for products of high quality. Trademarks, such as Campbell, Parke-Davis, Gerber and Hallmark, had powerful consumer franchises, and their owners did not desire to trade down. Industrial firms frequently felt the same, e.g. Sperry Univac, Allen Bradley, Brown & Sharpe and McNally-Pittsburgh. Black & Decker (not included in this study) demonstrated the profitability of a lower-quality approach when it developed a line of low-priced electrical tools for home use. Items, such as the eight-hour, ¼-inch electric drill, opened a whole new market many times the size of the traditional professional market.

Another special proviso, mentioned by 20 firms, was the mandate of low risk or conservatism in the product innovation function. Expressed in many different ways (e.g. 'no failures', 'evolutionary only', and 'minimal R&D dollar investment'), this mandate nevertheless clearly differentiated such a programme from one of high-risk, chance-taking innovation. Paramount Pictures (in its refusal to bankroll high-budget movies), National Semiconductor, Milton Bradley and General Foods (with its 'measured intro-duction' and 'orderly manner') were a few firms that included clearly restrictive policies in at least portions of their PICs. In contrast, Intel, Gould, Merck and Bendix were firms that had no apparent risk-avoidance mandate.

Other special directions included that of seeking market 'niches', an approach cited by the managements of American Motors, Iroquois Brands and others. Another was the mandate to serve 'real needs'. In Merck's charter, for instance, 'real needs' could easily be translated as 'the need for new pharmaceuticals'. This kind of mandate was also prominent with a large bank and with the industrial leader, Gould.

Gillette, P&G and Dean Foods told their developers to seek opportunities only in markets that were large or rapidly growing. Some managers were willing to say openly that their charters led their new products teams away from markets where certain competitors were strong. IBM and P&G were often named as firms to avoid, but there were others. For example, cosmetics firm A wanted to avoid Avon, and cosmetics firm B wanted to avoid both Avon and firm A. American Motors wanted to avoid all three of its automotive competitors' key segments.

Finally, there was a potpourri of unique situations. Fetterolf and Merck would not touch unpatentable products; a chemical company specifically stipulated that new product decisions would be made 'without sentiment': and a computer peripherals firms said 'no systems'. These considerations may seem almost incidental, but they were clearly not incidental to the firms citing them. In several cases the special proviso was the key factor in the strategy.

MULTIPLE CHARTERS WITHIN A FIRM

Small firms and nondivisionalized medium-sized firms often operate only one strategic business unit and need, therefore, only one PIC. Most organizations, however, have multiple plans and multiple charters. One such firm is Texas Instruments.[8] TI has at least one 'business', MOS memories, in which its strategy is highly innovative—internal only, inventive only, keyed to TI technologies, high risk, and probably having some very high ROI goals. A second TI business, toys, represents mostly innovative application. Its strategy calls for internal innovation with strong marketing involvement and for creation of new markets for technologies already developed. TI's success with Speak 'n Spell demonstrates both the creativity demanded and the potential reward from this particular strategy. A third business, watches and calculators, is geared to the experience curve. It is a classic example of the economic strategy. TI, apparently familiar with all of the basic alternatives, has developed a steadily changing mix of business arenas and activity modes according to existing conditions.

CONTRASTS WITHIN AN INDUSTRY

Several recent reports have given us the chance to compare different firms within a common industry setting, as these firms have developed their respective PICs.

Intel versus National Semiconductor

These two firms illustrate the contrasts between the inventive and economic strategies.[9] Robert N. Noyce, chairman of Intel Corporation, is known as 'a brilliant and outgoing scientist-entrepreneur whose reputation is built on technical breakthroughs'. He has tried to find new niches in the semiconductor market by applying highly advanced technologies. Using an inventive strategy, for example, he raised R&D spending during the 1975 recession. His strategy, in short, carries high risks, but has a potential for high returns. Charles E. Spork, on the other hand, has generated a sales-and-profit bonanza at National Semiconductor with precisely the opposite approach. His goal, 'achieved in almost every major line of semiconductor products, was to make National a super-efficient manufacturer of high-volume products'. Although neither firm intends its strategy to be totally restrictive of the other approach (indeed, National has recently emphasized a plan to change), the difference has been dramatic for many years.

Frito-Lay versus Nabisco versus Standard Brands

Frito-Lay has long dominated the snack market, but Standard Brands and Nabisco are now challenging the traditional Frito-Lay dominance.[10] Nabisco, for instance, has been 'experimenting with multigrain products and new textures and shapes'. In addition, it has repackaged in bags such items as Mister Salty pretzels, and moved them from the cookie section to the snack section. In the short term, it is following both an adaptive strategy (by improving some standard items) and an innovative applications path (by repackaging). In the long term, it has an inventive strategy. These strategies are being carried out internally, and they carry reasonably high risks.

Standard Brands is also applying some available packaging technology (the canister approach used by P&G's Pringles), and applying the Planter's name to some new products (obtained by acquisition) that it claims to be superior. Its strategy is adaptive, not inventive.

While Nabisco is in the lab and Standard Brands is acquiring, Frito-Lay is developing new items of its own. Its strategy is not inventive, however, since it regards snack inventiveness as having run its course. It is also expanding production, planning on an economic strategy if necessary, and strengthening its distribution.

The firearms business

The firearms business is a business 'with tired blood'. It is expected to have 'slow or no growth' or even to decline in the future.[11] As a result, the PICs of five firms have had to be altered. Colt has chosen not to innovate, but rather to raise prices and to continue its line of high-quality commemorative firearms. Remington is trying to apply its powdered metal and abrasive technologies to other business arenas. Winchester, defining an arena in consumer terms, is running a gun book club and franchising gun clubs. Smith & Wesson is also taking a consumer approach. Its particular arena, however, is law enforcement agencies. It is now developing handcuffs, holsters, police car lights and other products for these agencies. Sturm Ruger is trying to exploit its manufacturing facility, especially its foundry, by offering to produce for other (nongun) manufacturers. In the meantime, small firms and foreign firms are not idle in the industry. One, using the inventive approach, has developed do-it-yourself, muzzle-loading firearm kits. Another firm is following an economic strategy. It uses its plants in the South to assemble guns at the lowest possible cost.

SUMMARY

This article has reported on a study of the strategic plans of 125 firms. Such plans are usually quite confidential, but managements often have occasion to reveal, or even to expound at length on, selected aspects of their new product strategies. This study relied upon unusually complete business press reports and on personal interviews. It has resulted in the description of a strategic concept—what has been termed here the 'product innovation charter'.

The PIC is a recent spin-off of the strategic planning process. From the strategic planning process have come approved directions for the established functions—marketing plans, production schedules, financing requirements and budgets for specific R&D projects. The PIC, a more recent development, is designed to guide the organization's cross-functional subset of activities charged with developing new products, and to give clear direction to the diverse personnel involved in new products.

The outline of a composite charter presented in this article can be used by any management that is planning product or service innovation. It will enable the management to test the comprehensiveness of its own decision set, or to easily scan through its strategic planning process to identify missing elements. Use of the PIC in new product planning can help managers to develop coordinated and integrated plans, and ultimately to achieve their overall profit goals.

NOTES

1. The literature on strategic planning is rapidly mounting and is impossible to cite in total. However, several of the better sources are:
   D. F. Abell, 'Using PIMS and Portfolio Analysis in Strategic Market Planning' (Paper presented at the XXIII International Meeting of The Institute of Management Science, Athens, Greece, July 1977);
   G. S. Day, 'Diagnosing the Product Portfolio', *Journal of Marketing*, April 1977, pp. 29–38;
   B. Hendley, 'A Fundamental Approach to Strategy Development', *Long Range Planning*, December 1976, pp. 2–11;
   B. Hendley, 'Strategy and the Business Portfolio', *Long Range Planning*, February 1977, pp. 9–15;
   M. Laric and C. Jain Subhash, eds. *Strategic Planning for Growth Management* (Proceedings for the American Marketing Association and University of Connecticut Conference, March 14, 1978);
   W. Rothschild, *Putting It All Together* (New York: AMACOM, 1976), chs. 3–7;
   M. Hanan, 'Reorganize Your Company around Its Market', *Harvard Business Review*, November–December 1974;
   D. J. Luck and O. C. Ferrell, *Marketing Strategy and Plans* (Englewood Cliffs, NJ: Prentice-Hall, 1979), ch. 2. For an excellent summary of the literature on strategic planning, which includes the most complete bibliography, see H. W. Boyd, Jr. and J. Larreche, 'The Foundations of Marketing Strategy', in *Review of Marketing*, ed. G. Zaltman and T. V. Bonoma (Chicago: American Marketing Association, 1978), pp. 41–72.
2. Several researchers have begun to address the subject of new product strategy in a serious way. Their thinking helped stimulate the current research paper. See:
   B. Andrews, *Creative Product Development* (New York: Longman, 1975), chs 4 and 8 in particular;
   C. Freeman, *The Economics of Industrial Innovation* (Harmondsworth, England: Penguin, 1974), ch. 8;
   D. S. Hopkins, *Business Strategies for Problem Products* (The Conference Board, 1977);
   H. Nyström, 'Company Strategies for Research and Development', *Proceedings* (Strathclyde, New York: Macmillan Co. International Symposium on Industrial Innovation, 1978);
   L. W. Steele, *Innovation in Big Business* (New York: Elsevier, North-Holland Publishing, 1975), ch. 6 in particular;
   B. Twiss, *Managing Technical Innovation* (New York: Longman, 1974), ch. 2 in particular;
   R. C. Bennett and R. G. Cooper, 'Beyond the Marketing Concept', *Business Horizons*, June 1979, pp. 76–83.
3. For good examples, see:
   P. H. Engel, 'The Rubenstein Religion', *Across the Board*, October 1977, pp. 79–87;
   'Loctite: Ready to Fend off a Flock of New Competitors', *Business Week*, 19 June 1978, pp. 116–118;
   P. Berman, 'With Fashion Coming In, Can Levi Strauss Branch Out?' *Forbes*, 21 August 1978, pp. 41–45;

'Hallmark Now Stands for a Lot More than Cards', *Business Week*, 29 May 1978, pp. 57–58. Though business press reports are customarily scanty, the ones used for this study were surprisingly complete.

4. The proper manner of defining business targets has been the subject of considerable debate, though most of the controversy concerns the portfolio of present products. For a good discussion of the problem, see Abell (July 1977). See also Boyd and Larreche (1978), 46–60.

5. Again, the literature on market-share strategy is extensive. See:
   Boyd and Larreche (1978);
   R. D. Buzzell, B. T. Gale and R. G. M. Sultan, 'Market Share—A Key to Profitability', *Harvard Business Review*, January–February 1975, pp. 97–106;
   P. N. Bloom and P. Kotler, 'Strategies for High Market Share Companies', *Harvard Business Review*, November–December 1975, pp. 63–72;
   Perspectives on Experience (Boston: Boston Consulting Group, Inc., 1972).

6. See H. I. Ansoff and J. M. Stewart, 'Strategies for a Technology-Based Business', Harvard Business Review, November–December 1967, pp. 71–83. Others have also offered paradigms in this area: Twiss (1974); Steele (1975).

7. See Hopkins (1977). In addition, see B. Merrifield, 'Industrial Project Selection and Management', *Industrial Marketing Management* (1978): 324–330. The author offers a checklist which he recommended be used somewhat as a limited version of this report's Product Innovation Charter.

8. See 'Texas Instruments Shows U.S. Business How to Survive in the 1980s', *Business Week*, 18 September 1978, pp. 86–92.

9. See 'New Leaders in Semiconductors', *Business Week*, 1 March 1976, pp. 40–46. A very similar comparison of Digital Equipment Corporation and Data General can be found in B. Uttal, 'The Gentleman and the Upstarts Meet in a Great Mini Battle', *Fortune*, 23 April 1979, pp. 98–108.

10. See 'Innovators in the Salted Snacks Market', *Business Week*, 30 October 1978, pp. 73–74.

11. See 'Why the Firearms Business Has Tired Blood', *Business Week*, 27 November 1978, pp. 107–112.

6

The Strategy–Performance Link in Product Innovation

Robert G. Cooper

INTRODUCTION

The importance of new products and technological innovation as a route to corporate growth has long been recognized. But relatively few studies into what constitutes a 'high performance' new product strategy have been undertaken. This article reports the results of a study of a large sample of industrial product firms, whose objective was to identify the key strategy elements associated with firms' new product performance.

BACKGROUND

New products and technology are vital forces in the competitive environment of the modern firm. Technology and resulting new products bear an integral relationship to a company's strategic thinking by helping to define the range of its possibilities (Kantrow, 1980). But managements wishing to include technology strategy in their corporate strategy will find little help in the traditional literature (Maidique and Patch, 1982).

A major deficiency is the lack of empirical research to determine the components and results of firms' overall new product strategies: that is, how companies directly or indirectly chose new markets and areas of technology, and organize and focus their R&D efforts in different ways (Nyström, 1977). Most research on product innovation has centred on the product itself as the unit of analysis, rather than on the firm's total new product programme. Such a narrow focus has been criticized as myopic (Bennett and Cooper, 1981; Gold, 1980): conceivably, what leads to an individual successful new product may not result in a totally successful new product program from a corporate perspective.

Recently, researchers have begun to identify the strategy elements and results of firms' new product programs. For example, Crawford (1980) studied 125 firms' product innovation charters and uncovered scores of elements that characterize a new product strategy. Nyström and Edvardsson explored the innovation strategies of firms on six

Reprinted with permission from *R&D Management*, Vol. 14, No. 4, 1984, pp. 247–259 strategy dimensions and how these were tied to a multi-item index of performance (Nyström and Edvardsson, 1978, 1980; Nyström, 1977, 1979). Finally, the PIMS (profit impact of market strategy) studies considered R&D spending and product quality, among many market strategy elements, and their impact on firms' profitabilities (Buzzell, Gale and Sultan, 1975; Schoeffler, 1974).

Critical questions concerning new product performance and innovation strategies remain unanswered, however. The research reported in this article seeks to determine:

- how new product performance—at the firm level—can be conceptualized and measured;
- whether a group of high performer firms can be identified and contrasted with low performer firms;
- what these high performer firms share, if anything, in terms of common strategies or other distinguishing characteristics, especially when compared to lower performance companies.

The ultimate objective of the research was to learn more about explicit or implicit strategies and directions that result in a positive corporate new product performance.

A CONCEPTUAL FRAMEWORK

A conceptual framework was first developed in order to identify the elements of new product strategy and the components of performance (see Figure 1). The underlying hypothesis of the research is that *the new product strategy a firm elects determines the performance of the company's new product programme.* The firm's new product strategy includes the types of products, markets and technologies the firm chooses and the direction, commitment and stance of its innovation programme.

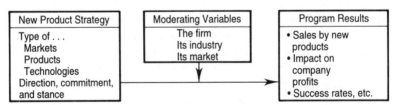

Figure 1. The Conceptual Framework for the Study. The new product strategy a firm elects determines its innovation programme results.

Four major blocks of variables to describe strategy were initially identified. These blocks were suggested by Crawford (1980), Kantrow (1980), Nyström (1977, 1979); Nyström and Edvardsson, 1978, 1980), and others:

1. The nature of products developed by the firm. For example:

- the level of product innovativeness (Cooper, 1979a, b; Crawford, 1980);
- product quality level (Buzzell *et al.*, 1975; Crawford, 1980; Schoeffler, 1974);
- product concentration versus diversification (Nyström, 1977; Nyström and Edvardsson, 1980);

- degree and nature of product differentiation or differential advantage (Cooper, 1979a, b);
- product customness (Cooper, 1979a, b).

2. The nature of markets sought by the firm with its new products. For example:

- market size, growth and potential (Crawford, 1980);
- market competitiveness (Crawford, 1980);
- stage of the product lifecycle (Bitondo and Frohman, 1981);
- marketing fit or synergy with the firm (Cooper, 1979a, b; Crawford, 1980);
- newness of the market to the firm (Bitondo and Frohman, 1981; Cooper, 1979a, b).

3. The nature of technology employed—design, development and production—in the firm's new product program. For example:

- maturity of the technology, e.g. state-of-art versus mature technologies (Bitondo and Frohman, 1981);
- technological fit or synergy of new products with the firm's technology resources (Crawford, 1979; Nyström, 1977; Nyström and Edvardsson, 1980);
- concentrated versus diversified technologies (Nyström, 1977; Nyström and Edvardsson, 1980).

4. The nature, orientation and commitment to the new product process. For example:

- whether the program is defensive versus offensive (Bitondo and Frohman, 1981; Crawford, 1980);
- sources of new product ideas (Crawford, 1980; Nyström, 1977; Nyström and Edvardsson, 1980);
- technological versus market orientation of the program (Nyström, 1977; Nyström and Edvardsson, 1980);
- applied versus pure R&D (Bitondo and Frohman, 1981);
- risk level of projects accepted (Crawford, 1980);
- spending levels, e.g. on R&D (Buzzell et al., 1975; Schoeffler, 1974).

A total of 66 strategy variables were identified in these four main blocks of strategy elements, and formed the basis of the research queestionnaire.

The components of performance of a firm's new product program were a second facet of the conceptual framework. Collier (1977) suggests financial criteria and objectives criteria as two major categories of performance, while Hopkins (1980) identifies other measures, including percent sales by new products, success rates and a global satisfaction score. Performance criteria used in this research included:

- the percentage of current company sales made up by new products introduced over the last five years;
- the success, failure and 'kill' rates (percent) of products developed in the last five years (two variables);

- the extent to which the new product program met its performance objectives over the last five years;
- the importance of the program in generating sales and profits for the company;
- the extent to which profits derived from new products exceed the costs of the new product program;
- the successfulness of the program relative to competitors;
- the successfulness of the program—a global rating.

THE DATA

A large sample of firms (located in Ontario and Quebec, Canada) provided the data to test the underlying hypothesis of the research. A total of 170 firms were contacted, firms which had been supplying data to the researcher over the years on their new product efforts and results. All were known to be active in the field of industrial product development. For the current research, a combination of telephone contacts and a pretested mailed questionnaire was used to obtain the data.

The 66 strategy elements were measured in each firm by presenting strategy statements and requesting the manager to indicate whether each described his/her firm's new product strategy and direction (agree/disagree, zero to ten scales). That is, both implicit and explicit strategies were determined. In the case of several strategy elements—for example, R&D spending and market research spending for new products—direct measures were obtained (dollars per year), later converted to percent of corporate sales.

Performance measures of the entire program were obtained in two ways: quantifiable gauges, such as success rates and percent sales by new products, were directly measured; other gauges, such as performance relative to competitors and overall satisfaction with performance, were measured on eleven point anchored scales.

The question of reliability of measures was dealt with in several ways. First, the data were collected via a questionnaire which had been extensively pretested on a limited subset of respondents; second, the respondents and researcher had an on-going relationship, suggesting more than a casual treatment of the questionnaire by the respondents; third, when data were analyzed, there was evidence of strong intercorrelation amongst variables (both strategy and performance variables), relationships which would have been attenuated had the measures been unreliable.

Of 170 firms originally contacted, 122 usable questionnaires were returned for a response rate of 72%. The breakdown by industry was:

Electrical and electronic	26.2%	32 firms
Heavy equipment	24.6%	30
Chemicals	19.7%	24
Materials and components	20.5%	25
Miscellaneous	9.0%	11
Total	100.0%	122 firms

Average annual sales were $156 million, while R&D spending averaged 3.95% of sales. Note that the sample of firms was not typical of industry in general: all firms were manufacturers (no process or service companies); they were involved in only certain industries and with industrial products (no consumer goods companies); and they were all known to be active in product development.

PERFORMANCE CLUSTERS: ANALYSIS

As might be expected, the individual performance measures were strongly interconnected. But the internal consistency of all eight performance gauges was surprisingly low, indicating that a single performance index was inappropriate. (The Cronbach alpha, a measure of internal consistency, was -0.31.) The conclusion was that several independent factors of performance might explain firms' new product results. Factor analysis was therefore used to identify the underlying dimensions of performance (principal factoring with iterations and varimax rotation; eigenvalues ≥ 1.0). Three strong and easily interpretable performance factors were identified (Table 1):

- *Success rate*: gauges the 'track record' of new products that the firm develops, and comprises the success and kill rates.
- *Program impact*: describes the impact or importance of the new product program on the firm's total operations, e.g. on the firm's sales and profits.
- *Relative performance*: captures how the new product program fares overall, versus objectives, versus competition and in terms of profits versus costs.

These three orthogonal factors explained 79.6% of the variance of the original eight performance measures. The factor analysis was validated by a split half method: successive analyses of randomly split halves of the sample consistently yielded the same factor solutions.

Cluster analysis was next employed in order to identify various performance groups of

Table 1. Dimensions of new product performance

Dimension name (% variance explained)	Variables loading on dimension	Variable loadings
1. Overall program performance (48.9%)[a]	Overall, new product program a success	0.837
	Program met performance objectives	0.769
	New product profits exceeded program costs	0.658
	Program a success relative to competitors	0.644
	Importance of program to company sales and profits	0.629
2. New product success rate (17.9%)	% of new products that were 'killed'	−0.913
	% of new products that were a commercial success	0.866
3. Program impact on company (12.9%)	% of current sales by new products	0.872
	Importance of program to company sales and profits	0.560

[a] % variance explained prior to rotation; add to 79.6%; eigenvalues ≥ 1.0.

firms. The performance factor scores were first computed for each firm: that is, the location of each firm in the three-dimensional performance domain. Ward's method of cluster analysis together with a relocation procedure was used to generate the clusters (Wishart, 1978).

Five well-defined performance groups or clusters were identified. A clustering level of five groups was chosen based on the criterion of maximum homogeneity within groups and parsimony of explanation. Firms were fairly evenly divided among the five performance clusters, and no outliers were detected. The cluster analysis was validated in two ways. First, cluster membership was related to the three performance factors and to the original eight performance measures (one-way ANOVAs), testing for homogeneity within and differences between clusters. This validation was very positive: cluster means were significantly different at the 0.0001 level for all three factors and for all eight performance gauges. The second validation involved the use of two-group discriminant analysis, where discriminant functions were developed between cluster membership (each cluster against the other four) and the three performance factors. On average, the discriminant functions classified 95.4% of the cases into the correct performance group (range: 90.9% to 100%), lending credibility to the cluster analysis solution. The five performance clusters were interpreted from the results of the ANOVAs together with Duncan multiple range tests. These results are shown in Table 2.

Table 2. Performance measures for each cluster

Performance measures	Cluster					All Firm Mean	Significance
	1	2	3	4	5		
Performance factors							
Success rate	**0.749**	(−2.214)	0.163	0.154	0.061	0.0	0.0001
Impact	(−0.650)	−0.476	0.131	**1.372**	(−0.580)	0.0	0.0001
Relative performance	0.335	−0.167	**0.882**	−0.137	(−1.267)	0.0	0.0001
Original performance variables							
% of sales by new products	19.4	17.8	40.6	**78.2**	(6.5)	36.5	0.0001
% successes	**90.1**	(16.5)	67.0	72.3	3.5	67.2	0.0001
% killed	**4.2**	(62.9)	15.8	11.0	13.8	15.8	0.0001
% failed	**5.7**	20.6	17.1	16.8	(32.6)	17.0	0.0001
Meets objectives	6.8	5.3	7.6	6.1	3.7	6.1	0.0001
Importance to company	6.2	5.1	**8.2**	**8.4**	(3.7)	6.6	0.0001
Profitability	6.9	5.7	**7.5**	6.0	(5.0)	6.4	0.0001
Rating *vs.* competitors	6.8	5.7	**7.7**	6.7	(5.1)	6.6	0.0001
Overall rating	7.1	5.2	**8.3**	7.5	(4.1)	6.7	0.0001
Cluster membership (no. of firms)	34	12	27	27	22	122	–

Notes: Values shown are means for each cluster. High performers are in bold type; low performers are in parentheses (based on Duncan multiple range tests; $p \leq 0.05$). Significance noted in Tables is based on one-way ANOVAs.

The strategies and types of firms associated with each performance group were next determined. Cluster membership was related to the 66 variables that described the firms' strategies and also the characteristics of the firm and its industry (one-way ANOVAs with Duncan multiple range tests). These results are in Tables 3 and 4. Of the 66 strategy variables, 26 were significantly tied to cluster membership ($p \leq 0.10$). Moreover, descriptors of the firm—including the technology level of the firm's industry, industry maturity, various firm strengths and firm ownership—were also related to performance groups ($p \leq 0.10$). Performance clusters, however, were independent of industry and firm size (sales).

Table 3. The strategies employed by each performance cluster

Strategy element	Cluster					Significance level
	1	2	3	4	5	
Firm's orientation and commitment						
R&D spending (% of sales)				VH		0.0001
R&D orientation	L		H	VH	VL	0.0001
Proactive in acquiring new technologies	L		H	VH	VL	0.01
Market research spending (% of sales)	L	H		H	L	0.01
Proactive on market need identification	H		VH	L	VL	0.01
Active new product idea search		H	VH		VL	0.0001
Offensive (vs defensive) program		L	VH	H	VL	0.005
Venturesome projects and program			H		L	0.10
Program a leading edge of corporate strategy			VH	VH	VL	0.005
High risk of projects	L			VH	L	0.001
Firm's new products are/have						
End use similarity to firm's existing products	H	L	L			0.05
Innovative products	L		H	VH	VL	0.01
Impact on customer			H		L	0.10
Closely related to each other	H		L	H		0.05
Meet customer needs better than competitors	H		VH	L	VL	0.05
High technology products	L		H	VH	VL	0.01
Technically complex products				H	L	0.10
Custom products		H	L			0.10
Technology employed for new products is/has						
Strong fit between products and firm's R&D resources	H		H		L	0.05
Sophisticated technology	L		H	VH	VL	0.005
Leading production technology	H	H		H	L	0.10
Focussed on one or few development technologies			L	H	L	0.10
Focussed on one or few production technologies			L	H		0.10
New product markets involve						
New customers to the firm	L	H	L		L	0.10
New channels for the firm	L	H				0.10
New competitors for the firm		H		L		0.10

Notes: of the 66 strategy elements measured and tested, only those significant at the 0.10 level (one way ANOVAs) are shown. VH, H, L and VL denote 'very high'; 'high'; 'low'; and 'very low', based on Duncan multiple range tests ($p \leq 0.05$).

Table 4. Firm type and industry by each performance cluster

Firm or industry characteristic	Cluster 1	2	3	4	5	Significance level
Industry						
Technology level of industry	L			H		0.0005
Industry growth						NS
Maturity of industry				Developing	Mature	0.005
Industry classification						NS[a]
Firm						
Size (annual sales)						NS
Financial strength	H		H	L	L	0.10
R&D strength,						NS
Engineering strength						NS
Management strength	H		H	L	L	0.005
Salesforce strength	H		H	L		0.10
Advertising strength			H	L		0.10
Market research strength						NS
Production strength						NS
Firm ownership	Foreign MNC	Domestic MNC	No distinct trend	Domestic	Domestic MNC	10[a]

Notes: H denotes 'high'; L denotes 'low'; based on Duncan multiple range tests ($p \leq 0.05$). Significance of one-way ANOVA is shown in last column. NS denotes not significant at the 0.10 level.

[a] Based on cross-tabulation; chi-squared test.

THE FIVE PERFORMANCE TYPES

Five distinct types of performance (clusters) were identified. Three groups of firms demonstrated positive performance (see Table 2):

- Cluster 3, the top performer, scored the highest on the factor 'relative performance', and by a considerable margin. New product programs in these firms met objectives, were important in generating corporate sales and profits, were more profitable, were rated higher versus competitors' programs, and overall were rated more successful than programs in the other four groups.
- Cluster 1, the largest group, contained firms with a high success rate, but low impact new product program. These firms had the highest success rate (90.1% versus an all firm average of 67%), the lowest failure rate (5.7%) and the lowest kill rate (4.2%). Unfortunately these firms also had among the lowest percent sales by new products, and scored the lowest on the 'impact' factor.
- Cluster 4, the high impact firms, achieved a remarkable 78% of corporate sales by new products. They scored the highest on the 'impact' factor, and the highest in terms of program importance to corporate sales and profits.

Two poor performance groups of firms were also uncovered:

- Cluster 5, the worst performer, contained firms with the lowest relative performance, and a low impact program. These firms' new product programs failed to meet objectives, were minimally important to the company, were not profitable, and were rated the lowest overall and relative to competitors. Percentage sales by new products was the lowest (15.6%), and failure rates were the highest of all clusters (32.6% versus an all firm mean of 17%).
- Cluster 2, the smallest cluster, was the low success rate performer. Firms in this group scored the worst on the 'success rate' factor, and also poorly on the 'impact' factor. These firms had the lowest proportion of successes (16.5% successes) and the highest kill rate (62.9%). Percent sales by new products was also low (17.8%).

Figure 2 helps to summarize these different types of performers.

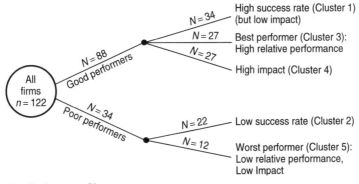

Figure 2. The Five Performance Clusters.

STRATEGIES, FIRMS AND PERFORMANCE

What are the unique and distinguishing characteristics and strategies of the top performer firms? Each group of firms was related to the 66 strategy variables and to a number of descriptors of the company and industry (ANOVAs).

Overall, the five performance types differed significantly on 26 strategy elements (Table 3). The most important strategy blocks were:

1. strategies that portrayed the orientation and commitment to the new product programme;
2. strategies that described the nature of the new products the firm seeks and develops;
3. strategies that captured the nature of technology employed in the program.

Surprisingly, strategies that described the types of markets that firms seek for their new products had relatively little effect on performance.

The most important strategies that separated the strong performers from poor performers lay in the orientation and commitment to the new product program. For example, the following were all strongly related to performance cluster membership ($p \leq 0.01$):

- R&D spending as a percentage of sales:
- degree of R&D orientation in the program;
- proactive search for ideas;
- offensive versus defensive program;
- role of the program in the corporate strategy;
- risk level of new product projects;
- market research spending for new products as a percentage of sales;
- proactive technology acquisition;
- proactive identification of market needs;
- venturesome projects.

Product strategies were also closely tied to performance, and included level of innovativeness of products developed, technology level of products and the degree to which the firm sought products with a differential advantage (met customer needs better than competing products). In contrast, only one technology strategy—namely the sophistication of technology employed—was strongly linked to cluster membership ($p \leq 0.01$), although other technology strategies were associated with performance, but in a weaker fashion ($p \leq 0.10$). Surprisingly, none of the market strategies was strongly related to cluster membership ($p \leq 0.01$), although three such strategies, describing markets with new customers, and involving new channels and new competitors, were somewhat tied to performance ($p \leq 0.10$).

Each of the five performance clusters is now described in terms of the strategies employed and the nature of the firms in each cluster.

Cluster 1. The high success rate, low impact strategy

This large group of firms, representing 27.9% of the sample, achieved a high success rate of new products (90.1%), but ended up with a low impact program: only 19% of sales by new products.

Such firms pursued a relatively conservative, but market-oriented, approach. They developed products that were very similar to their existing products in terms of end-use, and were closely related to each other. They avoided highly innovative products and high technology products, but did seek products that could serve customer needs better: a differential advantage. This conservative strategy avoided markets involving new customers to the firm and new channel systems. These firms avoided the use of sophisticated technologies, and sought products that fitted the firm's existing R&D skills and resources and involved leading production technologies. These conservative firms were proactive on market need identification, were not R&D oriented at all, and were not proactive on acquiring new technologies. R&D spending was the lowest of all groups (1.85% of sales), and market research spending for new products was also low as a percentage of sales.

Not surprisingly, these firms were often found in lower technology industries. The firms tended to be foreign-owned, and rated themselves strong financially and also in terms of management and salesforce.

For a high success rate, but low impact program, the picture of a conservative, 'stay close to home', market-oriented, but technologically unaggressive strategy emerges.

Cluster 2. The low success rate, low impact firms

This small group of firms, representing only 9.8% of the sample, stands in direct contrast to Cluster 1: the new product success rate was the lowest of all firms (16.5%); the kill rate the highest (62.9%); and new products had a minor impact on the company.

A review of strategies also shows certain differences versus Cluster 1. Such firms sought markets which were new to the firm: new customer types, new channels of distribution and new competitors. The products they developed were often custom products and served new end-uses; that is, end-uses that the firm's current products did not serve. These firms utilized leading production technologies and featured an active search for new product ideas. But they viewed their new product programs as defensive in nature. Such firms were not particularly heavy spenders on new products, nor were they technologically aggressive or sophisticated.

There were few distinguishing characteristics in terms of industry and firm strengths for these Cluster 2 companies. Many, however, were domestically owned multi-national corporations.

A picture of a 'non-strategy' begins to take shape in a review of these firms' directions: new markets, new end-uses, custom products, but with no real technological prowess, aggressiveness or commitment. The result was a fairly dismal programme, with a low success rate and low impact on the company.

Cluster 3: The top performers

This enviable group of companies, consisting of 22.1% of the sample, featured by far the highest relative performance: they scored highest in terms of meeting objectives, program profitability and program performance versus competitors and overall. Moreover, success rates, failure rates and kill rates were just about average, and percent sales by new products (40.6%) was somewhat above average.

What was the secret of these firms' outstanding performances? In the first place, such firms featured a strong, aggressive technological orientation: they were strongly R&D oriented, proactive in acquiring new technologies, and boasted a venturesome, offensive program that was a leading edge of corporate strategy. These firms developed innovative products, high technology products and products that had a marked impact on the customer. Also, these firms utilized sophisticated technologies in product development, but sought products with a high degree of fit with the firm's R&D skills and resources. They tended to avoid custom products, however.

At the same time, these top performing companies were also market oriented. They were particularly stronger than other firms in developing products which served customers' needs better than competitors' products: the quest for a differential product advantage. They boasted a very strong search effort for new product ideas, and were particularly proactive in identifying customer needs.

Surprisingly, another facet of these top performers' strategies included a lack of focus in their new product program: their new products were not closely related to each other;

nor did the firms rely on closely related or focussed development and production technologies; and the end-uses served by their new products tended to differ from their
existing products.

These top performers were not specific to any particular industry, nor did their
industries share any distinguishing characteristics (i.e. they included low and high
technology, developing and mature industries). Similarly, company size was about
average and no ownership trends were detected. But these firms did rate themselves high
in terms of financial, management, salesforce and advertising strengths.

The key to a high relative performance program appears not to depend so much on
the nature of the industry or firm, but rather on the strategy elected: a union of
technological prowess and aggressiveness with a strong market orientation.

Cluster 4. The high impact firms

This group of good performers, representing 22.1% of the sample, boasted a high impact
program with a remarkable 78% of corporate sales generated by new products introduced in the last five years. But relative performance and success rates were about
average.

Such firms were decidedly technologically oriented and driven. They spent heavily on
R&D, averaging 9.46% of sales, by far the most of any group. They were strongly R&D
oriented, were very proactive in acquiring new technologies, and featured an offensive
program. They viewed their new product program as a leading edge of corporate
strategy and were proactive in identifying needs for new products. They developed
highly innovative, high risk, high technology, technically complex products. These high
impact firms utilized very sophisticated technologies in their new products, and leading
production technologies. Both development and production technologies were focused,
i.e. in one or a few areas.

Where these firms differed from the top performers (Cluster 3) was in their degree of
market orientation. These high impact firms were not particularly market oriented, and
one of their greatest weaknesses was their inability to develop products that served
customer needs better.

As might be expected, these high impact firms were found in high technology, developing industries. The firms were typically smaller than the rest of the firms (mean sales
of $50 million versus an all firm mean of $156 million) and were domestic, non-
multinationals. Financial, management, salesforce and advertising strengths were all
rated low.

Cluster 4 portrays the stereotype strategy of the high technology, R&D-oriented,
smaller firm in a high tech industry. The strategy appears one-sided—heavily technologically driven—and lacking on the marketing side. The result is a high impact programme, but with only average performance in terms of success rates and relative
performance.

Cluster 5. The worst performers

The final group of firms, accounting for 18.0% of the sample, had by far the least
enviable new product program. The failure rate was the highest of all firms (32.6%); the

proportion of sales by new products the lowest (16.5%); and on every scaled measure of performance, these firms ranked the worst.

What was so terribly wrong with these firms' strategies? In the first place, such firms lacked technological aggressiveness and commitment. They were not R&D oriented at all: nor were they proactive in acquiring new technologies. The program was a defensive one, and they avoided venturesome, high risk projects. Moreover, the program was not considered to be a leading edge of corporate strategy.

The products these poor performers developed were the least innovative of all firms, had minimal impact on customers, were technically simple, and involved a low level of technology. These firms employed relatively simple development technologies, and no leading production technologies. In spite of this, there was often a lack of synergy between the products these firms developed and their R&D resources and skills.

A market orientation was also missing in these firms' strategies. They spent the least on new product market research of all firms (0.12% of sales versus an all firm average of 0.25%). They were not proactive on market need identification nor did they have an active search effort for new product ideas. Finally the products they developed were the worst of all firms in terms of serving customer needs better, not surprising in view of their lacklustre technological and market prowess. These firms, perhaps wisely, avoided markets involving new customers to the firm.

Who were these firms with such a doubtful new product strategy? Typically they were large firms with international facilities, operating in mature industries. In spite of their size, they rated their financial and managerial capabilities poorly relative to their competitors.

CONCLUSIONS

The underlying hypothesis of the research was supported by the research findings: The new product strategies firms elect are indeed closely tied to the performance results achieved. A total of 26 strategies were significantly related to performance types, 14 in a very strong way. These results have important implications for the management of new products, and point to the need for a carefully conceived innovation strategy. New product performance is not so much a matter of being in the right industry or simply being lucky; rather new product performance is largely decided by the strategy that top management elects.

There are more conclusions from the research, however, than merely the support of the major research hypothesis. Three dimensions of the performance of a firm's new product program were uncovered in the research. The fact that these dimensions were constructed to be independent of each other shows that a firm can strive for quite different types of new product performance. On the one hand, a realistic goal might be the attainment of a high success rate program—one where a high proportion of new products succeed, and few fail or are killed. Alternatively, management may seek a high impact program, where success rates may suffer, but where the total impact on the firm in terms of new product sales and profits is substantial. Finally, a high relative performance could be the objective—high performance relative to competitors, to objectives, and in terms of cost/benefit to the firm.

The identification of three dimensions of performance, rather than a single measure or index, helps to clear up confusion that surrounds the term 'a high performance new product program'. A review of the literature on new products reveals a great many prescriptions and divergent views on how management can improve the firm's new product efforts. This divergence is most notable in a comparison of engineering and R&D literature versus marketing literature. But rarely is there any reference to the performance goals sought. Perhaps what we witness are different prescriptions aimed at achieving quite different results. The identification of three independent directions of performance may help to explain these apparently divergent views.

The one piece of disconcerting evidence in the research was that no one group of firms performed well simultaneously on all three performance criteria. The results suggest that it may be unrealistic to expect a firm to achieve a high success rate, a high impact and a high relative performance concurrently. Ideally, one might have desired that the performance of the Cluster 3 and Cluster 1 firms could somehow be married in one group of firms. But comparisons of the strategies elected by Cluster 3 firms (the high relative performance firms) versus Cluster 1 companies (the high success rate programs) shows that in many cases the strategies elected are in direct conflict. For example, Cluster 3 firms are strongly R&D oriented, are proactive in acquiring new technologies, develop innovative high technology products and utilize sophisticated technologies. In contrast, Cluster 1 firms score very low on all of these strategy elements; moreover they develop products that have the same end-use as their existing products and are closely related to each. Cluster 3 firms do the opposite.

Overall, Cluster 3 firms—the high relative performance firms—achieved the most enviable new product record. Many firms may wish to emulate the outstanding results achieved by these top performers: a strong performance in terms of meeting objectives, impact on company sales and profits (40% of sales by recent new products), profitability of the program, performance versus competitors, and overall performance. Success rates, moreover, were satisfactory at 67%. The strategies leading to this high performance were characterized by a technologically aggressive, innovative, venturesome, proactive, diverse and market-oriented stance. They include:

- an aggressive technological orientation—strong R&D orientation and proactive in acquiring new technologies;
- a venturesome, offensive program that was viewed as a leading edge of corporate strategy;
- a market-oriented program, featuring a strong effort to identify customer needs, and a proactive search effort for new product ideas;
- the development of products with a differential advantage, which met customer needs better than competitive products, and had a marked impact on customers;
- the use of sophisticated technologies, but with a high degree of synergy with the firm's resource base;
- a relatively diverse new product program—products, technologies and end-uses not necessarily closely related to each other.

What we witness is not a single strategy, but a packet of strategies that differentiated these high performers from the rest of the firms. A marriage of technological prowess, a strong marketing orientation, the search for a differential advantage and a willingness to accept risk appears to be the key to a high performance program.

It is important to note that such strategies and firms were not unique to any one industry or set of industry characteristics. Conceivably, such strategies are applicable to a wide variety of firms and industries. This is an important finding: too many managers assume that they are victims of their firms' environment or industry when it comes to new products.

As product lifecycles shorten, technology advances, and competition from home and abroad heightens, increasingly managements recognize the central role that new products will play in their firms' future prosperity. The need to treat product innovation strategy as a central facet of corporate strategy becomes more evident. Ways of conceptualizing and measuring new product performance and strategies leading to alternative types of performance, as uncovered in this research, must be consciously considered as managers go about the development of a product innovation strategy.

ACKNOWLEDGEMENTS

The research report in this article was supported by grants from: Canadian Federal Government, Department of Regional & Industrial Expansion, Office of Technological Innovation; and the Canadian Industrial Innovation Center, Waterloo, Canada.

REFERENCES

Bennett, R. C. and Cooper, R. G. (1981) 'The Misuse of Marketing—An American Tragedy', *Business Horizons*, **24**(6): 51–61.

Bitondo, D. and Frohman, A. (1981) 'Linking Technological and Business Planning', *Research Management* (Nov.): 19–23.

Buzzell, R. D., Gale, B. T. and Sultan, R. G. M. (1975) 'Market Share—A Key to Profitability', *Harvard Business Review* (Jan.–Feb.): 97–107.

Collier, D. W. (1977) 'Measuring the Performance of R&D Departments', *Research Management* (March): 30–34.

Cooper, R. G. (1979a) 'Identifying Industrial New Product Success: Project NewProd', *Industrial Marketing Management*, **8**: 124–135.

Cooper, R. G. (1979b) 'The Dimensions of Industrial New Product Success and Failure', *Journal of Marketing*, **43**(3).

Crawford, C. M. (1979) 'New Product Failure Rates—Facts and Fallacies', *Research Management* (Sept.): 9–13.

Crawford, C. M. (1980) 'Defining the Charter for Product Innovation', *Sloan Management Review* (Fall): 3–12.

Gold, B. (1980) 'Rediscovering the Technology Foundations of Industrial Competitiveness', Editorial, *OMEGA*, **8**(5): 503–504.

Hopkins, D. S. (1980) *New Product Winners and Losers*, Conference Board Report No. 773.

Kantrow, A. M. (1980) 'The Strategy-Technology Connection', *Harvard Business Review* (July–Aug.): 6–21.

Maidique, M. A. and Patch, P. (1982) 'Corporate Strategy and Technological Policy', in Tushman, M. L. and Moore, W. L. (eds) *Readings in the Management of Innovation*, Marchfield, Mass: Pitman Publ.: 273.

Nyström, H. (1977) *Company Strategies for Research and Development*. Report from the Institute for Economics and Statistics, S–750 07, Uppsala, Sweden.

Nyström, H. and Edvardsson, B. (1978) *Research and Development Strategies for Four Swedish Farm*

Machine Companies. Report from the Institute for Economics and Statistics, S–750 07, Uppsala, Sweden.

Nyström, H. (1979) 'Company Strategies for Research and Development', in Baker, M. (ed.) *Industrial Innovation*, Macmillan Co.

Nyström, H. and Edvardsson, B. (1980) *Research and Development Strategies for Four Swedish Farm Machine Companies.* Report from the Institute for Economics and Statistics, S–750 07, Uppsala, Sweden.

Schoeffler, S. (1974) 'Impact of Strategic Planning on Profit Performance', *Harvard Business Review* (Mar.–Apr.): 137–145.

Wishart, D. (1978) *Cluster User Manual 3rd Edition*, Program Library Unit, University of Edinburgh, Report No. 47.

7

The Product Family and the Dynamics of Core Capability

Marc H. Meyer and James M. Utterback

Why is it that some firms introduce distinctive new products time and time again, when so many other firms are far less able to generate new products? More specifically, some firms, while strong in product design, fail to gain commercial reward, but their more successful counterparts exhibit the right mix of capabilities in implementation, manufacturing, and distribution as well as product design. Much current management thought addresses developing single products as rapidly as possible. Product development when seen from this perspective has two essential problems: redundancy of both technical and marketing effort and lack of long-term consistency and focus. We will argue for a broader approach to managing new products.

Concentrating at the level of the product family, and more specifically on the development and sharing of key components and assets within a product family, is the vital issue. The benefit of examining elements shared by products within a family is that firms will then develop the foundation for a range of individual product variations. At an even broader level, one can examine relationships between product families themselves to achieve even greater commonality in both technologies and marketing. For an existing product family, renewal is achieved by integrating the best components in new structures or proprietary designs to better serve evolving customer needs. Integration improves all products within the family. Diversification can be achieved by building on and extending capabilities to build the foundations of new but related product families. For example, Hewlett-Packard built on a foundation of core capabilities in scientific instruments to create families of computers and peripherals, and also to enter into the medical systems business. Similarly, Canon built on its copier and facsimile machine platforms to create laser printer and scanner businesses.

Figure 1 portrays a set of products and their relationships over time that we believe is conducive to sustained success. Each generation of a product family has a platform used as the foundation for specific products·targeted at different or complementary market applications ('Platform Development Family A', Products 1–4). Successive generations refresh older platforms with improved designs and technologies ('New Generation Platform Family A', Products 1–6). Starting work on the next product platform while

Reprinted from 'The product family and the dynamics of care capability' by Marc H. Meyer and James M. Utterback, *Sloan Management Review*, Spring 1993, pp. 29–47 completing specific products based on the current platform helps the company maintain product leadership. In terms of creating new businesses, new product families branch from existing ones, expanding on their technical skills, market knowledge, and manufacturing capabilities ('Platform Development Family B'). Thus, the development of new technologies is focused. Market extensions are related. High levels of customer recognition are the cumulative effect of a robust product family. These factors all contribute to growth.

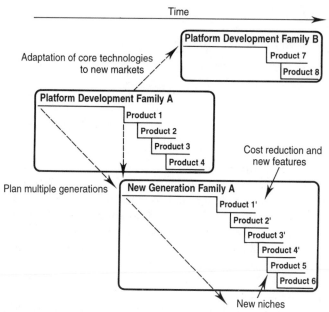

Figure 1. The Product Family Approach to New Product Development.

Deliberately building product families rather than single products requires management of a firm's core capabilities.[1] Quinn, Doorley and Paquette view the firm as an intellectual holding company in which products and services are the application of the firm's knowledge assets. By targeting and focusing on the best of these assets, a firm can dominate its rivals.[2] Core capabilities cannot be divorced or viewed separately from the actual products that a company makes and sells on a daily basis. Core capabilities are the basis of products. Nondistinctive capabilities lead to nondistinctive products. Strong capabilities lead to strong product families because these capabilities are embodied in the people and assets applied to building a company's new products.

Our purpose in this article is to synthesize the two central concepts of the product family and core capabilities. Many managers with whom we have worked in the past have expressed a strong desire to understand better the evolution of their product families and leverage achieved from underlying architectures and designs. Many have also wanted to identify more clearly the core capabilities of their organizations and how these capabilities have also changed over time. To address both needs, we have developed a method to map product families and assess their embodied core capabilities. We will apply this method to three product families developed by a large corporation for the electronic imaging market and then use that application to more broadly consider how firms may better manage the development of new products.

DEFINING THE PRODUCT FAMILY

What is a product family? What are those characteristics and properties shared by and therefore common to a series of related products grouped into a family?

The term 'product platform' was used earlier in its common meaning: encompassing the design and components shared by a set of products. A robust platform is the heart of a successful product family, serving as the foundation for a series of closely related products. For example, Chrysler has just released three new lines of cars, the Chrysler Concorde, Eagle Vision and Dodge Intrepid, based on a common platform in which all share the same basic frame, suspension and drive train. New products are refinements or extensions of the platform. For example, Chrysler's forthcoming upscale New Yorker model will be based on a longer version of the new platform.

We will call products that share a common platform but have specific features and functionality required by different sets of customers a product family. A product family typically addresses a market *segment*, while specific products or groups of products within the family target *niches* within that segment. The commonality of technologies and markets leads to efficiency and effectiveness in manufacturing, distribution and service, where the firm tailors each general resource or capability to the needs of specific customer groups.

The technology embodied in a product family has two key parts: the design and the implementation of the design. Design groups dedicated to new product platform research create basic designs, standard components, and norms for subsystem integration. Implementation teams create different product models, integrating component technologies to achieve specific product goals.[3,4]

To illustrate the ideas of the product family, platforms, and extensions of platforms as products, consider Sony's Walkman. Sanderson and Uzumeri catalogued all products introduced in the portable tape cassette segment.[5] Sony introduced more than 160 variations of the Walkman between 1980 and 1990. These products were based on a platform that Sony refreshed with four major technical innovations.[6] The company combined these major innovations with incremental improvements to achieve better functionality and quality, while lowering production costs. Sony's trademark is virtually synonymous with the portable cassette player.

Black & Decker's power tool business pursued a deliberate strategy to share major elements of product platforms across different product families.[7] In 1970, the company had hundreds of products. The products used more than 30 different motors, 60 different motor housings and dozens of different operating controls. Further, each of the hundreds of power tool products had its own unique armature. Management determined that, in order to remain competitive, it would have to decrease its cost of goods sold by about a third in the coming decade. Black & Decker created a plan to design and manufacture product families based on shared components and modules. Nearly $20 million was allocated to the effort. First, the company developed a hexagonal, copper-wire-wrapped motor field with standard electrical plug-in connections that would serve all its power tools.[8] Engineers designed standard motor housings and controls as well as a more standardized, adhesive-bonded armature. The company tackled each product family in succession (drills, jigsaws, sanders etc.). The results were dramatic: product costs were reduced by 50%, market share rose from 20% to a dominant share, and the number of competitors declined from more than 20 to three. The case also shows the extent to which product families can share technical designs and components, an understanding of market requirements, and production capabilities.

MAPPING PRODUCT FAMILIES

Individual products are therefore the offspring of product platforms that are enhanced over time. Product families and their successive platforms are themselves the applied result of a firm's underlying core capabilities. In well-managed firms, such core capabilities tend to be of much longer duration and broader scope than single product families or individual products.

We believe that the product family can be used as a basis for assessing the dynamics of a firm's core capabilities, in other words, how these capabilities grow, decline and integrate with one another over extended periods of time. The first step is to *map* the chronology of a product family. The following pages will describe our method as we applied it to three product families in a large corporation engaged in the electronic imaging business.

Figure 2 shows a product family map. The general application of the products shown has been to reproduce computer screen images onto various presentation media. We refer to them as a *horizontal market* application in that they are general-purpose solutions for different customer groups in different industries that nonetheless have a common need.

In order to map this product family, we assembled a study group of ten people, all actively involved in the family development for many years and representing business, technology and marketing functions. Producing the map required several intensive meetings. The top half of Figure 2 is the summary, and the bottom half the detail, showing the market introduction and termination date for each product. The product family is represented in four hierarchical levels:[9]

- The product *family* itself. Figure 2 shows one product family.
- *Platforms with a family* are encapsulated in large rectangles in the top half of Figure 2. There were four basic product platforms in that family: two platforms generated internally (one analog, the other digital) and two acquired from vendors as private-labeled products ('OEM initiatives').
- *Product extensions* are denoted by oval forms starting at the beginning of the research and ending with the cessation of active marketing of platform-based products. 'Skunk works' projects, having no commercial product offspring, can be the first iteration of a product platform and provide important technological and market knowledge for subsequent platform extensions. The first product platform in Figure 2 has had two successive platform extensions.
- Specific *products* (numbered here to disguise real product names) are placed at and

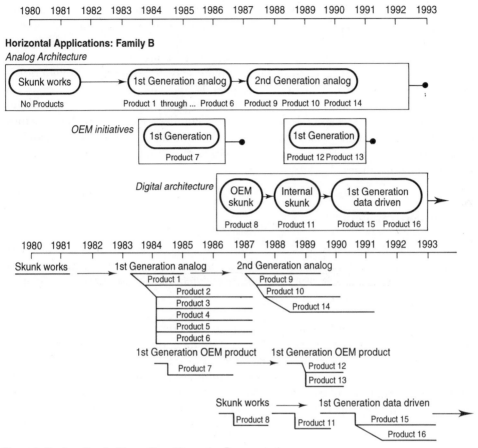

Figure 2. Product Family Map—Two Alternative Representations.

numbered in order of the market introduction dates and, in the bottom half of the figure, extend out to the date of marketing termination.

Product family maps convey a sense of continuity or the lack thereof in product development. For example in Figure 2, there have essentially been three overlapping streams of development: analog architecture products, products resold from other vendors (called OEM initiatives), and the current digital architecture products. All have been carried forward by different groups in the company. The original development team chose not to abandon its initial analog platform in favor of the newer digital platforms being introduced by competitors. Its products became obsolete. Seeing that this was happening, management tried to short cut its lack of effective products with two private-label initiatives that were early digital systems. Meanwhile, two product champions resurrected the company's internal technical initiative by recruiting engineers from corporate research to create a new digital platform. The result, after four years of determined technical effort and marketing development, has been the delivery of what many would call world-class products.

Figure 3 includes the product family map described above as well as maps for two other, related businesses in the same company that addressed different areas of electronic imaging. Family A is a turnkey system made for a specific industrial vertical market. It is sold primarily through the company's own direct salesforce and requires systems integration at the customer's site. Family B contains the horizontal electronic imaging applications described above. The company sells these products through distribution channels. Family C consists of peripherals and components sold through a number of different channels; they have been aimed at both industrial and consumer market segments. Management selected these three families for us to study because they represented different points along the spectrum from making components to building turnkey systems and therefore provided a good test of mapping product families and assessing core capabilities.

Assessing core capability

The product family idea serves as a basis for assessing the evolution of a firm's core capabilities. Figure 4 presents a detailed core capability assessment for Family B. Figure 5 represents a summarization of that detail. We generated similar charts for the other two families. The charts have four basic parts:

- The product family map as a legend is plotted against time in both charts. Key product events serve as anchors for subsequent data gathering and analysis.[10]
- In Figure 4, the product family team's strengths are assessed in relation to existing competition for specific core capabilities within four basic dimensions: product technology, understanding of customer needs as reflected by products sold at that time, distribution and manufacturing.[11] The solid line running across the measurement strips is a mean of responses from team members, the details of which will be described shortly.
- Figure 5 summarizes the means for responses for the core capabilities within the four basic dimensions.
- Figure 5 also shows a final summary of core capability strength as embodied within the product family.

All four parts show the ebb and flow of core capabilities over time for the product family.

The process of gathering data started with a group meeting of the product family team members.[12] At this initial meeting, the team defined the product families, groups, generations, and specific products under a product scope established earlier by the study's executive sponsors. This process required several iterations, using recollections of product histories and archived project documents to create product maps. We also noted key product events, some made by the company itself and others by its competitors. These served as anchors for gathering information and then presenting it.

The study team was then reconvened in a second series of meetings to identify the general product technologies, the major customer segments, the distribution channels used over time, and the key manufacturing processes required for the product.[13] These are the specific core capabilities embodied in a product family and constitute the vertical legend running down the left side of Figure 4.

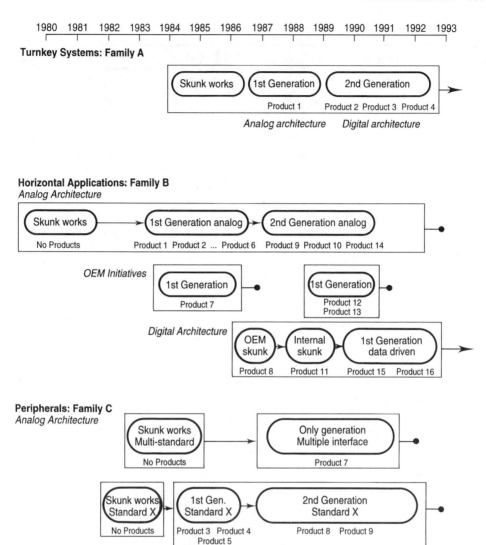

Figure 3. Three Product Family Maps.

Our model posits that *generic* core capabilities in any product family exist in product technology, market understanding and so on; the team defines the specific core capabilities within each of these areas. For example, the respondents who provided data for Family B developed a consensus that three basic technical capabilities were central to their products. These technologies were higher-level groupings of more numerous individual technologies. Participants must determine the appropriate level of grouping using their understanding of the technologies employed in a product family. Examples of

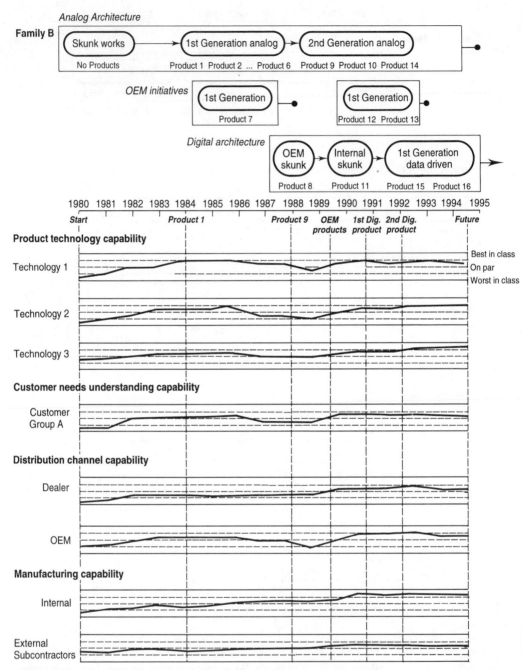

Figure 4. Core Capability Assessment for Family B.

technological core capability categories from this company and others where we have applied the method include 'PC graphics hardware', 'signal processing' or 'circuit packaging' or 'networked computing', and 'applications software development'. Since

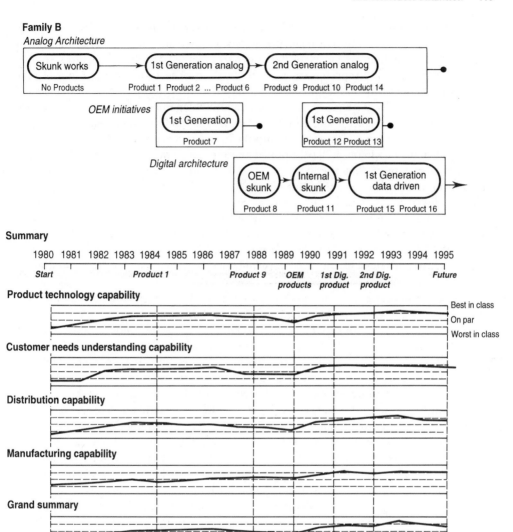

Figure 5. Summary Core Capability Assessment for Family B.

the purpose of the study is to facilitate *managerial* analysis and action, too much detail will obfuscate major trends in the past and a firm's needs in the future.

Figure 4 also shows that Family B had one major industrial customer group. The company sold the products through independent dealers and original equipment manufacturers. The team felt most comfortable combining specific manufacturing processes into one 'internal manufacturing' core capability, and relationship management with suppliers and manufacturing subcontractors into an 'external subcontractors' capability.[14]

We produced blank survey forms for each product family. These forms appeared exactly as shown in Figure 4 but with the measurement strips left empty for respondents to complete. Each measurement strip has five levels. These levels represent the degree of capability (from best in class to worst in class) *relative to competitors at that time*, for each of the years in the product family's history as perceived by respondents.[15] This assessment method can be further anchored by having participants identify competitors that at different points in time represented 'best in class' or close to it for each area of core capability. Competitors' names are simply inserted at the appropriate point along each capability measurement strip. (We could not include the names of best-in-class competitors for Family B in Figure 4 and still keep the case adequately disguised.)

Measurement strips can be extended into the future to learn a team's expectations. In fact, in other firms where we have applied the method, managers have included new areas of core capability that a product family will require in the future or, in other words, that appear as measurement strips starting in 1994 or 1995.

Respondents then completed the survey forms, using the same response scale for all core capabilities. We instructed them to indicate levels of strength relative to existing competitors for capabilities for only those years when they had worked on the product family. We also asked respondents to assess capability strength for the key product anchor points and then fill in the intervening years for which they had knowledge. Figure 4 shows average responses.[16]

Figure 5 summarizes the company's capabilities with unweighted means.[17] The bottom of Figure 5 shows a grand average of these capabilities.

Figure 6 shows the core capability assessments for all three product families in the study. We use the width of line and shading to represent levels of strength in core capability, so the reader can more quickly and clearly surmise meaning. The core capability embodied in Family A has gradually increased over the years to a moderate level of strength. Family B experienced strong initial strengthening, then a strong decline, and, more recently, an even stronger rebound in its embodied core capabilities. The company has yet to build significant core capability in Family C.

This method for identifying and assessing core capabilities is flexible. As noted above, each firm will identify those areas of core capability most important for each product family studied. Further, while the managers in Families A, B and C chose to treat each area of core capability as equal in importance, other companies may wish to assign different weights to different capabilities for computing averages. These weights can be adjusted to accommodate changes in the relative importance of core capabilities over time. Further, we have used the same survey forms with long-term customers, which provides a way to validate a team's self-assessments and to gain new perspectives on benchmarking its competencies.

CORE CAPABILITIES AND PERFORMANCE

Higher levels of core capability should be associated with sustained success, be it in terms of product development effectiveness, financial performance or learning and employee satisfaction.[18]

We asked divisional management of the sponsoring company to provide their assessment of the *success of the product family over its history relative to other new business developments undertaken by the company at that time.* Using a scale representing levels of performance, six senior vice presidents completed a measurement strip chart for each product family, basing their assessments on financial return.[19] We asked them to assess product families

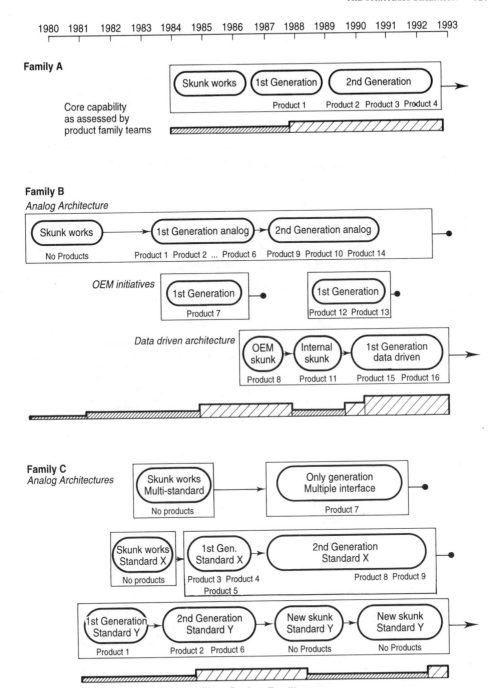

Figure 6. Core Capability Assessments for Three Product Families.

only for those years in which they had actively monitored and otherwise participated in the management of the product family. We plotted an average of these responses in Figure 7.[20]

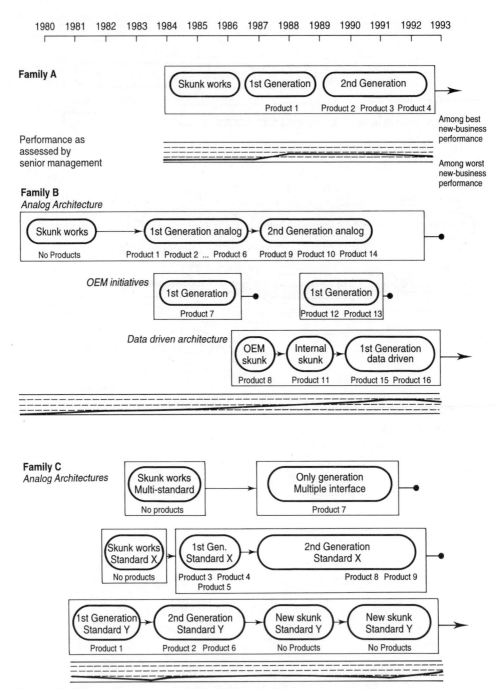

Figure 7. Performance Assessments for Three Product Families.

Data for core capabilities and performance are compared in Figure 8, using width of line and shading to convey degree. Higher levels of core capability have tended to precede and then coincide with higher levels of performance. For example, Family B gained moderate levels of core capability in 1985, and better performance came in 1987. The obsolete analog platform in Family B for the two-year period between 1987 and 1989 did not significantly depress performance because customers were not quick to abandon the familiar product. However, participants indicated that the new digital platform arrived just in time in 1990. By 1991, the product family achieved very high levels of performance. Family A achieved moderate levels of overall core capability in 1988; better performance followed in 1989. Family C's levels of embodied core capability and performance have also been closely matched, i.e. poor, over the course of ten years. The history of these three product families appears to support a cause-and-effect relationship between core capability and performance.[21]

Achieving high levels of capability can be expected to have less impact in declining markets. We have recently completed a similar analysis for an electronic capital equipment company where, despite continuously growing core capability in its traditional mainstream product line, declining market conditions (slower growth and more competitors) have nonetheless yielded poorer performance relative to prior years. This company must find new market applications for its core technologies.

Market dynamics temper the relationship between core capability and performance. We asked each family study team to indicate changes in the rate of market growth,[22] the level of competition[23] and the effective product life cycle for their product families.[24] Figure 9 shows the results for Family B. For all three product families, market growth rates in target markets are now moderate to fast, and competition has intensified. Product life cycles have also shortened.

USING CORE CAPABILITY ASSESSMENT TO IMPROVE A PRODUCT FAMILY

A company must continue to invest in renewing product platforms, particularly for markets with accelerating rates of product introduction and competitive intensity. For example, if management does not continue to invest to renew Family B's platform, the 'dip' experienced before will probably occur again.

How is management to choose which requests to satisfy fully, or whether the resources requested are indeed sufficient? Many, if not most, firms allocate resources by individual product effort on an annual basis. Further, allocation requests tend to be summarized by functional area (R&D versus marketing versus manufacturing). Single-product funding impedes the development of a core for product families and therefore inhibits creation of the type of leverage that we have discussed throughout this paper.

What does a firm need to do to achieve best-in-class status in technology, market knowledge, distribution, manufacturing and service? Product family maps combined with core capability assessment may be useful in this regard.

For example, Figure 10 shows the core capability assessments for product technologies in Family A. While the first two technologies have risen above the industry average, the third (applications software development) continues to be well below par. The company must address this area of weakness to be more successful. Specific areas of need in the other product families also emerged from these more detailed core capability assessment charts.

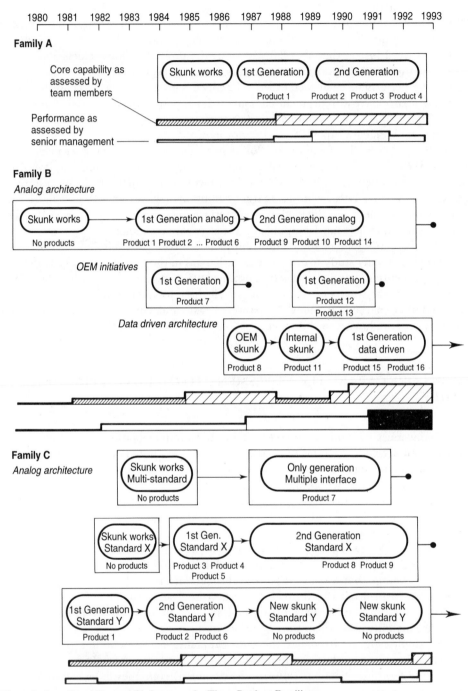

Figure 8. Core Capability and Performance for Three Product Families.

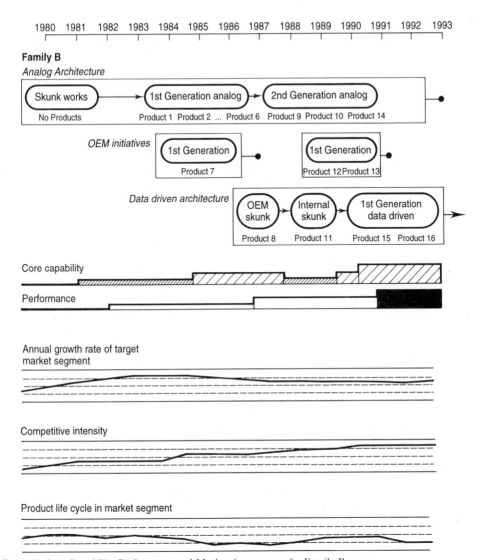

Figure 9. Core Capability Performance and Market Assessments for Family B.

EXPLAINING THE EBB AND FLOW OF CORE CAPABILITIES

Core capabilities are inherently dynamic. They result from the efforts of individuals and are thus affected by the organization of teams, the selection of products and markets, and the nature and quality of those markets. Once gained, competence can be readily lost. Ill-considered managerial policies and approaches can destroy hard-won capabilities, impede learning, hurt the effectiveness of product development and, ultimately, damage the profitability of the company. Our work suggests this and illustrates what managers intuitively know and feel.

Four fundamental inhibitors of core capability creation have emerged as common themes in our work.

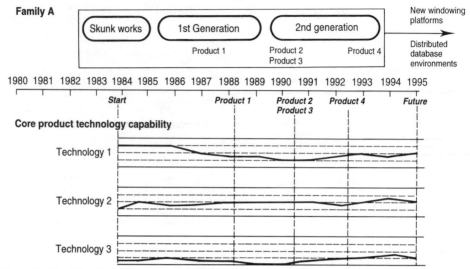

Figure 10. Identifying Problems in Family B's Product Technology Capabilities.

Lack of patience

Using unrealistic, short time horizons for the development of new businesses invariably leads promising technical and marketing development efforts to be killed before capability, visible on the horizon, is realized and exploited. How long should it take to achieve excellence in the relevant core capabilities in a new area?

A visual presentation of a product family powerfully conveys the nature of the embodied core capabilities, how painstakingly they may be gained, and how quickly lost. Of the three product families studied, the company achieved competitive levels of capability in only one family, and in that case, only after approximately ten years. This experience is by no means atypical. Other studies have produced time ranges from seven to 20 years.[25]

Failure to adopt innovations and new architecture

Technological discontinuities can quickly make a company's products obsolescent.[26] Radical technological innovation in an industry can make any given capability irrelevant. In fact, companies often get trapped in their earlier successes.[27] Thomas Edison dramatically improved the efficiency and reliability of carbon filaments in light-bulbs when his business was attacked by more efficient but expensive metal filaments. Later, he was forced to spend large sums to license metal filament technology from these same competitors to replace his own carbon filament capability and create a new light-bulb platform for his company. Other firms have consistently looked forward. In workstations, for example, Sun Microsystems abandoned more quickly than its competitors complex instruction set processing (CISC) to embrace a simpler, more elegant, reduced instruction (RISC) architecture.

Planned renewal of product platforms combined with sustained development of core capabilities is a defense against technological surprises and obsolescence. We have observed that early planning and development of new product platforms must also be coupled with high levels of modularity in designs and emphasis on layering technologies within an overall product architecture. Modularity in designs allows a firm to more readily focus on critical areas of proprietary technology to advance internally. Modularity also allows a firm to upgrade components with newer and better variations from suppliers.

Coasting on success

Management can dissipate the firm's capabilities by failing to invest in product and manufacturing technology required to maintain competitive distinctiveness. Members of our study groups called this the *coast mentality*. Once a product family reaches high levels of success, management allocates only maintenance-level resources and shifts resources to other product families in earlier stages of development. Maintenance is a strategy prone to disaster.

The coast mentality is probably more a result of a portfolio management approach to new product development than anything else: diversity, spread risk and invest by stage of maturity. Portfolio management leads large corporations to have too many irons in the fire. Rather than produce many successful products, the portfolio approach yields many mediocre products.[28] Strategic focus and aggressive reinvestment are essential to rapidly changing markets with high levels of technological change.

Breaking up design teams

The staffing of business and technical teams has a strong bearing on the development of core capabilities. Surely core capabilities cannot be developed or maintained if key individuals do not have the chance to work with one another in a concentrated way for extended periods of time. In many companies, while management brings multifunctional 'hit teams' together to design and complete a product, once that product is finished, management disbands the team and assigns its personnel to other high-priority product efforts.

Perhaps there is another way. Is it possible for firms to keep the heart of a multifunctional design team together for at least a generation of a product family? Momentum would then build behind a product platform that meets customers' needs and is amenable to effective manufacturing and sales. At the same time, management can rotate people into the development effort more frequently to implement the product platform and create specific variations using the latest skills and techniques.

MANAGING TOWARD A BETTER FUTURE

Companies can manage toward a better future by thinking in terms of the product family, product platforms, and the policies required to enrich core capabilities. Management must fashion planning horizons and financial commitments toward periods longer than current practice in many companies. Management must also have multifunctional design teams stay together longer than current practice. The more diverse a corporation's various businesses, the greater will be the pressure not to do these things.

The common understanding of product platforms focuses on technology and designs. We propose a broader definition (see Figure 11). A successful product family requires a clear and deep understanding of target customers' need for the product, how they will use it and how the customer will integrate the product within their technical and business infrastructures.[29] Further, while product technology and market understanding are usually most important, in some situations, competences in manufacturing or distribution or service will explain success more than other factors.[30] For example, in a paper pulp manufacturer, the rate of new product introduction is low. However, within its long-lived product family of pulp variations, the rate of continuous improvement in manufacturing quality and costs can be high, making its manufacturing core capabilities the keys to success. Similarly, a large retailer might well find its capabilities in logistics, selling and customer service the levers of competitiveness since it neither creates nor manufactures its own products.

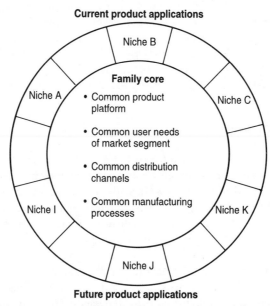

Figure 11. The Product Family: Core and Product Applications.

The idea that a product family requires a multidimensional core is summarized in a framework for managing successive development efforts in Figure 12. Product families consist of cores on which products are based to address specific market niches. Different functional aspects of the core undergo substantial improvements on a periodic basis. Platforms are improved. New manufacturing processes are used. The firm may implement new techniques and technologies to improve service. It can improve or add new channels of distribution. All such improvements to the family's core raise the effectiveness of the individual products within the family. If a company can enhance the capabilities undergirding the current family core, the result should be better products.

Conversely, if core capabilities dissipate, families will lose their competitive edge and their products will fare poorly. Ideally, the percentage of the platform's contribution to individual products should increase from generation to generation based on the principles of modularity and technology layering in design.

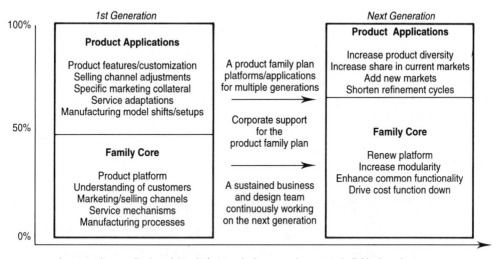

• Increase the contribution of the platform and other core elements to individual products
• Improve quality
• Product refinement cycle time continuously shortened
• Marketing emphasizes good products today, better ones tomorrow

Figure 12. The Product Family Infrastructure and Product Applications.

For the product family idea to have impact, we believe that the firm must consider several basic steps. First, management must transform product planning into product *family* planning that includes, over several generations, ways in which its platforms and other aspects of its core must change in the form of specific product variations and their market applications. Second, management must adapt its budgeting to multiyear planning for related products. In many companies, individual new product efforts compete for resources. To our way of thinking, a company must try to consolidate these individual efforts into basic product families. Each family management requests *multiple year* commitments from senior management based on its plans; one major part is for core development, and the other major part is for the completion and marketing of specific products.

A disciplined approach to developing and extending product families presents a compelling basis for achieving rapid delivery cycles in the creation of new products. If one adopts this approach to making new products, then a strategy for 'speed management' emerges. A company must be patient and forward thinking in developing product platforms and other dimensions of the family core. The completion of a strong platform then facilitates the far more rapid development of specific product variations. In fact, rather than release a single new product, the firm may simultaneously introduce many products, each aimed at a specific market niche. Concurrently, the company must begin designing the product platform for the next generation of the family and consider changes to its basic manufacturing, selling and service capabilities.

Product obsolescence is inescapable. The issue is who takes control of the process. Winning companies retire their own products rather than let competitors do it for them. Methods such as ours will help management see its past activities more clearly and to better plan the future.

ACKNOWLEDGEMENTS

The authors wish to thank the Center for Innovation Management Studies at Lehigh University and MIT's Leaders for Manufacturing Program and International Center for Research on the Management of Technology for their support of the research reported in this article.

NOTES

1. D. Teece, 'Profiting from Technological Innovation: Implications for Integration, Collaboration, Licensing, and Public Policy', *Research Policy*, **15** (1986): 285–306; and C. K. Prahalad and G. Hamel, 'The Core Competence of the Corporation', *Harvard Business Review*, May–June 1990, pp. 79–91.
2. J. B. Quinn, T. L. Doorely and P. C. Paquette, 'Technology in Services: Rethinking Strategic Focus', *Sloan Management Review*, Winter 1900, pp. 79–87.
3. Sanderson posited that 'virtual designs' serve as the basis for a series of 'product realizations' within particular generations of a product family. See S. Sanderson and V. Uzumeri, 'Cost Models for Evaluating Virtual Design Strategies in Multicycle Product Families', Troy, New York: Rensselaer Polytechnic Institute, Center for Science and Technology Policy, 1991, and forthcoming in *Journal of Engineering and Technology Management*.
4. R. Henderson and K. Clark, 'Architectural Innovation: The Reconfiguration of Existing Product Technologies and the Failure of Established Firms', *Administrative Science Quarterly*, **35** (1990): 9–30.
5. Sanderson and Uzumeri (1991).
6. The four major innovations were miniature stereo headphones, miniature super flat motors, disk drive mechanisms and small rechargeable Ni-Cd batteries.
7. A. Lehnerd, 'Revitalizing the Manufacture and Design of Mature Global Products', *Technology and Global Industry: Companies and Nations in the World Economy*, B. R. Guile and H. Brooks (eds) Washington, D.C.: National Academy of Engineering Press, 1987, pp. 49–64.
8. By simply varying the length of the motor field, power from 60 to 650 watts could be achieved.
9. Wheelwright and Clark employ a similar framework in their new book on product development. See S. C. Wheelwright and K. B. Clark, *Revolutionizing Product Development*, New York: Free Press, 1992.
10. Events and years to anchor data gathering and analysis over a span of time have been used to study and illustrate that successful R&D teams pursue a number of alternative technical solutions before arriving at final solutions. See T. J. Allen, *Managing the Flow of Technology*, Cambridge, Massachusetts: MIT Press, 1977, pp. 13–26.
11. A fifth basic dimension, service, has been made part of our research with other companies.
12. For Family A, seven individuals participated in the study; for Family B, ten individuals; for Family C, nine.
13. We settled on these four dimensions of core capability based on the literature. We are also examining core capabilities for data gathering and analysis.
14. In our work with other firms, managers have chosen to identify specific manufacturing processes as core capabilities for data gathering and analysis.
15. The metric used to assess capability was as follows:

     5. Best in class—industry leadership
     4. Above par
     3. On par
     2. Below par
     1. Worst in class

16. The underlying databases for these studies can be quite large. For example, over a thousand data points were gathered for the horizontal application family alone. We computed standard deviations to examine the variance in responses among participants for each core capability These have been left out of this article to simplify the presentation.

17. In our work for other firms, participants have requested that we weight certain core capabilities more heavily than others to reflect their importance in the products studied.

18. Prahalad and Hamel (1990); Quinn, Doorley and Paquette (1990).

19. The scale for performance was:
     5. Among the most successful new business development efforts in the company
     4. Above par
     3. On par
     2. Below par
     1. Among the least successful new business development efforts in the company.

20. In another study at the same company, we have gathered data on individual product performance for recent years. Grouping individual products into their respective families provided a cross-check on the validity of the executives' relative assessments. Cross-checks for earlier years were not feasible because performance data for individual products were not recorded.

21. We are presently applying this method to a number of other product-developing firms in order to gather sufficient data to generalize the finding reported here with meaningful statistics.

22. The scale for market growth was:
     5. >25% per year: rapid growth
     4. >10% and <25%: fast growth
     3. >5% and <10%: moderate growth
     2. ≥0% and <5%: slow growth
     1. <0%: contracting market

23. The scale for level of competition was:
     5. Many competitors, with several dominant firms
     4. Many competitors, but no dominant firms
     3. A few large competitors
     2. A few small competitors
     1. No competitors

24. The scale for effective product life cycle was:
     5. Five or more years
     4. Four years
     3. Three years
     2. Two years
     1. One year

25. Sony spent approximately twenty years in basic research for the development of its video camera products. See M. Cusumano, Y. Mylonadis, and R. Rosenbloom, 'Strategic Maneuvering and Mass-Market Dynamics: The Triumph of VHS over Beta', Cambridge, Massachusetts: MIT Sloan School of Management, International Center for Research on the Management of Technology, Working Paper 40–91, 1991.

26. W. J. Abernathy and J. M. Utterback, 'Patterns of Innovation in Industry', *Technology Review* **80** (1978): 40–47; R. N. Foster, 'Timing Technological Transitions', *Technology in the Modern Corporation*, M. Horwitch (ed.) (Cambridge, Massachusetts: MIT Press, 1986); W. J. Abernathy and K. B. Clark, 'Innovation: Mapping the Winds of Creative Destruction', *Research Policy* **14** (1985): 3–22; and M. Tushman and P. Anderson, 'Technological Discontinuities and Organizational Environments', *Administrative Science Quarterly* **31** (1986): 439–465.

27. J. M. Utterback, *Mastering the Dynamics of Innovation*, Boston: Harvard Business School Press.

28. M. H. Meyer and E. B. Roberts, 'Focusing Product Technology for Corporate Growth', *Sloan Management Review*, Summer 1988, pp. 7–16; Quinn, Doorley and Paquette (1990).

29. C. Freeman, *The Economics of Industrial Innovation*, Cambridge, Massachusetts: MIT Press, 1986; R. G. Cooper, *Winning at New Products*, Reading, Massachusetts: Addison-Wesley, 1986; M. A. Maidique and B. J. Zirger, 'The New Product Learning Cycle', *Research Policy* **14** (1985): 299–314.
30. J. M. Utterback, 'Innovation and Industrial Evolution in Manufacturing Industries', *Technology and Global Industry: Companies and Nations in the World Economy*, B. R. Guile and H. Brooks (eds), Washington, D.C.: National Academy of Engineering Press, 1987, pp. 16–48; E. B. Roberts and M. H. Meyer, 'New Products and Corporate Strategy', *Engineering Management Review* **19** (1991): 4–18.

8

Product Development Strategy: An Integration of Technology and Marketing

Harry Nyström

It is becoming clear that new product strategies are important determinants of long-run company success in many, if not all, industries (Cooper, 1984; Crawford, 1980). At the same time, a systematic framework for the analysis of product strategy problems has not yet been developed. This article presents some ideas that can contribute to such a framework.

A common view of strategy is that success depends on whether the strategy and structure of the company matches its environment. For product development strategies, the most important environmental factors are linked to market and technological change (Day, 1975; Gold, 1975; Kiel, 1984; Maidique and Patch, 1982). Companies thus need both marketing strategies and technology strategies to deal effectively with product development. But in particular, they need (1) to make their marketing and technology strategies more explicit, and (2) to integrate them into an overall new product strategy.

This article provides a framework for characterizing and integrating marketing and technology strategies. Its purpose is to provide a way of evaluating existing strategies and proposed strategy alternatives.

SOME COMMON FACTORS

The framework developed here has been proven applicable in industrial goods as well as consumer goods industries; in research intensive industries as well as those where research spending is relatively low—in pharmaceuticals and electronics instruments; in food processing and steel. The framework was developed in five major research projects where managers in 171 firms in eight industry categories were interviewed over a ten-year period, beginning in the mid-1970s (Nyström, 1979a; Nyström and Edvardsson, 1978, 1980, 1982). In the course of the interviews, case histories of 365 new products were examined in the search for details of implemented strategies as compared to stated or written strategies. The interviews were supplemented by the analysis of written materials such as company reports and product documents.

Reprinted with permission from *Journal of Product Innovation Management*, Vol. 2, 1985, pp. 25–33.

The majority of the firms and products that were examined were in the farm machin-ery industry, but the elements of the analytical framework were equally useful for structuring the strategies of the other firms in the studies. The list of industries in the research programme is shown in Table 1.

Table 1. Industries studied in the ten-year research programs[a]

Study	Industry	Number of companies studied	Number of new products studied
A	Pharmaceutical	3	24
	Electronic instruments	4	31
	Industrial chemicals	2	13
	Steel	2	23
B	Farm machinery	140	166
C	Farm machinery	4[b]	27[b]
D	Food processing	20	121
E	Pulp and paper	4	14
		171	365

[a] References: Study A, Nyström (1979a); Study B, Nyström and Edvardsson (1978); Study C, Nyström and Edvardsson (1980); Study D, Nyström and Edvardsson (1982); Study E, reported in this article.
[b] Included in Study B total.

The common thread running through the studies is that, in most industries and in most companies, what I have called an open, innovative product development strategy is more successful than a closed strategy. The rate of success varies among firms, but our data show that, by and large, the same strategic factors that are associated with success in high-technology firms are also associated with success in low-technology firms. In the following discussion, I define what I mean by 'open' and 'closed' strategies and present the elements of the product development strategy framework.

After outlining the elements of the framework, I use four firms in the Swedish pulp and paper industry to illustrate the use of the framework as a tool for strategic analysis. Some notes on the research methodology are provided in the Appendix.

TECHNOLOGY STRATEGY

It is only in recent years that the notion of a technology strategy has been getting widespread and explicit attention. Ten years ago, when the research behind this article was first initiated, product development was mainly viewed as a marketing problem, at least in the business literature. Technology strategies for finding and developing new products were seldom discussed either in the business literature or in firms. Our com-pany interviews at that time clearly pointed to the need for a specific formulation of technology strategies.

Two dimensions of technology strategy emerged from the data as having crucial importance: technology use and technology orientation. Technology use refers to the way technologies are applied to the critical technical problems in product development. Technology orientation refers to the extent to which a company relies on its own internal technical competence and resources in new product development or depends on outside sources.

Technology use

Technology use can be *isolated*, where research and development work on new products is mainly within a given established area of technology, such as microelectronics or optical measurement. The technology is seen as a relatively well defined and delineated body of knowledge, usually the basis for professional and academic specialization. Isolated technology use is intradisciplinary and can be carried out by individuals or firms working in relative isolation from one another.

Technology use can be *synergistic*, where new product R&D combines technologies. Synergistic technology is interdisciplinary in nature and requires the bridging of gaps between specialized experts from otherwise disjunct areas of knowledge. It requires that good contacts be maintained among the disciplines to achieve effective combinations. There are good chances for more innovative solutions when there are diverse approaches to problems. Synergistic technology use then can be said to be more open and innovative, compared to the more closed and static nature of isolated technology use. Some examples of isolated and synergistic technology uses by companies that were examined in the research are shown in Table 2.

Table 2. Examples of isolated and synergistic technology use

Isolated technology use	Synergistic technology use
Biochemistry	Biochemistry and immunology
Steel metallurgy	Microbiology, pharmacology and
Hydromechanics	bacteriology
Separation chemistry	Steel metallurgy and welding technology
Paper chemistry	Optical measurement, mechanical con-
Extrusion	struction and microelectronics
Thermotechnology	Extrusion and mechanical construction
Data programming	Paper chemistry and mechanical con-
Microelectronics	struction

Source: These were technology use examples as delineated by managers and R&D personnel who had direct involvement in product development.

Technology orientation

Few firms lie at the extremes of an *internal* orientation, where there is complete self-reliance, or an *external* orientation, where there is complete reliance on outside resources, but there is often a strong tendency in one direction or the other. External cooperation may be with, for instance, universities, research institutes, other companies or independent inventors.[1] An external orientation, by involving the outside technological environment to a larger extent, can be called an 'open' element of technology strategy. An internal technology orientation restricts the possible solutions to product development problems and is a more closed orientation.

MARKETING STRATEGY

Marketing strategy can be defined in terms of the product and customer focus of the company. On the dimension of product focus, a company can concentrate on developing products that are essentially variations of existing products—*product modifications*, or it can focus on products that fall outside the established product line—*product diversifications*.

The second dimension of marketing strategy is customer focus. If new products are primarily aimed at getting new customers, the strategy is *offensive*. If they are mainly directed toward tying existing customers closer to the company, the strategy is classified as *defensive* (Nyström, 1977).

Product design

Whether the marketing strategy is offensive or defensive, it may be implemented through products that are directed either toward a wide range of customer needs—a *general* product design; or it may result in products that are aimed at a more narrow spectrum of customer needs—a *specific* product design. The choice of general or specific product design orientation is an important factor in characterizing the overall product development strategy. In a sense, it is an intervening variable in a model that relates strategy to product development success.

Process design

Closely related to the choice of marketing strategy is the choice of process, especially in those industries, such as steel, chemicals and food processing, where product and process innovations are closely connected. A *general* process is used for producing many types of end products. A *specific* process is one designed to produce a narrow range of end products, or even just one. In this sense, the process design can also be considered to be an intervening variable between product development strategy and product development success.

PRODUCT DEVELOPMENT OUTCOMES

Ultimately, the measure of success of a strategy is its effects on new product performance (Cooper, 1984). Of course, strategy alone is not the sole determinant of success. Nevertheless, it is worth defining some of the ways success can be measured in order to assess some part of the relationship between product development strategy and product development outcome. Three dimensions of performance are specified in the product development framework: technological, competitive and financial.

Technological outcome

The main measure of technological outcome is the level of *technological innovation*. This is defined as the degree of novelty companies have to employ to solve the critical technical problems when developing new products. The underlying assumption is that a relatively high level of technical creativity is usually a necessary, but not sufficient, condition for achieving highly competitive new products, particularly in research and technology intensive industries. A high level of technological innovation also, as a rule, makes it easier to achieve patent protection. Further, as a rule, it requires a longer period of development time than more routine technical developments.

In the research program, there were three measures of the level of technological innovation achieved by the companies. The principal measure was our rating of the degree of novelty or uniqueness of technological solutions. These were derived after intensive discussions with individuals in the firms. The ratings were highly correlated with the other two measures: degree of patent protection and time for development. Since companies, for competitive reasons, may not apply for patents, the patent situation is an imperfect indicator of the level of technological novelty. Development time is also an imperfect indicator, but its high correlation with the other two measures gives some confidence in the overall measures that were made.

Competitive outcome

In our framework, the measure of market outcome was the *uniqueness* or the *interchangeability* of the product from the buyer's point of view at the time it is introduced on the market. If buyers consider the product to be more or less interchangeable with competing products already on the market, the product's uniqueness is low. The assumption is that, the more unique it is—the more that buyers see it as different in features and performance from competing products—the greater the market potential.

Financial outcome

Commercial success for new products is ultimately the *profitability* of the product over its life cycle. For this research, the measure was an estimate of the profitability over the time period, as judged and as justified to the researchers by company executives. Of course, as noted earlier, the profitability depends on many factors other than product development, so it is difficult to be conclusive about apparent relationships between strategy for product development and product development outcomes. The technological and competitive outcomes are similarly limited as a measure of strategy success although they are more direct consequences than profitability.

The general analytical framework for product development strategies is shown in Figure 1.

OPEN AND CLOSED STRATEGIES

From a general point of view, product development strategies can be viewed as lying along the dimension of *open* or *closed*. Synergistic technology use and external technology

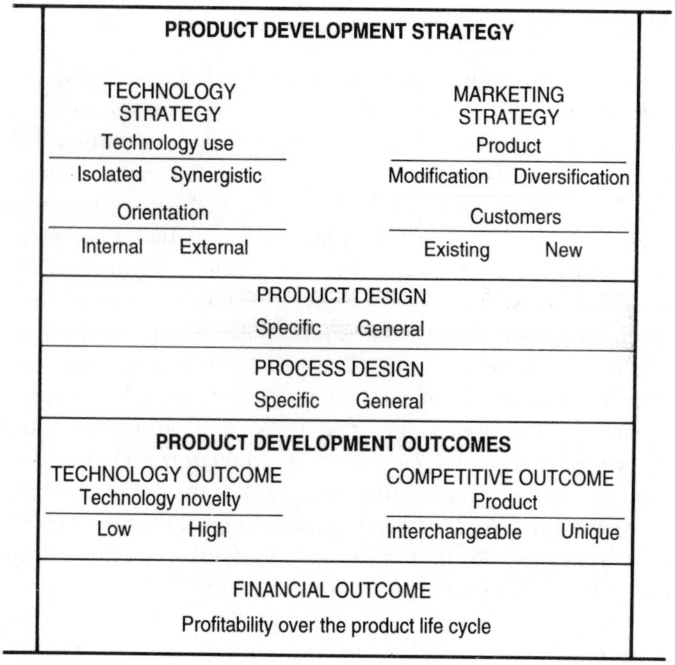

```
┌─────────────────────────────────────────────────────────────┐
│              PRODUCT DEVELOPMENT STRATEGY                    │
│                                                             │
│      TECHNOLOGY                    MARKETING                 │
│       STRATEGY                     STRATEGY                  │
│     Technology use                  Product                 │
│   ─────────────────        ─────────────────────────        │
│   Isolated   Synergistic    Modification   Diversification  │
│      Orientation                   Customers                │
│   ─────────────────        ─────────────────────────        │
│   Internal    External       Existing        New            │
│  ┌──────────────────────────────────────────────────────┐  │
│  │                 PRODUCT DESIGN                        │  │
│  │                Specific    General                   │  │
│  ├──────────────────────────────────────────────────────┤  │
│  │                 PROCESS DESIGN                        │  │
│  │                Specific    General                   │  │
│  └──────────────────────────────────────────────────────┘  │
│            PRODUCT DEVELOPMENT OUTCOMES                      │
│   TECHNOLOGY OUTCOME              COMPETITIVE OUTCOME        │
│    Technology novelty                  Product              │
│   ─────────────────        ─────────────────────────        │
│    Low        High          Interchangeable      Unique     │
│  ┌──────────────────────────────────────────────────────┐  │
│  │               FINANCIAL OUTCOME                       │  │
│  │     Profitability over the product life cycle        │  │
│  └──────────────────────────────────────────────────────┘  │
└─────────────────────────────────────────────────────────────┘
```

Figure 1. Analytical Framework for Product Development Strategies.

orientation contribute to an open technology strategy. Product diversification and an emphasis on new customers are open aspects of marketing strategy. Conversely, an isolated technology use, an internal technology orientation, product modification approach, and an emphasis on existing customers are all elements of a closed strategy.

General product designs to suit a wide range of customer needs and general process designs for a wide range of production operations can also be considered to be part of an open strategic orientation. Specific product and process designs are a part of a more closed strategic orientation.

The main underlying assumption that has emerged from the research program has been that more open, explorative strategies offer a greater creative potential and therefore should be more appropriate in highly changing and uncertain environments. More closed strategies, on the other hand, should focus the efforts of a company more efficiently and therefore should be better in more stable and predictable environments. A summary of the characteristics of open and closed strategies is provided in Table 3.

THE ANALYSIS OF FOUR FIRMS

The strategy framework was used to analyze the product development strategies of four Swedish pulp and paper companies. The first step was to develop a picture of the company strategies from annual reports, internal company documents, and discussions with managers in the firms. Then, a series of case histories of new product developments was compiled and analyzed to see what the company's actual or *realized* strategies were.

Table 3. Characteristics of open and closed product development strategies

	Open: creative potential for changing, uncertain environments	Closed: focus for efficiency in stable environments
Technology orientation	External	Internal
Technology use	Synergistic	Isolated
Product line focus	Diversification	Modifications
Customer focus	New	Existing
Product design	General needs	Specific needs
Process design	General production	Specific production

We had some expectation that there might be a difference between the stated strategies and the realized strategies, and as it turned out, the two were not always consistent. What managers and their documents said they did—their intended strategies—was not what we found they actually did—their realized strategies—when we examined the product development case histories.

Company A

Company A's sales in 1982 were 4 billion Swedish Crowns (about US $500 million) and it had about 8000 employees. Its product mix was mainly pulp, carton board, paper sacks, wall-paper, chemicals and lumber. Its overall policy was to concentrate on existing product lines and achieve cost rationalization. Its international strategy was to add value to its own raw materials by further processing in subsidiary companies abroad. The idea was that final processing in its subsidiaries would give better market contact and better technical adaptation to foreign markets than would direct exporting.

In terms of our analytical framework, Company A's product development had a pronounced closed, defensive strategy, with R&D and production technology geared, to a large extent, to specific process innovation and existing products and customers.

Company B

In 1982, Company B had about 10 000 employees and sales of 4.8 billion Swedish Crowns (about US $600 million). Its product mix was mainly pulp, fine paper, lumber and chemicals. In its overall strategy, it had stressed diversification within existing product lines. The company was trying to achieve this by changing its emphasis from mainly process innovations to more product innovations. Marketing, R&D and production technology were giving more emphasis to product diversification and new customers, especially in comparison to Company A.

Company B had a relatively open product development strategy.

Company C

Company C had about 6200 employees in 1982 and sales of 3.7 billion Swedish Crowns (just over US $450 million). Its products were mainly pulp, craft liner, journal paper, lumber and paper machines. As an overall strategy, it concentrated on existing product lines with its own forestry and power system as its strategic resource base. The company had stressed both biological research (for its forestry) and technical product development.

From the point of view of our framework, Company C had a pronounced closed product development strategy, similar to Company A, with R&D, production technology (as well as marketing) aimed primarily at process innovations for existing products for existing customers.

Company D

Company D had about 630 employees in 1982 and sales of 350 million Swedish Crowns (almost US $45 million). Its product mix was more concentrated than in the other three companies and consisted mainly of pulp, craft liner and carton board. Its overall strategy was to diversify its existing product line within the limits imposed by a reliance on its own pulp as a raw material.

This company had emphasized production flexibility and had concentrated on selecting market segments to increase the value added to its basic raw material, pulp. In the terms of our analytical framework, Company D had a more open, offensive product development strategy than any of the other three companies. Its R&D was more fully directed toward product, rather than process innovation, and towards new customers.

REALIZED STRATEGIES

To a great extent, the descriptions of the strategies of the four firms, as outlined above, represent a summary of what the companies had done in the past and what their managers intended should happen. Descriptions of actual product histories can give a clearer picture of the product development strategies as they were actually implemented.

Choice of products

Company representatives were asked to give examples of products developed and marketed over a period, usually, of about ten years. To be included in the study, the products had to be new from both a technological and a marketing view, and the companies themselves had to have taken an active part in the products' technical development and market introduction.

The sample groups of products from each company were to be representative of the total range of new products developed and introduced during the period studied. Both successful and unsuccessful products were to be included. These selection criteria gave a sample of products that, even in large companies, tended to be close to the total number of new product cases that were available. A total of 14 product case histories were developed, three or four from each of the four firms.

During interviews with the company representatives, information was collected that allowed ratings to be subjectively applied by the company personnel and the interviewers to the strategy dimensions outlined in the model shown in Figure 1. These ratings were very rough evaluations and should not be taken as precise, objective measures. Nevertheless, they do serve to indicate differences in strategy elements among the companies and to suggest some relationships between strategy and performance. The ratings were on a scale from 1 to 5. For the three 'performance' or outcome dimensions, 1 indicate the lowest level of success, 5 the highest. For the strategy elements, 1 indicates a closed strategy characteristic, 5 an open characteristic. The details of the rating system are outlined in the Appendix.

PRODUCT ANALYSIS

In each firm, there was some variety in the type of product and in the development process used. For this analysis, the ratings for the product cases were averaged to give the rating for the firm. The overall strategy ratings and outcomes are shown in Table 4.

Table 4. Ratings of company strategies and outcomes[a]

Company	Original strategy rating	Marketing strategy	Competitive outcome	Technology strategy	Technology outcome	Financial outcome
A	Pronounced closed	3.7	4.0	1.7	3.7	4.3
B	Relatively open	3.0	3.0	1.0	2.0	3.5
C	Pronounced closed	3.5	3.8	3.0	3.2	3.5
D	Most open	3.0	3.3	3.5	2.8	3.7

[a] Higher ratings indicate more open strategies and more successful outcomes.

The company we originally classified as having the most open strategy, Company D, expressed, in the product cases, clearly the most open technology strategy but one of the two most closed marketing strategies. The two companies with, originally, the pronounced closed strategies, had the two most open marketing strategies. There was some consistency in the ratings for Company B. It showed in its product cases the most closed technology strategy, and the poorest technology outcome; and one of the two most closed marketing strategies and the poorest competitive outcome. But the consistency fails when we compare the product ratings to the original rating of a relatively open strategy.

The only apparent relationship between strategy and outcome is that an open marketing strategy—aiming at new customers and product diversification—was associated with a good competitive outcome—product uniqueness. Otherwise there was no clear pattern of relationship.

COMPANY-SPECIFIC ANALYSIS

The results of this study and those of the earlier studies in our research program point to the need for a company-specific analysis of strategy and its relationship to performance. It is difficult to generalize across companies except with regard to one dimension—

technology strategy. Although the records of the four pulp and paper companies are somewhat inconsistent in this regard, in all of our other studies in our research program over the past ten years, there is a tendency for more open technology strategies to be associated with more technological success.

Technology success is measured in our model by the level of technological innovation, that is, the degree of novelty required and realized in critical aspects of new product design. To achieve competitive new products in any industry, some degree of technical creativity is necessary. In our data, synergistic technology use and an external orientation is more clearly related to higher levels of technological innovation than isolated technology use and internal orientation.

More closed strategies may lead to a more efficient use of existing resources. Achieving the right balance between open and closed strategies, in both marketing and technology, is a major management issue. The integration of marketing and technology strategies is another major management issue.

It is in the skillful management of these sets of marketing and technology variables that successful companies excel. Our framework is designed to help managers address the difficult new product strategy questions.

ACKNOWLEDGEMENT

Financial support for the study has been received from the Swedish Council for Research in Agriculture and Forestry, which is gratefully acknowledged.

APPENDIX: METHODOLOGICAL NOTE ON DEFINITION AND MEASUREMENT

Marketing strategy

[1] Most closed	[3] Intermediate value	[5] Most open
Defensive and product modification (variation of existing product to existing customers)	Defensive and product diversification *or* Offensive and product modification	Offensive and product diversification (new products, new customers)

More open marketing strategies are thus aimed at generating new business by product and market development. More closed strategies are aimed at maintaining existing product types and markets.

The distinction between product modification and product diversification is based on product usage, as reflected in how companies themselves view the products in their technical descriptions and sales promotion.

Technological strategy

[1]	[3]	[5]
Most closed	Intermediate value	Most open

Internal R&D orientation and isolated technology use	Internal R&D orientation and synergistic technology use *or* External R&D orientation and isolated technology use	External R&D orientation and synergistic technology use

More open technological strategies are thus aimed at generating new technological knowledge and competence by cooperation with the outside environment and the combining of technologies. More closed strategies are aimed at efficiently using the companies' own technological knowledge and specialized competence.

The technologies companies are working in and the extent to which they are utilized to solve critical problems in developing specific products are given by company representatives. This is also the case with regard to information on R&D cooperation for specific products.

Marketing innovation

[1]	[5]
Product essentially similar to competing products	Unique product

Marketing innovation is measured on a scale from 1 to 5 based on information from the companies. This refers to how different a product is judged to have been, at its market introduction, from existing competing products. In this way competitive response and the effect of marketing promotion and price is eliminated from our measure of market success.

This measure then becomes a pure measure of how successful a company has been in developing a product which at the time of market introduction fulfills previously unsatisfied buyer needs. The extent to which this market potential is actually realized by the companies and transformed into profit is determined by competitive parameters, such as price and promotion.

Technological innovation

[1]	[5]
Conventional technological solution, based on existing knowledge	Unique technological solution, based on new knowledge

As in the case of marketing innovation, technological innovation is measured on a scale from 1 to 5, based on company information. With regard to each specific product, companies provided detailed information on the extent to which solving the critical technical problems required solutions novel not only to the company, but to society.

Essentially this is a measure of technical creativity, similar to that required by patent law. A direct measure of technological innovation was used to avoid the incompleteness of more indirect measures such as patent data. Companies, for competitive reasons, often do not apply for patent protection, even it if is likely that it might be granted.

In the present study development time is therefore used as the only validity check on our estimates of technological innovation. It should be pointed out, however, that in our other studies we have found a relatively high correlation between both the degree of patent protection and development time on the one hand and our estimates of the level of technological innovation on the other hand. As we have noted in the main text, the present study also shows that development time increases with the level of technological innovation, which is what we would expect if our measurement of the level of technological innovation accurately reflects our intention.

Commercial outcome

'[1]	[2]	[3]	[4]	[5]
Large loss	Small loss	Break-even	Small profit	Large profit

The commercial outcome for the products studied were assessed by company representatives on a scale from 1 to 5. This outcome refers to estimates over the total product life cycle and requires that the product has been on the market for some time.

NOTE

1. From the Editor, *JPIM*: A full discussion of the use of external technology sources is given by Håkansson, H. and *Laage*-Hellman, J. (1984) 'Developing a network R&D Strategy'. *Journal of Product Innovation Management*, 224–237.

REFERENCES

Cooper, R. G. (1984) 'How New Product Strategies Impact on Performance'. *Journal of Product Innovation Management* (Jan): 5–18.

Crawford, C. M. (1980) Defining the Charter for Product Innovation', *Sloan Management Review* (Fall): 3–12.

Day, G. S. (1975) A Strategic Perspective on Product Planning', *Journal of Contemporary Business* (Spring): 1–34.

Gold, B. (1975) Alternate Strategies for Advancing a Company's Technology', *Research Management*, **4**: 24–29.

Kiel, G. (1984) Technology and Marketing: the Magic Mix. *Business Horizons*, **3** (May/June): 7–14.

Maidique, M. A. and Patch, P. (1982) 'Corporate Strategy and Technological Policy', in *Readings in the Management of Technology*, Tushman, M. L. and Moore, W. L. (eds), Boston: Pitman, pp. 273–285.

Nyström, H. (1977) Market Strategy and Market Structure: Learning and Adaptation in Market Relations. *Marknadsvetande*, **1**: 41–45.

Nyström, H. (1979) Company Strategies for Research and Development. In: *Industrial Innovation: Technology, Policy, Diffusion*, Baker, M. J. (ed.), London: MacMillan, pp. 417–440.

Nyström, H. and Edvardsson, B. (1978) Research and Development Strategies for Swedish Companies in the Farm Machine Industry. Report from the Institute for Economics and Statistics, No. 139. Uppsala, Sweden.

Nyström, H. (1979) *Creativity and Innovation*, New York: Wiley.

Nyström, H. and Edvardsson, B. (1980) Research and Development Strategies for Four Swedish Farm Machine Companies. Report from the Institute for Economics and Statistics. Uppsala, Sweden.

Nyström, H. and Edvardsson, B. (1982) Product Innovation in Foodprocessing: a Swedish Survey. *R&D Management* (April): 67–72.

Part III

New Product Development Models

CONTENTS

Introduction to Part III

Susan Hart

Once the strategic direction of new product development has been set, the company embarks upon the actual process of developing new products. This process of new product development has been represented by numerous empirically-based models. These models encapsulate many of the key tasks involved from generating and evaluating new product ideas through development of the concepts and physical products, their functional and market testing to the final launch. The representation of these tasks has changed considerably over the past 30 years. The articles chosen in this section provide an overview of the evolution of models as well as an indication of how companies actually do use these models, if at all.

The opening reading of Part III, by Hart and Baker (1994), provides a review of the evolution of models since their early department-by-department approach to NPD through to the recent advocating of a more parallel approach to the NPD process. Indeed, parallel, simultaneous and concurrent processing and cross-functional integration are recurrent themes of the readings in this part. Hart and Baker's review of the literature leads them to propose a further model, that of 'multiple convergent processing', which is claimed to allow not only for cross-functional integration, but the integration of parties external to the firm. The literature reviewed sets in context several of the articles that follow in the remainder of this part. In contrast to Hart and Baker, the article by Mahajan and Wind (Reading 10) reports empirical data on whether and how companies use new product development models. The basic model used in the article is based on the linear representation—with particular investigation of market research techniques used. The findings are fascinating, showing that while new products contribute significantly to the total sales of a strategic business unit, the use of market research techniques and the following of model steps is not widespread. Companies who do use models and techniques appear to be satisfied with them. However, the findings should cause researchers to question the direction of their work. Cooper's (1984) article suggests that companies following the Booz–Allen–Hamilton model more comprehensively fare better in their new product endeavours than those who skip several stages. On the other hand, the increasing need for speed in development, the high cost of carrying out market research at several points in the process may be prohibitive. Mahajan and Wind raise many other questions from their findings, and issue a word of caution to the market research industry regarding the perceived utility of its own product offering.

Gehani's paper (Reading 11) is much less closely argued than others in this section, but uses examples of major companies and the Japanese experience to call for a concurrent approach to new product development which speeds up the process and fosters greater integration across functions. Gehani also points out that *effective* implementation of a concurrent approach may demand more of an organization than it is prepared to give. For example, investment, not only in soft and hardware, but also in terms of human resource which may have to be retrained and developed to remove, or at least minimize, long-untracked attitudes. Gehani's perspective has been adequate without specific reference to what might be termed 'NPD literature', and thus brings extra newness to the field by its reference points in the more general management writers such as Drucker and Ouchi, together with practitioners such as Gary Reiner, VP of the Boston Consulting Group and Akio Morita, former chairman of the Sony Corporation.

The final paper in this section, by Griffin (Reading 12), introduces some empirical data on the use of an integrative NPD model, first developed at Mitsubishi's Kobe shipyards in the early 1970s, called quality functions deployment (QFD). In the context of the current limitations of US NPD processes, Griffin explains the nature and benefits of using QFD. The model's primary advantages relate to its focus on customer needs and wants, its necessity for a cross-functional response to those needs and wants and the ensuing reduction in development times associated with cross-functional, as opposed to linear, development. (A fuller history of QFD is included in Griffin and Hauser (Reading 13) in Part IV.)

The article then reports from an in-depth study of nine US companies using QFD. The findings show a mixed response to QFD, with a number of conclusions and hypotheses being drawn. The articles in this section give a clear view of theory and practice regarding NPD models, as a whole. The next two sections, by contrast, look at parts of that process in greater detail, focusing on the 'action details' of the various stages germane to the development of new products.

9

The Multiple Convergent Processing Model of New Product Development

Susan J. Hart and Michael J. Baker

INTRODUCTION

The field of new product development (NPD) is widely researched in a variety of organizations such as universities, consulting firms and manufacturing companies and is located in a wide range of disciplines, including technology management, business policy, marketing and engineering. Much of that research has specifically focused on discovering what organizational, strategic and process-related factors characterize successful new product developments. There is, therefore, a wealth of knowledge regarding 'successful' NPD, which has been the subject of several literature reviews (Craig and Hart, 1992; Johne and Snelson, 1988; Lilien and Yoon, 1989; Rothwell, 1977). A parallel focus of research has been to develop conceptual models of new product development which might be used by managers to conduct and organize their new product endeavours. Many versions of models, for example, by Booz, Allen and Hamilton (BAH, 1982), The British Standards Institutions (BSI, 1989), Cooper (1988) and Pugh (1983), have been validated by research in that manufacturers do claim to use them. However, it is equally true to say that problems experienced by product developers often seem to relate to the application of factors identified by the NPD 'success' literature. For example, a recent worldwide survey by Arthur D. Little (1991) noted that 87% of Japanese respondents experienced a lack of systems and guidelines for product development, 90% felt there was insufficient attention paid to product specification to meet customer requirements, while 72% cited a compartmentalized, sequential process as an obstacle to improving product innovation. Yet, factors such as these have long been documented as important to success in new product development.

This article takes as its point of departure the view that NPD process models have not been sufficiently adapted to take account of the findings of the NPD 'success' literature. It proposes an alternative model, The multiple convergent process (MCP), to incorporate the lessons from the NPD success literature, based on interaction among several

Reprinted with permission from *International Marketing Review*, Vol. 11, No. 1, 1994, pp. 77–92.

parties throughout the development of new products. In addition, network analysis is forwarded as an appropriate analytical framework in which to investigate the usefulness of the MCP. In order to expand on these propositions, the balance of the article is divided into four parts. The first will examine the models that currently represent the new product development process, the second will review these models in the light of the insights provided by the 'success and failure' literature, while the third proposes a new conceptual framework and the final part examines network analysis as an appropriate research paradigm for the new framework.

NEW PRODUCT DEVELOPMENT MODELS

Saren's (1984) taxonomy, where he categorized new product development models into five types, is a useful basis upon which to examine the multifactors representation of the new product development (NPD) process:

(1) departmental-stage models;
(2) activity-stage models;
(3) decision-stage models;
(4) conversion process models;
(5) response models.

Each of these is described briefly in turn, before going on to examine in greater detail the activity- and decision-stage models, which are felt to be the most useful for reasons detailed below.

The 'departmental stage' models view the new product development process in terms of the departments or functions that hold responsibility for various tasks carried out. For example, in an industrial context, the ideas are furnished by the R&D department, the detailed design is then carried out by the design department, engineering will then 'make' the prototype after which production will become involved to work on the manufacturing problems. Finally, marketing will become involved to plan and carry out the launch. In addition to the criticism levelled by Saren (1984) and Biemans (1992), such representations are now rather out-moded, failing, as they do, to take cognizance of the lessons to be learned from the research into success and failure in NPD. It is now widely accepted that the 'pass-the-parcel' approach to NPD from one department to the next, is deficient in several respects. First, there is the likelihood that the prototype differs (for sound engineering reasons) from the accepted design, which was, in itself, merely one representation of the ideas from R&D, and that the prototype requires modification for manufacturing. Thus control of the process is lost as the idea is adapted, in an isolated way, from one set of functional exigencies to another. Second, it is unnecessarily time-consuming. Third, it does nothing to foster ownership of, or strategic responsibility for, new products (Hegarty and Hoffman, 1990; Kortge and Okonkwo, 1989; Ramanjam and Mensch, 1985) and, finally, there is nothing in the way of market feedback, since marketing is presented with the product to market (Cooper, 1984; Nyström, 1985).

Activity-stage models improve on departmental-stage models in that they focus on actual activities carried out, including various iterations of market testing. However, they too have been criticized for continuing a pass-the-parcel approach to NPD since the activities are still seen to be the responsibility of separate departments or functions (Takeuchi and Nonaka, 1986). Refinements to the activity-stage models have been proposed in order to counter this problem and these are discussed later in the article.

Decision-stage models represent the NPD process as a series of evaluation points, where the decision to carry on or abandon the project is made (Cooper, 1983b; Ronkainen, 1985). This approach underlines feedback loops, which, although not impossible within the framework of activity-stage models, are certainly not highlighted either. And yet, such feedback loops are critical, since the NPD process is one of continual refinement, until an ideal technical solution, which is easily manufactured and still relevant to customer needs, is produced. How such a goal might be achieved without feedback from one task to another is difficult to see. Furthermore, if the necessity of feedback loops is accepted, the dimension of 'information exchange' as a fundamental element of NPD flows naturally. This is a facet of the work in hand and will be developed further in the article.

Conversion process models view NPD as a 'black box' in an attempt to eschew the imposed rationality of departmental-, activity- and decision-based models. The alternative conversion process is a collection of unspecified tasks which may or may not be carried out, depending on the nature of the innovation (Cooper, 1982; Schon, 1967). Essentially, a series of inputs is envisaged, which may be composed of information on customer needs, a design drawing or an alternative manufacturing procedure. Over time, depending on a multiplicity of factors, including human, organization and resource-related, this input is converted into an output. Such a holistic view underlines the importance of information in the process, but has little else to commend it, given its lack of detail.

Finally, response models take change at the beginning of the NPD as their focus, based on the work of Becker and Whistler (1967) who use the framework derived from behavioural psychologists, typified by the perception–search–evaluation–response iteration. These models focus on the individual's or organization's response to change such as a new product idea, or R&D project proposals in terms of acceptance or rejection of the idea or project. A number of factors influencing the decision to accept or reject the proposal are helpful to the extent that they provide a new angle on what might otherwise be called the screening stage of the NPD process.

Saren's typology is sufficiently comprehensive to encapsulate most NPD process variants that have been proposed since its publication in 1984. One strand of research in NPD that it does not cover is that of managing NPD in networks, which de-emphasizes the manufacturer-active paradigm (Biemans, 1992; von Hippel, 1988). Instead the various parties, both inside and outside the firm, are portrayed as key players throughout the process. This work does not reject manufacturer-active models *per se*, for as Biemans (1992) points out the decision-staged models can be adapted to incorporate input from third parties. However, both the linear models classified by Saren and the network models have been evolved without specific attention to the implications that the success literature may hold for process models and it is to those issues that we now turn.

SUCCESS AND FAILURE IN NPD: IMPLICATIONS FOR THE NPD PROCESS

The vast literature on new product success and failure brings to light a host of factors that influence success. The literature has been reviewed extensively (Craig and Hart, 1991; Snelson and Hart, 1991) and from these reviews three sets of issues continually are reinforced and validated:

(1) *The need for interdisciplinary inputs.* One discussion of the various NPD models shows that the tasks involved generally fall within the domain of different functions, themselves based on professional education, training and certification. The 'success' literature consistently shows that where these various professions actively collaborate through the NPD process, its outcome is more successful (Cooper and Kleinschmidt, 1990; Maidique and Zirger, 1984; Pinto and Pinto, 1990). As the development of a new product may be the only purpose for which these people meet professionally, it is important that the NPD process adopted ensures that they work well and effectively together.

(2) *The need for quality inputs to the process.* Both technical and marketing information, which are building blocks of NPD, have to be both accurate and timely, and must be constantly reworked in the light of changing circumstances during the course of the development. In addition, customer and supplier inputs need to be encouraged to ensure user-relevance and supplier support.

(3) *The need for speed in the process.* The NPD process has to be managed in such a way as to be quick enough to capitalize on the new product opportunity before competitors do so. The value of being first into the market with a new product is often significant and the window of opportunity for a new development may be fleetingly open. The speedy undertaking of the complex and intricate product development task will require careful consideration.

Although there are many other factors shown to be important to the success of NPD (for a full review see Craig and Hart, 1992), the first two have consistently appeared in new product success literature for the past 25 years, as for example in the work of Carter and Williams (1957) while the third has been fairly constant over the past 10–15 years. This, then, leads us to enquire whether the widely-accepted models of NPD take full cognizance of these issues. The Booz, Allen and Hamilton (1982) model is a useful basis for such an enquiry, as it represents the major elements of many activity based models. To it, we add dimension to decision-stage models which capture information inputs and decision outputs at each stage. This helps us to view the usefulness of the models in the light of the success literature because the information needs and decision outputs are taken from the findings of this body of literature. Figure 1 represents a summary, therefore, of NPD models based on these traditions.

The model shown in Table 1 shows each 'task' in terms of the required information input, the source of such information and the output- or decision-objective of the task.

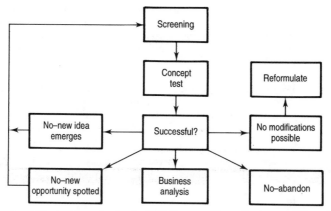

Figure 1. Horizontal and Vertical Iteration in the NPD Process. (*Source*: Snelson and Hart, 1991.)

Thus it uses the BAH model to construct an 'information processing' view of NPD. This is the inherent strength of the activity- and decision-stage approaches, namely, that they can be expanded to show what each task requires of various departments to fulfil each decision stage. However, representation of the NPD process by the BAH and other activity- and decision-stage models has been criticized on two further counts:

(1) In reality, the NPD process is idiosyncratic to the firm and to the project in question. It depends on the type of new product being developed and its relationship with the firm's current activities (Cooper, 1988; Johne and Snelson, 1988), with so-called 'radical' new products requiring a fuller process than 'modifications'.

(2) There is no clear beginning, middle and end to the NPD process. For example, from one idea, several product concept variants may be developed, each of which might be pursued. Also, as an idea crystallizes, the developers may assess the nature of the market need more easily and the technical and production costs become more readily identified and evaluated. The issue, problems and solutions become clearer as the process unfolds; it is easier to decide on which variants to pursue and how worthwhile the whole endeavour may be later in the process. This is important given that commentary attached to the process models stress the importance of early assessment and evaluation, precisely at those stages when the credibility and accuracy of the information to be assessed are at their weakest.

The iterative nature of the NPD process results from the fact that each stage or phase of development can produce numerous outputs which implicate both previous development work and future development progress. Using the model provided by Booz, Allen and Hamilton, if a new product concept fails the concept test, then the development itself is terminated. In reality, a number of outcomes may result from a failed concept test, and these are described below.

It is possible that although the original product concept is faulty, a better one is found through the concept tests; it would then re-enter the development process at the screening stage. Alternatively, a new customer may be identified through the concept testing stage, since the objective of concept testing is to be alert to customer needs when formulating a

Table 1. An analysis of the NPD Process based on Booz, Allen and Hamilton (1982)

Stage of development	Information needed for stage: nature of information	Sources of information	Likely output of stage in light of information
Explicit statement of new product strategy, budget allocation	Preliminary market and technical analysis: company objectives	Generated as part of continuous MIS and corporate planning	Identification of market (NB not product) opportunities to be exploited by new products
Idea generation (or gathering)	Customer needs and technical developments in previously identified markets	Inside company: salesman, technical functions Outside company: customers, competitors, inventors etc.	Body of initially acceptable ideas
Screening ideas: finding those with most potential	Assessment of whether there is a market for this type of product, and whether the company can make it. Assessment of financial implications: market potential and costs. Knowledge of company goals and assessment of fit	Main internal functions: R&D Sales Marketing Finance Production	Ideas which are acceptable for further development
Concept development: turning an idea into a recognizable product concept, with attributes and market position identified	Explicit assessment of customer needs to appraise market potential. Explicit assessment of technical requirements	Initial research with customer(s). Input from marketing and technical functions	Identification of key attributes that need to be incorporated in the product, major technical costs, target markets and potential
Business analysis: full analysis of the proposal in terms of its business potential	Fullest information thus far: Detailed market analysis Explicit technical feasibility and costs Production implications Corporate objectives	Main internal functions Customers	Major go/no-go decision: company needs to be sure the venture is worthwhile as expenditure dramatically increases after this stage. Initial market plan. Development plan and budget
Product development: crystallizing the product into semi-finalized shape	Customer research with product. Production information to check 'makeability'	Customers Production	Finalize product specification Explicit marketing plan

Table 1. (*continued*)

Test marketing: small-scale tests with customers	Profile of new product performance in light of competition, promotion and marketing mix variables	Market research: production sales, marketing, technical people	Final go/no-go for launch
Commercialization	Test market results and report	As for test market	Incremental changes to test launch Full-scale launch

Source: Hart and Snelson (1991).

new product. Any new customers would then feed into the idea generation and screening process. Figure 1 shows these and other possibilities and illustrates how, viewed as linear or sequential, the BAH model is inadequate, particularly regarding up-front activities. The existence of related strands of development complicates the picture further because they mean that product development activity is not only iterative *between* stages but also *within* stages. These related strands of development refer to marketing, technical (engineering design) and production tasks or decisions that occur as the process unwinds. Each strand of development gives rise to problems and opportunities within the other two. For example, if, at the product development stage, production people have a problem which pushes production costs up, this could affect market potential. The marketing and technical assumptions need to be reworked in the light of this new information. A new design may be considered, or a new approach to the marketplace may be attempted. Whatever the nature of the final solution, it has to be based on the interplay of technical, marketing and manufacturing development issues. These interplays are illustrated in Figure 2, using the example of the development of variable ratio steering columns for passenger cars. The crucial issue here is that the BAH model does not adequately communicate the horizontal dimensions of the NPD process.

Drawbacks such as these have given rise to the idea of 'parallel processing', which acknowledges the iterations between and within stages, categorizing them along functional configurations. The idea of parallel processing is highly prescriptive: it advises that major functions should be involved from the early stages of the NPD process to its conclusion. This, it is claimed, allows problems to be detected and solved much earlier than in the classic task-by-task, function-by-function models. In turn, the entire process is much speedier, which is now recognized to be an important element in new product success. It is said also to encourage a multi-disciplinary approach, which has also been proved important to the outcome of new products. It is interesting to note that much has been written about the concept of parallel processing in the engineering domain (Finger and Dixon, 1989; Murrin, 1990; Stoll, 1986). Also named 'simultaneous engineering', the approach is one aimed at synthesizing the demands of various technical disciplines in developing successful new products. However, the wider issues in general and specific ones, like the market perspective, tend, on the whole, to be 'tacked on' to the process, where simultaneity of input is confined to the technical dimension. Crawford (1991) depicts the parallel processes of technical, evaluative and planning tasks, and these are reproduced in Figure 3.

While this is clearly a step forward in that different functional tasks are shown, there are two conceptual problems embedded in the notion of parallel processing. First, it

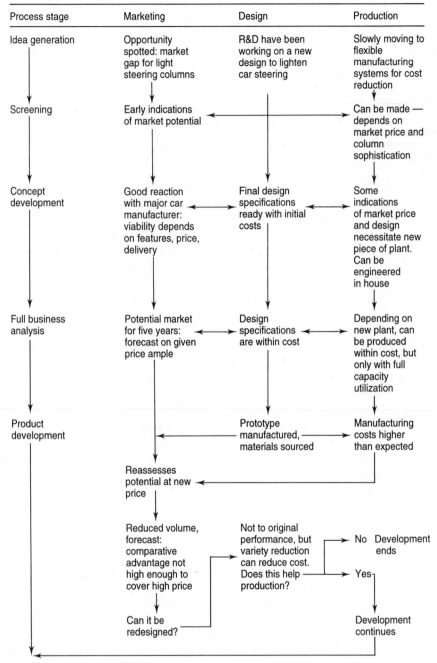

Figure 2. An Example of the Impact of Individual Interrelated Strands of Development. (*Source*: Snelson and Hart, 1991).

ignores the important inputs to NPD that are provided by customers and suppliers. Second, if functions are to work *in parallel* then when do they *converge* to take decisions and move on to the next stage?

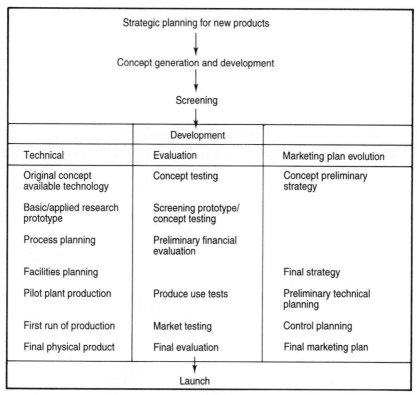

Figure 3. New Product Development Process.(*Source*: Crawford, 1991.)

MULTIPLE CONVERGENT PROCESSING: A PROPOSED FRAMEWORK

Dictionary definitions of 'parallel' refer to 'separated by an equal distance at every point' or 'never touching or intersecting', and while there are references to simultaneity, particularly when related to computers, it is a somewhat troublesome notion that suggests functional separation, when all the performance indicators in NPD point to the need for functional integration. On the other hand, 'to converge' is defined as 'to move or cause to move towards the same point' or to 'tend towards a common conclusion or result', and is therefore, a more precise indicator of what is required of NPD management.

Realizing, however, that there are still functionally distinct tasks which must be carried out at specific points throughout the NPD process, it is clear that the tasks will be carried out simultaneously at some juncture and that the results must converge. Due to iterations in the process, this convergence is likely to happen several times, culminating at the time of product launch. As previously mentioned, the process is a series of information gathering and evaluating activities, and as the new product develops from idea to concept to prototype and so on, the information gathered becomes more precise and reliable and the decisions are made with greater certainty. Therefore as the development project progresses, there are a number of natural points of evaluation and a number of types of evaluation (market, functional) which need to be carried out in an

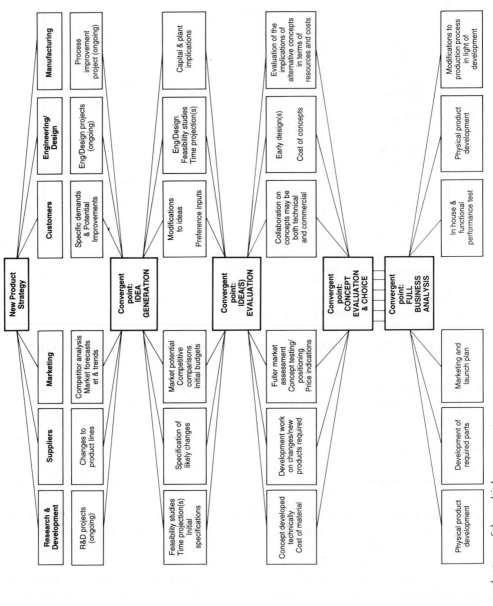

Figure 4. The early stages of the multiple convergent process

integrated fashion. Hence, there are multiple convergent points. An example of the early stages of the multiple convergent process is shown in Figure 4.

The advantages of viewing the process this way are:

(1) iterations among participants within stages are allowed for;
(2) the framework can easily accommodate third parties;
(3) mechanisms for real integration throughout the process among different functions are set in the convergent points.

While the first two advantages compensate for the problems of linear models, which are derived within the manufacturer-active paradigm (von Hippel, 1988) the third deals with some of the disadvantages forwarded by Biemans (1922) regarding the management of NPD in networks. In his analysis of 22 new product developments, Biemans noted the extent of user involvement and gives ample evidence on the functioning of networks in the development of new products. Indeed, at several points in the work, the problems associated with manufacturer-active models of the NPD process are explained and concur largely with the thread of argument presented in this paper. However, several problems associated with developing products within networks are also introduced (Biemans, 1992):

• integration of marketing and R&D;
• performance of the predevelopment activities;
• resources allocated to the actual development activities;
• testing prototypes with users;
• timing of the market launch;
• use of the names and reputations of users during market launch;
• co-operation between industrial firms and universities;
• specific problems of small firms.

The multiple convergent model deals directly with the first two in enhancing integration and allowing for full execution of the predevelopment activities. Each of these is dealt with in turn.

Only two of the companies in the study by Biemans characterized their NPD process as being a balanced mixture between marketing and R&D, yet this is a fundamental element of the success literature (Moenaert and Souder, 1990a, b; Bonnet, 1986) and has been the focus of numerous detailed articles by Gupta et al. (1986) and Gupta and Wilemon (1988, 1990). Given the amount of attention that this issue has received from researchers working both in and outside the network paradigm, it is still not adequately incorporated into NPD process models.

In Biemans' study, most of the companies showed an understanding of the need to integrate R&D and market activities, although the desirability of this is not considered to be automatic, based on the evidence of the companies surveyed. In Gupta, Raj and Wilemon (1985, 1986) and Gupta and Wilemon (1988), it is also stressed that the appropriate level of integration must be decided upon, and that this level is dependent upon organizational strategies, environmental uncertainty, organizational factors and individual factors. The key element in integration is the amount of information sharing, and the multiple convergent process provides the opportunity for information sharing which is neglected by other models. Clearly, a host of other factors are likely to influence the amount of cross-functional information sharing, including organizational climate and structure. This said, the multiple convergent model carries within it the impetus for information sharing though the convergent points that can be located liberally throughout the process.

Moving on to the second problem identified by Biemans (1992), namely, the performance of predevelopment activities, again this echoes the work of researchers outside the network paradigm (Cooper, 1988). Of importance here is the attention given to a series of essential early activities, such as undertaking a preliminary market assessment based on previously-identified criteria and consulting relevant parties (customers, suppliers, production, distributors etc.) thoroughly before freezing the design. Biemans' work showed that these activities were neglected with a limited number of co-operative partners being involved in the early stages and a superficial performance of the predevelopment activities due to a lack of experience and knowledge.

In the work of Cooper and Kleinschmidt (1986, 1987, 1990) particular reference is made to the 'initial screening, preliminary market assessment, preliminary technical assessment, detailed market study and business/financial analysis', which should be carried out before any development activities take place. Again, the multiple convergent process specifically addresses this by incorporating evaluation points from the earliest stages in the process, based on technical and market assessments as well as those early activities with customers, suppliers and other outside bodies.

To sum up, the proposed model of multiple convergent processing addresses problems present in both the manufacturer-active activity- and decision-staged models and network models, by focusing upon the multifarious and multi-participant tasks that compose the NPD process and by incorporating the opportunity for these tasks to be evaluated in an integrative fashion at several points throughout the iteration of the process. However, it is, at present, a conceptual development requiring trial and validation in the field. It is proposed that network analysis provides a most promising analytical paradigm, a proposition to which we now turn.

THE ROLE OF NETWORK ANALYSIS IN STUDYING MULTIPLE CONVERGENT PROCESSING

In analysing the cases under study, Biemans suggested that networks in NPD could and should be considered at two different levels: external and internal. He argues that although part of the wide network of different organizations, each of the major parties in the network has, in turn, its own internal network. However, this aspect of networking has been largely neglected by the literature on NPD and networks, despite the fact that 'the functioning of the internal networks directly influences the efficiency and efficacy of the external network' (Biemans, 1992, p. 176). On the other hand, research which has been focusing on the interactions between R&D from the perspective of survey research within the manufacturer-active paradigm, have had limited success in explaining the nature of the interaction because of the linearity of the models and an incomplete view of the role of information in integration. According to Gupta et al. (1986), integration comprises information sharing, decision-making agreement and decision-making authority agreement. However, beyond stating the need for information sharing between marketing and R&D throughout the process, very little is said regarding how this might be researched and nothing is said about the integration of other parties in the process. However, if we look at network analysis, we find a framework for research which throws more light on this issue.

External networks are based on exchange among various firms whose aim is to pool different resources and competences (Richardson, 1972). A key resource in a network is often information, and nowhere is this more so than in the case of new product development (Imai *et al.*, 1985; Kenney and Nonaka, 1989; von Hippel, 1988). Indeed, a recent article by Campbell (1991) underlines the importance of information in Japanese multi-nationals, where collecting and analysing information is everyone's job, where lots of interaction between all levels of the organization is required and listening to all external actors is encouraged. The author appears to suggest that the importance of information and the way in which Japanese companies use networks of independent firms and the separation of manufacturing and marketing are mutually reinforcing aspects of organizational design. Thus the extent of information sharing and involvement of several parties are issues inherent to network analysis. The appropriateness of network analysis is further justified because of its grounding in the theories of exchange, power and resource dependence (Aldrich, 1979; Aldrich and Whetten, 1981; Auster, 1990; Cook, 1982) which have been only partially included in studies of integration in NPD to date.

The tools of network analysis, however, provide a framework for mapping the nature of the internal and external networks within new product development. These tools, as summarized by Auster (1990) are:

- *Size*: number of functions/outside parties in the network.
- *Density*: number of linkages among functions and parties.
- *Diversity*: linkage; number of different types of linkages in the network.
- *Reachability*: organizational—number of different types of functions and outside parties in the network; number of links separating the different functions and parties.
- *Stability*: linkage—whether the network remains the same throughout the NPD process; organizational—whether the actors in the functions and outside parties remain the same throughout the NPD process; frequency of change in linkages or organization; magnitude of change in linkages or organization.
- *Stars*: the number of functions and outside parties with greater than X number of ties.
- *Isolates*: the number of functions and third parties with no linkages to others.
- *Linking pins*: functions or outside functions with extensive and overlapping ties to different parts of a network.

Using this format, the changing roles of the actors and the structure of the network can be mapped as the new product evolves. The advantage of using the multiple convergent process as the level of analysis is that greater understanding of the dynamic forces at play is afforded than by using the company as the investigative level. Furthermore, as a basic tenet of networks is their dynamism, the extent to which they change as the NPD process unfolds can be monitored.

Finally, although networks are more than a series of interactive relationships, the latter are the basic building blocks. Here, too, the well-developed analytical frameworks might be applied in order to provide insights into the key linkages (stars, see list above), that are critical in reducing the duration of the process. Biemans (1992) usefully distinguishes five characteristics of interaction:

(1) type of interaction (vertical/horizontal; competitive/complementary);
(2) purpose of interaction (task performance or task stimulation);
(3) intensity of interaction;
(4) duration of interaction;
(5) formalization of interaction.

By combining these two analytic frameworks to study the nature of the relationships throughout a set of specific tasks, the scope for understanding why some processes are effective and efficient has greater potential than research based on the traditional manufacturer active paradigm, which tends towards ignoring iteration and multiple inputs in the NPD process.

SUMMARY AND CONCLUSION

This article essentially discusses the status of research into new product development and synthesizes the insights gained via research into success and failure into a prescriptive view of the decision-making process. It traces the development of process models of NPD from the early departmental-stage models through to the more recent parallel processing models and shows how the development of successful new products is essentially a task of cross-functional information, management and decision-making. Integrating the contributions that have been forwarded by those studying NPD in networks, the article argues that a new model of multiple convergent processing provides a dynamic and cross-functional context in which to examine and advance the practice of NPD. The MCP overcomes the manufacturer-active paradigm that dominates 'mainstream' research into NPD, but in focusing on networks internal to the company also tackles some of the shortcomings of analysing NPD solely externally. It is hoped that this greater synthesis of two powerful research traditions will bring more insightful, relevant and ultimately beneficial comments to bear on the way in which companies advance new products from ideas to commercialization.

REFERENCES

Aldrich, H. (1979) *Organizations and Environments*, Prentice-Hall, Englewood Cliffs, NJ.
Aldrich, H. and Whetten, D. (1981) 'Organisation-sets, Action-sets and Networks: Making the Most of Simplicity', in Nyström, P. C. and Starbuch, W. (eds), *Handbook of Organisational Design*, Vol. 1, Oxford University Press, London, pp. 385–408.
Arthur D. Little (1991) *Survey of the Product Innovation Process*, Arthur D. Little Inc., Cambridge, MA.
Auster, E. R. (1990) 'The Interorganisational Environment', in Williams, F. and Gibson, D. V. (eds), *Technology Transfer: A Communication Perspective*, Sage, London.
Becker, S. and Whistler, T. I. (1967) 'The Innovative Organisation: A Selective View of Current Theory and Research, *Journal of Business*, **40**(4): 462–469.

Biemans, W. (1992) *Managing Innovations within Networks*, Routledge, London.

Bonnet, D. (1986) 'The Nature of R&D Marketing Co-operation in the Design of Technologically Advanced New Products', *R&D Management*, **16**(2): 117–26.

Booz, Allen and Hamilton (1982) *New Products Management for the 1980s*, Booz, Allen and Hamilton, New York, NY.

British Standards Institution (1989) *British Standard 7000: Guide to Managing Product Design*, BSI, London.

Campbell, N. (1991) 'The Borderless Company: Networking in the Japanese Multinational', *Proceedings of the 7th IMP Conference*, September, Uppsala, Sweden.

Carter, C. and Williams, B. (1957) *Industry and Technical Progress*, Oxford University Press, London.

Cook, K. (1982) 'Network Structures from an Exchange Perspective', in Marsden, P. and Lin, N. (eds), *Social Structure and Network Analysis*, pp. 177–199.

Cooper, R. G. (1982) 'New Product Success in Industrial Firms', *Industrial Marketing Management*, **11**, 215–223.

Cooper, R. G. (1983a) 'The New Product Process: An Empirically-based Classification Scheme', *R&D Management*, **13**(1): 1–13.

Cooper, R. G. (1983b) 'A Process Model for Industrial New Product Development', *IEEE Transactions on Engineering Management*, **EM-30**(1): 2–11.

Cooper, R. G. (1984) 'The Performance Impact of Product Innovation Strategies" *European Journal of Marketing*, **18** (5): 5–54.

Cooper, R. G. (1988) 'Predevelopment Activities Determine New Product Success', *Industrial Marketing Management*, **17**, 237–247.

Cooper, R. G. and Kleinschmidt, E. (1986) 'An Investigation Into the New Product Process: Steps Deficiencies and Impact', *Journal of Product Innovation Management*, **3**, 71–85.

Cooper, R. G. and Kleinschmidt, E. (1987), 'What Makes a New Product a Winner: Success Factors at the Project Level', *R&D Management*, **17**(3).

Cooper, R. G. and Kleinschmidt, E. (1990) 'New Product Success Factors: A Comparison of 'Kills' versus Success and Failures', *R&D Management*, **20**(1): 169–184.

Craig, A. and Hart, S. J. (1991) 'Dimensions of New Product Success: A Literature Review', *Proceedings of the 23rd Annual Conference of the Marketing Education Group*, July, Cardiff.

Craig, A. and Hart, S. J. (1992) 'Where to Now in New Product Development', *European Journal of Marketing*, **26**(11): monograph.

Crawford, M. C. (1991) *New Products Management*, Irwin, Homewood, IL.

Dwyer, L. and Mellor, R. (1991) 'Organisational Environment, New Product Process Activities and Project Outcomes', *Journal of Product Innovation Management*, **8**, 39–48.

Finger, S. and Dixon, J. R. (1989) 'A Review of Research in Mechanical Engineering Design, Part II: Representations, Analysis and Design for the Life Cycle, *Research in Engineering Design*, **1**, 121–137.

Gupta, A., Raj, S. P. and Wilemon, D. (1985) 'The R&D-Marketing Interface in Hi-tech Firms', *Journal of Production Innovation Management*, **2**, 12–24.

Gupta, A., Raj, S. P. and Wilemon, D. (1986) 'A Model for Studying the R&D-Marketing Interface in the Product Innovation Process', *Journal of Marketing*, **50** (April), 7–17.

Gupta, A. and Wilemon, D. (1988) 'The Credibility-Cooperation Connection at the R&D Marketing Interfacer', *Journal of Product Innovation Management*, **5**, 20–31.

Gupta, A. and Wilemon, D. (1990) 'Improving R&D-Marketing Relations: R&D's Perspective', *R&D Management*, **20**(4): 4.

Hart, S. J. and Baker, M. J. (1992) 'Multiple Convergent Processing for Faster Time to Market', *Proceedings of the Annual Conference of the IMP Group*, September, Lyons.

Hegarty, H. and Hoffman, R. C. (1990) 'Product/market Innovations: a Study of Top Management Involvement among Four Cultures', *Journal of Product Innovation Management*, **7**, 186–199.

von Hippel, E. (1988) *The Sources of Innovation*, Oxford University Press, New York, NY.

Hise, R. T., O'Neal, L., McNeal, J. U. and Parasuraman, A. (1989) 'The Effect of Product Design Activities on Commercial Success Levels of New Industrial Products', *Journal of Product Innovation Management*, **6**, 43–50.

Imai, H., Nonaka, I. and Takeuchi, H. (1985) 'Managing the New Product Development Process:

How Japanese Companies Learn and Unlearn', in Clark, K., Hayes, R. and Lorenz, C. (eds), *The Uneasy Alliance*, Harvard Business School, Boston, MA.

Johne, F. A. and Snelson, P. A. (1988) 'Success Factors in Product Innovation: A Selective Look at the Literature', *Journal of Product Innovation Management*, **5**, 114–128.

Kenney, M. and Nonaka, I. (1989) 'Innovation as an Organizational Information Creation Process', discussion paper, Hitotsubashi University.

Kortge, D. G. and Onkonkwo, P. A. (1989) 'Simultaneous New Product Development: Reducing the New Product Failure Rate', *Industrial Marketing Management*, **18**, 301–306.

Lilien, G. and Yoon, E. (1989) 'Determinants of New Industrial Product Performance: A Strategic Re-examination of the Empirical Literature', *IEEE Transactions on Engineering Management*, **36**(1), 3–10.

Maidique, M. A. and Zirger, B. J. (1984) 'A Study of Success and Failure in Product Innovation: The Case of the US Electronics Industry', *IEEE Transactions on Engineering Management*, **EN31**(4): November.

Moenaert, R. K. and Souder, W. E. (1990a) 'An Information Transfer Model for Integrating Marketing and R&D Personnel in New Product Development Projects', *Journal of Product Innovation Management*, **7**(2): 91–107.

Moenaert, R. K. and Souder, W. E. (1990b) 'An Analysis of the Use of Extrafunctional Information by R&D and Marketing Personnel', *Journal of Product Innovation Management*, **7**(2): 213–219.

Murrin, T. J. (1990) 'Design for Manufacturing: An Imperative for US Global Competitiveness', *Design Management Journal*, **1**(2): 37–41.

Nyström, H. (1985) 'Product Development Strategy: An Integration of Technology and Marketing', *Journal of Product Innovation Management*, **2**: 25–33.

Pinto, M. B. and Pinto, J. K. (1990) 'Project Team Communication and Cross-functional Cooperation in New Program Development', *Journal of Product Innovation Management*, **7**: 200–212.

Pugh, S. (1983) 'Design Activity Model', Engineering Design Centre, Loughborough University of Technology, June, 28–22.

Ramanjam, V. and Mensch, G. O, (1985) 'Improving the Strategy-innovation Link', *Journal of Product Innovation Management*, **2**(4): 213–223.

Richardson. J. B. (1972) 'The Organization of Industry', *Economic Journal*, **82**.

Ronkainen, I. A. (1985) 'Criteria Changes across Product Development Stages', *Industrial Marketing Management*, **14**: 171–178.

Rothwell, R. (1977) 'The Characteristics of Successful Innovations and Technically Progressive Firms, with Some Comments on Innovation Research', *R&D Management*, **7**(3): 191–206.

Saren, M. (1984) 'A Classification of Review Models of the Intra-firm Innovation Process', *R&D Management*, **14**(1): 11–24.

Schon, D. (1967) 'Champions for Radical New Inventions', *Harvard Business Review* (March–April) 77–86.

Snelson, P. A. and Hart, S. J. (1991) 'Product Policy: Perspectives on Success', in Baker, M. J. (ed.), *Perspectives on Marketing Management*, **1**: 193–225.

Stoll, H. W. (1986) 'Design for Manufacture: An Overview', *Applied Mechanics Review*, **39**(9): 1356–1364.

Takeuchi, H. and Nonaka, I. (1986) 'The New Product Development Game', *Harvard Business Review* (January–February): 137–146.

10

New Product Models: Practice, Shortcomings and Desired Improvements

Vijay Mahajan and Jerry Wind

INTRODUCTION

Given the emphasis on market orientation in the development of strategic business plans (Kohli and Jaworski, 1990; Narver and Slater, 1990), the $2.4 billion market research industry witnessed a successful growth in its revenues at an 8% average annual rate in the 1980s (*Business Week*, 1991). The inflation-adjusted revenues for the industry, however, declined 1% in 1990 and a similar decline has been predicted for 1991 (*Business Week*, 1991). Industry analysts report that marketing executives are increasingly becoming skeptical about marketing research and are 'bewildered by scanner technology, computer models and the proliferation of consumer surveys' (*Business Week*, 1991).

One of the major businesses of the market research industry is new product research (Mahajan and Wind, 1988; Urban and Hauser, 1980; Wind, 1981). For example, since its introduction in the 1970s, simulated test marketing has grown and is now approximately a $40 million dollar business (Shocker and Hall, 1986; Sabel and Katz, 1989). Similarly, Wittink and Cattin (1989) estimate that about 200 to 400 commercial applications of conjoint analysis were carried out during the early 1980s. Most of these applications dealt with new product concept identification, competitive analysis, pricing, segmentation and product repositioning (Green and Srinivasan, 1990; Green and Wind, 1975). This is a remarkable track record for a method that was introduced such a short time ago (Green and Srinivasan, 1990). Despite their phenomenal success in the 1980s, the validity and reliability of new product models has also been challenged (*Business Week*, 1987, 1991; Sobel and Katz, 1989).

Given the above trends in the market research industry, it is imperative that the developers, suppliers and users of market research assess the role it plays in the practice of marketing. Towards this objective, this article reports the results of a study conducted in the spring of 1990 to understand the role of new product models in supporting and improving the new product development process. In that respect, this study is unique and complements the earlier studies by Booz, Allen and Hamilton (1982) and Cooper and Kleinschmidt (1986) that focused on the scope and steps used in the new product development process.

This article is organized in three additional sections. The following section includes the study objectives and approach. The study results are presented next. The article concludes with implications of the results and presents a research and implementation agenda to further foster and benefit from advances in new product models.

STUDY OBJECTIVES AND APPROACH

The aim of the reported study was to determine the role of new product models in supporting and improving the new product development process. A new product was defined to include innovative new products (new to the world), a new product line and an addition to an existing line. The study was sponsored by the *Marketing Science Institute* (MSI) and it raised the following four questions in addressing this objective:

(1) How do companies go about developing new products and services?
(2) Which models and methods are used in the new product development process?
(3) How do users assess the models and methods employed?
(4) What improvements are needed to further foster and benefit from advances in new product models?

To address the above questions, a questionnaire was developed and pre-tested with one strategic business unit (SBU) each from eight major firms (two each from consumer packaged, industrial, durable and service firms). As the questionnaire asked for very detailed information on the models and methods, the scope of the study was limited to members from the Fortune 500 firms of the Product Development and Management Association (PDMA). Given the focused objectives of PDMA related to the advancement of management practice in all of the functions involved in the total process of product innovation, its members were considered the best initial contacts for informed responses. The selected members were mailed a letter including the study description. The letter further requested these individuals to either participate themselves or nominate individuals from their firms who they thought were most qualified to participate in the study. Such contacts yielded a sample of 338 respondents from 200 Fortune 500 firms. An initial mailing of the questionnaire and a subsequent telephone follow-up to these respondents resulted in 78 responses from 69 firms yielding a response rate of about 35% for the firms. It should be noted, however, that as the use of new product models within a firm can vary across the various SBUs, the responding SBU may not be representative of its firm. The responding SBUs, however, collectively did provide a broad cross-section of industry types; 40% industrial, 29% durables, 17% consumer packaged goods and 14% services.

Some of the underlying characteristics of the responding SBUs are highlighted in Figure 1 and Tables 1 and 2. The following sample summary is warranted from these exhibits:

(1) The average percent of total SBU sales attributable to new products developed

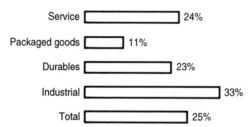

Figure 1. Percent of Total Sales due to New Products Developed in Last Three Years.

within the last three years was 25%, ranging from a low of 11% for packaged-goods SBUs to a high of 33% for industrial-product SBUs (Figure 1).

(2) The market focus for 60% of the SBUs was domestic (as opposed to global). Similarly, the new product development focus for 65% of the SBUs was also domestic (Table 1).

(3) The rank ordering of the average number of new product introductions per year by SBU type was packaged goods (9), industrial (8), durable (5) and service (4). The trend has been to introduce more products per year, on average, per firm, independent of SBU type (Table 2). A very small number of these introductions were of innovative products (Table 2).

The above summary suggests that the responding sample SBUs were actively involved in developing new product lines or additions to new product lines and produced most of these new products to meet the domestic market needs. Based on these characteristics, the responding firms should clearly be the right target group to explore the four study questions outlined earlier. Their characteristics also compare favorably with some of the characteristics of the SBUs included in the 1982 new product management study by Booz, Allen and Hamilton (1982). The median number of new products introduced by the SBUs included in the Booz, Allen and Hamilton study was 5 and they contributed about 30% of the total company profits.

THE STUDY RESULTS

As mentioned earlier, the objective of the study was to address the four questions related to the new product development process and the use of new product models. To facilitate exposition of the findings, the study results are organized below around these four questions.

How do companies go about developing new products and services?

To probe into this question, the study focused on three key aspects of the new product development process: objectives and criteria used to measure the performance of a new product, new product development organization and specific activities used to develop a new product. The results are summarized in Figures 3–5. It should be noted here that

Table 1. Market and new product development focus

		SBU market focus (%)		
		Domestic	Global	Total
New product focus (%)	{ Domestic	56	9	65
	{ Global	4	31	35
	Totals	60	40	

these three aspects have served as the main focus of the studies by Booz, Allen and Hamilton (1982) and Cooper and Kleinschmidt (1986). Wherever appropriate, results reported in Figures 3–5 are compared with results reported in these studies.

Figures 2 and 3 indicate that firms take a short-term perspective when evaluating a new product's success. In fact, the objective to increase market penetration dominates all other objectives. Similarly, profits and sales volume seem to be the dominant criteria used to evaluate the performance of a new product. The top six criteria identified in the new product management study by Booz, Allen and Hamilton included profit contribution, sales volume, return on investment (ROI), pay-back period, internal rate of return and net present value. This ranking is similar to the ranking reported in Figure 3.

Figure 4 suggests that new product development is organized in many different ways within the firms. This general finding has also been reported by Booz, Allen and Hamilton (1982). As summarized in Figure 4, the top three organizational approaches are marketing department (27%) and separate corporate new product development groups (17%).

Figure 5 lists 10 activities typically associated with the new product development process ranging from new product idea generation to market launch planning. Respondents were asked to indicate the activities they use in new product development. Figure 5 summarizes their responses. For the most part, each activity was undertaken by 70–90% of the SBUs for at least one product (except for detailed market study for concept development testing, pre-market volume forecast using prototype and market test/trial sell). However, the frequency with which an activity was performed for all new products and the importance of an activity varied more widely. As detailed in Table 3 and Figure 6, product development and business and financial analyses were performed for all new products by 79% and 70% of the SBUs, respectively. These two activities were also considered the two most important activities in the development of a new product. Detailed market study for concept development testing, pre-market volume forecast using prototype and market test/trial sell were performed most infrequently. Not surprisingly, there is a strong relationship between frequency of use and the relative importance of an activity in the new product development process (Figure 6).

In their study of 252 actual new product introductions, Cooper and Kleinschmidt (1986) found that in only 2% of the new product introductions were all of their identified 13 new product steps used by firms. The three most used steps were initial screening, product development and in-house product testing. The least three used steps were market test/trial sell, detailed market study for positioning and pre-commercialization business analysis. Despite the differences in survey approaches, the correspondence between these results and the results reported in Table 3 and Figure 6 are remarkable.

Table 2. Average number of new products introduced in 1987–1989[a]

SBU type	Year							
	1989		1988		1987		Average	
	All new products	Innovative products	All new products	Innovative products	All new products	Innovative products	All new products	Innovative products
Service	5 (3)	1.4 (1.3)	4 (3)	0.8 (1.4)	4 (4)	0.7 (1.2)	4	1.0
Packaged goods	12 (24)	2.5 (4.4)	9 (19)	1.5 (2.6)	7 (13)	1.4 (3.5)	9	1.8
Durables	6 (9)	1.4 (1.8)	6 (8)	1.7 (2.0)	4 (4)	0.8 (0.9)	5	1.3
Industrial	13 (54)	2.8 (9.0)	6 (18)	1.2 (2.3)	6 (19)	1.6 (4.2)	8	1.9
Total	10 (35)	2.1 (6.0)	6 (14)	1.3 (2.1)	5 (13)	1.2 (3.0)	7	1.5

[a]Standard deviations are given in parentheses.

OBJECTIVE

Produce products at lower cost ▢ 4%

Utilize by-products of existing products ▢ 10%

Offset seasonal cycle ▢ 13%

Utilize exess capacity ▢ 17%

Preempt emerging market segment ▢ 32%

Establish a foothold in a new market ▢ 46%

Capitalize on a new technology ▢ 53%

Combat major competitive entry ▢ 58%

Capitalize on existing markets ▢ 74%

Increase market penetration ▢ 77%

Figure 2. Objectives for Developing New Products (Percent SBUs).

CRITERION

Net present value ▢ 28%

Payback period ▢ 37%

Market share ▢ 55%

ROI (Return on investment) ▢ 56%

Sales volume ▢ 80%

Profit ▢ 81%

Figure 3. Criteria Used to Measure the Performance of New Products (Percent Respondents).

ORGANIZATION

Part of plannning department ▢ 3%

Combination of marketing, R&D and planning ▢ 4%

Task force venture team ▢ 9%   q

Part of an R&D team ▢ 14%

Separate corporate new product development group ▢ 17%

New product development department at each SBU with permanent staff ▢ 21%

Marketing department ▢ 27%

Figure 4. Organization of the New Product Development Process (Percent Respondents).

Which models and methods are used in the new product development process?

Twenty-four different models and methods were cited by respondents. Table 4 lists the 11 most frequently used models and methods along with the percentage of SBUs using them. By far the most often used method in the new product development was focus groups (used by 68% of the respondents). Conjoint analysis was the sixth most cited

Figure 5. Activities Performed in the New Product Development Process (Percent Respondents).

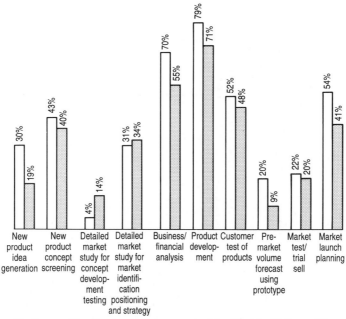

Figure 6. Relationship Between New Product Development Activity Used in All Cases (□) and Their Critical Importance (■).

method (used by 15%). It is interesting to note that the eighth most frequently used method was a Japanese method, relatively new to the United States, called quality function deployment (QFD) or 'house of quality' (Crawford, 1984; Hauser and Clausing, 1988.) In addition to the 11 models and methods listed in Table 4, the remaining 13 models and methods mentioned by 5%, or less than 5% of SBUs, included (in order of decreasing percentages) sensory work with panels, behavior scan, DEMON, ENTRO,

Table 3. Frequency of use and importance of new product development activities

Activity	Frequency (%)			Importance (%)			
	In all cases	In some cases	In very few cases	Critical	Important	Marginal	Not at all important
New product idea generation	30	49	20	19	50	26	3
New product concept screening	43	40	15	40	38	13	6
Detailed market study for concept development testing	4	53	41	14	43	31	6
Detailed market study for market identification, positioning and strategy	31	41	23	34	43	11	8
Business/financial analysis	70	23	6	55	38	3	4
Product development	79	17	3	71	23	1	1
Customer test of products	52	27	18	48	37	9	1
Pre-market volume forecast using prototype	20	33	47	9	47	27	16
Market test/trial sell	22	31	42	20	42	18	16
Market launch planning	54	30	14	41	45	12	1

Table 4. Frequently used models and methods in the new product development process[a]

Model/method	SBUs (%)
Focus groups	68
Limited rollout	42
Concept tests	26
Show tests and clinics	22
Attitude and usage studies	19
Conjoint analysis	15
Delphi	9
Quality function development (QFD)	9
Home usage test	9
Product life-cycle models	8
Synectics	8

[a] The remaining 13 models and methods mentioned by 5%, or less than 5% of SBUs, included (in order of decreasing percentages (sensory work with panels, behavior scan, DEMON, ENTRO, LTM, response surface analysis, sales wave research, AdTEL, ASSESSOR, CRITIQUE, diffusion models, ESP and LITMUS.

LTM, response surface analysis, sales wave research, AdTel, ASSESSOR, CRITQUE, diffusion models, ESP and LITMUS.

Table 4 suggests that only one method (focus groups) is used by more than half of the SBUs. In general, the use of new product models, especially analytical models, is not widespread. Data further indicated that a number of these models and methods were being used for several activities in the new product development process. For example, focus groups were cited being used (with different percentages) for all new product activities mentioned in Figure 5 except for business and financial analysis, product development, pre-market volume forecasting and market test/trial sell. Similarly, conjoint analysis was also mentioned being used for all new product development activities (with different percentages) except for idea generation, market study for concept development testing, market test/trial sell and market launch planning. The use of the various models and methods for several new product activities is summarized in Table 5. This exhibit suggests, in addition to their low use (Table 4), that the usage positioning of these models and methods is not focused. Overall, as indicated in the last column in Table 5, the top three new product development activities for which models and methods are used most often are new product idea generation, new product screening and consumer testing of products. Similarly, they are used most infrequently for pre-market volume forecasting, business/financial analysis and market launch planning.

How do users assess the models and methods employed?

Despite the low use of models and methods by the respondents, some interesting questions remain. Are the users of the various models and methods satisfied with the models and methods they use? What are some of the major reasons for their use of the

Table 5. Use of models and methods across new product development activities

Activity	Focus groups	Limited rollout	Concept tests	Show tests and clinics	Attitude/ usage studies	Conjoint analysis	Delphia	QFD	Home usage test models	Product life-cycle models	Synectics	% SBUs
New product idea generation	X	X	X				X	X		X	X	51
New product screening	X	X	X	X	X		X					41
Market study for concept development testing	X	X	X	X	X	X					X	28
Market identification positioning, marketing strategy specification	X	X	X	X	X	X		X		X		22
Business/finance analysis			X		X	X				X		10
Product development		X	X	X		X		X				19
Consumer test of products	X	X	X	X		X			X			32
Pre-market volume forecasting				X		X			X			6
Market test/trial sell		X		X								17
Market launch planning	X	X	X	X	X					X		10

[a] X: Indicates use of a particular model/method for the new product activity.

Table 6. Level of satisfaction, usage reasons and shortcomings of the various models and methods

Model/method	No of respondents	Level of satisfaction (%)[a]			Primary usage		Major shortcomings	
		High	Medium	Low	Reason	% citing	Shortcoming	% citing
Focus group	60	25	67	7	Improve success rate	62	Forecasting inaccuracy	48
							Market too complex to capture with model	48
Limited rollout	34	29	53	15	Identify problems	65	Too much time to implement	56
Concept tests	21	19	71	10	Improve success rate	81	Forecast inaccuracy	62
Show test/clinics	18	33	67	0	Improve success rate	72	Too much time to implement	67
Attitude and usage studies	15	40	47	7	Identify problems	72	Forecast inaccuracy	53
Conjoint analysis	11	55	45	0	Identify problems	72	Too expensive	45
					Improve success rate	100	Market too complex to capture with model	45
Delphi	7	43	57	0	Improve success rate	100	Market too complex to capture with model	85
							Forecast inaccuracy	57
QFD	7	43	29	29	Improve success rate	71	Too much time to implement	57
Home usage test	7	57	43	0	Improve success rate	100	Too much time to implement	85
							Too expensive	85
Product life-cycle models	6	17	83	0	Improve success rate	67	Forecast inaccuracy	67
					Identify problems	67		
Synectics	6	17	83	0	Improve success rate	50	Forecast inaccuracy	16
							Too expensive to implement	16

[a] Because of rounding, total percentage may not equal 100%.

models and methods? What do they feel are the major shortcomings of these models? Table 6 summarizes their responses to these questions for the 11 models and methods listed in Table 4.

Satisfaction with models and methods was measured as being either high, medium or low. As shown in Table 6, nearly all responses were in the high or medium categories. Although the number of respondents for a few models and methods is small, the general trend seems to indicate an overall satisfaction among the users with those models and methods.

Although the respondents indicated several reasons for the use of each method and model, two primary reasons stood out across all models and methods. As summarized for each respective model and method in Table 6, these reasons were that the method/model:

(1) improves the success rate of new products;
(2) identifies problems with the product and alternative marketing strategies.

When queried, respondents provided several shortcomings for each of the models and methods. Again, major shortcomings mentioned for each model and method are summarized in Table 6. Overall, the respondents seem to concern themselves about forecasting inaccuracy. For some of the models and methods, however, the time it takes to implement them (e.g. limited rollout and QFD) and their incapability to capture the complexity of the market (e.g. focus groups and conjoint analysis) were two major shortcomings mentioned by respondents.

What improvements are needed to further foster and benefit from new advances in new product models?

Respondents collectively gave 21 suggestions to improve the models and methods. The suggestions for each new product development activity are tabulated in Table 7. Despite their small sample size, two reasonable trends stand out:

(1) Overall, about 36% of the respondents (28 out of 78) suggested that the new product development process can further benefit from more formal and quantitative approaches. Surprisingly, although forecasting inaccuracy was mentioned as one of the major shortcomings of the models and methods, not many (only five out of 78 respondents) suggested improving accuracy. Other than the need for more formal and quantitative approaches, the top three suggestions to further enhance the use of new product models included time reduction, better top management involvement and the need to add better forecasting models to some activities of the new product development process (such as concept screening, market study for concept development, market study for market identification and positioning and business/financial analysis).
(2) Among the new product development activities, although some suggestions were made to improve the use of models and methods for each one of them, the activities receiving the most suggestions (top three) were idea generation, concept screening, market study for market identification and positioning and product development. In

fact, the least number of suggestions were made to improve the models for pre-market volume forecasting, market test/trial sell and market launch planning.

The above observations suggest that the new product development process can benefit from more formal and quantitative approaches. Furthermore, most of the improvements will be more beneficial for activities dealing with the earlier stages of the new product development process. In that respect the new product development process called the 'stage-gate system' presented by Cooper and Kleinschmidt (1991) may be useful in integrating the various activities.

CONCLUSIONS

Given the proliferation of new product introductions and intensifying domestic and global competitiveness in the new product market, the survey reported in this article serves to shed light on the current industry practices related to the use of various models and methods, their shortcomings and desired improvements. The sample responses from the SBUs of the major Fortune 500 firms leads to the following major findings:

(1) New products contribute significantly (about 25% per year) to the total sales of SBUs.
(2) The product and the market foci of most SBUs are domestic (as opposed to global).
(3) Most of the SBUs take a short-term perspective when evaluating a new product's success.
(4) Most of the SBUs typically do not follow all the new product development activities. However, two activities, product development and business/financial analyses, are used most often by the SBUs.
(5) The use of new product models is not widespread. Focus groups tend to be used more often than any other new product model and method.
(6) The usage positioning of many new product models and methods is not focused. A particular model and method tend to be used for several different new product development activities. Overall, the models and methods tend to be used for new product idea generation, new product screening and consumer tests of products.
(7) Despite their low use, users of the various models and methods tend to be satisfied with them. They use these models to (a) improve the success rate of new products and (b) identify problems with the product and develop alternative marketing strategies.
(8) Forecast inaccuracy of models and methods seems to be a major shortcoming. Other shortcomings include long implementation time and incapability to capture the complexity of the market.
(9) The new product development process, especially the earlier stages of the process such as idea generation, concept screening, market identification and positioning and product development, can benefit from more formal and quantitative approaches.

Based on the above findings, the following research and implementation agenda is proposed:

Table 7. Suggestions for improvements of models/methods by new product activity area[a]

	Idea generation	Concept screening	Market study for concept development	Market study for market ID positioning strategy	Business/financial analysis	Product development	Customer test of product	Pre-market volume forecasting	Market test/trial sell	Market launch planning	Total suggestions
More formal/quantitative approach	8	5	4	2	3	2	2	1	1	1	28
More in-depth probing							2				2
Add forecasting model		1	2	3	2						8
Add R&D assessment				1	1						2
Increase accuracy of forecast		1		1	1			1	1		5
Better financial analysis				2							2
Improve quality and validity of model/method		1		1			1				3
Simplify	3			1	1	1	1				7
Better customer feedback/get involved	1	1				1					3
Identify and incorporate lead users/key customers			1								1
Involve field sales	1					1					2

Suggestion										Total
Larger and better samples	1									1
More international focus	2	1								3
Methods customized to my industry	1			1	1		1			4
Better people/training	2		1	2					1	5
Better integration across functions	2	3		1						8
Better top management involvement/commitment funding		1								1
Longer term orientation—'life beyond 12 months'	1		1	3	1	1	1	1		9
Reduce the time, do it earlier	1									1
On-line information				1						
Reduce cost										2
Total suggestions	18	16	10	13	10	13	8	2	4	4

[a] Numbers in the table indicate the number of respondents who made a suggestion for a specific new product development activity.

(1) *Reasons for low use.* Overall, the findings suggest that most of the new product models and methods are not being utilized by the major potential users. The question is, why? Are they unaware of these models and methods? Did they use them and then decide not to use them? Are there other reasons, for example, unsupportive organizational culture, lack of top management commitment, no institutional learning (high turnover among individuals who know and appreciate new product models and hence there is no institutional memory), poor implementation etc.?

(2) *Demonstrated model value.* Despite their low use, the users of the various models and methods tend to be satisfied with them. This clearly offers an opportunity to develop live cases that echo the actual use and benefits of the various models and methods. Such dissemination programs, for example, can be undertaken by organizations such as the Marketing Science Institute, Product Development and Management Association, The Institute of Management Science and the American Marketing Association. The leading marketing journals should encourage publication of such actual implementations. Is the high new product failure related to the low use of new product models? Empirical studies investigating this relationship are clearly needed to demonstrate the value of models.

(3) *Model developments.* To overcome issues such as forecast inaccuracy, implementation time and inability to capture market complexity, model usage must be simplified and 'black box' rationals must be avoided. Models must be improved conceptually to reflect the emerging market dynamics including globalization of markets and the advances in information technology (Kleinschmidt and Cooper, 1988; McKenna, 1991). Additional work is needed in the area of validation, data interaction and development of models that capture market complexities such as the competitive response. More formal and quantitative models are needed to evaluate 'go/no/go' decisions at the early stages of the new product development process

(4) *Limitations and future studies.* The reported study is based on a relatively small sample from the Fortune 500 firms and, hence, is not without shortcomings. For example, a very small number of new products introduced by the responding SBUs were innovative products (Table 2) and the sample included only 17% consumer packaged-goods SBUs who are traditionally the major users of new product models (Mahajan and Wind, 1988). Consequently, differences across the various industry types and new product types could not be studied. Because of the limited representation of the consumer packaged-goods SBUs in the sample, it could be argued that the survey results may not present a realistic picture of the current use of new product models. In addition, it is likely usage practices and perceived benefits of new product models and methods may be respondent-specific and hence may vary within an SBU and across SBUs in a firm. Therefore, more studies are needed to develop generalizable conclusions across industry types and new product types. These studies may suggest a need to develop other models and methods for firms not involved in consumer packaged-goods industries.

Given the recent declining sales trends in the market research industry, it is imperative that this industry try to understand its users and the 'products/services' it markets. The search for total customer satisfaction and market orientation mandates that firms understand the role new product models and methods can play in further improving their new product development processes. These models and methods provide an explicit mechanism to capture market dynamics. New product development only benefits from the understanding of such dynamics.

ACKNOWLEDGEMENTS

The authors thank the Marketing Science Institute, the Product Development and Management Association and M/A/R/C, Inc. for their support. Helpful comments were provided by Professors George Day and David Schmittlein of The Wharton School, Professor Don Lehmann of Columbia University, Professor Alvin Silk of the Harvard Business School, Professor Tom Hustad, Editor *JPIM* and two anonymous reviewers.

REFERENCES

Booz, Allen and Hamilton, Inc. (1982) *New Products Management for the 1980s*, New York, NY: Booz, Allen and Hamilton.

Business Week (1991) 'The "Bloodbath" in Market Research', *Business Week*, (February 11): 72–74.

Business Week (1987) 'A Case of Malpractice in Marketing Research', *Business Week*, (August 10): 28–29.

Cooper, R. G. and Kleinschmidt, E. J. (1986) 'An Investigation into the New Product Process: Steps, Deficiencies and Impact', *Journal of Product Innovation Management*, **3** (June): 71–85.

Cooper, R. G. and Kleinschmidt, E. J. (1991) 'New Product Processes at Leading Industrial Firms', *Industrial Marketing Management*, **20** (May): 137–147.

Crawford, C. M. (1984) 'Protocol: New Tool for Product Innovation', *Journal of Product Innovation Management*, **1** (April): 85–91.

Green, P. E. and Srinivasan, V. (1990) Conjoint Analysis in Marketing Research: New Developments and Directions. *Journal of Marketing*, **54** (October): 3–19.

Green, P. E. and Wind, Y. (1975) New Way to Measure Consumer's Judgement. *Harvard Business Review*, **53** (July–August): 107–117.

Hauser, J. R. and Clausing, D. (1988) The House of Quality. *Harvard Business Review*, **66** (May–June): 63–73.

Kleinschmidt, E. J. and Cooper, R. G. (1988) The Performance Impact of an International Orientation on Product Innovation. *European Journal of Marketing*, **22**: 56–70.

Kohli, A. K. and Jaworski, B. J. (1990) Market Orientation: The Construct, Research Propositions and Managerial Implications. *Journal of Marketing*, **54** (April): 1–18.

Mahajan, V. and Wind, Y. (1988) New Product Forecasting Models: Directions for Research and Implementation. *International Journal of Forecasting*, **4**: 341–358.

McKenna, R. (1991) Marketing is Everything. *Harvard Business Review*, **69** (January–February): 65–79.

Narver, J. C. and Slater, S. F. (1990) The Effect of a Market Orientation on Business Profitability. *Journal of Marketing*, **54** (October): 20–35.

Shocker, A. D. and Hall, W. G. (1986) Pretest Market Models: A Critical Evaluation. *Journal of Product Innovation Management*, **3** (June): 86–107.

Sobel, K. and Katz, G. (1989) Why Simulated Test Marketing Doesn't Work. Working Paper. Market Simulations, Inc.

Urban, G. L. and Hauser, J. R. (1980) *Design and Marketing of New Products*, Englewood Cliffs, NJ: Prentice-Hall.

Wind, Y. (1981) *Product Policy: Concepts, Methods and Strategy*, Reading, MA: Addison-Wesley.

Wittink, D. R. and Cattin, P. (1989) Commercial Use of Conjoint Analysis: An Update. *Journal of Marketing*, **53** (July): 91–96.

11

Concurrent Product Development for Fast-Track Corporations[1]

R. Ray Gehani

FAST TRACKS FOR CORPORATIONS

The 1980s have forced three major competitive trends on business corporations in manufacturing industries world-wide. These are: internationalization of technology-driven competition, globalization of manufacturing due to faster transnational flows of materials and money, and a compression of product life cycles with increasingly sophisticated customers. Not all high-tech firms have been able to adapt well to these dynamic environmental influences. Business organizations which were leaders for decades in their industrial sectors now can lose their positions in a few years. Some high-tech products, which were in high demand for years, now can disappear in a few months.

For example, Xerox, the pioneer of photocopying technology, had over 80% of the market share of copiers in 1978, but lost its overall lead, with its market share falling to under 45% in 1982 (Reiner, 1990). Xerox then took four to five years to develop a new product, while its more nimble competitors entered their products in the market in under two years (Bussey and Sease, 1988). Xerox recognized its slackness and recovered some of the lost ground in market by modifying its approach to develop its new 10-series photocopier products in a matching shorter time frame. By 1984, Xerox slashed its cycle time for product development by half (*Business Week*, 1984).

ROLE OF PRODUCT DEVELOPMENT IN BUSINESS

According to Drucker (1990), in the 'post modern' factory of the 1990s 'manufacturing is [going to be] seen as an integrated process that converts goods ... into economic satisfactions'. Drucker's systems approach 'embeds the physical process of making things, that is manufacturing, in the economic process of creating business value'. According to a 1982 study by Booz, Allen and Hamilton, US organizations are likely to derive one-third of their profits from their new products (Fraker, 1984). In today's

Reprinted with permission from *Long Range Planning*, Vol. 25, No. 6, 1992, pp. 40–47.

technology-governed competitive highways, only the organizations which innovate their added-value products and processes frequently and speedily are likely to survive.

Japanese manufacturing organizations did a particularly good job of this. For instance, the Japanese producers of projection television gained worldwide market shares by developing a new television in one-third of the time taken by their counterparts in the USA. The Japanese plastic injection moulders developed their moulds at one-third the cost and one-third the time required by their counterpart US moulders (Stalk, 1988). In the world-wide auto industry, the key factor cited behind the success of Japanese auto makers is their shorter time required to develop a new car model (Sasaki, 1991).

Several technology-driven US companies have also recognized and accepted this market challenge. In 1989, *Fortune* reported that Motorola reduced its throughput time for a pager from three weeks to just two hours, and that AT&T cut its design time for a new telephone by half, to one year. Bell Atlantic cut a major corporate service from several weeks to two days. Compaq Computer Corporation, one of the fastest growing Fortune 500 companies in the US, achieved its super-fast growth by reducing the computer industry's average product development cycle time of 12 to 18 months, to less than six to nine months. Compaq took only 1½ months to introduce its DeskPro 386 microcomputer *after* Intel introduced its 80386 microprocessor chip in the market. Compaq worked very closely with Intel, its chip supplier, and developed compatibility of its new product development process with that of Intel's new product development process.

AN ANALYTICAL APPROACH

In this article, we comprehensively analyse different aspects of a concurrent product development process. We discuss the internal and external benefits of an accelerated product development process. This is coupled with an analysis of the anatomy of a product development process. New processes for product development are compared with the conventional approaches used to develop new products. Three alternative approaches to product development are described. These are: a serial 'relay race' approach, an iterative 'ping-pong' approach and a parallel 'rugby' approach. We then discuss three different ways organizations bring about integration. These include hardware-based integration, humanware-based integration and software-based integration. Finally, managerial implications of a faster concurrent product development process are discussed.

CONCURRENT PRODUCT DEVELOPMENT: A SYSTEMIC WEAPON

Simultaneous engineering, or organization-wide concurrent product development process, is a systemic weapon that can be deployed by high-tech companies to accelerate their new product development programmes. Eastman Kodak Company of Rochester, New York, used concurrent engineering to develop its single use 'Funsaver' cameras to gain competitive advantage over its international competitors. Eastman Kodak used computer-aided design (CAD) tools and a close co-operation between its product development group and production group. This resulted in shortening of the journey from a concept to commercially marketable product to a record nine-month period (personal communication from Kodak executives affiliated with Funsaver programme). Eastman Kodak also used a similar concurrent product development programme to develop its sharper Kodak Ektar film in a quarter of its usual film development cycle time (Wheeler, 1991).

It is thus clear that most companies in the 1990s, and particularly those that are technology driven, must create, design and develop products faster; produce them faster; and service their customers faster. Customers want their needs satisfied 'just-in-time'— as they conceive them. They do not have patience for producers to start and conclude their product development programmes months or years later. The new globalized market place can be compared to viewing a television, as customers zap through different products and services until they get what they want.

Before we discuss how organizations can accelerate their product development programmes, let us first set the stage by reviewing some recent developments in microeconomic environments facing technology-driven organizations.

EVOLVING PRODUCER–CONSUMER RELATIONSHIPS

In recent years, the relationship between producers of goods and the consumers of goods, has gone through a major metamorphosis. For decades a majority of customers was forced to accept whatever goods were *handed down* to them by the producers. And, due to a lack of alternatives, the customers typically paid the asking prices.

About six decades ago, Henry Ford innovated the auto assembly line for producing automobiles in large volumes to offer them at lower prices and reach a larger number of customers. Ford thus gained competitive leadership by coupling standardization of parts and economies of scale, and reducing the price of an automobile drastically. Ford proclaimed that any US customer could have 'a car of any color provided it was black'.

Later Henry Ford's product standardization was outdated by Alfred Sloan of General Motors, who recognized and responded to the diversity of customer preferences in a segmented market. Sloan created different divisions in his holding auto company to cater to choices of different customers, and then developed over-arching structures to help head-office to co-ordinate between those divisions. Sloan's General Motors, however, still relied on a 'supply driven' approach. Typically, the US auto companies also took many years, sometimes decades, to develop their new car models. During this period customers waited patiently for these new products to arrive in showrooms.

JAPAN'S ENTRY

In the 1970s, as the oil shocks sent the price of petroleum oil sky high, the Japanese auto makers quickly entered the world markets with their more fuel efficient, compact cars. To retain their new found foreign customers, and to improve their market shares further, the Japanese auto makers relied heavily on their high product quality and quick response to fast-changing customer preferences. The Japanese auto makers cut in half the time taken by the US auto makers for development of a new car model, and thus penetrated deep into the US and the world-wide automarkets (Sasaki, 1991).

The Japanese auto makers achieved this by using new forms of organizational structures in their manufacturing activities (Lincoln, 1986). According to Stalk, new product development programmes in most Western organizations are carried out by functional centres, whereas their Japanese counterparts used cross-functional team cells to do the same tasks.

ANATOMY OF A PRODUCT DEVELOPMENT PROCESS

To understand the characteristics of different product development processes, we will next consider how a typical product development process originates, and what the various stages are in such a process.

Origins of product development process

In an organization, the process of product development programme can begin in one of two ways. Shanklin and Ryans (1984a, b) consider technology driven markets as either 'supply-side' driven or 'demand-side' driven processes. In the supply-side approach for product development (sometimes referred to as technology push), the ideas for product development originate in the organization's research and development (R&D) department, where scientific discoveries lead to new product concepts. Sony Corporation of Japan represents an organization with such a supply-side approach. In 1950, Sony launched its tape-recorder, even though the general public did not feel a need for recording their own or other people's speech. The general public initially treated Sony's new tape-recorder like a toy and not as an appliance for any significant daily usage. With a technology push driven process, organizations like Sony create entirely new markets in an 'entrepreneurial' manner (Morita, 1981).

On the other hand, the 'demand-side' approach to product development (also referred to as marketing pull) begins the process in the marketing department of the organization. The marketers identify some unfulfilled need of a critical mass of customers. They then involve the organization's R&D department to develop a product to respond to the specific market need defined by the marketing department.

In the 1950s and early 1960s, while the market environment and production technologies were stable for most of the products and organizations, the technology push for initiating a product development process worked quite effectively for opening new business avenues. In this manner, E. I. du Pont, a leading US chemical manufacturer, successfully introduced a series of polymer-based synthetic materials such as rayon, nylon, polyester, aramid etc. to create many new business streams. Many of these products are still quite profitable because of their significant technological edge over competition.

But later in the 1980s, and particularly for emerging technologies, such as in the microcomputer industry, the competitive advantage gained by an organization with technology push approach disappeared quickly because its competition caught up with it in a very short time. For example, first Apple and later IBM gained growth with introduction of their personal computers, but this was quickly eroded by a follower organization such as Compaq. Compaq, a relatively new entrant in computer industry, quickly gained competitive advantage over IBM and Apple in personal computer segment by fast introduction of its new product based on a newly emerging Intel 80386 microprocessor chip.

With time, as the market environments have become more dynamic and turbulent, the technology-driven organizations have to stay closer to their customers to take cues from their changing needs or preferences. Thus, the stimulus for initiating the process of a new product development programme has increasingly shifted from the internal R&D centre to the external marketplace.

Stages in product development process

In either case, whether the new product development process was initiated in R&D or marketing department, it generally traverses through a set of milestones in its journey from conception to commercialization.

For a continuous chemical process manufacturer like Eastman Kodak of Rochester, New York, a new product development programme comprises six distinct stages. These are:

(1) conceptual design;
(2) technology demonstration;
(3) feasibility demonstration;
(4) process capability demonstration;
(5) design review;
(6) production readiness.

Each stage is defined by a set of recommended actions and specific deliverables. For instance, the conceptual stage must 'define the basic concept and manufacturing technology for a new product, establish the financial requirements and returns, and identify whether the risks for developing the new product are high or low'. Similarly, the downstream process capability demonstration stage involves study of 'process capabilities on prototype equipments, completion of the preliminary production system design, and meeting requirements for product-process interactions'. The deliverable of this stage is a 'confirmed production process and product design'. A programme to reduce the product development cycle time reduces the idle time in each stage of the product development process, but does not lessen the number of these stages,

The typical process for a product development programme of a new car model also involves a similar set of six different activities. These include: design of the product concept; research and development of materials and mechanisms; analysis of market and profit potential; product design; production planning; and finally development of market strategy and product launch in market (Sasaki, 1991). Each of these stages take different time periods. Typically, the US auto makers take a total cycle time of 60 months, whereas the Japanese auto makers take only about 36 months to develop their new auto models. The delays for the US auto makers are caused by a number of factors related to the way they use their machines, deploy their manpower, or the way they structure their organizations. Factors for accelerating product development cycle will be discussed later.

DISINTEGRATION OF PRODUCT DEVELOPMENT PROCESS

Traditionally, to develop new products and to run day-to-day business operations, most organizations were organized by functional departments. These departments were organized to work independently and carry out individual functional operations such as marketing, manufacturing, design, research and development, logistics or distribution. In many organizations, departments are still formed by collecting employees with similar educational or skill backgrounds, and making them work together to do only parts of overall business operations.

The hierarchical division of work between workers and their supervisors is generally split according to the principles of 'scientific management' proposed by Frederick Taylor. Around the turn of the nineteenth century, Taylor's scientific management ushered in enormous growth and profitability in US manufacturing organizations with the notion of 'one best way'. This became very popular with managers because of its contribution to efficiency of production of standardized products for mature stable markets.

The relationship between different functional departments in industrial organizations is generally governed by Max Weber's principles for ideal bureaucracy. With extensive rules and procedures in place, the different departments operate almost independently of each other, and the work moves from one department to another, across the organization. This can take place in the following different ways:

Serial relay race or bucket brigade approach

Using the above mentioned principles, for many years, different departments involved in a product development process functioned independently and sequentially like in a 'relay race' or a 'bucket brigade' of fire-fighters (Figure 1).

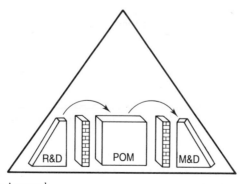

Figure 1. Serial Relay Race Approach.

In this NASA (National Aeronautical and Space Agency) styled sequential phase programme, once the marketers have identified a customer need, they pass this idea 'over their departmental wall' to the next door neighbour: development department. The developers use the received idea to develop a product concept and throw it 'over the wall' to the engineering department. The engineers design a product and throw the blueprints over to the manufacturing department. The manufacturers produce the products and throw them 'over the wall' to the marketing department. In this relay process, a particular department is rarely consulted by preceding department(s) and the department refuses to recognize the reason to involve the next department in its own decision-making process. Managerially, this is a simple but time-consuming organization design to control and monitor a product development programme.

Iterative ping-pong match

Very often, and particularly in the absence of a fire-like competitive crisis facing a business organization, the 'bucket' or the relay 'baton' does not always steadily move forward in the brigade or relay race. The designers and developers have a tendency to reject the marketers' suggestions for new products for being too 'idiosyncratic'. The engineers tend to reject quickly the developers' product concepts as 'impossible', or 'too idealistic', and insist that the designs must be fixed or revised. The product development process thus resembles more like a 'ping-pong match', where the task on hand goes back and forth between the interacting departments, with extensive delays in the progress of a task from one stage to the next stage in the product development programme, as shown in Figure 2.

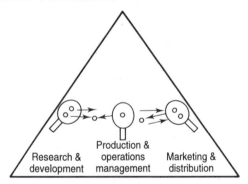

Figure 2. Iterative Ping-Pong Match.

For many years the delay and the cost thus caused in development of new products did not hurt most companies' bottom line very much. The customers generally waited patiently for new products to appear in the market. With few new organizations entering an oligopolistic and mainly domestic US economy, there was no significant erosion in the customer base of an organization due to such delays.

But, with globalization of competition in the 1980s and ease of trans-continental movements of goods, money, and information, foreign competitors started entering as soon as some gaps appeared in the highly valued US or European markets. Thus the US customers had to wait no more for their domestic producers' products to appear in the market. They had alternative products—often cheaper or superior to what they had been receiving for years from their domestic producers.

Parallel rugby approach

To capitalize quickly on market gaps appearing in distant offshore markets in the US or in Europe, the Japanese competitors structured their companies with more flexible organizational designs. In order to lower inter-departmental bureaucratic barriers and be able to respond quickly to customers' changing needs, they organized teams which 'overlapped' or worked 'concurrently' (Nonaka, 1986; Takeuchi and Nonaka, 1986). The Japanese competitors transformed their operating style into a 'rugby' approach, where the team members from different upstream and downstream departments are involved simultaneously in the product development process from the very beginning (Figure 3).

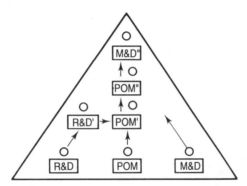

Figure 3. Parallel Rugby Approach.

For example, when Fuji Xerox was developing its FX3500 photocopier, each phase from planning to production overlapped with other phases in a parallel concurrent manner. This concurrence in process compressed the total product development time to 24 months. Earlier a similar programme with a linear and sequential 'relay-race' approach took 36 months. The Big Three US auto makers have also now adopted the 'parallel engineering' programmes to replace their earlier sequential approach for product development programmes (Bussey and Sease, 1988).

With the concurrent 'rugby' approach for product development, marketers do not keep developers, engineers and manufacturers in the dark until the very last minute. They share their information about customers' needs, even when customers' preference patterns are not fully developed. This gives the downstream 'receivers' in the organization enough lead time to prepare and position themselves for a future pass from their upstream teammates.

Furthermore, with a joint ownership in the final outcome, the downstream team players do not quickly reject ideas from their upstream partners as they did before. And, the most significant benefit of such pre-emptive involvement and organization-wide sharing is in the rate of conversion of new ideas generated within an organization into more numbers of commercially successful new products launched into the market.

IMPLEMENTATION OF CONCURRENT PROCESS: ALTERNATIVE INTEGRATING MECHANISMS

The faster, concurrent product development process, described above, requires a higher degree of integration across different parts of an organization for more simultaneous progress across the organization. By nurturing and generating synergies of integration across various subunits of a high-tech organization, the process of new product development can be accelerated many times over. To integrate across different departments, different organizations tend to rely on different competencies. These approaches involve organization-wide integration by introduction of integrating hardware, humanware, or software, which will be discussed next.

Organization-wide integration by hardware

Organizations can introduce hardware technologies, such as computer-aided design (CAD), computer-aided manufacturing (CAM), computer-aided engineering (CAE), computer-integrated manufacturing (CIM), flexible manufacturing system (FMS) etc., to integrate and share common useful information and other resources across different departments. This is shown in Figure 4. These integrating hardware technologies, sometimes called flexible or 'programmable' automation, have facilitated significant improvements in speed and delivery of products (Hayes and Jaikumar, 1988). Earlier an example was cited regarding use of CAD hardware in concurrent development of single use camera in Eastman Kodak, with significant improvements in cost and quality. Hayes and Jaikumar (1988) caution that generally, the integrating technologies such as CAE, CIM, FMS, cannot be profitably introduced in parts or on an incremental basis. Their high returns on investment are synergized only by their enterprise-wide introduction and implementation. This is best illustrated by the hub-and-spoke transportation system pioneered by Federal Express, and emulated subsequently by commercial airlines in the US. Many other companies earlier tried to adopt only one or some of the integrating technologies used by Federal Express (in their 'islands of automation') and gained only limited improvements in their competitive advantages.

Organization-wide integration by humanware

Whereas new technology-based hardware solutions can be brought into an organization relatively easily, their acceptance and success is slow. Acceptance is not delayed by the slow process of bringing about changes in long-entrenched human behaviour and attitudes. The affected employees tend to resist any changes in technologies and organizational processes because of their fear or lack of familiarity with the likely outcomes.

To successfully introduce and exploit the integrating technologies listed above, employees in different parts of an organization have to be taken into confidence to

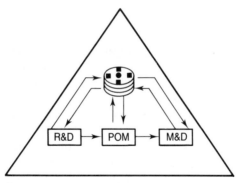

Figure 4. Integration by Hardware.

perform their different tasks in unison. To do so, the organization's human resource may have to be trained to share, communicate and exchange ideas with team members from other parts of the organization in a non-confrontationary manner. Figure 5 shows a linking-pin arrangement where members from different departments are involved in cross-functional teams to do so.

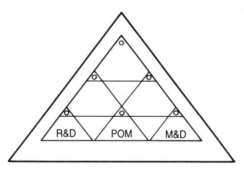

Figure 5. Integration by Humanware.

In a traditional 'serial' organization, product and process innovations may emerge independently in different parts of the organization. On the other hand, in an integrated 'parallel' organization, the product and process innovations in different parts of an organization develop and grow concurrently in a sharing and 'systemic' manner.

AT&T and Ford of the USA use cross-functional teams staffed with members from different disciplines such as product engineering, manufacturing, marketing, and purchasing (Bower and Hout, 1988). These multi-functional teams work together throughout the developmental phase, with real authority to make critical decisions regarding development of new telephones or new cars. By doing so these companies save enormous time and expense in their new product development programmes.

Organization-wide integration by software

New management practices and-processes may also be used to integrate and speed up a product development process. Collective decision making with open communication and information sharing across different parts of an organization can help to counter the bureaucratic effects of large industrial organizations (Figure 6). A cross-functional business team with responsibility sharing is increasingly becoming the effective unit of organizing in fast-track organizations.

For organization-wide understanding needed in a faster product development process, Nonaka (1990) has postulated that 'information redundancy' is fundamental. Nonaka defines information redundancy in Japanese organizations as 'a condition where ... excess information is shared in addition to the minimal amount of requisite information held by every individual, department (group), or sub-organization involved in performing a specific function'. He stresses that in the Japanese organizations, 'the excess information helps to clarify the information held by different individuals, and stimulates ... generation of information with new meanings'. Information redundancy also implies that the new ideas are not prematurely rejected, or considered 'eccentric' because of limited view of one's own role in the overall product development process.

Furthermore, the Japanese organizations nurture organization wide integration with an in-built 'multi-functionality' (Nonaka, 1990). With long-term employment, non-specific recruitment, and extensive job-rotation over the working life of a Japanese employee, a Japanese manager of a product development team is likely to be much more multi-functional in his or her approach that his or her counterpart, a functional specialist in a Western organization (Ouchi, 1981).

With cross-functional team membership, new technologies for multi-criteria decision making are needed for evaluation during the integrated multi-functional process of new product development (Gehani, 1990). The centre of gravity of decision making for integrated product development must also move down the organizational hierarchy, from a supervising manager to the active team players (such as a designer, an assembler, or a salesman). With this new decentralized approach, many managers who typically relied on top-down decision making for short-term bottom-line returns, may feel uncomfortable regarding the erosion of their power and control. They are forced to share information with lower cadres of their organization. On the other hand, such delegation by managers also relieves some of their time and attention for more innovative and creative contributions to the overall product development process.

COMPETITIVE BENEFITS OF A CONCURRENT PROCESS

According to Gary Reiner, Vice President of Boston Consulting Group, an accelerated product development process produces both internal as well as external benefits to an organization. The external or competitive benefits include market penetration due to faster customer responsiveness, premium pricing, precise flow of market research information and 'ability to incorporate latest technology into a product'.

The accelerated product development process also helps the organization internally by:

(1) rapid generation of economics of learning curve with lower overhead and labour costs;
(2) more information sharing and problem solving across the organization;
(3) higher quality of goods and services;
(4) lower requirement of working capital;

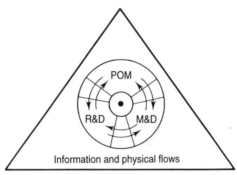

Figure 6. Integration by Software.

(5) less need for engineering and design changes due to environmental variations.

One must, however, be careful that a faster product development process requires some zero-base improvements in the way an organization's product development programmes function. Managers have to genuinely try for zero-defects, remove all the 'bugs' from their existing operations and make their overall business process more streamlined for faster deployment of resources. A faster but inefficient organization is likely to produce a large volume of wastage with defective goods and poor service, resulting in a devastating effect on the bottom line of the organization.

MANAGERIAL IMPLICATIONS OF CONCURRENT PROCESS

The central question is: does concurrent product development process provide the much needed elixir for growth and survival of corporations during the current cut-throat global competition of the 1990s? It is definitely not likely to be so, if it is implemented half-heartedly and in a hurry. If that is the case, it will produce large quantities of substandard products which no customers want.

As the concept of concurrent product development is still relatively new to most organizations, the proponents of this strategy tend to extol the virtues of concurrent programmes in a one-sided manner. They rarely point out that not all employees are mentally or physically geared to operate effectively in a team or group environment. Some individuals function better individually, moving on self-assigned targets, and making progress in their 'own ways'. The motivation levels are also likely to vary from one person to another. Some individuals are motivated merely by the excitement of seeing their design concepts patented or converted into real products in the market, whereas others *must* have quick and substantial monetary returns for their long hours of work.

Finally, in an integrated and inter-dependent chain of people linked together with the common objective of developing new products faster, the overall strength of the organizational chain is likely to be determined by the weakest element in the chain. Thus, if an organization has a weak marketing function, then no matter how innovative its R&D department is, and no matter how skilful its engineers are, the organization is likely to miss the weak but significant signals from customers. Such an organization is likely to fail in launching its new products successfully into the market.

Thus, the concurrent product development approach demands a balance in individual and departmental capabilities of different parts of an organization. In the absence of an intensive Japanese-like training and development programme in most of the US or European organizations, the concurrent product development process will find no dearth of sites of friction generating interpersonal rifts that will interrupt or discontinue the concurrent product development programmes. Organizations must increase and distribute their training efforts to avoid such premature conclusions.

We hope that the foregoing discussion and a comprehensive exploration of different elements of a concurrent product development process will be helpful in curtailing the employees' anxieties and improving their comfort level with respect to adopting this new way to develop new products. A judicious evaluation of the portfolio of alternate ways to implement organization-wide integration in an organization will also help organizations to reduce the probability of a premature failure.

This will result in improving chances for a steady and frequent stream of successful new products launched into their target markets.

NOTE

1. This study is related to 'Theory of Integration Research Project, stimulated by Center for Integrated Manufacturing Studies (CIMS) at RIT, Rochester, New York.

REFERENCES

Bower, J. L. and Hout, T. H. (1988) Fast-cycle capability for competitive power, *Harvard Business Review*, 110–118 (November/December).

Business Week (1984) 'How Xerox Speeds up the Birth of New Products', *Business Week*, 19 March: 58–59.

Bussey, J. and Sease, D. (1988) 'Manufacturers Strive to Slice Time Needed to Develop Products', *Wall Street Journal* (23 February): 1, 24.

Drucker, P. (1990) 'The Emerging Theory of Manufacturing', *Harvard Business Review* (May/June): 94–103.

Fraker, S. (1984) High Speed Management for the High-Tech Age, *Fortune* (5 March): 38. (This reports the Booz, Allen and Hamilton Survey).

Gehani, R. R. (1990) 'Strategic Multi Criteria Considerations for Innovation in Technology Driven Organizations', paper presented at the *Second International Conference on Management of Technology*, organized by Institute of Industrial Engineers and University of Miami.

Hayes, R. H. and Jaikumar, R. (1988) Manufacturing's Crisis: New Technologies, Obsolete Organizations, *Harvard Business Review* (September/October): 77–85.

Lincoln, J. R., Hanada, M. and McBride, K. (1986) Organizational Structures in Japanese and US Manufacturing, *Administrative Science Quarterly*, **31**, 338–364.

Morita, A. (1981) Creativity in Modern Industry, *Omni* (March): 6.

Nonaka, I. (1990) Redundant, Overlapping Organization: a Japanese Approach to Managing the Innovation Process, *California Management Review* (Spring): 27–38.

Ouchi, W. G. (1981) *Theory Z: How American Business Can Meet the Japanese Challenge*, Avon Books, New York.

Reiner, G. (1990) 'Cutting Your Competitor to the Quick', in Asman, D. (ed.), *Wall Street on Managing: Adding Value Through Synergy*, Doubleday Currency, New York.

Sasaki, T. (1991) How the Japanese Accelerated New Car Development, *Long Range Planning*, **24** (1), 15–25.

Shanklin, W. L. and Ryans, J. K. Jr. (1984a) Organizing for High-Tech Marketing, *Harvard Business Review* (November/December): 164–171.

Shanklin, W. L. and Ryans, J. K. Jr. (1984b) *Essentials of Marketing High Technology*, Lexington Books, Lexington, Mass.

Stalk, G. Jr. (1988) Time—the Next Source of Competitive Advantage, *Harvard Business Review* (July/August): 41–51.

Takeuchi, H. and Nonaka, I. (1986) The New Product Development Game, *Harvard Business Review*, **64**, (January/February): 137–146.

Wheeler, J. M. (1991) Cycle Time Reduction and Increased Productivity, Lectures Delivered to High Tech Task Force in Rochester, New York on 3 April , and to the MBA class of Technology Management at Rochester Institute of Technology on 17 April.

12

Evaluating QFD's Use in US Firms as a Process for Devellloping Products

Abbie Griffin

This article outlines a relatively new process for developing products, Quality function deployment (QFD), and presents the results of a field research study of QFD's use in American firms. Although using QFD produces some major benefits and has the potential to provide even more, it is not the panacea that some proponents would have managers believe. Implementing QFD requires significant up-front investment in training, project facilitation and frequently, market research. Most tangible benefits (speed to market, cost to develop) become visible only through repeated use of the process in one product family. In the short term, however, QFD may provide significant intangible (unmeasurable) benefits, such as reducing cross-functional barriers and aiding changes in corporate culture. In deciding whether or not to implement QFD, managers must trade-off whether the impacts of these intangible benefits will be strong and visible enough to allow them to keep investing in using the process until measurable effects on shortening speed to market can be realized.

THE PROBLEM: SHORTCOMINGS IN US NEW PRODUCT DEVELOPMENT

Developing new products is a complex managerial process (Cooper, 1983) that involves multiple functional groups, each with a different orientation (Dougherty, 1987; Lorsch and Lawrence, 1965). Commercializing successful new products requires melding customer needs to technical solutions and manufacturing capabilities, and shepherding the result through the corporate infrastructure. Because customer needs and technological solutions change over time, repetitively developing successful products is very difficult.

Although many US industries depend on new products for significant amounts (50% or more) of their total sales (Pessemier, 1986), over one-third of 13 000 consumer and industrial products commercialized between 1976 and 1981 failed to meet company-specific financial and strategic performance criteria (Booz, Allen and Hamilton, 1982). In a more recent study, Page (1991) found that 45% of the products introduced to the

Reprinted with permission from *Journal of Product Innovation Management*, Vol. 9, 1992, pp. 171–187

marketplace did not meet their profitability goals. Additionally, US companies find that they take longer to shepherd projects into the marketplace than their foreign competitors (Hayes, 1988; King, 1987; Scott, 1985).

Several studies place the blame for poor product development performance on the development *processes* corporations now use (Gupta, Raj and Wilemon, 1985; Hayes, Wheelwright and Clark, 1988; Scott, 1985). Scott (1985) concluded that US firms have a serious inability to convert new technology into the products desired by the marketplace and manufacture those products reliably and inexpensively, a problem leading to declining market shares, profitability and manufacturing incomes for most major industrial sectors. A 1987 Department of Defense (DoD) Task Force on the Industrial Base Initiative also concluded that multifunctionally oriented foreign firms take products and processes from R&D into production more effectively than many US firms (Kimzey, 1987).

CURRENT PROCESSES FOR DEVELOPING NEW PRODUCTS

If you walk into almost any US corporation and ask how they develop new products, the reply would most likely be 'We use a phase-review process'. Phase-review processes divide development into a series of phases, with tasks to be completed in each phase, and a management review and approval step before the next phase can be started (Figure 1) (Urban and Hauser, 1980). Development proceeds sequentially, with different functional groups participating in different development phases, then passing their results on to the next functional area (Rosenthal and March, 1991). Indeed, the DoD Task Force found that US firms generally follow this sort of 'over-the-wall' design process. Design engineers rarely, if ever, communicate directly with manufacturing engineers, marketing personnel or others involved in development (Kimzey, 1987).

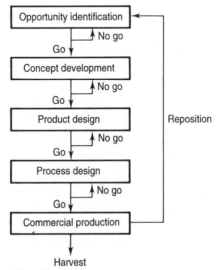

Figure 1. Product Development: Phase Review Process
(Adapted from Rosenthal and March, 1991; Urban and Hauswer, 1980).

Using a phase-review process for product development can easily lead to undesirable development results. A sequential process has no early warning system to indicate that planned features are not manufacturable. Commercialization cycles lengthen as the project iterates back through design to correct the problem. The DoD study found that sequential processes also lead to lower conformance quality and market appeal (Kimzey, 1987).

Some research (Cooper, 1983; Dougherty, 1987; Gupta et al., 1985; Souder, 1978, 1988) suggests that corporations might improve new product development performance by integrating the process across the functions involved. Other writing offers evidence that treating new product development as a holistic process produces products successful in the marketplace and reduces time to market (Hayes et al., 1988; Takeuchi and Nonaka, 1986). Several processes stressing cross-functional integration have been experimented with recently by US firms, including Cooper's (1990) stage-gate process and QFD (Eureka, 1987; Hauser and Clausing, 1988). This article focuses on QFD's use and results in US companies.

QUALITY FUNCTION DEVELOPMENT: A DEVELOPMENT PROCESS FROM JAPAN

QFD is one new formal management process (Sullivan, 1986) for product development that US companies are implementing. QFD is an industry-initiated process, whose primary aim is to capture and convert the 'voice of the customer' (Griffin and Hauser, 1991) into the product and process requirements that profitably deliver the identified customer needs and wants. QFD manages *across* individual functional aspects of new product development (market research, engineering design), providing mechanisms that weave the industrial functional tasks into a coherent process (Hauser and Clausing, 1988; Sullivan, 1986a). It allows development teams to bring together and manage all the elements needed to define, design and deliver a product that will meet or exceed customer needs (Daetz, 1990).

In QFD, cross-functional teams use a series of interaction matrices to translate from customer needs to process step specifications, as shown in Figure 2 (Eureka, 1990). QFD matrices explicitly relate the data (assumptions) produced in one stage of the development process to the decisions that must be made at the next process stage.

US users are most familiar with the 'house of quality', QFD's first matrix (Hauser and Clausing, 1988). As shown in Figure 3, the house of quality relates data generated from market research on customer wants and needs (the 'voice of the customer') to proposed performance characteristics of the product (engineering design inputs). The house of quality can be thought of as the negotiated protocol containing the record of agreement as to exactly what the design will achieve (Crawford, 1984). The second QFD matrix relates potential product features to the delivery of performance characteristics. The third and fourth matrices bring process characteristics and production requirements into the engineering and marketing relationships. The series nature of the charts allows team members to trace the impact of any proposed project change across all functional areas. Table 1 shows how QFD differs from the more traditional US phase-review approach to product development.

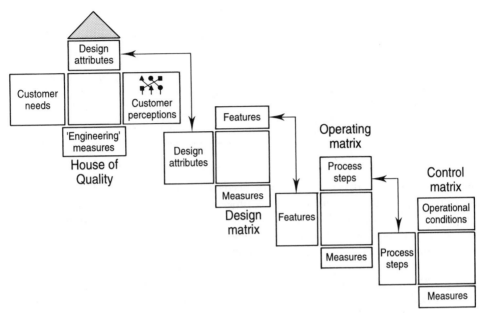

Figure 2. QFD's Interaction Matrices.

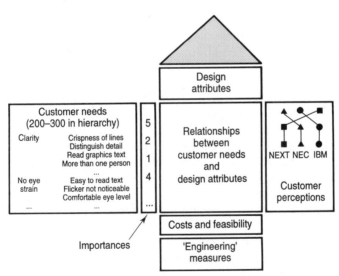

Figure 3. House of Quality.

The cross-functionally developed matrix nature of QFD leads to several specific process-related benefits (Daetz, 1990). First, the matrices bring together all the data required to generate good product definition, design, production and delivery decisions in a highly visual and compact form. Assumptions behind each decision are linked back to expressed customer wants and needs. Second, building the charts quickly highlights

Table 1. Contrasting QFD and phase-review processes

Characteristics of QFD	Phase-review process elements
Simultaneous development across functions	Sequential, iterative development
All functions participate from start	Function involvement by phase
Team empowered to make decisions	Management approval after each phase
Tasks shared across functions	Tasks assigned by function
Consensus decisions about trade-offs	Functionally led trade-off decisions
Working meetings to develop results jointly	Presentation meetings to present results

any areas where the development team needs to acquire additional information to bolster the validity of the decision-making process. Third, the matrices store the plan so that none of the details are lost over time. Finally, the charts quickly communicate the plan and its assumptions to management, new team members and those responsible for implementing the results later in the development process.

Mitsubishi's Kobe shipyards are credited with developing QFD in 1972 (Kogure and Akao, 1983). In 1978 Toyota adopted QFD. Fuji-Xerox initiated QFD to decrease their product development cycle time in 1983. Ford also adopted QFD in 1983 as a defensive move against Toyota. Since 1983, major US firms including Cummins Engine, Digital Equipment Corporation, General Motors, Hewlett-Packard, Procter & Gamble and Polaroid have adopted QFD.

Much of QFD's US acclaim comes from articles describing Toyota's success with the process (Eureka, 1987). Toyota claims that QFD virtually eliminated all warrantee problems associated with rust. It also has allowed them to reduce development costs and time to market by as much as 40% (Eureka, 1987; Sullivan, 1986a, b).

THE RESEARCH

Much has been published on QFD. Articles provide specific instructions on QFD process steps (Clausing, 1986; King, 1987); of what the matrices consist and how to calculate the numbers. Others pose potential benefits for implementing QFD (Daetz, 1990; Sullivan, 1986b) and present US case studies (McElroy, 1987). However, several issues pertinent to managing the process are not addressed in the literature, including:

(1) Does QFD really work *in US companies*?
(2) Why/how does QFD improve new product development performance?
(3) What factors (product type or context) affect QFD's utility?
(4) How is QFD successfully managed in corporations? Are there pitfalls?

The field-based qualitative research reported here investigates these four questions. Because the research of Lorsch and Lawrence (1965) suggests that environmental or contextual factors may affect product development success for any specific process, this study compared outcomes from implementing and managing QFD across projects and firms.

Research methods

Several contextual factors affecting successful new product development have been identified previously (Dougherty, 1987; Gupta *et al.*, 1985; Souder, 1978, 1988). Lawrence and Lorsch (1967) also identified some factors associated with successfully implementing integrated management processes. While these studies provide direction, additional factors may affect implementing and managing new product development projects employing QFD approaches across various situations. This research is an exploratory study using two qualitative research methods, participant observation and in-depth retrospective interviewing, whose combined purpose was to cast the broadest possible information-gathering net to identify success- and failure-related factors.

Participant observation has been used to investigate how groups form and function (Kidder, 1981). QFD teams were observed to develop a dynamic view of how the process works and how QFD teams function. In an inductive process, a participant–observer researcher starts with data, generating hypotheses ad a theory from the ground up (Glaser and Strauss, 1967). Participant observation allows a researcher to mould his or her own frameworks and hypotheses without respondent bias. Nine projects were studied using participant observation.

In-depth retrospective interviewing (focused interviewing in Pessemier (1986)) delves into what others think about a situation; why things did or did not happen, what was and was not successful, how the person felt, and why. It accesses frameworks, conceptual structures and hypotheses developed by others with experiences not had by the researcher (Kidder, 1981). It also allows a researcher to acquire information about aspects of the investigation (s)he has not observed, either because they occurred before the researcher arrived, or they were not visible (i.e. judgments, thoughts). Focused interviewing allows a researcher to test interpretations of previously observed situations.

Interviews with leaders and members of 35 new product development teams using QFD covered a broad range of project- and environment-related topics and gathered project histories. Senior managers evaluated the differences between QFD and other processes for developing new products, such as the traditional phase-review processes frequently found in corporate policy manuals. Senior managers also discussed general corporate characteristics, and why and how QFD was initiated at their company. Over time the interview structure changed as hypotheses formed from the observed groups and an analytical framework coalesced.

The research in the field extended across a year. Several introductory interviews were used to develop a list of issues, then groups were observed. Both observation and interviewing continued throughout the year in the field. Field data are captured in (extensive) notes of each interview and observed team meeting. Data analysis integrates the findings across projects into a coherent framework that could be used in the future for more quantitative investigation.

The sample

The research investigated projects whose goals were to develop new products, and which used QFD as the development process rather than the more traditional phase-review process. As identified from trade journals, conference agendas, other literature and word-of-mouth, around two dozen US companies were using QFD to some extent as a product development process by 1987. Nine of these companies, representing a wide array of corporate contexts, provided information for this research (Table 2). The particular research sites were chosen because they had significant experience in implementing QFD (they had already used QFD in multiple projects) and because they agreed to cooperate.

Table 2. Major business and codenames for research sites

Business category	Number of firms	Firm codenames
Consumer package goods	2	Goods A, B
Complex durable products		
consumer durables	2	Durables A, B
high-tech durables	2	High-tech A, B
Components for complex durables	3	Parts, A, B, C

Firms with significant experience in QFD were identified from published reports of QFD use and success, QFD and total quality management conference speaker listings or as referrals from other contacts. Seven sites evolved from cold calls to project leaders. One site contacted John Hauser (of MIT) after reading his article on QFD (Hauser and Clausing, 1988). One site resulted from a consulting contact.

Project characteristics

Three dimensions of project characteristics that one might expect *a priori* to impact the difficulty of successfully developing products or the speed with which a product could be commercialized are summarized in Table 3. These characteristics, specifically tracked in the projects investigated, vary independently of each other and may correlate with QFD's ability to improve new product development. A number of other project characteristics also were tracked that did not lead to any discernible differences in development outcomes.[1]

Goods and services in the sample differ in levels of inherent project complexity. Managers of complex projects must manage inputs from multiple functional groups and worry about subsystem interfaces. One would expect higher levels of project complexity to lengthen commercialization time and increase the need for a formalized process that manages across functional interfaces. The sample runs the gamut from simple-to-manage component-type products such as shampoos and computer modems to very complex systems like computers and trucks.

Projects differed by type of manufacturing process. Manufacturing processes for physical goods are generally hidden from customers. These processes can be designed to operate successfully given semiskilled and skilled workers. Services are experiential in nature. Manufacturing processes for services involve customers in service delivery. Service manufacturing processes must be designed to operate despite perturbations from the 'unskilled' customers who form a part of the process. 'Manufacturing' for computer software is really the software development process—each software product is unique, and the' line workers' in the process are software engineers.

Table 3. Project characteristic summary

	Total number	Percent of 35
Inherent project complexity		
Complex system	7	20
Subsystem	14	40
Component	14	40
Project type		
Physical good	20	57
Service	7	20
Software	8	23
Change in this project		
Incremental ≈25%)	3	9
Major change (≈50%)	6	17
Next generation (≈75%)	8	23
Clean sheet (≈100%)	18	51

Physical goods-producing firms generally have a formal process by which they design their manufacturing processes. In general, they understand the role manufacturing plays in new product development, and most have developed some specific protocols for process design. Service firms, on the other hand, tend to use more *ad hoc* methods for service delivery process design. They are less sophisticated in designing their delivery processes than they are in outlining the service benefits package. Service firms might benefit greatly from a process that helps them design both the service and its delivery.

Finally, projects in the sample varied in the amount of change incorporated into the product, compared with the last generation of the product. The projects ranged from ones embodying only incremental changes to a current product (less than 25% different) to designing completely new products (100% change, or clean sheet developments).

Projects coalesce with different levels of project-based characteristics. The combinations of variables add up to impact the time to, and/or success of, commercialization. For example, one would expect that less complex projects with only incremental changes made to a currently used design (developing a 'new and improved' shampoo) would be much easier to manage and faster to develop than complex systems designed from scratch (Ford's original Taurus program, for example).

Implementation characteristics

As Lorsch and Lawrence (1965) demonstrated, how companies implement different processes also may affect its use success. Table 4 shows how a number of characteristics associated with QFD implementation varied across the projects. These characteristics were investigated for correlation with outcomes (success and failure of QFD) across the projects.

QFD was introduced via one of three corporate sources: management (top-down implementation), one or more persons on the project team (bottom-up) or some other neutral party, frequently the quality assurance group,. Team commitment, or buy-in, to the QFD process ranged from high, with everyone on the team and their management

Table 4. Implementation characteristic summary

	Number	Percent of 35
Who pushes QFD use		
Top-down	8	23
Bottom-up	10	29
Neutral other	17	49
Level of team buy-in to QFD		
High	10	29
Moderate	12	34
Low	13	37
Team orientation		
Process-oriented	20	57
Result-oriented	15	43
Corporate attitude to QFD		
Investment	21	60
Expense	14	40
Number of functions involved		
1 out of 4	2	6
2 out of 4	8	23
3 out of 4	15	43
4 out of 4	10	28
Team familiarity		
High	3	9
Moderate	14	40
Low	18	51

fully backing its use, to low, where one functional group was dragging the rest of the functions into reluctantly using QFD. Less than half the projects understood QFD as a means to an end (affective goals). Most teams implemented QFD for process-oriented reasons ('If the Japanese are using QFD, we should too'). One proxy for upper management's commitment to QFD was whether QFD was treated as an investment (high commitment), with time, space and money set aside for the process or as an expense (low commitment) to be minimized. The team's familiarity with each other ranged from high, where the whole group had worked together on a previous generation of the product or on some other project, to low, where the team was assembled from people who had never previously worked together.

FIELD RESEARCH RESULTS

This article presents three sets of results from the research. First, QFD's overall impact on product development performance is summarized. Then a number of differences between successful and failed QFD products are presented. Finally, the article puts forth several generic characteristics for new product development processes that perform, in the eye of development-process users, better than current processes.

QFD: Relatively little measurable short-term improvement

Industry practitioners claim QFD decreases the cost and time required to develop new products (Eureka, 1987; Sullivan, 1986b). These effects, if realized, are quantifiable and visible. They are the 'tactical' benefits made possible by implementing QFD because measurable results show up on the short term—'in this project'. Identifying QFD's impact on tactical product development improvements is necessary because many US managers have promoted QFD use in their firms based on these immediate benefits.

Unfortunately, these measurable improvements do not seem to be readily obtained through QFD. As indicated in Table 5, the distribution of projects across the four outcome categories outlined below does not statistically differ from a random assignment of projects across the categories.[2] 'Tactical' outcome categories include:

Table 5. QFD process success and failure summary[a]

Tactical success strategic category	Number of projects	Percent of total[b]	Number with benefits
Tactical success	7	27	7
No change	7	27	7
Mixed results	8	31	8
QFD failures	4	15	2
No information	9	–	5
Total	35		29

[a] This table presents success/failure results for the *process* of QFD. While all products generated by these projects were commercialized, this study does not measure or report on commercial success rates for the products in the marketplace.
[b] Percent of the 26 with known tactical outcomes.

- successful—QFD produced measurable project improvements;
- no change—projects exhibit no difference from expected performance;
- mixed—some performance aspects were worse, others improved;
- failed—the QFD process is abandoned or rejected.

QFD success. A project is 'successful' if it demonstrates improvement in *any* of the possible indicators of tactical success, without worsening any other facet. Increased product performance, quality levels or customer satisfaction indicate product improvement. Process improvements include decreased commercialization time or cost. QFD also may affect profits directly through changing the product in ways that increase sales volume or decrease product cost.[3] Just over a quarter of the projects were 'successful' by these definitions.

No change. About a quarter of the projects exhibited no measurable difference from expected product or development process performance. Each project, however, found that other benefits associated with QFD warranted its continued use in product development, even though expected project improvements were not realized.

Mixed performance. Mixed performance occurs when overall benefits outweigh penalties associated with worsened facets. For example, in one software development QFD lengthened the project's development time. However, the manager supported continued QFD use because he was convinced the process had forced the team to come to a more explicit and detailed understanding of customer needs and how they might best be translated into product features. The product met customer needs better and produced higher sales than the product the manager believes would have been developed using another development process. In mixed result cases, management chooses to continue using QFD or tries to modify it to eliminate performance problems. Nearly a third of the QFD projects produced mixed outcomes.

QFD process failure. No project in this data set had failed in the marketplace or due to technical difficulties at the time of analysis. Thus, indications of QFD's failure are process abandonment before project completion or design rejection by management. When QFD was abandoned, the team reverted back to a phase-review development process. Four (15%) of the projects failed by these definitions.

Because a development project may take five or six years to complete, some projects (nine of 35) cannot yet be categorized. All analyses are therefore based on the results from the project subsets from which data are available.

The good news: QFD produces significant intangible benefits

QFD seems to be a better tool for producing long-term development benefits than for obtaining short-term 'this project' improvements. In addition to short-term, tactical benefits, teams identified a number of benefits attributable to QFD that are not quantifiable in terms of improving specific project results. Benefits were identified from responses to two open-questions posed to project members and leaders: 'What did QFD do for this project?' and 'What benefits did using QFD produce?' Because respondents were not prompted, the benefits gathered and reported (Table 6) for these projects should be only the largest of the strategic effects for each project.

Table 6. Strategic benefit summary

	Number
Process benefits	
Make rational decisions	18
Improve information flow	16
Solidify design early	13
Meld team together	9
Non-specific value	
Would/did use QFD again	9
Produced a change	7
'Liked it'; saw value	3
Long-term corporate	
Captures knowledge	7
Forges cross-functional relationships	4

Intangible benefits, like better understanding customer needs and building cross-functional bridges, accrue very slightly in initial process applications and may produce little or no *measurable* impact on specific outcomes. In following projects those benefits may spread across the organization until they have instituted sweeping changes in the way product development is performed. In the long run these benefits may be more instrumental in advantageously changing the culture and environment for product development than the tactical project-related benefits. I call these the strategic benefits of implementing QFD because of their potential long-term impact on product development. With the exception of two QFD failures, all completed QFD applications provided strategic benefits to the development process (Table 5).

Almost two thirds of the strategic benefits cited by the groups related to product development *process* improvements that helped the team compete its task. Interestingly, team members for the projects with 'mixed' and 'no change from expected' outcomes cited more strategic benefits from QFD, and especially more process-related strategic benefits, than the 'successful' teams cited (Figure 4).[4] These teams consistently cited merit in the process changes brought by QFD even though they couldn't claim that QFD measurably improved product development. Perhaps the successful teams did not recognize as many strategic benefits because they were already focused on QFD's measurable benefits.

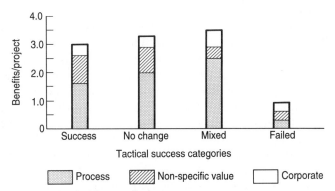

Figure 4. Strategic Benefits by Tactical Success Category.

What project characteristics contribute to success and failure?

Contributors to QFD success

As Table 5 indicates, only seven QFD applications (27%) improved upon expected outcomes. Table 7 illustrates that there are few discernible patterns between outcomes and project characteristics.

QFD improved product outcomes for two physical goods (10%) and five service projects (71%), resulting in increased performance levels (at the same product cost), higher sales or higher customer satisfaction. QFD also improved the development process by decreasing the time or cost to commercialization in only the two projects

Table 7. Summary of project characteristics

	Total number	Percent of 35	Number successful	Number failed	Number mixed	Number no changes
Inherent project complexity						
Complex system	7	20	1	2	2	2
Subsystem	14	40	3	2	3	2
Component	14	40	3	0	3	3
Project type						
Product	20	57	2	2	4	5
Service	7	20	5	1	1	0
Software	8	23	0	1	3	2
How much change in this development project						
Incremental	3	9	0	0	2	1
Major change	6	17	1	0	0	1
Next generation	8	23	6	1	0	0
Clean sheet	18	51	0	3	6	5

developing products. Service developers were unable to judge whether QFD helped or hindered their development process.[5]

Both successful product projects were for the least-complex 'component' category, QFD did not improve outcomes for any of the more complex-to-manage subsystem or complex system product-developing projects. The QFD success rate, even for the component projects, was low. Of nine component-type products in the sample for which results are available only two (22%) showed measurable improvements. These two projects are associated with two differentiating implementation characeristics (Table 8): they are the only component teams that undertook QFD with specific affective goals in mind and with high levels of team buy-in to using QFD from both the members and their managers.

QFD did not produce tactical improvements for only two service-developing projects in the sample. The only difference between these two projects and the five successful service projects is in the level of buy-in to QFD. Everybody was committed to using QFD in the successful projects. While the managers of the other two service projects were committed to using QFD, the groups developing the project were not.

Contributors to QFD failure

The four failed QFD projects had a number of similar context and implementation factors (see Tables 7 and 8) including:

- low team or management QFD commitment;
- attitude toward QFD as an expense, not an investment;
- low to moderate team familiarity;
- low levels of functional integration in the corporation;
- personnel movement primarily within function;
- high levels of planned product change.

Table 8. Summary of implementation characteristics

	Total number	Percent of 35	Number successful	Number failed	Number mixed	Number no changes
Who pushes QFD use						
Top-down	8	23	0	1	2	3
Bottom-up	10	29	4	1	1	1
Neutral other	17	49	3	2	5	3
Level of team buy-in or commitment						
High	10	29	7	0	0	2
Moderate	12	34	0	0	5	4
Low	13	37	0	4	3	1
Project orientation						
Process-oriented	20	57	1	2	5	5
Results-oriented	14	43	6	2	3	2
Corporate attitude to QFD						
Investment	21	60	7	0	7	3
Expense	14	40	0	4	1	4
Number of functions involved						
1 out of 4	2	6	1	0	1	0
2 out of 4	8	23	3	2	1	0
3 out of 4	15	43	1	2	5	5
4 out of 4	10	28	2	0	1	2
Team familiarity						
High	3	9	0	0	0	2
Moderate	14	40	5	2	4	2
Low	18	51	2	2	4	3

QFD was a failure in four of the five projects in this sample with all these characteristics. The two most important contributors to failure are the top two: four of the seven projects with low QFD commitment and for which QFD was treated like an expense were implementation failures. Obtaining high levels of team commitment and treating QFD as an investment in people and information seem crucially linked to preventing QFD failures.

Characteristics of mixed result projects

Overall, eight QFD projects ended up with mixed results. In each case, the worsened outcome was a slower time (compared with that expected from the 'traditional' process) to commercialization.

The eight teams with mixed results had several factors in common (Table 8). None of the eight was highly committed to QFD. Personnel on the teams were not highly familiar with each other nor had they worked together prior to this project. The level of cross-functional integration also was low in each of the companies with a mixed-result project and people were promoted predominantly within their own functional area.

That all the 'slow' teams had these common factors leads to speculation that perhaps the reason QFD lengthened these projects was because the unfamiliar members of the team first had to be built into an integrated group. Because the firms' functions were not well integrated, forging the cross-functional relationships needed to make QFD work took significant amounts of time. Five of the mixed-result teams (63%) specifically cited 'better, stronger teams' or 'improved cross-functional relationships' as a strategic benefit of using QFD, which seems to provide support for the above speculation.

A total of 14 projects in the sample have the characteristics that are common across the eight mixed-result projects. Of those 14, almost three quarters (ten) resulted in longer development time with QFD.[6] This research suggests that in companies where the functions are not well integrated, using QFD is quite risky and may take longer to complete than the traditional product development process, especially when team members and their managers are not highly committed to using QFD.

These analyses of the impact of project characteristics on QFD application success and failure lead to several hypotheses that future work should investigate further:

(1) Process-related improvements are more difficult to achieve than product-related improvements.
(2) QFD may benefit service developers more than product developers.
(3) Improvements are more difficult to achieve for more complex products than for simple ones.
(4) Improvements are more difficult to achieve for projects that seek radical product redesign or are developing a clean sheet product.
(5) Implementation characteristics may significantly affect project outcomes.

This last hypothesis will be examined next.

QFD implementation affects success

Throughout the analysis of the project-related characteristics, variables associated with how QFD was implemented seemed to affect whether or not the QFD application was successful at least as much as did the project variables. However, of all the implementation variables traced, only two cleanly differentiate between QFD successes and failures (Table 8). Firms always treated successful QFD projects like investments in people and information. They spent money and provided facilities for the groups to work as a team. Additionally, all involved management and team members of the successful projects were highly committed to using QFD as the development process. They attended and actively participated in meetings, completed any between-meeting assignments and worked toward breaking down cross-functional barriers.

Failed projects were always treated like expenses. Management was loath to spend money on additional market research, provide facilitators to smooth process implementation or even release personnel from their 'real' jobs to participate on QFD teams. Ultimately, only one functional subset of the development team was committed to using QFD in the failed projects. Champions cannot implement QFD by themselves for developing new products.

An additional implementation variable that seems necessary but not sufficient for project success is the goal orientation of the project. QFD is unlikely to produce measurable development improvements when undertaken as a 'demonstration' project to gain expertise with the method or when implementing the process is the goal of using QFD instead of the means to an end. Affective goals can take multiple forms, including 'faster to market', 'best product' and 'cheaper to produce'. Six of the seven successful QFD projects were undertaken to affect a specific change in some aspect of the product or development process. All five successful service projects used QFD affectively, to either drive service offerings based on customer needs (two) or change the service-providing operations (three). However, an affective goal did not ensure success. Two of the failed QFD projects had affective goals.

One can hypothesize that project goals contributed to QFD commitment. Perhaps buy-in to QFD was high in the successful projects because the team was targeting a goal they believed QFD would allow them to reach, but that they could not foresee reaching using any other means. The findings of this research suggest that to be successful, QFD projects should not only have specific goals the team wants to achieve, they also must be committed to the idea that QFD is the most appropriate means to achieve them.

When project members are the ones pushing for QFD, the effort is almost always at least partially successful. Dictating QFD's use from the top of the division or corporation seems to be associated with fewer cases of successful or partially successful implementation.

Table 9 summarizes the project and implementation characteristics associated with producing more and less successful applications of QFD. From the research it appears that these factors are not always independent; for example, stretch goals may lead to QFD buy-in. It also appears that higher probabilities of success with QFD are achieved by simultaneously attaining more of these favorable factors.

Table 9. Factors leading to QFD application success and failure

Factors increasing success	Factors leading to failure
Project characteristics	
Service projects	Apply to physical goods
Less complex projects	More complex projects
Incremental change	Clean sheet designs
Implementation characteristics	
Treat as an investment	Treat as an expense
High commitment to QFD	Single function champions QFD
Project members champion QFD use	Management dictates QFD use
Team members familiar to each other	Team members are strangers
QFD as a means to achieving an end	Using QFD is the goal
Goals that stretch capabilities	Goals attainable with current processes
High cross-functional integration	Isolated functional groups

Suggestions for improving product development processes in general

While analyzing the short-term QFD benefits leads to relationships between project and implementation characteristics and success and failure, analyzing the strategic benefits that teams attribute to QFD leads to identifying three characteristics of a product development process that may be superior to most currently used processes. Characteristics of an improved process include the ability to:

- structure decision-making processes across functional groups;
- build a solidly organized, highly motivated team;
- move information efficiently from its origin to the ultimate user.

These three generic characteristics were identified by the majority of teams as the major process improvements provided by QFD. Identifying these process characteristics is important because this research suggests that Japanese-originated QFD does not produce consistent *immediate* product development improvements in US applications. Given that Japanese firms are managed very differently than American firms and have vastly different organizational structures and corporate cultures (Abegglen and Stalk, 1985), it is not really surprising that QFD achieves somewhat different results in American firms than it does in Japan.

However, QFD did consistently improve some aspects of development for US firms. The improved process aspects US teams attribute to using QFD may be a desirable set of characteristics for any new product development process. US firms should then be able to construct product development processes that are more appropriate than QFD for the way they are managed, based on these desirable characteristics.

A process needs to structure thinking across functional areas. One process improvement identified is a method of structuring the development group's thinking across functional areas. QFD explicitly lays out decision steps across all functions simultaneously through a series of relational matrices, reducing or eliminating the previously sequential and functionally isolated nature of decision making. The assumptions supporting the decisions are clearly exposed to all participants. Anyone not agreeing with an assumption has the opportunity to contest it and understand how it was derived.

While QFD uses matrices to structure group thinking, other structuring tools could achieve the same purpose. Simple structuring tools include checklists and root cause diagrams. More sophisticated methods include Pugh concept analysis (King, 1987), Crawford's 'protocols' (Crawford, 1984), and stage-gate systems (Cooper, 1984). The important factors are to ensure that the right information is developed and that all the needed information is developed.

A process needs to meld people into a team. The QFD data suggests that an improved development process builds a solidly organized, highly motivated team. QFD melds the individual 'thought-worlds' (Dougherty, 1987) of the functional groups (e.g. marketing, engineering and manufacturing) into one joint thought-world encompassing all project facets by developing a common language, broadening functional understanding and introducing new ways to resolve disagreements.

In executing QFD, the project team develops their own language—a language all participants speak, which contains numerous project-specific connotations for otherwise ordinary words. Some teams even compile dictionaries of the special meanings they develop. As nomenclature develops, working relationships form between individuals participating in the process. Understanding grows about how other functions work, what task functions have traditionally been assigned in product development and how each function goes about completing their tasks.

Although QFD's language-building creates links between team members, conflicts between team members still arise because of the natural differences in their orientations (Lawrence and Lorsch, 1967). To maintain a team over time, these conflicts must be constructively resolved. QFD provides a mechanism for effectively resolving conflicts between people with different perspectives concerning a decision.

In QFD, setting priorities and making complex trade-offs results from straightforward calculations based on a rather large set of relatively simple assumptions. If team members find the results of the calculation unexpected or disagree with them, they can go back and check the assumptions. People stop arguing among themselves about which way the overall, difficult-to-analyze, trade-off should be made and together start scrutinizing specific assumptions that go into the analysis. QFD thus changes conflicts from interpersonal in nature (and inherently destructive) to fact-based (and more logically resolvable) by explicitly laying out decision assumptions in numerical terms.

A process to move information efficiently. The teams indicated that, as a process, QFD provided efficient ways to:

- explicitly define the information required to make good product development decisions;
- identify information sources;
- quickly obtain needed information;
- transmit information directly to the users without an intervening filter.

QFD uses team meetings to develop and directly diffuse a large amount of the information used in decision making verbally, on line and in real time, from sources to *all* potential users. Questions are asked and answered until all implications of the information are understood by the group. The group identifies and agrees on what information is required but currently unavailable. Individuals publicly commit to responsibility for sourcing the information. The group also agrees on assumptions about what it believes the obtained information is and uses those assumptions in the development until the information is available.

Use QFD—or build your own process? While QFD seems to exhibit the three general product development process improvements outlined above, some of QFD's inherent drawbacks may make it especially difficult for some US firms to implement effectively and secure substantial benefit. These drawbacks include an enormous up-front planning effort before the 'real work' of product design can begin, a need for market research data that are more detailed and direct from customers than obtained in the past and the active participation of all the functions of the organization in product development from project inception through commercial production. Resolving these problems will require many managements to change ingrained operating procedures (sequential functional involvement) and corporate cultures (fire, then aim; cross-functional barriers), very difficult tasks, before QFD's benefits can be obtained.

However, other processes providing these same benefits also can be imagined. Instead of choosing only between implementing QFD and a traditional sort of phase-review process, product development groups can use the above precepts to evaluate the strengths and weaknesses of other product development processes (for instance, stage-gate) or develop new product development processes attuned to the particular needs of their own firm, environment or product type.

CLOSING REMARKS ABOUT QFD'S APPARENT UTILITY

Project-related results across the 35 new product development projects in this sample suggest that QFD is not a short-term panacea. QFD does not consistently deliver the measurable development process improvements cited by Japanese users. Furthermore, the way QFD is implemented may greatly impact a firm's ability to see any measurable benefit at all from the process. When all team members in all functional areas and their mangers are committed to QFD as the means to achieve a specific affective goal, and when they and upper management treat the time, energy and money spent on implementing the process as an investment in the product and team, QFD may provide at least some of the tactical benefits touted by QFD proponents. QFD is a cross-functional investment in people and information. As with other corporate assets, expecting to recoup the investment over just one project may overestimate QFD's ability to affect new product development.

On the other hand, QFD may have the potential to drive long-term improvements in the way new products are developed in the United States. Over 82% (29 out of 35) of the projects believe that using QFD provided definite strategic product development benefits. The teams specifically identified three major development process improvements that the QFD process provided them over their previous development process.

However, judging from the number of unimproved QFD projects, guiding implementation is not easy. Implementation can be hampered by a lack of support from any one of the four functional areas involved in new product development or by granting inadequate time for going through the process, especially early in the development effort.

In companies with poorly integrated functional staffs, QFD may actually lengthen development time as personnel learn to work together. Indeed, before realizing any tactical benefits from QFD in one of these companies, it may be necessary to increase the company's level of cross-functional integration. Perhaps QFD could even be a useful change agent in moving the company toward higher levels of cross-functional integration.

In conclusion, QFD is probably one technique corporate managers who want to improve the way new product development is done would want to have available for development teams. However, managers promoting QFD use have a fine line to walk; they should make the technique available and support its use with time and money, but should not push it on teams without their consent and commitment. Managers also probably need to guide projects with little chance of using QFD successfully (clean sheet, complex, strictly process-oriented groups) away from QFD. QFD needs to be one technique in an arsenal of methods available to groups for developing new products.

ACKNOWLEDGEMENTS

Financial support for this research was provided by the Industrial Research Institute, the Marketing Science Institute, an American Fellowship of the American Association of

University Women and various of the companies studied in this research. I thank all nine participating companies for providing me with very open access to their QFD efforts. I also thank John Hauser, Harry Roberts, George Easton, Tom Hustad and two anonymous reviewers for their suggestions on improving this manuscript.

NOTES

1. Two additional characteristics are the number of customer groups from which market research information must be obtained, and whether the products are dependent (they become part of or work only in concert with another product or service) or not. *A priori*, one would expect dependent goods and multiple customer groups to increase the complexity of managing the product development.
2. I assume that a random distribution would produce an even distribution of projects across outcome categories. A chi-square test of the QFD outcome distribution does not detect a difference ($P > 0.1$) from an even distribution across outcome categories. This finding holds for the four outcome-category case as well as for the three outcome-category case (combine mixed plus failed categories into one grouping comprising all projects with any worsened performance aspects).
3. The real measure of interest is increased profits, but so many other variables intervene between process change and profit that decreased cost is the measure used to infer profit increase.
4. The incidence of strategic benefits differs across tactical outcome categories, but as with overall project outcomes the distribution does not differ significantly from an evenly distributed sample (chi-square test, $P > 0.1$).
5. That service developers may not be able to judge whether QFD helped or hindered their process is not unexpected. Very few service companies have more than an *ad hoc* system for developing new services. Thus, they have no basis against which to judge QFD's process capabilities.
6. Of the ten slower projects, two failed and were abandoned and eight were continued. The other four projects fell in the 'no change' category.

REFERENCES

Abegglen, J. C. and Stalk, G. Jr. (1985) *Kaisha: The Japanese Corporation*, New York, NY: Basic Books.

Booz, Allen and Hamilton (1982) *New Products Management for the 1980s*, privately published research report.

Clausing, D. (1986) *QFD Phase II: Parts Deployment*, American Suppliers Institute Publication.

Cooper, R. G. (1983) The New Product Process: An Empirically-Based Classification Scheme, *R&D Management*, **13**(1): 1–13,

Cooper, R. G. (1990) 'Stage-gate Systems: A New Tool for Managing New Products', *Business Horizons* (May–June): 44–54.

Crawford, C. M. (1984) 'Protocol: New Tool for Production Innovation', *Journal of Product Innovation Management*, **1**(2): 85–91.

Daetz, D. (1990) 'Planning for Customer Satisfaction with Quality Function Deployment', *Proceedings: Eighth International Conference of the ISQA*, Jerusalem, Israel, November.

Dougherty, D. (1987) '*New Products in Old Organizations: The Myth of the Better Mousetrap in Search of the Beaten Path*', Unpublished PhD. thesis MIT, June.

Eureka, W. E. (1987) 'Introduction to Quality Function Deployment. Section III', in *Quality Function Deployment: A Collection of Presentations and QFD Case Studies*, American Suppliers Institute Publication.

Glaser, B. G. and Strauss, A. L. (1967) *The Discovery of Grounded Theory*, Chicago, IL: Aldine Publishing, 1967.

Griffin, A. J. and Hauser, J. R. (1991)'The Voice of the Customer', University of Chicago Working Paper.

Gupta, A. K., Raj, S. P. and Wilemon, D. K. (1985) The R&D–Marketing Interface in High-Technology Firms. *Journal of Product Innovation Management*, **2**(1): 12–24.

Hauser, J. R. and Clausing, D. (1988) The House of Quality. *Harvard Business Review* (May–June): 63–73.

Hayes, R. H., Wheelwright, S. C. and Clark, K. B. (1988) *Dynamic Manufacturing*, New York, NY: The Free Press.

Kidder, L. H. (1981) *Sellitz, Wrightsman, and Cook's Research Methods in Social Relations*, New York, NY: Holt, Rinehart and Winston.

Kimzey, C. H. (1987) 'Summary of the Task Force Workshop on Industrial Base Initiatives', Office of the Assistant Secretary of Defense, Production and Logistics, Washington, DC, August 18.

King, R. (1987) *Better Designs in Half the Time: Implementing QFD in America*, Methuen, MA: GOAL/QPC.

Kogure, M. and Akao, Y. (1983) Quality Function Deployment and CWQC. *Quality Progress*, **16**(10): 25–29, October.

Lawrence, P. R. and Lorsch, J. W. (1967) *Organization and Environment*, Boston, MA: Harvard Business School Press.

Lorsch, J. W. and Lawrence, P. R. (1965) Organizing for Product Innovation. *Harvard Business Review* (January–February): 109–120.

McElroy, J. (1987) For Whom Are We Building Cars? *Automotive Industries* (June): 68–70.

Merton, R. K., Fiske, M. and Kendall, P. L. (1956) *The Focused Interview*, Glenco, IL: The Free Press.

Pessemier, E. A. (1986) *Product Management: Strategy and Organization*, Malabar, FL: Robert E. Krieger Publishing Company, Inc.

Page, A. L. (1991) *'PDMA's New Product Development Practices Survey: Performance and Best Practices'*, PDMA 15th Annual International Conference, Boston, MA, October 16.

Rosenthal, S. and March, A. (1991) *'Speed to Market: Disciplines for Product Design and Development'*, Boston University School of Management Manufacturing Roundtable Research Report.

Scott, B. R. (1985) US Competitiveness: Concepts, Performance and Implications. In: *US Competitiveness in the World Economy*. Scott, B. R. and Lodge, G. D. (eds.), Boston, MA: Harvard Business School Press.

Shapiro, B. P. (1987) 'The New Intimacy', Harvard Business School Note, ICCH #788010, October 1.

Souder, W. E. (1978) Effectiveness of Product Development Methods. *Industrial Marketing Management 7.*

Souder, W. E. (1988) Managing Relations Between R&D and Marketing in New Product Development Projects. *Journal of Product Innovation Management* **5**(1): 6–19.

Sullivan, L. P. (1987) The Power of Taguchi Methods. *Quality Progress*, **12**(6): 76–79 (June).

Sullivan, L. P. (1986) *QFD Benefits*, American Suppliers Institute Publication IC.

Sullivan, L. P. (1986) Quality Function Deployment. *Quality Progress*, **19**(6): 39–50 (June).

Takeuchi, H. and Nonake, I. (1986) The New Product Development Game. *Harvard Business Review* (January–February): 137–146.

Urban, Glenn L. and Hauswer, John R. (1980) *Design and Marketing of New Products*. Englewood Cliffs, NJ: Prentice-Hall, Inc.

Part IV

The Early Stages of the New Product Development Process

CONTENTS

Introduction to Part IV

Susan Hart

Thus far, readings have shown various representations of the new product process. The 'early stages' are defined here as idea generation, idea screening, concept development and concept testing, as they occur before a physical representation of the product has been developed. This is the point in the process where costs start to rise dramatically, as resources to developing (and re-developing) the physical product are needed. It is important, therefore, on the basis of cost alone, that the concept taken forward to development is close to what is finally required. It is far cheaper to change a concept than a physical product. The articles chosen for Part IV represent these various tasks of the early stages of new product development. The first article, by Griffin and Hauser (Reading 13), develops several of the themes introduced by Griffin's article at the end of Part III. It develops one issue in QFD, namely, how the 'voice of the customer', that is, customer needs and preferences, can be fed into the product development process, to educate the design, engineering, marketing and manufacturing elements of that process. The identification and privatization of needs can be seen as a fact of 'idea generation' and concept development, although in QFD, they are purposefully fed into later stages as well. The thrust of the article by Griffin and Hauser is the examination of how to identify and prioritize customer needs and wants *effectively*. They raise and answer questions regarding market research methodology, sample sizes, number of analysts required and statistical methods required to eliciting the 'voice of the customer'.

Throughout, the concepts of QFD are related and compared to other 'traditional' market research techniques, thereby avoiding the re-invention of the wheel. The article is a useful exposé of the first 'house' of quality, the voice of the customer.

Rochford's article (Reading 14) reports on the extent and nature of the usage of idea generation and screening techniques in six industrial firms. She found that there are two basic approaches to 'opportunity identification' (a term largely synonymous with idea generation, although some would argue that the latter is restricted to *actual* techniques for generating ideas from both within and outside the firm, such as brainstorming, synectics and so forth). The first is similar to the normative models whereby ideas are generated from identified market needs. The second emanates from fortunate technical discussion, line extensions and current product modifications. The article gives a good overview of the possibilities and practices for idea generalization and screening.

A very different approach is taken by von Hippel (Reading 15) in his article on ideas from customers. This article is now classic, presenting as it does, the 'customer active paradigm'. Von Hippel notes, from his research, that market research techniques such as perceptual mapping tend to be used by consumer goods companies, where the manufacturer is actively developing and testing new products to a largely passive, responsive market. In industrial markets, 'customers' tend to be far less passive and often actively seek new products to fit their needs. These two crestaliens are called the manufacturer-active paradigm (MAP) and the customer-advice paradigm (CAP). The two are compared and contrasted in this seminal work. The paper by de Brentani (Reading 16) is one of few to focus exclusively on screening. She analyses the issues used by companies to screen new product ideas and categorises these into 11 dimensions, four of which dominate: the financial potential of the idea; its synergy with various aspects of the overall company's operation; technological and production synergy; and the idea's product differential advantage. The research then goes on to examine the extent to which this general pattern changes in firms of different size and with different new product goals. As might be expected, the pattern does change somewhat, although the common decision criteria are far more important than those which might be specific to any one type of firm. The four document screening dimensions cover the key issues for managers involved in new product development, and it is to be expected that most companies might candidate their screening on these. Another issue to be kept in mind here is that when screening has taken place, there is relatively little information available upon which to make adjustments. It is therefore necessary to use broad indicators at this stage, until a clearer picture of the idea—in the form of a clearly articulated concept—evolves. The stage of concept testing benefits from a 'new product' concept which should contain some detail of the dimensions, materials, functions, price, appeal and comparative advantage of the product. This makes it easier to assess financially, both in the market, and as a manufacturable, deliverable item.

The last paper in this part, by Moore (Reading 17), gives insights into the different kinds of concept—tests that exist, and the extent to which they are used. In his article, however, the term 'concept' is used to cover 'idea' and the early paragraphs of the article refer to what has been termed 'idea generation and screening' by a majority of writers. This type of semantic difference is typical of what was referred to in the introduction to the reader. Under the section on 'concept generation', however, the detail of the content is synonymous with 'concept development' as used by other writers. This is the task of articulating fully the nature and appeal of the new proposed product, so that reaction to it might be guessed. Moore gives an interesting discussion of the purpose, methods, decisions and pitfalls of concept testing.

With the completion of the concept test, the 'early stages' of the new product process are complete. If, upon completion of the concept test, there is a positive reaction, the company will go on to perform a full business analysis, which, if acceptable, will be followed by product development, testing and launch. Such is the traditional linear view.

However, as the articles describing models have suggested, a linear view of the new product process is rather naive, and whilst it might be a convenient way to organize discussion of the process, the reality is that from the generation of an idea, through to the final product launch, the idea, the concept, the prototype and pre-production products undergo development, functional and market testing and redevelopment. This, in turn, means that evaluation, especially in relation to market potential, is the recurrent failure of new product development processes.

13

The Voice of the Customer

Abbie Griffin and John R. Hauser

INTRODUCTION

Many leading US firms are focusing on total quality management techniques. For example, in 1991, 106 firms applied for the Baldrige Award (the national quality award)—an application process that is tedious, costly and time-consuming but carries tremendous prestige for the winner. There were 180 000 requests in 1990 for copies of the Baldrige criteria (NIST, 1991; Reimann, 1991) and another 190 000 in 1991 (NIST, personal communication). This interest is based on the belief that quality improvements lead to greater profitability. For example, based on a study of the Baldrige finalists, the General Accounting Office (GAO, 1991; Stratton, 1991) suggests that those firms which adopt and implement total quality management tend to experience improved market share and profitability, increased customer satisfaction and improved employee relations.[1]

One aspect of the focus on total quality management has been the widespread adoption of quality function deployment (QFD). QFD is a product (service) development process based on interfunctional teams (marketing, manufacturing, engineering and R&D) who use a series of matrices, which look like 'houses', to deploy customer input throughout design, manufacturing, and service delivery. QFD was developed at Mitsubishi's Kobe shipyards in 1972 and adopted by Toyota in the late 1970s. In part, because of claims of 60% reductions in design costs and 40% reductions in design time (see Hauser and Clausing, 1988), it was brought to the US in 1986 for initial applications at Ford and Xerox. By 1989 approximately two dozen US firms had adopted QFD for some or all of their product and service development.[2] We estimate that in 1991 well over 100 firms use some form of QFD. (For those readers unfamiliar with QFD we provide a brief review in the next section of this paper.)

From the perspective of marketing science, QFD is interesting because it encourages other functions, besides marketing, to use, and in some cases perform, market research. Each of these functions brings their own uses and their own demands for data on the customer's 'voice'. For example, engineers require greater detail on customer needs than is provided by the typical marketing study. This detail is necessary to make specific tradeoffs in engineering design. For example, the auto engineer might want data on

Reprinted by permission of Abbie Griffin and John R. Hauser, 'The voice of the customer', *Marketing Science*, Vol. 12 No. 1, Winter 1993 customer needs to help him (her) place radio, heater, light and air-conditioning controls on the dashboard, steering column and/or console. However, too much detail can obscure strategic design decisions such as whether the new automobile should be designed for customers interested in sporty performance or for customers interested in a smooth, comfortable ride. Because QFD is an interfunctional process it requires market research that is useful for both strategic decisions (performance vs. comfort) and for operational decisions (placement of the cruise control).

To address both strategic and operational decisions, industry practice has evolved a form of customer input that has become known as the 'voice of the customer'. The voice of the customer is a hierarchical set of 'customer needs' where each need (or set of needs) has assigned to it a priority which indicates its importance to the customer. Developing products based on the voice of the customer becomes a key criterion in total quality management. The first key concept in the Baldrige Award criteria is that 'quality is based on the customer' (NIST, 1991, p. 2). See also Juran (1989).

This paper focuses on the customer input used for new-product development. We adopt industry terminology for the customer input and we work within the QFD framework. Marketing readers will notice a similarity between many of the QFD constructs and those that have long been used in marketing. One goal of our paper is to introduce the problems and challenges of QFD to the marketing audience. Another goal is to present new data on some of the techniques that are commonly used by industry.

Following the philosophy of total quality management, we focus on incremental improvement of the techniques for QFD's customer input. In most cases we draw from the rich history of research in marketing and focus on the changes and modifications that are necessary for QFD. We cite new data on comparisons that we have made. Naturally, we cannot compare all the possible techniques for any given step in the customer input. Instead, based on experience over the past four years with over 25 US corporations[3] and based on discussions with market research suppliers, we focus on those techniques that are applied most often within the QFD framework. Because comparative research provides incremental improvement, it is never completed. Based on the data presented in this paper we fully expect that other researchers will experiment with additional techniques and provide improvements relative to the techniques we report.

We begin with a review of QFD and the voice of the customer. We define customer needs and indicate briefly how they are tied to design goals and decisions. We then focus on each of three steps in the measurement and analysis of QFD's customer input: (1) identifying customer needs, (2) structuring customer needs and (3) setting priorities for customer needs. Because QFD's voice of the customer should help the product-development team understand how to satisfy the customer, we close with data on QFD's stated goal of customer satisfaction. We format our presentation within each section around those research questions that we have heard most often in applications (and for which we have data to address).

QUALITY FUNCTION DEPLOYMENT—A BRIEF REVIEW

Well-established research in the management of technology suggests that co-operation and communication among marketing, manufacturing, engineering, and R&D leads to greater new-product success and more profitable products.[4] QFD improves communication among these functions by linking the voice of the customer to engineering, manufacturing, and R&D decisions. It is similar in many ways to the new-product-development process in marketing (Pessemier, 1986; Shocker and Srinivasan, 1979; Urban and Hauser, 1992; Wind, 1982), the Lens model (Brunswick, 1952; Tybout and Hauser, 1981), and benefit structure analysis (Myers, 1976). Like these marketing processes QFD uses perceptions of customer needs as a lens by which to understand how product characteristics and service policies affect customer preference, satisfaction, and ultimately, sales. One advantage of QFD is that it uses a visual data-presentation format that both engineers and marketers find easy to use. This format provides a natural link among functions in the firm. Since its development in 1972, QFD has evolved continuously to meet the usage requirements of the product-development teams.

QFD uses four 'houses' to present data.[5] As show in Figure 1 the first house, the 'house of quality', links *customer needs* to *design attributes*. Design attributes are engineering measures of product performance. For example, a computer customer might state that he (she) needs something which makes it 'easy to read what I'm working on'. One solution to this need is to provide computer customers with monitors for viewing their work. Design attributes for the monitor might be physical measurement for the illumination of alphanumeric characters, for the focus of the characters, for the judged readability at 50 centimeters (on an eye-chart-like scale) etc.

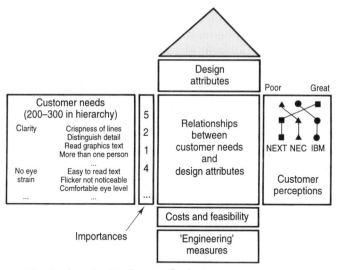

Figure 1. The House of Quality from Quality Function Deployment.

The second house of QFD links these design attributes to *actions* the firm can take. For example, a product-development team might act to change the product features of the monitor such as the number of pixels, the size of the screen, the intensity of the pixels, or the refresh rate. The third house of QFD links actions to *implementation* decisions such as manufacturing process operations, and the final house of QFD links the implementation (manufacturing process operations) to *production planning*.

The voice of the customer

Customer needs

QFD lists customer needs on the left side of the house. A customer need is a description, in the customer's own words, of the benefit to be fulfilled by the product or service. For example, when describing lines on a computer monitor a customer might want them 'to look like straight lines with no stair-step effect'. Note that the customer need is not a solution, say a particular type of monitor (VGA, Super VGA, XGA, Megapixel etc.), nor a physical measurement (number of noticeable breaks in the line), but rather a detailed description of how the customer wants images to appear on the monitor. The distinction has proven to be one of the keys to the success of QFD. If the product-development team focuses too early on solutions, they might miss creative opportunities. For example, a computer-monitor team might be tempted to focus on the size of the monitor (12″, 14″, 16″) to affect the size of the alphanumeric characters on the screen. However, the size of the alphanumeric characters is only one of the design attributes that affects the customer need of 'easy to read text'. The readability of a text string also depends on the ambient room light and reflections, the colors that the software designer chooses, the ratio of the height of small letters to that of capital letters, and even the style of the typeface (serif or sans-serif, proportional or fixed etc.). All of these design attributes interact with the size of the monitor to affect the customer need of 'easy to read text'. Some may be less costly and more effective, some may be synergistic with changing the monitor's size, but all should be considered before a final design is chosen for the monitor.

Discussions with customers usually identify 200–400 customer needs. These customer needs include basic needs (what a customer will tell you that he, she or they want a monitor to do) and exciting needs (those needs which, if they are fulfilled, would delight and surprise the customer).

Hierarchical structure

Not everyone on the product-development team works with the detail that is implied by a list of 200–400 customer needs. QFD structures the customer needs into a hierarchy of primary, secondary and tertiary needs.[6] Primary needs, also known as strategic needs, are the five-to-ten top-level needs that are used by the team to set the strategic direction for the product or service. For example, the primary needs help the product-development team decide whether to develop a computer viewing system that emphasizes clarity and resolution, ease of viewing, viewing interactiveness or visual impact.

Each primary need is elaborated into three-to-ten secondary needs. (Secondary needs are also known as tactical needs.) Secondary needs indicate more specifically what the team must do to satisfy the corresponding primary (strategic) need. For example, if clarity is the primary need, then the secondary needs tell the team how the customer judges clarity, say by the crispness of the lines, the ability to distinguish detail on all parts of the screen, the ability to read graphically generated text and the ability of the user to see what he (she) will get on hard copy. These tactical needs help the team focus their efforts on those more-detailed benefits that fulfill the strategic direction implied by the primary need. Typically, the 20–30 secondary needs are quite similar to the 20–30 'customer attributes' in marketing research that often underlie perceptual maps (see Green *et al.*, 1988; Lehmann, 1985; Urban and Hauser, 1992).

The tertiary needs, also known as operational needs, provide detail so that engineering and R&D can develop engineering solutions that satisfy the secondary needs. For example, a person may judge the crispness of a line (a secondary need) by the following tertiary needs: the lack of a stair-step effect, the ability to distinguish lines from background images and text, and the ability to distinguish among individual lines in a complex drawing.

Importances

Some customer needs have higher priorities for customers than do other needs. The QFD team uses these priorities to make decisions which balance the cost of fulfilling a customer need with the desirability (to the customer) of fulfilling that need. For example, the strategic decision on whether to provide improved clarity, improved ease of viewing, or some combination will depend upon the cost and feasibility of fulfilling those strategic needs and the importances of those needs to the customer. Because the importances apply to perceived customer needs rather than product features or engineering solutions, the importance measurement task is closer to marketing's 'expectancy value' tradition (e.g. Wilkie and Pessemier, 1973) than to the conjoint tradition (e.g. Green and Srinivasan, 1978); however recent hybrid techniques (Green, 1984; Green and Srinivasan, 1990; Wind *et al.*, 1989) have blurred that distinction.

Customer perceptions of performance

Customer perceptions are a formal market-research measurement of how customers perceive products that now compete in the market being studied. If no product yet exists, the perceptions indicate how customers now fulfill those needs. (For example, existing patterns of medical care served as generic competition for health maintenance organizations in a study by Hauser and Urban, 1977.) Knowledge of which products fulfill which needs best, how well those needs are fulfilled, and whether there are any gaps left between the best product and 'our' existing product provide further input into the product-development decisions being made by the QFD team.

Segmentation

In many firms, each product-development team focuses on one particular segment of the customer population. A complete 'voice' is obtained for each segment. In other firms, only the importances differ among segments. The issue of segmentation is an important research topic; however, for the purposes of this paper, we assume that the team has already decided to focus on a particular customer segment.

Engineering input

The team identifies those measurable aspects, called *design attributes*, of the product or service which, if modified, would affect customer's perceptions. Objective *engineering measures* of existing products (the team's and competitors') on the design attributes are obtained and displayed. The *relationship matrix* displays judgments (or experiments) indicating which design attributes affect which customer needs and by how much. The *'roof matrix'* specifies the engineering relationships among the design attributes. (For example, engineering realities might mean that increasing the illumination of the screen decreases the life of the screen material or the speed of screen refreshes.) Finally, most applications include rows in the matrix which summarize the *projected costs* and *technical difficulty* of changing a design attribute.

Using the house of quality

By collecting in one place information on both customer needs and engineering data on fulfilling those needs, the house of quality forces the interfunctional product-development team to come to a common understanding of the design issues. In theory, the goal of a house-of-quality analysis is to specify target values for each of the design attributes. However, different teams use the house in different ways. In some cases it is central to the design process and is used to make every decision, in others its primary function is communication, and in still others formal arithmetic operations provide formal targets for the design attributes. For example, some teams multiply the importances times gaps in customer perceptions (best competitor vs. our product) to get 'improvement indices'. Other teams multiply importances times the coefficients in the relationship matrix to get imputed importances for the design attributes. (For these operations we require strong scale properties of the measures.)

In closing this section, we note that QFD seems to work. In a study of 35 US projects Griffin (1992) reports that QFD provided short-term benefits (reduced cost, reduced time, increased customer satisfaction) in 27% of the cases and long-term benefits (better process or better project) in 83% of the cases. Griffin and Hauser (1992a) report that, in a head-to-head comparison with a traditional product-development process, QFD enhanced communication among team members. Collections of articles by Akao (1987) and the American Supplier Institute (1987) contain many case studies of successful applications.

IDENTIFYING CUSTOMER NEEDS

Identifying customer needs is primarily a qualitative research task. In a typical study between 10 and 30 customers are interviewed for approximately one hour in a one-on-one setting. For example, a customer might be asked to picture himself (herself) viewing work on a computer. As the customer describes his or her experience, the interviewer keeps probing, searching for better and more complete descriptions of viewing needs. In the interview the customer might be asked to voice needs relative to many real and hypothetical experiences. The interview ends when the interviewer feels that no new needs can be elicited from that customer. Interviewers might probe for higher-level (more strategic) needs or for detailed elaborations as in the laddering and means–ends techniques (Gutman, 1982; Reynolds and Gutman, 1988). Other potential techniques include benefit chains (Morgan, 1984), subproblem decomposition (Ruiz and Jain,

1991), Echo techniques (Barthol and Bridge, 1968; Barthol, 1976), and repertory grids (Kelly, 1955). While many applications use one-on-one interviews, each of these techniques can be used with focus groups (Calder, 1979) and with mini-groups of two-to-three customers.

The three questions which we have hard most often are:

(1) Do group synergies identify more customer needs?
(2) How many people (groups) must be interviewed?
(3) How many team members should analyze the data?

Groups vs. one-on-one interviews

Many market research firms advocate group interviews (se also Calder, 1979) based on the hypothesis that group synergies produce more and varied customer needs as each customer builds upon the ideas of the others. A concern about focus groups is that 'airtime' is shared among the group members. If there are eight people in a two-hour group then each person talks, on average, for about 15 minutes.

We compared focus groups to one-on-one interviews in a proprietary QFD application. The product category was a complex piece of office equipment. The QFD team obtained customer needs from eight two-hour focus groups and nine one-hour interviews. (The data were collected by an experienced, professional market research firm.) The entire set of data was analyzed by six professionals to produce a combined set of 230 customer needs. With our students (Silver and Thompson, 1991) we analyzed the data to determine, for each customer need and for each group or individual, if that group or individual voiced that need.

Figure 2 plots the data. On average, a single one-on-one interview identified 33% of the 230 needs and two one-on-one interviews identified 51% of the customer needs. The average is taken over all combinations of two interviews.

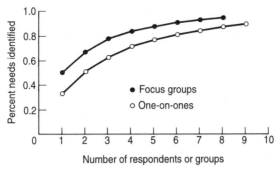

Figure 2. Focus Groups vs. One-on-One Interviews for Office Equipment (from Silver and Thompson, 1991).

The data in Figure 2 suggest that while a single two-hour focus group identifies more needs than a one-hour one-on-one interview, it appears that two one-on-one interviews are about as effective as one focus group (51% vs. 50%) and that four interviews are about as effective as two focus groups (72% vs. 67%). As one manager said when he examined the data, an hour of interviewing is an hour of interviewing independently of whether it comes from a one-on-one interview or a focus group.[7] If it is less expensive to interview two consumers for an hour each than to interview 6–8 customers in a central facility for two hours, then Figure 2 suggests that one-on-one interviews are more cost-efficient. At minimum, Figure 2 suggests that group synergies do not seem to be present in this data.

How many customers?

We would like to know how many customers need be interviewed to identify most of the customer needs. Besides intellectual curiosity, there are many reasons for industry to seek an answer to this question. First there is the monetary cost. While the field costs per interview are moderate, analysis costs are quite high. It is typical for some team members to observe each interview and for four or more team members to read each transcript. One major US firm estimates that the typical out-of-pocket costs for 30 interviews are only \$10–20 000 but that the implicit team costs include over 250 person-hours to observe the interviews, read the transcripts, and summarize the customer needs. Even based on a low estimate of \$100 per person-hour (fully-loaded) for professional personnel, this means that the total costs per interview are in the range of \$1000–2000. If you multiply this by 5–10 segments (typical in a complex category) and 5–10 major product lines within a firm, then the cost savings of setting a policy of 20 customers per segment rather than 30 customers per segment can be substantial (\$250 000–\$2 000 000).

Time delays accrue if too many interviews are used. Because the timely introduction of new products is important in today's competitive environment, product-development teams seek to avoid unnecessary delays in data collection. Some of these delays are market research time (recruiting and interviewing), but much of the delay is the time the team devotes to observing and analyzing the transcripts. There is a high opportunity cost for the teams' time.

On the other hand there are benefits to more interviews. The goal of total quality management and the philosophy of QFD is to base product development on customer needs. In one application, a service firm was able to gain an additional \$150 million in profit by reallocating operating procedures from fulfilling one customer need to fulfilling a different, more important customer need. When the product-development team defended their recommendation to top-level managers, the team was asked to certify that the initial list of needs was based on a sufficient number of customers to justify the decision.

Firms also want to be confident that they have interviewed enough customers to uncover most of the exciting needs. Exciting needs, if fulfilled, provide important competitive advantages. For example, Kao developed highly-concentrated laundry detergent, Attack, that fulfills the need of Japanese customers and retailers for a product that takes significantly less space to store. This product (and imitators) now command a significant fraction of Japanese sales.

Firms seek to balance the cost of additional interviews with the benefits of identifying a more complete set of needs. However, the cost (in person-hours) to analyze this tradeoff is quite high. A complete coding of transcripts to identify, for every interview and for every need, whether that customer voiced that customer need is tedious and time-consuming. We have found few product-development teams willing to undertake such analyses for a typical QFD project. However, because of the general interest in obtaining a 'ballpark' estimate of the number of customers required, we have obtained funding for two applications—the office equipment application described above and a low-cost durable application described below.

The data

We interviewed 30 potential customers of portable food-carrying and storing devices (coolers, picnic baskets, knapsacks, bike bags etc.). The interviews were transcribed and each interview was read by seven analysts. The needs were merged across analyst and customers and redundancy was eliminated to obtain a core list of 220 needs. We recorded which customers and which analysts identified each need. Naturally, some needs were mentioned by more than one customer (see Figure 3). For example, 38 needs were identified by one customer out of 30, 43 needs were identified by two customers out of 30, 29 needs by three customers out of 30 etc. One need was identified by 24 of the 30 customers.

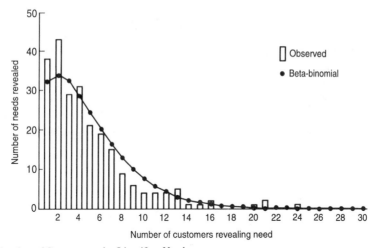

Figure 3. Number of Customers who Identify a Need.

To calculate how many needs we would have expected to obtain from interviewing fewer customers, we consider all possible orderings of the 30 customers and determine the average percent of nonredundant needs we would have obtained from n customers for $n = 1$ to 30. (Note that we are temporarily defining 100% as that obtained from 30 customers. We address missing needs below.) Because the number of possible orderings, 30!, is a very large number, we randomly sampled 70 000 orderings. The results, plotted in Figure 4 as 'observed', show that interviewing 20 customers identifies over 90% of the needs provided by 30 customers.

To generalize to more than 30 customers we need a model. We draw upon a model developed by Vorberg and Ulrich (1987, p. 19) and define for a given customer c, and a given customer need i, the probability p_i that customer c voices need i at least once

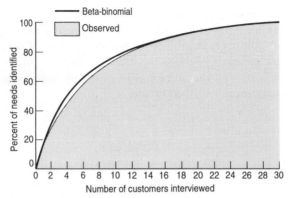

Figure 4. Percent of the Customer Needs Identified by N Customers (where 30 customers = 100%).

during the interview. In our data we observe the outcome of this binomial process. That is, we observe whether or not customer c voices customer need i. This model is related to Morrison's (1979) search model and to concepts developed by Dawkins (1991) and Efron and Thisted (1976).

For 30 customers we observe the outcome of 30 binomial processes. Thus, for 30 interviews we observe how many customers voiced need i. We simplify the model by assuming that customers are more or less equivalent in their ability to articulate needs. Then for each need i, we can consider our customers as 30 successive random draws from the same binomial distribution. We now assume that the probabilities p_i are described by a beta distribution across customer needs.[8] This assumption, combined with the binomial processes, gives a beta-binomial distribution for the number of times that needs are voiced in the 30 interviews. The best-fit beta-binomial distribution[9] is plotted in Figure 3. While not perfect it does appear to be a reasonable model.[10]

Analysis

We use the beta-binomial model in Figure 3 to estimate the average number of needs obtained from n customers. Consider need i with probability p_i. Because each customer is considered an independent draw, the probability that customer need i is identified in a sample of n customers is simply $1-(1-p_i)^n$. However, the probabilities p_i are distributed by the beta distribution. Thus, if the beta-binomial distribution[11] has parameters α and β, then the expected value E_n of the probability of observing a need from n customers is

$$E_n = 1 - \frac{\Gamma(n + \beta)\,\Gamma(\alpha + \beta)}{\Gamma(n + \alpha + \beta)\Gamma(\beta)}. \tag{1}$$

Figure 4 plots equation (1) for α and β estimated for our data. For comparison in Figure 4, we have normalized equation (1) to correspond to a percentage of the 30 customer needs. A Kolmogorov–Smirnov test for goodness of fit between the actual and modeled cumulative distributions indicates that they do not differ at a statistical significance level of 0.05. The analysis is slightly optimistic in the range of 2–12 customers, but fits quite well beyond 12 customers. Since most decisions will be made in the range above 12 customers, the model appears accurate enough for our purposes.

What are we missing?

While 30 customers produce 100% of our data, they may not produce 100% of the needs. We may have missed those needs which have a low p_i. Fortunately, equation (1) gives a means by which to estimate the magnitude of our error. That is, we estimate the number of needs that were given zero times out of 30 tries. The model estimates that our 30 customers gave us 89.8% of all the needs. The complete plot of E_n is given in Figure 5.

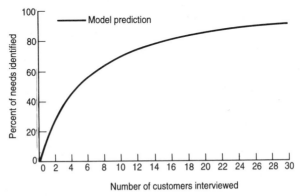

Figure 5. Predictions Based on the Beta-binomial Model.

Office equipment

The low-cost durable application was completed in 1988. In the past three years interviewing techniques have evolved so that interviewers are more effective in eliciting customer needs. For example, interviewers attempt to keep track of the customer needs voiced by the customers who have been interviewed already and focus their questions to probe for new customer needs. With the improved interviewing techniques, we expect that fewer customers need be interviewed. Indeed, in the 1991 analysis of office equipment (review Figure 2) the beta-binomial analysis ($\alpha = 1.88$, $\beta = 2.88$) suggests that the nine customers and eight focus groups identified 98% of the customer needs. Based on the transcript-hour equivalence discussed above, this means that 25 hours of interviews identified 98% of the office-equipment needs. However, we caution the reader that this difference may also be due to the difference in product categories. Hopefully, subsequent applications will supplement the data in Figures 2 and 3.

How many analysts?

While many applications assign 4–6 team members to read and analyze transcripts, other applications rely on qualitative expert(s) to read transcripts and identify needs. To test this strategy we asked seven 'analysts' to code the transcripts in the portable food-carrying device application. One was an experienced analyst of qualitative data, two were undergraduate students, and four were engineering development teams who would be using the customer needs in their development efforts. The students and teams, which split the transcripts among themselves, were provided with about 30 minutes of training in identifying customer needs. (This is typical of the amount of training given to corporate product-development team members who use these techniques to identify customer needs.)

On average, the analysts were able to identify 54% of the customer needs with a range of 45%–68% across analysts. The qualitative expert was at the low end of the range while the engineering teams were at the high end. The students were in the middle of the range. Figure 6 plots the average cumulative percent of attributes identified as more analysts read the transcripts (observed) compared to a beta-binomial ($\alpha = 22$, $\beta = 19$) model. Based on the model, we estimate that the seven analysts identified 99% of the customer needs obtainable from the transcripts.

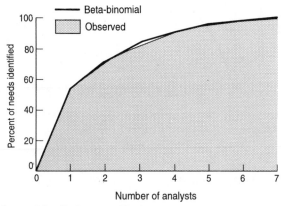

Figure 6. Ability of Analysts to Identify Customer Needs.

Besides the low-cost durable study, we have observed many multiple-analyst applications. Analysts with different backgrounds interpret customer statements differently. This variety of perspectives leads to a larger set of customer needs and a richer understanding of the customer than is feasible with a single expert. Sometimes readers who claim category expertise have preconceived notions which causes them to miss surprising or unexpected statements of needs.

If Figure 6 is representative of other categories more than one analyst should read the transcripts. The use of product-development team members brings the added value of team buy-in to the data and greater internalization of the 'voice' for later design work. Such ancillary benefits are lost if the team relies on outside experts to interpret the data.

Summary

Based on our data, we hypothesize that

(1) one-on-one interviews may be more cost-effective than focus groups,

(2) 20–30 interviews are necessary to get 90–95% of the customer needs;
(3) multiple analysts or team members should read and interpret the raw transcripts.

STRUCTURING CUSTOMER NEEDS

In this paper we compare the dominant structure-generating method, a group consensus process (affinity charts and tree diagrams), with a proposed customer-based structure-generating method, customer sorting and clustering.

Group consensus process

In most American and Japanese applications, customer needs are structured by group consensus using affinity charts (K–J diagrams[12]) and tree diagrams, two of the 'seven new tools' used in Japanese planning processes (King, 1987; Imai, 1986). This group consensus process uses the product-development team to impose structure on the customer needs. The advantage of a consensus process is that it assures group buy-in to the structure; the disadvantage is that there is no assurance that the team's structure represents how customers think about their needs or make decisions.

The process we used in our comparison is typical of both American and Japanese applications. To create the affinity chart each team member is given a roughly equal number of cards, each card bearing one customer need. One team member selects a card from his (her) pile, reads it aloud, and places it on the table (or wall). Other members add 'similar' cards to the pile with a discussion after each card. Sometimes the card is moved to a new pile; sometimes it stays. The process continues until the group has separated all the cards into some number of piles of similar cards, where each pile differs from the others in some way. The team then structures the cards in each pile into a hierarchical tree diagram with more-detailed needs at lower levels, and more-tactical and strategic needs at the upper levels. To select a higher-order need, say a secondary need, to represent a group of tertiary needs, the group can either select from among the tertiary needs or add a new card to summarize the group of relevant tertiary needs. Throughout the process the team can rearrange cards, start new piles or elaborate the hierarchy.

Customer sort and cluster process

Green et al. (1969), Rao and Katz (1971) and Green and McMennamin (1973) applied a technique known as subjective clustering in which subjects sort stimuli (e.g. television programs) or activities (e.g. sunbathing) into piles, a similarity matrix is calculated, and either a similarity map or a hierarchical cluster is derived. We modify that data collection procedure to apply to customer needs.

In a customer-sort process, customers are given a deck of cards, each bearing one customer need. They are asked to sort the cards into piles such that each pile represents similar needs and differs from the other piles in some way. The number of piles and the exact definition of similarity is left unspecified. After completing the sort, each respondent is asked to choose a single need from each pile, called an exemplar, which best represents the customer needs in the pile. From the sort data we create a co-occurrence matrix[13] in which the i–jth element of the matrix is the number of respondents who placed need i in the same pile as need j. We also label each need with the number of times it was chosen as an exemplar.

To develop a structured hierarchy we cluster[14] the co-occurrence matrix. To name the clusters we use the exemplars. When there is no clearly dominant exemplar within a cluster, we either choose from among the exemplars in the cluster or add a label to the data.

The use of exemplars rather than labels is an attempt by the product-development teams to maintain as close a link as possible to the actual words used by customers. For example, one might label a group of statements about computer viewing devices as 'appropriate ergonomics', but this may be misleading if the customer really said 'everything is blurred after a day using my computer'. The 'blurred-vision' statement provides the product-development team with more realistic clues about product use which the sanitized label does not.

The data

The group-consensus chart for portable food-carrying devices was constructed by a team of engineering managers, chosen from M.I.T.'s Management of Technology Program. The team had studied the product category, had read all of the interview transcripts, and had reviewed the list of customer needs. The team was lead by Abbie Griffin, who had observed and/or participated in almost 20 industry applications of group-consensus charts at that time. Sixty M.I.T. graduate students who use food-carrying devices participated in the customer sort. Because we funded this data collection ourselves, we report the actual customer needs.

In addition we compared group-consensus charts and customer-sort hierarchies for a major consumer good with almost 200 customer needs. Two group-consensus charts were developed: one by a team at the consumer-products company who had worked on the product category, and another by a team of graduate students from M.I.T.'s engineering school. The customer-sort hierarchy was based on a sample of 60 consumers chosen randomly from active users of the product category. Because the data are proprietary, we report summary statistics and our qualitative impressions only.

Finally, we report on a computer-product application in which a team-based consensus chart was compared to a customer-based consensus chart, and we report the qualitative experience of approximately 20 proprietary applications of the customer-sort methodology.

Food-carrying device structures

Table 1 compares the top levels of the group-consensus chart and customer-sort hierarchies for food-carrying devices. (The complete hierarchies are available in Griffin, 1989.) Consider first the number of secondary and tertiary needs and the number of exemplars within each primary grouping. The customer-sort technique provides a more even distribution. While an even distribution is no guarantee that a hierarchy is better, an even distribution is one of the desirable features for which product-development teams look. An even distribution makes it easier to assign responsibilities. Notice also that 27 labels were added to the group-consensus chart by the development team (247 total needs) while only ten labels were added to the customer-sort hierarchy (230 total needs). This means that more of the customers' semantics are used directly in the primary and secondary levels of the customer-sort hierarchy.

The more interesting comparison is based on qualitative impressions. (Primary labels are shown in Table 1.) We have shown these hierarchies to a number of people including the team that created the consensus chart and executives at firms which use the voice of the customer in their product-development processes. In all cases, including the team that did the consensus chart, judgments were that the customer-sort hierarchy provided a clearer, more-believable, easier-to-work-with representation of customer perceptions than the group-consensus charts. Only one of the five group-consensus primary groupings is specific to the category (not generic), while four of the seven customer-sort groupings are specific to the category. The qualitative reaction seems to be summarized by: 'The group-consensus chart is a good systems-engineering description of the problem while the customer-sort hierarchy is really the customer's voice'.

To compare the hierarchies formally we report two statistical measures of structure similarity, Kruskal's λ (Goodman and Kruskal, 1954) and an information theoretic measure, U^2 (Hauser, 1978). For the primary needs we calculate $\lambda = 0.28$ and $U^2 = 0.30$ and for the secondary needs we calculate $\lambda = 0.51$ and $U^2 = 0.63$. The group-consensus chart agrees more with the customer-sort at the tactical (secondary) level than at the strategic (primary) level.

Consumer-product structures

Qualitatively, the customer-sort hierarchy seems to be superior to the group-consensus chart for food-carrying devices. We sought to replicate this comparison for another category. In this category we were fortunate that an experienced product-development group at a world-class new product organization developed a group-consensus chart and then tested it with a customer-sort analysis of 198 customer needs. While similar in most aspects to the above comparison, this comparison differs because (1) the group-consensus chart was developed by category experts, and (2) the products in the category are less complex and more familiar to consumers than food-carrying devices. To separate these effects, we had 'nonexpert' engineering students develop a second group-consensus chart.

As before, the distribution of tertiary needs is more uniform for the customer-sort hierarchy than for the product-development team consensus chart. Furthermore, the product-development-team consensus chart contained 20 labels that were not in the customer-sort chart. (The student team added 14 labels.) In retrospect some of these labels obscured the true customer voice. Statistical analysis suggested that there was more agreement between group-consensus charts and customer-sort hierarchies for the consumer product than for the food-carrying device. We hypothesize that this is due to the less complex nature of the consumer product. It is not totally attributable to the expertise of the professional product-development team because the student team did almost as well as the professional team in their agreement with the customer-sort.

Table 1. Comparing group-consensus and customer-sort food-carrying-device hierarchies

	Affinity chart				Customer-sort		
Primary need	Secd. needs	Tert. needs	Exemplars	Primary need	Secd. needs	Tert. needs	Exemplars
Price	4	0	3	Attractiveness	4	20	9
Container utility	2	14	2	Carries many things	2	23	2
Phys. characteristics	10	30	10	Maintains temps.	2	29	6
Thermal attributes	4	34	6	Right size	3	29	6
Convenience	5	139	21	Easy to move	2	30	4
				Convenience	4	31	9
				Works as container	5	39	6
Total	25	217	42		22	201	42
Coeff. of variation	0.6	1.4	0.9		0.4	0.2	0.4

The most compelling evidence of the customer-sort method's utility is its face validity. The product-development team felt that the customer-sort hierarchy was a better representation of consumer perceptions than either group-consensus chart. After looking at all three structures, the product-development team concluded that the in-house structure reflected the way the firm *developed* the product (technology by technology). The customer-sort structure, on the other hand, reflected the way customers *use* the product (function by function). The product-development team chose to use the customer-sort hierarchy for product-development and segmentation activities (with some minor modifications).

Other applications

In a computer product application with 469 customer needs, we compared team-based and customer-based consensus charts. The team sorted the needs into 14 primary and 57 secondary groups while the customers sorted the needs into 11 primary and 50 secondary groups. The coefficients of variation were comparable, 0.6 for the team and 0.5 for the customers, but the team added more labels (50% vs. 18% of the primary needs were labels). Qualitatively, the team consensus chart structured the needs to reflect an engineering view while the customers sorted the needs to reflect product use. After seeing the customer-consensus chart, the team accepted it as a better structural representation. The resulting change in organizational emphasis led to a number of fundamental changes in product development.

The customer-sort hierarchies have been applied over 20 times by one supplier.[15] That supplier reports that in every application the product-development team accepted the customer-sort data as a better representation of the customer's voice and that, in some cases, the customer-sort structure changed dramatically the philosophy of the product-development effort. See also Cooper (1992), Roberts (1992), Ross (1992) and Yie (1992).

Team buy-in

One argument that has been advanced in favor of the team-based consensus charts is that they result in greater team buy-in to the hierarchical structure. Recent applications of customer-sort and customer-consensus structures have addressed this issue by having the team complete the customers' task in parallel with the customers. As the team sorts the cards they begin to ask themselves: 'I sort the cards like this, but how would the customer sort the cards?' Indeed, while the customer instructions state that there is no right or wrong answer, the team begins to realize that for them there is a right answer— how the customer sorts the cards.

In the end, the QFD philosophy of focusing on the customer and the scientific evidence that products are more successful if marketing input is understood by engineering and R&D, both suggest that the customer's perspective on the structure of customer needs should be given serious consideration. Note also that while we focus on the customer hierarchy for the customer's voice, the design attributes (engineering inputs to the house of quality) can be (and often are) structured as the product is built. The relationship matrix (Figure 1) provides the necessary link.

Summary

While the customer-sort analyses have not enjoyed the popularity of group-consensus charts, we feel that they deserve serious consideration for developing the hierarchical structure of customer needs that is used in QFD.

MEASURING OR ESTIMATING IMPORTANCES

The next step in QFD's voice of the customer is to establish priorities for the customer needs in the form of importance weights. These priorities aid in allocating engineering resources and guide the team when it is forced to make tradeoffs among needs. For example, if a product-development team increases the thickness of the insulation in a food-carrying device, then they are likely to improve satisfaction relative to the primary need of *maintains food temperatures* while degrading *carries many things*. Naturally, we prefer engineering strategies that stretch the frontier and improve satisfaction relative to both primary needs (such as changing the insulating material to obtain more insulating power per inch), but at times tradeoffs must be made and priorities set.

In the interest of brevity we resist reviewing the academic literature[16] which is rich in the study of obtaining importances for *attitude*, *preference* or *utility*. (However, this literature has not addressed explicitly the challenges of obtaining importances for large numbers (200–400) of customer needs.[17])

In this section we focus on importances within the QFD framework of primary, secondary and tertiary needs. We report some new data collected within the QFD framework that attempts to address four questions that we have heard from industry.

(1) Do survey measures of importances have any relation to customer preferences among products designed based on customer needs?
(2) What is the best survey measure?
(3) Can we avoid data collection for importances by using frequency of mention in the qualitative research as a surrogate for importance?
(4) Are revealed techniques (with satisfaction as the dependent measure) superior to survey measures?

Do customers prefer product concepts that emphasize the fulfillment of 'important' customer needs?

The data

This analysis is based on data collected by an unnamed consumer products firm. The consumer-products firm measured or estimated customer's importances for 198 customer needs using three different methods:[18]

(1) Nine-point *direct-rating scale* in which customers answered for each need, 'How important is it or would it be if . . . ?'.
(2) *Constant-sum scale* in which customers allocated 100 points among the seven primary needs, then allocated 100 points to each set of secondary needs within each primary-

need group, and finally allocated 100 points among each set of tertiary needs within each secondary-need group.

(3) *Anchored scale* in which customers allocated 10 points to the most important primary need and up to 10 points to the other six primary needs. Similarly up to 10 points were allocated to secondary needs corresponding to each primary need and to tertiary needs corresponding to each secondary need.

Questionnaires were mailed to 5600 randomly selected consumers (1400 for each method plus 1400 who rated products on the customer needs). Response rates were very good (75–78%). (All recipients of the questionnaires were given a $5 incentive. Those that responded in a week were entered in a lottery for $100.) In addition, the constant-sum questionnaire was mailed to an additional 1400 consumers from a national panel. The response rate for that sample was 90%. The rank-order correlation of the importances as measured by the random sample and the panel sample was 0.995.

Customer reactions to product concepts

To test whether the importances made sense for setting priorities among product-development programs, the professional product-development team in the consumer-products company created seven product concepts. Each concept was created to emphasize one of the primary customer needs while stressing that the other six customer needs would not be any better or worse than existing products. The concepts went through two pretests with actual consumers and were modified until the firm felt that they did indeed 'stretch' the consumer needs. (The actual concept statements are proprietary.) Consumers were asked to evaluate the concepts by expressing their interest in (nine-point scale) and preference for (rank order) the concepts. Table 2 indicates that consumers' interest and preference is highly correlated with the self-stated measures of primary needs.

Table 2. Rank correlations between concept evaluations and importances

		Importances		
		Direct	Anchored	Co.-sum
Concept evaluations	{ Interest	0.89	0.93	0.93
	{ Preference	0.96	0.96	0.96

Which survey measure is best?

The direct, anchored and constant-sum measures give similar rank-order results (Table 3) and each correlates with interest and preference (Table 2).[19] We have also completed comparisons for two other product categories, the portable food-carrying device described earlier (Griffin, 1989) and a proprietary application to a high-cost durable product.[20] In both cases there was agreement between the survey measures of importance. Qualitatively we prefer the anchored scale,[21] but the scientific data to date suggest that any of the three scales could be used to measure importances.

Table 3. Correlations between ranks of mean importances

	Direct	Anchored
Primary needs		
Anchored	0.96	
Constant-sum	0.96	1.00
Secondary needs		
Anchored	0.78	
Constant-sum	0.67	0.94
Tertiary needs		
Anchored	0.84	
Constant-sum	0.71	0.89

We asked the product-development team at the consumer product company to judge the face validity of the importance measures. They felt that the measured importances (direct, anchored and constant-sum) corresponded to their beliefs about the category—beliefs based on experience and a large number of other market studies. They felt that the simpler self-explicated measures provided sufficiently accurate importance measures for the QFD process and used them to select customer needs upon which to focus. See Hauser (1991) for details.

Is frequency of mention a surrogate for importance?

It is a reasonable hypothesis that customers will mention most those needs that are most important. If this were true, then we could save time and money by using frequency of mention as a surrogate for importance. To test this hypothesis we measured, with a nine-point direct scale, importances for the primary, secondary, and tertiary customer needs identified for the portable food-carrying device. We then reanalyzed data as described in Figures 3, 4 and 5, but for only the most important needs. The results are plotted in Figure 7, where for comparison, we have normalized the data so that 30 customers equals 100%. Figure 7 suggests that important needs are no more likely to be mentioned by a customer than needs in general. (The distributions do not differ at the 0.05 level by a Kolmogorov–Smirnov goodness-of-fit test.) Regrettably, frequency of mention does not appear to be a good surrogate for importance.

Are revealed techniques (based on satisfaction) superior to survey measures?

Econometricians advocate revealed preference measures where the importance weights of attributes are derived statistically (Manski and McFadden, 1981; Ben-Akiva and Lerman, 1985). For the consumer good we measured customer's perceptions of their chosen product with respect to the primary needs and regressed those perceptions on customer's satisfaction with that product. Regrettably, the revealed importances did not correlate with either preference for or interest in the concepts (−0.36 with interest, −0.14 with preference). This poor predictive ability may be due to the collinearity

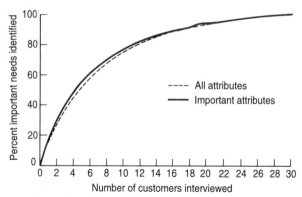

Figure 7. Important Needs vs. Total Needs (from Griffin and Hauser, 1991b).

among primary needs (71% of the correlations are above 0.20). Also, as argued in the next section, monadic satisfaction may be a poor dependent measure.

We have also attempted to estimate revealed importances for a high-cost durable product, for the portable food-carrying devices (Griffin, 1989), and for the secondary needs of the consumer product. In all cases collinearity was severe. It was not uncommon that less than 20% of the importances were 'revealed' to be significant and several had negative signs. In none of the applications did the revealed estimates have high face validity. While we cannot rule out revealed satisfaction techniques for the large numbers of customer needs in QFD, we do feel that collinearity poses formidable barriers to such estimation.

Summary

Based on the data examined to date we feel that survey measures of importance can predict how customers will react to product concepts. However, we have not yet identified a single 'best' measure. On the other hand, frequency of mention does not appear to be a good surrogate for importance and revealed techniques suffer from collinearity in customer perceptions.

CUSTOMER SATISFACTION AS A GOAL

Industry accepts customer satisfaction as the goal of QFD because its advocates believe that, in the long-run, satisfied customers are an asset of the firm. Future short-run strategies can be adjusted to draw profitably on this asset.

Self-selection bias

Given the academic interest in revealed importances, the poor showing of the revealed technique is sobering. While this may be due entirely to collinearity among customer perceptions, we (and the consumer-product firm) suspected that there was something more fundamental about the measure of satisfaction. For example, the firm's leading brand had been number one in the category for over 20 years, but its average satisfaction score was below that of many other brands. The brand with the highest satisfaction score was a small niche brand. (This phenomenon was also identified in Swedish data. See Fornell, 1991.)

Recall that the satisfaction measure asks customers to rate the brand they have chosen. We call such a measure a monadic measure. At minimum this measure contains a self-selection bias—presumably customers prefer most (price and promotion considered) the brand they chose. Indeed, a niche brand may satisfy only a few customers, but it may satisfy them quite well. On the other hand, a market-share leader might satisfy its customers more than other brands, but, because its customers are diverse, its satisfaction score (for leading-brand customers) might be lower than the niche brand's score (for niche-brand customers). Thus, while satisfaction is a different construct than market share, a low correlation between measured satisfaction and market share would suggest the presence of such a self-selection bias.

One initial test of this hypothesis is presented in Table 4. This table compares rank-order primary-brand share with monadic satisfaction and with relative satisfaction from ongoing tracking data at the consumer-products company.[22] For the ten brands for which data from both studies is available, monadic satisfaction did not correlate with primary-brand share. However, the relative satisfaction measure did correlate with primary-brand share. The correlation was marginal (0.15 level) among consumers who have used the brand in the last three months, but highly significant (0.01 level) among consumers who have heard of the brand.

Table 4 highlights the dilemma in choosing an appropriate satisfaction measure. When evaluating a product programme we prefer to base satisfaction on customers who have used the brand and, perhaps, not include those who have only heard of the brand. However, the used-brand sample is subject to the same criticism as the monadic satisfaction measure—it confounds people and products (albeit to a lesser degree). The used-brand sample includes only people who have evaluated a brand and who, at least once, believed that it would meet their needs. The heard-of-brand sample includes more consumers including many who have evaluated the brand and rejected it. It should not surprise us that the latter measure is more like a market-share measure.

Table 4. Comparison of monadic satisfaction, relative satisfaction and primary-brand share

Brand	Primary-brand share	Monadic satisfaction measure	Relative satisfaction (brand user)	Relative satisfaction (heard of brand)
Q	1	6	1	1
R	2	3	5	3
S	3	8	4	2
T	4	2	8	6
U	5	9	7	7
V	6	1	9	5
W	7	4	3	8
X	8	7	2	4
Y	9	10	6	9
Z	10	5	10	10
Rank correlation		0.20	0.39	0.83
t-statistic		0.58	1.21	4.21

The self-selection bias with respect to the commonly-used satisfaction measure is extremely important to designed-in-quality programmes. Many American corporations are using measures of customer satisfaction as part of employee rewards and bonuses. For example, GTE and Montgomery Ward both tie management compensation to customer-satisfaction and quality measurements (Phillips *et al.*, 1990). If our hypothesis about the satisfaction measure holds up, then there is a real danger that these corporate programmes based on monadic satisfaction may be sending the wrong signals to product design. For example, suppose that a product-development group is rewarded only on monadic satisfaction. Then they might choose to design a product that gets extremely high satisfaction scores from a small niche of the target customers. They might avoid designs that capture a large market share of diverse customers. On the other hand, a relative measure of satisfaction would give better incentives. The niche product might satisfy its niche, but not the large set of diverse customers.

Implications for technique comparisons

Self-selection bias also has implications for academic research comparing different measures and estimates of importance weights.[23] Many of the comparisons in the literature (including some that we have published) are based on the correlation of a 'preference index' with measured preference. When the preference, attitude or utility measure is monadic, such correlations may confound the self-selection bias with differences in the predictive ability of the importances.

Summary

Our data caution firms that monadic measures of satisfaction lead to counterproductive incentives when evaluating products and product programmes. Furthermore self-selection biases (and/or collinearity) can give misleading results when evaluating alternative measures of importance.

APPLICATIONS[24]

The development of Puritan-Bennett's Renaissance™ Spirometry System is typical of voice-of-the-customer applications. (A spirometer is a medical instrument that measures lung capacity—an important indicator of general health.) Puritan-Bennett's (PB's) PB900A was a major player in the market but in 1989 its share slipped from 15% to 7% as a result of a new product by Welch Allyn (WA). WAs PneumoCheck was introduced at a dramatically lower price ($1995 vs. $4500 for WA) made possible by a reduced functionality—the PneumoCheck measured a person's ability to exhale while the PB900A measured both exhaling and inhaling. PB considered a cost-reduction programme but felt that the basic design of PB900A would make it impossible to come close to the WA price. Instead, they started the design from scratch based on QFD and the voice of the customer.

An interfunctional team drawn from marketing, customer service, sales, engineering,

R&D, manufacturing and management began with qualitative interviews and focus groups with their customers to identify the customer needs. Following procedures discussed in this paper, PB structured the customer needs into a hierarchy, measured importances and measured customer perceptions of both PB and competitive products. For example, the secondary needs are shown in Table 5.

Table 5. Customer needs for spirometry

• Produce is affordable	• Easy to hold
• Easy to operate	• Right size for patient
• Easy to clean	• Easy to set up first time
• Convenient-sized output	• Easy to calibrate
• Sanitary	• Availability machine/supplies
• Quick service response	• Good training/education
• Provides accurate readings	• Sleek appearance
• Eliminates technician variability	• Good printer quality
• Good printout quality	• Low cost of repairs/service
• Reliability	• Portability
• Diagnostic information meets needs	• Effective data storage/retrieval
• Easy-to-interpret diagnostic information	• Environmentally safe
• Fast to use	

By focusing development on these needs, within a year they designed an entirely new modular spirometry system that could be customized by each user segment (hospitals, large laboratories, small clinics and general practitioners). For example, 'affordability' was achieved with the modular prices, 'good printout quality' by using the customers' existing printers rather than the traditional approach of a built-in thermal printer, 'effective data storage and retrieval' by plug-in patient data cards, 'easy to hold' by a detachable, rechargeable unit that makes and stores measurements without the base station etc. Each customer need was met at a level that matched or exceeded competition. An occasional-screening system was priced $405 below WA, but heavy users could increase functionality and productivity with a system of three spirometers, two base stations, two charging stations, two memory cards, and a Canon Bubblejet™ printer at a cost of $4088.

DISCUSSION AND SUMMARY

Quality function deployment (QFD), which promises decreased product-development costs, decreased product-development time, and improved customer satisfaction, has been adopted widely by US and Japanese product-development teams. QFD begins with the voice of the customer—a prioritized list of 200–400 customer needs in a hierarchical tree of primary strategic needs, secondary tactical needs and tertiary operational needs.

Our data suggest interviews with 20–30 customers should identify 90% or more of the customer needs in a relatively homogeneous customer segment. Both one-on-one experiential interviews and focus groups seem to be effective at identifying needs, but the group synergies expected from focus groups do not seem to be present. Multiple analysts (4–6) should analyze the transcripts.

While group-consensus charts are the most popular method for obtaining a hierarchical structure, our data suggest that different structures are obtained by analyzing customer-sort data. The customer-sort hierarchies seem to group the needs to reflect how the customer uses the product, while team-consensus charts group the needs to reflect how the firm builds the product.

Our comparison of importance-measurement techniques suggest that if product concepts are created based on measured importances, then customers prefer and are interested in those products which stress important customer needs. However, for our data, estimated importances (regressing perceptions on satisfaction) do not seem to correlate with preference or interest. We suspect that this is due to the collinearity in the data (inherent in QFD) and/or the self-selection bias of the dependent measure, monadic satisfaction. Regrettably, frequency of mention does not appear to be a surrogate for importance.

The stated goal of QFD is customer satisfaction. Our data suggest that a self-selection bias might be present in standard customer-satisfaction data collected by corporations. This bias could give counter-productive incentives encouraging firms to retreat to small segments of easy-to-satisfy customers, or to (inadvertently) implement policies that increase average satisfaction by getting rid of dissatisfied customers.

Many challenges remain. Perhaps other techniques will prove superior to those that we studied. While data on two applications suggest that 20–30 customers per segment are sufficient, we do not know how this varies with the characteristics of product categories. Satisfaction measurement is a complex issue. We have only indicated one potential bias. In these and in many other ways we hope that other researchers build upon the data presented in this paper.

We have also seen research problems in industry. For example, industry is concerned with balancing the expense of multiple voice-of-the-customer studies, for each segment and for each product category, with the opportunity cost of doing a common voice-of-the-customer which has the same structure and mostly the same customer needs, but different importances for different segments. Fulfilling exciting customer needs leads to breakthrough products. Perhaps leading-edge user studies (von Hippel, 1986) can be developed to identify these exciting needs.

ACKNOWLEDGEMENTS

Funds for the research in the paper were provided by M.I.T.'s programme for the Management of Technology, Kirin Brewing Company, the Marketing Science Institute, the Industrial Research Institute, an anonymous office-equipment manufacturer and an anonymous consumer-products company. Abbie Griffin was partially supported by an AAUW American Fellowship.

NOTES

1. If only those firms that do well on these criteria can be expected to apply, then these data may contain some self-selection bias.

2. Among the US and Japanese firms reporting QFD applications in 1989 were General Motors, Ford, Navistar, Toyota, Mazda, Mitsubishi, Procter & Gamble, Colgate, Campbell's Soup, Gillette, IBM, Xerox, Digital Equipment Corp., Hewlett-Packard, Kodak, Texas Instruments, Hancock Insurance, Fidelity Trust, Cummins Engine, Budd Co., Cirtek, Yasakawa Electric Industries, Matsushita Densko, Komatsu Cast Engineering, Fubota Electronics, Shin-Nippon Steel, Nippon Zeon and Shimizu Construction.

3. These applications include computers (main-frame, mid-range, work stations and personal), software, printers, cameras, airline service, paints, surgical instruments, diagnostic instruments, office equipment, consumer products, portrait services, tools, retirement plans, movie theaters, health insurance, financial services, telephone service, gas and electrical service, distribution networks, automobiles and automobile subsystems and components.

4. See Cooper (1983, 1984a, b), Cooper and de Brenani (1991), Cooper and Kleinschmidt (1986), Dougherty (1987), de Brentani (1989), Griffin and Hauser (1992b), Gupta et al. (1985), Hise et al. (1990), Moenaert and Souder (1990), Pelz and Andrews (1976), Pinto and Pinto (1990), Souder (1978, 1987, 1988) and others.

5. For greater detail see Clausing (1986), Eureka (1987), Griffin (1989), Hauser and Clausing (1988), King (1987), Kogure and Akao (1983), McElroy (1987), and Sullivan (1986, 1987), as well as collections of articles in Akao (1987) and the American Supplier Institute (1987).

6. When necessary the hierarchy can go to deeper levels. For example, when Toyota developed a QFD matrix to help them eliminate rust from their vehicles, the hierarchy had eight levels (Eureka, 1987). The most-detailed level included a customer need relating to whether the customer could carry rotten apples in the bed of a pick-up truck without worrying about the truck body rusting.

7. In related research, Fern (1982) compared the ability of focus groups and individuals to generate ideas. Reanalysis of his data suggest that approximately 1.2 ideas were generated per minute, independently of whether subjects worked in focus groups or individually.

8. Note that we 'flip' the normal beta-binomial analysis. In most applications (e.g. Greene, 1982) the customer probabilities are beta-distributed across customers; in our model customers are replications. In our model the probabilities p_i are beta-distributed across customer needs i.

9. Morrison (1979) assumes that needs are voiced with Poisson rate λ_i. Then the probability that a need is voiced at least once is $p_i = 1 - e^{-\lambda_i t}$. Morrison shows that there exists a $G(\lambda_i)$ such that p_i is beta-distributed. Because the beta distribution appears to fit the data we prefer to work directly with p_i rather than λ_i.

10. If we smooth the small 'lump' at 21 customers, the observed frequencies are not statistically different than the beta distribution (Kolmogorov–Smirnov test). We feel that this 'lump' does not seriously impair the model. Note that we can also assume that customers are heterogeneous in their abilities to voice needs. However, we feel that the assumption of two forms of heterogeneity complicates the model needlessly. Our data are available should anyone wish to extend the model in this direction.

11. The beta distribution is given by

$$f(p) = p^{\alpha-1}(1 - p)^{\beta-1}/B(\alpha,\beta) \quad \text{where} \quad B(\alpha,\beta) = \Gamma(\alpha)\Gamma(\beta)/\Gamma(\alpha+\beta).$$

Method of moments estimation gives $\alpha = 1.45$ and $\beta = 7.64$.

12. K–J is the registered trademark of Jiro Kawakita for his version of the affinity chart. For the remainder of the paper we use the more generic name.

13. If the number of piles varies dramatically across respondents one can weight the data by a monotonic function (e.g. log [·]) of the number of piles that a respondent uses. This gives a greater weight to respondents who are more discriminating in their sorting task. To assure a simpler and more straightforward comparison we have not included this complication for food-carrying devices. Recent modifications collect importances and customer perceptions for the piles or exemplars.

14. We have found that Ward's method, the average linkage method, and the complete linkage (farthest neighbor) provided similar structures in our data (see Griffin, 1989). For example, when comparing a Ward's-based cluster solution and an average-linked-based cluster solution, only 3% of the customer needs appeared in different primary groupings. Single linkage

(nearest neighbor) led to 'chaining' in which customer needs were merged to a large cluster one at a time. Because the difference between the three clustering algorithms is slight, we chose Ward's method for the comparisons in this paper. It is used more often in industry (Romesburg, 1984) and, when shown the three solutions, the management team believed that Ward's structure was slightly superior in terms of face validity to the other two. (In Ward's method, clusters are merged based on the criterion of minimizing the overall sum of squared within-cluster distances.) Deciding where to cut the hierarchy remains an exercise in qualitative judgment. However, exemplars help identify the cuts.

15. Private communication with Robert Klein of Applied Marketing Science, Inc. for their Vocalyst™ technique.

16. Extensive reviews have been published in attitude theory (Wilkie and Pessemier, 1973), information integration (Lynch, 1985), concept development (Shocker and Srinivasan, 1979), conjoint analysis (Green and Srinivasan, 1978, 1990), behavioral decision theory (Huber, 1974), formal choice models (Corstjens and Gautschi, 1983), and the analytic hierarchy process (Wind and Saaty, 1980). For comparisons of methods see Akaah and Korgaonkar (1983), Cattin et al. (1982), Einhorn and Hogarth (1975), Green (1984), Hauser and Koppelman (1977), Hauser and Urban (1979), Hoepfl and Huber (1970), Lehmann (1971) and Schendel et al. (1971).

17. While a few applications in hybrid conjoint analysis have dealt with large numbers of attributes, e.g. Wind et al. (1989) use 50 product features, the norms in these academic literatures are for far fewer attributes than the 200–400 customer needs that are typical in QFD.

18. For the constant-sum and anchored scales, the importance of a tertiary need reflects the cascaded allocations to the primary and secondary needs. We also tried a 100-point satisfaction measure and a nine-point like/dislike scale. Results were similar methodologically. We did not test the analytic hierarchy process (AHP) because it would have required 602 pairwise judgments by each respondent.

19. Tables 2 and 3 report rank correlations. We get similar results for Pearson correlations.

20. Griffin's study was a pretest of 133 students for the 230 customer needs discussed earlier. She found direct, anchored, and constant-sum measures to be similar. The proprietary study compared direct ratings and constant-sum measures for almost 150 customer needs. The sample size was 350 customers.

21. One must be cautious in using either the anchored or constant-sum scale. In both of these scales the rated importance of the primary need is cascaded down as a multiplying factor for the corresponding secondary and tertiary needs. If the primary need is poorly worded, then any measurement error affects all corresponding secondary and tertiary needs. For this reason, the consumer-goods company prefers the direct measures.

22. Rank-order data preserves confidentiality better. The qualitative insights were similar for the interval-scaled data. Primary-brand share is the share of consumers who use the brand as their primary product. It is similar to, but not identical to, a market-share measure. The relative measures are relative in the sense of customers, all customers who have heard of (used) the brand rate it, and in the sense of brands, customers rate the brand relative to all brands that they have heard of (used). The ten brands reported comprise approximately 80% of the market.

23. This discussion applies to those studies that measure or estimate importances for groups of customers. It is mute on the many conjoint studies in which an individual's importance weights are used to predict preference among holdout profiles, that is, where the experimenter chooses the product profiles. It is also mute on studies where subjects evaluate products or product concepts chosen by the experimenter. It applies to studies where subjects evaluate only those products that they would consider seriously.

24. For more details and for eight additional application vignettes see Hauser (1992). The application vignettes include a stationery-products manufacturer, a construction-tools manufacturer, a financial institution, an insurance company, an entertainment provider, a manufacturer of office equipment, a manufacturer of surgical instruments and a manufacturer of a lightweight chemical mixing device.

REFERENCES

Akaah, I. P. and Korgaonkar, P. K. (1983) 'An Empirical Comparison of the Predictive Validity of Compositional, Decompositional, and Hybrid Multiattribute Preference Models', *Journal of Marketing Research*, **20** (May): 187–197.

Akao, Y. (1987) *Quality Deployment: A Series of Articles*, Lawrence, MA: GOAL, Inc. (G. Mazur, Trans.) American Supplier Institute (1987) *Quality Function Deployment: A Collection of Presentations and QFD Case Studies*, Dearborn, MI: American Supplier Institute, Inc.

Barthol, R. P. (1976) 'ECHO: Estimating Values in Familiar and Unfamiliar Cultures', in Sinaiko, H. W. and Broedling, L. A. (eds), *Perspectives on Attitude Assessment: Surveys and Their Alternatives*, Champaign, IL: Pendelton Press.

Barthol, R. P. and Bridge, R. G. (1968) 'The Echo Multi-Response Method for Surveying Value and Influence Patterns in Groups', *Psychological Reports*, **22**: 1345–1354.

Ben-Akiva, M. and Lerman, S. R. (1985) *Discrete Choice Analysis: Theory and Application to Travel Demand*, Cambridge, MA: MIT Press.

Brunswick, E. (1952) *The Conceptual Framework of Psychology*, Chicago, IL: University of Chicago Press.

Calder, R. J. (1979) 'Focus Groups and the Nature of Qualitative Marketing Research', *Journal of Marketing Research*, **14** (August): 353–364.

Cattin, P., Hermet, G. and Pioche, A. (1982) 'Alternative Hybrid Models for Conjoint Analysis: Some Empirical Results', in *Analytical Approaches to Product and Market Planning: The Second Conference*, Cambridge, MA: Marketing Science Institute (October): 142–152.

Clausing, D. (1986) 'QFD Phase II: Parts Deployment', Dearborn, MI: American Supplier Institute.

Cooper, L. K. (1992) 'The Structure of Recruiter Need at the Sloan School of Management: A Quantitative Assessment', Master's Thesis, Cambridge, MA: Sloan School of Management, MIT.

Cooper, R. G. (1983) 'The New Product Process: An Empirically-Based Classification Scheme', *R&D Management*, **13**(1): 1–13.

Cooper, R. G. (1984a) 'New Product Strategies: What Distinguishes the Top Performers?', *Journal of Product Innovation Management*, **2**: 151–164.

Cooper, R. G. (1984b) 'How New Product Strategies Impact on Performance', *Journal of Product Innovation Management*, **2**, 5–18.

Cooper, R. G. and de Brentani, U. (1991) 'New Industrial Financial Services: What Distinguishes the Winners', *Journal of Product Innovation Management*, **8**: 75–90.

Cooper, R. G. and Kleinschmidt, E. (1986) 'An Investigation into the New Product Process: Steps, Deficiencies, and Impact', *Journal of Product Innovation Management*, **3**: 71–85.

Corstjens, M. L. and Gautschi, D. A. (1983) 'Formal Choice Models in Marketing', *Marketing Science*, **2**(1): 19–56.

Dawkins, B. (1991) 'Siobhan's Problem: The Coupon Collector Revisited', *The American Statistician*, **45**(1): 76–82.

de Brentani, U. (1989) 'Success and Failure in New Industrial Services', *Journal of Product Innovation Management*, **6**: 239–58.

Dougherty, D. J. (1987) 'New Products in Old Organizations: The Myth of The Better Mousetrap in Search of the Beaten Path', Unpublished Ph.D. Thesis, Cambridge, MA: Sloan School of Management, MIT.

Efron, B. and Thisted, R. (1976) 'Estimating the Number of Unseen Species: How Many Words Did Shakespeare Know?', *Biometrika*, **63**(3): 435–447.

Einhorn, H. J. and Hogarth, R. M. (1975) 'Unit-weighting Schemes for Decision Making', *Organizational Behavior and Human Performance*, **13**, 171–192.

Eureka, W. E. (1987) 'Introduction to Quality Function Deployment', Section III of *Quality Function Deployment: A Collection of Presentations and QFD Case Studies*, Dearborn, MI: American Suppliers Institute.

Fern, E. F. (1982) 'The Use of Focus Groups for Idea Generation: The Effect of Group Size, Acquaintanceship, and Moderator on Response Quantity and Quality', *Journal of Marketing Research*, **19** (February): 1–13.

Fornell, C. (1991) 'A National Customer-Satisfaction Barometer: The Swedish Experience', *Working Paper*, The Office for Customer Satisfaction Research, Ann Arbor, MI: University of Michigan.

General Accounting Office, US (1991) 'Management Practices: US Companies Improve Performance Through Quality Efforts', GAO/NSIAD–91–190 (May), Gaithersburg, MD.

Goodman, L. A. and Kruskal, W. H. (1954) 'Measures of Association for Cross-Classification', *Journal of the American Statistical Association*, **49**, 732–764.

Green, P. E. (1984) 'Hybrid Models of Conjoint Analysis: An Expository Review', *Journal of Marketing Research*, **21**(2): 155–169.

Green, P. E., Carmone, F. J. and Fox, L. B. (1969) 'Television Programme Similarities: An Application of Subjective Clustering', *Journal of the Market Research Society*, **11**(1): 70–90.

Green, P. E. and McMennamin, J. L. (1973) 'Market Position Analysis', in Henderson Britt, S. and Guess, N. F. (eds), *Marketing Manager's Handbook*, Chicago, IL: Dartnell Press: 543–554.

Green, P. E. and Srinivasan, V. (1978) 'Conjoint Analysis in Consumer Research: Issues and Outlook', *Journal of Consumer Research*, **5** (September), 103–123.

Green, P. E. and Srinivasan, V. (1990) 'Conjoint Analysis in Marketing Research: New Developments and Directions', *Journal of Marketing*, **54**(4): 3–19.

Green, P. E., Tull, D. S. and Albaum, G. (1988) *Research for Marketing Decisions*, 5th Edition, Englewood Cliffs, NJ: Prentice-Hall.

Griffin, A. (1989) 'Functionally Integrated New Product Development', Unpublished Ph.D. Thesis, Cambridge, MA: Sloan School of Management, MIT.

Griffin, A. (1992) 'Evaluating Development Processes: QFD as an Example', *Journal of Product Innovation Management*, **9** (September).

Griffin, A. and Hauser, J. R. (1992a) 'Patterns of Communication Among Marketing, Engineering and Manufacturing—A Comparison Between Two New Product Teams', *Management Science*, **38**(3): 360–373.

Griffin, A. and Hauser, J. R. (1992b) 'The Marketing and R&D Interface', University of Chicago Working Paper (October).

Gupta, A. K., Raj, S. P. and Wilemon, D. (1985) 'R&D and Marketing Dialogue in High-Tech Firms', *Industrial Marketing Management*, **14**: 289–300.

Gutman, J. (1982) 'A Means-End Chain Model Based on Consumer Categorization Processes', *Journal of Marketing*, **46** (Spring): 60–72.

Hauser, J. R. (1978) 'Testing the Accuracy, Usefulness, and Significance of Probabilistic Choice Models: An Information-Theoretic Approach', *Operations Research*, **26**(3): 406–421.

Hauser, J. R. (1991) 'Comparison of Importance Measurement Methodologies and their Relationship to Consumer Satisfaction', MIT Working Paper, Cambridge, MA: Sloan School of Management, MIT.

Hauser, J. R. (1992) 'Puritan-Bennett—The Renaissance™ Spirometry System: Listening to the Voice of the Customer', MIT, Working Paper, Cambridge, MA: Sloan School of Management, MIT.

Hauser, J. R. and Clausing, D. P. (1988) 'The House of Quality', *Harvard Business Review*, **66**(3): 63–73.

Hauser, J. R. and Koppelman, F. S. (1977) 'Effective Marketing Research: An Empirical Comparison of Techniques to Model Consumers' Perceptions and Preferences', in *Analytic Approaches to Product and Market Planning*, Allan D. Shocker, (ed.) Cambridge, MA: Marketing Science Institute.

Hauser, J. R. and Urban, G. L. (1977) 'A Normative Methodology for Modeling Consumer Response to Innovation', *Operations Research*, **25**(4): 579–619.

Hauser, J. R. and Urban, G. L. (1979) 'Assessment of Attribute Importances and Consumer Utility Functions', *Journal of Consumer Research*, **5** (March): 251–62.

Hise, R. T., O'Neal, L., Parasuraman A. and McNeal, J. U (1990) 'Marketing/R&D Interaction in New Product Development: Implications for New Product Success Rates', *Journal of Product Innovation Management*, **7**(2): 142–155.

Hoepfl, R. T. and Huber, G. P. (1970) 'A Study of Self-explicated Utility Models', *Behavioral Science*, **15**: 408–414.

Huber, G. P. (1974) 'Multi-attribute Utility Models: A Review of Field and Field-like Studies', *Management Science*, **20**(10): 1393–1402.

Imai, M. (1986) *Kaizen: The Key to Japan's Competitive Success*, New York: McGraw-Hill Publishing Company.

Juran, J. M. (1989) *Juran on Leadership for Quality: An Executive Handbook*, New York: The Free Press: 14–19.

Kelly, G. A. (1955) *The Psychology of Personal Constructs*, vol. 1., New York: W. W. Norton.

King, R. (1987) *Better Designs in Half the Time: Implementing Quality Function Deployment (QFD) in America*, GOAL: Lawrence, MA.

Kogure, M. and Akao, Y. (1983) 'Quality Function Deployment and CWQC', *Quality Progress*, **16**(10): 25–29.

Lehmann, D. R. (1971) 'Television Show Preference: Application of a Choice Model', *Journal of Marketing Research*, **8** (February): 47–55.

Lehmann, D. R. (1985) *Market Research and Analysis*, 2nd Edition, Homewood, IL: Irwin.

Lynch, J. G., Jr. (1985) 'Uniqueness Issues in the Decompositional Modeling of Multi-attribute Overall Evaluations: An Information Integration Perspective', *Journal of Marketing Research*, **22** (February): 1–19.

Manski, C. F. and McFadden, D. (1981) *Structural Analysis of Discrete Data with Econometric Applications*, Cambridge, MA: MIT Press.

McElroy, J. (1987) 'For Whom are We Building Cars?', *Automotive Industries*, (June): 68–70.

Moenaert, R. K. and Souder, W. E. (1990) 'An Information Transfer Model for Integrating Marketing and R&D Personnel in New Product Development Projects', *Journal of Product Innovation Management*, **7**(2): 91–107.

Morgan, A. I. (1984) 'Point of View: Magic Town Revisited (A Personal Perspective)', *Journal of Advertising Research*, **24**(4): 49–51.

Morrison, D. G. (1979) 'An Individual Differences Pure Extinction Process', *Journal of Mathematical Psychology*, **19**(3): 307–315.

Myers, J. H. (1976) 'Benefit Structure Analysis: A New Tool for Product Planning', *Journal of Marketing*, **40** (October): 23–76.

National Institute of Standards and Technology (NIST) (1991) '1991 Application Guidelines: Malcolm Baldrige National Quality Award', Department of Commerce, Gaithersburg, MD 20899.

Pelz, D. C. and Andrews, F. M. (1976) *Scientists in Organizations*, Revised Edition, Ann Arbor, MI: University of Michigan Press.

Pessemier, E. A. (1986) *Product Management: Strategy and Organization*, Malabar, FL: Robert E. Krieger Publishing.

Phillips, S., Dunkin, A., Treece, J. and Hammonds, K. H. (1990) 'King Customer: At Companies that Listen Hard and Respond Fast, Bottom Lines Thrive', *Business Week* (March 12): 88–94.

Pinto, M. B. and Pinto, J. K. (1990) 'Project Team Communication and Cross-Functional Cooperation in New Program Development', *Journal of Product Innovation Management*, **7**: 200–212.

Rao, V. and Katz, R. (1971) 'Alternative Multidimensional Scaling Methods for Large Stimulus Sets', *Journal of Marketing Research*, **8** (November): 488–494.

Reimann, C. (1991) 'The Baldrige Award Criteria Speak for Themselves', *Quality Progress*, **24** (May): 43–44.

Reynolds, T. J. and Gutman, J. (1988) 'Laddering Theory, Method, Analysis, and Interpretation', *Journal of Advertising Research*, **28**(1): 11–31.

Roberts, J. W. (1992) 'M.B.A. Recruiters' Needs: Voice of the Customer Analysis', Master's Thesis, Cambridge, MA: Sloan School of Management, MIT.

Romesburg, H. C. (1984) *Cluster Analysis for Researchers*, Belmont, CA: Lifetime Learning Publications.

Ross, L. G. (1992) 'A Voice of the Customer Analysis of M.B.A. Schools: The Student Segment', Master's Thesis, Cambridge, MA: Sloan School of Management, MIT.

Ruiz, D. and Jain, D. (1991) 'Designing and Developing New Products: The Subproblem Decomposition Approach', Working Paper, Kellogg Graduate School of Management, Northwestern University, Evanston, IL 60208.

Schendel, D. E., Wilkie, W. L. and McCann, J. M. (1971) 'An Experimental Investigation of Attribute Importance', *Proceedings: Second Annual Conference*, Association of Consumer Research: 404–416.

Shocker, A. D. and Srinivasan, V. (1979) 'Multi-attribute Approaches for Product Concept Evaluation and Generation: A Critical Review', *Journal of Marketing Research*, **16** (May): 159–180.

Silver, J. A. and Thompson, J. C. Jr. (1991) 'Understanding Customer Needs: A Systematic Approach to the "Voice of the Customer"', Master's Thesis, Cambridge, MA: Sloan School of Management, MIT.

Souder, W. E. (1978) 'Effectiveness of Product Development Methods', *Industrial Marketing Management*, **7**.

Souder, W. E. (1987) 'Managing the R&D/Marketing Interface', *Managing New Product Innovations*, Chapter 10, Lexington, MA: Lexington Books.

Souder, W. E. (1988) 'Managing Relations Between R&D and Marketing in New Product Development Projects', *Journal of Product Innovation Management*, **5**: 6–19.

Stratton, B. (1991) 'The Value of Implementing Quality', *Quality Progress*, **25**(7): 70–71.

Sullivan, L. P. (1986) 'Quality Function Deployment', *Quality Progress*, **19**(6): 39–50.

Sullivan, L. P. (1987) 'The Power of Taguchi Methods', *Quality Progress*, **12**(6): 76–79.

Tybout, A. M. and Hauser, J. R. (1981) 'A Marketing Audit Using a Conceptual Model of Consumer Behavior: Application and Evaluation', *Journal of Marketing*, **45** (Summer): 82–101.

Urban, G. L. and Hauser, J. R. (1992) *Design and Marketing of New Products II*, Englewood Cliffs, NJ: Prentice-Hall.

von Hippel, E. (1986) 'Lead Users: A Source of Novel Product Concepts', *Management Science*, **32**(7): 791–805.

Vorberg, D. and Ulrich, R. (1987) 'Random Search with Unequal Search Rates: Serial and Parallel Generalizations of McGill's Model', *Journal of Mathematical Psychology*, **31**: 1–23.

Wilkie, W. L. and Pessemier, E. A. (1973) 'Issues in Marketing's Use of Multi-attribute Attitude Models', *Journal of Marketing Research*, **10** (November): 428–441.

Wind, Y. (1982) *Product Policy: Concepts, Methods, and Strategy*, Reading, MA: Addison-Wesley.

Wind, Y., Green, P.E., Shifflet, D. and Scarbrough, M. (1989) 'Courtyard by Marriott: Designing a Hotel Facility with Consumer-Based Marketing Models', *Interfaces*, **19** (January–February): 25–47.

Wind, Y. and Saaty, T. L. (1980) 'Marketing Applications of the Analytic Hierarchy Process', *Management Science*, **26**(7): 641–658.

Yie, S. (1992) 'The Core Curriculum at Sloan: Establishing a Hierarchy of Needs', Master's Thesis, Cambridge, MA: Sloan School of Management, MIT.

14

Generating and Screening New Product Ideas

Linda Rochford

INTRODUCTION

Opportunity identification (OI) is the initial stage in the new product development process where ideas for new products are generated and screened. It is an area of importance to marketers and industrial firms because of its primary role in the new product development process. Ideas are the raw materials for product development, and the whole planning process depends on the quality of the search and screening process. Although new products are essential to a firm's continued growth in revenues and profits, the development and marketing of new products is an expensive and risky undertaking for the firm (Pessemier and Root, 1973; Calantone and Cooper, 1981). Since idea generation and screening are relatively less costly stages in the new product development process (in terms of investment in funds, time and personnel, and escalation of commitment), it makes sense to manage the process in the most efficient and effective manner for the organization.

WHAT IS A NEW PRODUCT?

A product can be 'new' in the sense that it is either: (1) new to the firm, taking the company into new markets, new technologies or new production methods; (2) new to the market, the first of its kind, what some call an innovation; or (3) new in the sense that it is better for the customer with the product yielding some net benefit to the customer (Cooper, 1981a). For the purposes of this study, a new product will be defined as a product not previously manufactured by the firm (Myers and Marquis, 1969; Crawford, 1987). In other words, a product that is new to the firm.

THE OPPORTUNITY IDENTIFICATION PROCESS

The opportunity identification process involves basically two processes: identifying and collecting new product ideas and screening and evaluation of these ideas. The oppor-

Reprinted with permission from *Industrial Marketing Management*, Vol. 20, 1991, pp. 287–296

tunity identification process is intimately tied to strategic planning and strategy formulation as illustrated in Figure 1. The strategic planning process provides direction to the OI process by establishing the corporate financial and marketing goals and guiding selection of the fields to investigate for new product ideas. Mathot describes two functions of the strategic planning process as determination of innovation need (situation assessment) and determination of fields of search (Mathot, 1982). These two steps provide direction to idea generation and collection and screening.

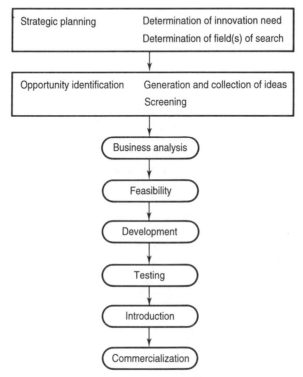

Figure 1. The New Product Process.

- *Determination of innovation need.* The innovation need is determined by situation analysis and often market research. Assessment of the firm's environment, competitive situation, and internal strengths and weaknesses help to determine the charter for innovation within the firm. Determination of innovation need provides the basis for establishing the firm's new product objectives and the resources to be committed to new product development.
- *Determination of fields of search.* The fields of search are the potential market and/or technology areas to be investigated for new product ideas. Fields of search are areas within which it is probable that many ideas exist that suit the opportunities of the market and the strong points of the firm. Fields of search are often indicated by situation analysis, the firm's corporate mission statement and the firm's new product objectives. Methods are available to map organizational strong points against opportunity areas to identify and evaluate potential fields of search including the well

known portfolio planning models such as the Boston Consulting Group, BCG portfolio model and models developed specifically for the OI process (Mathot, 1982).
- *Idea generation and collection.* The idea generation and collection process is the actual
  creative process of coming up with potential new product ideas. Many techniques are
  available which will be discussed in detail later.
- *Screening.* The screening process evaluates the new product ideas identified during the
  idea generation stage in order to devote the firm's resources to only those ideas
  worthy of additional attention.

SOURCES OF IDEAS

Sources for new products include sources both internal and external to the organization
(Calantone and Cooper, 1981; Mathot, 1982). Ideas can be thought of as driven by
market or technology (Cooper, 1983). Appendix 1 lists various sources for ideas. Firms
collect randomly identified ideas by means of some process and/or choose to generate
ideas in a formal manner. Firms can develop extensive information systems that collect
user-generated ideas and user needs while attempting to develop a high level of
employee and customer involvement (Von Hippel, 1978).

Ideas can be generated by individuals or one of several group methods using either
internal or external sources at various organizational levels. Types of group methods
which can be used to develop ideas include Delphi groups, focus groups, innovation or
new product development groups or teams, and management groups. Most authors
favor a multidisciplinary 'innovation group' for idea generation as being most effective
(Buijs, 1979; Chohan, 1979; Davies and Pearson, 1980; Lantis, 1970; McLellan and
Kelly, 1981), although Tauber (1975) and Davies and Pearson (1980) argue that individual idea generation produces better and more creative solutions than groups.

The issue of what constitutes an effective or successful idea generation process has not
been addressed in the literature, although success factors in new product development
have been studied in some detail (Calantone and Cooper, 1981; Cooper, 1983, 1984). If
the success of idea generation can only be measured in terms of new new product
success, it will be very difficult for managers to assess the specific effect of successful idea
generation.

IDEA GENERATION TECHNIQUES

There are many different formal methods for generating new product ideas. Table 1 lists
some of these methods (Hubka, 1983). Mathot has classified idea generation techniques
as either systematic analytical techniques (which split the problem into smaller parts,
for example, morphological analysis), associative techniques, such as brainstorming, or
analogical techniques, such as synetics (Mathot, 1982). Crawford, on the other hand,
has classified various idea generation techniques in terms of whether the general
approach is to identify unmet needs and problems and develop solutions to these
problems (problem find/solve approach) or to modify or improve existing products to
create new products (fortuitous scan approach) (Crawford, 1987). Problem find/solve

approaches includes the use of market research to find problems and brainstorming to identify possible solutions. The fortuitous scan approach includes such methods as analysis of properties (attribute listing) of existing products and technoeconomic design which may result in more incremental improvements/products, as well as creative and serendipitous discoveries of 'breakthrough' new products.

The various idea generation techniques have several limitations. Some require more information than may be readily available at the opportunity identification stage of new product development. A few methods may be difficult to implement due to their complexity or may be rather time-consuming. Some of the techniques are better suited to identification of product modification ideas than to new product or new market ideas as Crawford (1987) has pointed out. In addition, some techniques are more applicable to idea generators with specific functional backgrounds (Hubka, 1983).

STIMULATION FOR IDEA GENERATION

Idea generation may be part of an ongoing new product development program or may be initiated as needed. Stimulus for idea generation may be technology based (Chohan, 1979) or result from new product and market developments, performance improvements or changes, product cost minimization, or product demand.

Sherman (1969) describes how organizational change can stimulate the flow of new product ideas. Reorganizing the new product program, acquiring a new company and bringing in new staff or consultants can refocus energies and revitalize the idea generation process. Sherman also illustrates how a new product program can become 'stale' as the usable ideas from established, well-defined search areas are 'mined out'. The firm typically will redefine its areas of interest and can refocus to stimulate a new flow of ideas. As the need to introduce successful new products increases, managers turn toward more formal processes for the generation of ideas (McLellan and Kelly, 1981).

FACTORS IN IDEA GENERATION SUCCESS

Although the effectiveness of idea generation has not been measured, nor has effectiveness been defined in any normative manner, many 'success factors' have been suggested for effective idea generation. Shocker, Gensch and Simon (1969) emphasize the need for a well-publicized, clearly defined process for success. Shocker et al. suggest that there are probably many people within an organization who do not know how to enter an idea into the new product development process. Many people do some sort of screening themselves and eliminate the idea rather than submitting it for consideration. Often the mechanics of the product development process flow are not well specified so ideas are forwarded to the wrong person or place or not at all.

Sherman (1969) discusses the need for top management involvement in the opportunity identification process. There must be a philosophical and operational link between the people working on new products and their top level management. Hamilton (1980) states that managers need to be receptive to ideas and encourage investigation of

Table 1. Idea generation techniques

Method	Characteristics	Objectives
Abstraction (progressive abstraction)	Make problem or situation more abstract	Insights into new solutions
Adaptation	Modifying or partial transformation of an existing product for different conditions	Reliable solution for new conditions
Aggregation	Combination of product characteristics into a single product or of functions of a number of products into one product	New properties, simplified structure
Analysis of properties (attribute listing)	Thorough analysis of every property of the product	Improvement of an existing product
Application	Application of an existing product for new functions	Application of a proven product to new areas of use
Attribute-based discriminant analysis (PREFMAP)	Market segments developed on basis of brand preferences, geometric representation developed by discriminant analysis from brand's effective attributes, then mapped and analyzed	Market structure generated and searched for new product opportunities
Brainstorming	Collect ideas in freewheeling discussion without criticism	Find many new ideas
Combinations with interactions	Combining of a product or of properties to obtain new and more complicated effects	Derive new solutions from existing products
Critical path network	Graphic representation of activities and their duration	Create an overview of the sequence and timing and find the critical path to identify opportunities
Descartes	Four principles: criticism, division, ordering, create overview	Correctness and effectiveness of thought process stimulates ideas
Dimensional investigation	Technical and economic properties of the product brought together into a mathematical relationship and extreme values found	Find optimal solution on product properties
Division of totality	Tactical procedure based on division of a whole concept or problem into component parts	Create overview, generate partial solutions
Evaluation	Find technical and economic valuation by point counting	Find best variant among a few
Experimentation	By measuring and testing, obtain desired values	Determination of product
Incubation	After thorough preparation of the problem, take a break	Find ideas by intuition
Iteration	Starting from assumed values, obtain progressively closer approximation of all values	Solution of a system with complicated interactions
Market research	Systematic collection and classification of market information	Establishing market conditions and opportunities
Mental experiment	Observe an idealized mental model at work	Testing of an idea, determination of behavior

Table 1. (*continued*)

Method	Characteristics	Objectives
Methodical doubt (scientific skepticism)	By systematic negation of existing solution, search for new solution paths	Find new solutions, opportunities
Method '6–3–5'	6 participants: each writes down 3 ideas within 5 minutes, passing ideas on to the next person for 3 similar ideas, working all the way around the group	Find many solutions, ideas
Morphological analysis/matrix	Split up problem into parts and look for partial solutions to each, leading to generation of solutions to original problem	New solutions by combinations of functions
Problem inventory analysis (reverse brainstorming)	Generate list of negative attributes of existing products	Find product improvements
Problem-purpose expansion	Expand problem, reformulate by stating objective in standard format	Look for new solutions
Questioning	By applying a system of questions, find gapless information or produce mental stimulation	Obtain most complete information possible
Step forwards/ backwards	Attempt both solution directions from 'is' to 'should be' and reverse	Find most favorable path to a solution
Synetics	Team analyzes problem and searches for new solutions through analysis	Discover new solutions, opportunities
Systematic search of field	Research all directions starting from fixed points of the region	Obtain most complete information possible
Systems approach	Systematic working in every situation requiring a solution or decision	As far as possible complete investigation
Technoeconomic design	By technical and economic evaluation find and improve the strong features of the product	Improve product
Technological environmental forecasting	Develop broad scenarios about the future in general, then technology in particular	Insight into the future
Value analysis or engineering	Analysis and criticism of the existing solution from the economic viewpoint	Improve economic properties of the product

each suggestion. Lantis (1970) criticizes random idea generation as 'too haphazard a procedure' for a successful opportunity identification process.

There is also a widely held view that firms should generate as many ideas as possible to increase the probability of locating an appropriate idea which satisfies the firm's needs (Chohan, 1979). Setting time aside for idea generation is considered an important factor for success. Planning, efficient discussion, hard agreements on meeting frequency and duration, diversity in participant backgrounds, multiple inputs, training and experience of the idea generators, organizational and managerial commitment, allocation of priority to new project development, personal motivation, the firm's reward system and the firm's ability to absorb related risk of failure are all suggested as factors which can affect idea generation success (Martino, 1972).

SCREENING

The purpose of the screening process is to 'select from a large list of ideas the few that warrant extensive and expensive analysis' (Hamilton, 1974). The recommended approach for screening is to utilize a multistage process (Cooper, 1983; Buijs, 1979; Hamilton, 1974). Hamilton separates screening into three steps: culling, rating and scoring, with possible substeps within each category (Hamilton, 1974). Others recommend a two-step process utilizing a quick or coarser screen and then subjecting the ideas to a finer screen. The main point of the multistage approach is to subject ideas to the lower-cost (in terms of time and information required) and more 'brutal' screens first and then to pass the fewer prescreened ideas through the more costly screens.

The first step in screening is developing the criteria used to evaluate the ideas. These criteria should be formulated before the ideas are generated, keeping in mind the objective and limits of screening (in terms of information available, cost and time), corporate new product objectives and factors related to the success of the new product which can be identified at this stage of the new product development process (Cooper, 1983; Hamilton, 1974). The first criteria an idea may be subjected to in the initial screening stage may be as simple as: 'Does the idea fit the company's new product guidelines or mission?' and 'Is the project do-able?'

Beyond a very preliminary screen, criteria for evaluation can become quite extensive. O'Meara's (1961) model classifies screening criteria into the categories of marketability, durability, productive ability and growth potential. Cooper's (1981a) criteria (based on analysis of new product successes and failures) fall into categories of resource compatibility, 'newness' of the project to the firm, nature of the product, nature of the market and nature of the project. Appendix 2 lists typical screening criteria.

Depending on the number of screening stages employed, one or more screening methods may be used. The screening methods may be categorized as qualitative and quantitative. More qualitative, yes/no methods may be employed in the primary stages of screening and more quantitative methods utilized later. Criteria may be further classified or weighted on the basis of 'must' objectives (or criteria) and 'want' objectives (Buijs, 1979). Appendix 3 lists various screening methods. The particular method used will be based on realism, flexibility, capability, ease of use and cost considerations.

Criticism of various screening methods has often focused on the subjective nature of some of the models (e.g. checklists, scoring methods). However, at the screening stage, management opinion may be the only 'data' available (Cooper, 1981b). The objective of screening is not in-depth analysis of each idea. When the objectives and limitations of the screening process are considered, it becomes obvious that much of this criticism is unwarranted. Davies and Pearson comment that there should not be 'undue emphasis on numerical accuracy' in the screening process and suggest that more quantitative types of approaches do not work well (Davies and Pearson, 1980).

Information for the screening process cannot be expensive to obtain but should be effective in rejecting concepts that do not have a good chance for success. Generally this information consists of managerial experience and information collected from the literature and possibly the telephone. There is generally insufficient information available at this point in the new product process to calculate ROI, for example.

Other criticisms are the arbitrariness with which weights are assigned to screening factors, the oversimplification of reducing a complex decision to a composite score, the fact that there are no generally accepted cutoff criteria and that many of the criteria factor variables are not independent. Shocker, Gensch and Simon (1969) suggest the use of factor analysis to reduce screening variables to a subset of independent factors to eliminate the interdependencies of ratings. Cooper's (1981b) empirical work to identify realistic, independent screening criteria related to new product successes is an encouraging step in this direction. Subjective ratings of the criteria remain, but as Cooper points out, 'the screening decision will always be plagued by a high degree of uncertainty and objectivity'.

Ideas can be processed through the screening process individually or in batches, depending on whether time constraints are a serious concern, whether an even flow of ideas into later stages of the new product development process is important and whether there are significant economies in processing several ideas at a time. Management may have to decide, based on company objectives and resources, between having an array of ideas at different stages of the screening (or new product development) process and getting an idea to commercialization as quickly as possible (Hamilton, 1974).

Buijs (1979) and Davies and Pearson (1980) state that the screening process is perhaps more important than its results. The selection of 'must' objectives from 'want' objectives, for example, is an important focus for interaction. The group screening process encourages commitment by all parties and may relate to implementation at later stages of the new product development process. Davies and Pearson comment that screening is used to test ideas for relevance, to highlight uncertainties, to identify potential problems and to get commitment to implement projects.

The ideas that are discarded from the screening process should be saved as alternatives to be picked up when selected ideas are either passed on to later stages in the new product development process, dropped, or additional resources are made available (Sherman, 1969; Gutman and Bennett, 1979). Market or technology changes can occur which can change the disposition of previously rejected ideas. Wilson and Hlavacek (1980) discuss project 'unshelving' as an overlooked source of potentially successful project ideas within a firm.

OPPORTUNITY IDENTIFICATION IN PRACTICE

In order to determine how organizations apply opportunity identification (OI) in practice, the author interviewed technical directors and new business development, planning or marketing managers at the divisional or SBU level of six industrial firms. The sample was selected on the basis of convenience. No attempt was made to undertake a rigorous study, the objective being to learn and compare how firms actually identify opportunities. The interviews were conducted in person and by telephone.

Each of the firms interviewed was categorized in terms of the primary type of idea generation approach used (problem find/solve approach versus fortuitous scan), the primary source of new product ideas (internal or external), the primary method used for generating ideas (group versus individual) and the formality of the screening approach employed. The results are displayed in Table 2.

Table 2. Comparison of OI processes among six industrial firms

Firm	Idea generation approach	Idea source	Generation method	Screening method
A	Problem find/solve	External	Group	Informal
B	Fortuitous scan	Internal	Individual	Informal
C	Problem find/solve	Both	Group	Formal
D	Fortuitous scan	Both	Individual	Semi-formal
E	Fortuitous scan	Both	Individual	Formal
F	Problem find/solve	External	Group	Formal

Some tentative generalizations can be made from this limited sample. Those organizations that primarily use a problem find/solve approach (Firms A, C and F) rely largely on external idea sources. For Firm A, whose major market is the Department of Defense, the customer defines the need. For Firms C and F, the customer plays a less significant but still important role in identifying new opportunities. Several of Firm F's past new products were based on ideas and input from vendors. The problem find/solve approach also appears to be associated with group idea generation. This may be due to the fact that many of the ideas originated from external sources (customers) and that the firm developed or elaborated on the identified need to come up with a solution or product.

Those firms with a fortuitous scan approach to idea generation tend to use an individual rather than a group to generate ideas and use either internal sources or both internal and external sources for ideas. Firms B, D and E developed both 'breakthrough' new products involving new technology that were 'new to the market' as well as new products considered line extensions or modifications of existing technology or products. While these firms recognized that a new product idea would ultimately require market need for success, this was not the primary emphasis or concern in identifying new product ideas.

While the problem find/solve approach firms and fortuitous scan approach firms seemed to share certain characteristics with respect to idea generation, the screening methods used and general approach to screening were different. Firms A and B both had an informal screening process. In fact, these organizations were characterized by a pronounced unwillingness to formally screen or evaluate ideas, the logic being that the potential of a truly novel idea is not always recognized by management. Furthermore, these managers recognized that they might not know what criteria should be applied or how to evaluate a truly new idea. As a result, new product ideas were often 'bootlegged' or sheltered from management scrutiny until technical or market feasibility could be demonstrated or until significant financial resources were required which made screening by management a necessity. The screening process, when implemented, did not rely upon detailed quantitative screening techniques. No concrete screening criteria were offered as a means for evaluating a new product idea. The new product idea was generally screened or reviewed as an individual case rather than evaluated against competing new product ideas in a batch process.

Firms C, E and F exhibited characteristics of the classic, formal screening process and techniques described in the literature. Elaborate scoring methods, checklists and criteria had been developed for each firm.

Firm D had what might be described as a 'semiformal' screening process. New product projects that are the result of research efforts are described as 'continually reviewed' but a new product opportunity may remain in R&D for years before it is necessary to submit the new product project for screening and review outside of R&D. Firm D appears to use informal screening criteria within R&D until it is necessary to obtain commitment for serious funding. At the point where strategic investments in people or equipment need to be made, a more formal 'screening' appears to take place.

Characterizing the opportunity identification process

It appears that there may be at least two basic types of OI processes used in industrial organizations. The first type of process, referred to as Pattern A, is a classic, formal opportunity identification process very similar to and characteristic of most normative descriptions of idea generation and screening in the marketing literature. Pattern A is characterized by idea generation from identified market needs (marketing concept) and a formal screening process. The second type of process, referred to as Pattern B, is informal and much less structured. It is characterized by random idea generation associated with serendipitous technical discovery, and line extensions and modifications of existing products and technologies. Pattern B organizations have a pronounced unwillingness to screen or evaluate ideas.

Table 3. Types of OI processes

	Pattern A	Pattern B
OI process	Classic, formal process Idea generation driven by market needs Structured More concerned with the risk of accepting a bad idea	Informal Idea generation not limited to defined market needs Less structured More concerned with the risk of rejecting a good idea
Company characteristics	Slow to modestly changing environments	More rapidly changing environments Strong technological culture

The Pattern B process firms could be characterized as being more reluctant to accept a Type I error, the risk of rejecting a good idea. The Pattern A process firms were also concerned about Type I errors but placed more emphasis on avoiding a Type II error, the risk of accepting a bad idea.

The Pattern B firms seemed to have stronger technology cultures than the Pattern A organizations. The organizations also differed as to the degree of change in their 'base' industry. The Pattern A process firms seemed to be in environments with less uncertainty than the Pattern B process firms with respect to both technology and market. All of the firms generated ideas across the continuum of product 'newness', from product modifications to truly new or novel ideas, although the processes, criteria, and emphasis within the firms differed.

Of the six firms, two seemed to easily fall into the Pattern A process category and two into the Pattern B process, while the remaining two firms had some characteristics of both types, suggesting that there may be a continuum of OI processes from Pattern A to Pattern B.

This exploratory study provides some evidence for different types of opportunity identification processes. Research is needed to determine under what conditions different OI processes arise. For example, characteristics of the OI processes may depend on firm culture, environment, resources and strategy. Further research could be valuable in providing insight into those organizations that do not appear to follow the normative OI process described in the literature.

Appendix 1. Sources of ideas

Internal sources
Employees
  Sales
  Marketing
  Research and Development
  Technical Service
  Customer Service
  Production
  Quality Assurance/Control
  Management
  Finance
Internal market study reports
Existing research and development programs
Technological surveys
Normal design development process

External sources
Customer needs
Competitive pressures
Absorption (Diffusion of technology)
Licensing
Patent office
Data banks
Existing needs analysis
Research institutes
Universities
Government reports/agencies
Shows/exhibits
Public reports
Scientific and trade publications
Consultants
Competitors
Customers
Vendors

Appendix 2. Typical screening criteria

Initial criteria
Consistent with company objectives?
Is the project 'do-able'

Secondary criteria
Market

Size (current and potential)
Growth (current and potential)
Appeal
Role for the company
Product
   Uniqueness
   Exclusivity (patentability)
Feasibility
   Product development
   Technology
   Production
   Personnel
   Financial
Compatibility of fit with respect to:
   Organizational infrastructure
   Personnel and managerial experience and expertise
      Marketing
      Sales
      Technical
      Production
      Financial
      Customer/market needs
Time
   Needed to develop the idea
   Needed to commercialize
Financial
   Investment requirements
   Costs
   Profitability
Other
   Gut feel
   Is it realistic
   Probability of success

Appendix 3. Screening methods

Ranking
Checklists
Scoring models
Network models
Attribute based discriminant analysis
Numerical weighting methods
Line profiles
Block profiles
Idea sort
Profitability index models
Lexiographic evaluation

REFERENCES

Anderson, C. R. and Paine, F. T. (1975) 'Managerial Perceptions and Strategic Behavior', *Academy of Management* (December): 811–823.

Barclay, I. (1984) 'Profitable Product Analysis (Improving Established Products–Value Analysis)', *Plastics and Rubber International*, **7**(5): 177–179.

Bergen, S. A. and Pearson, A. W. (1983) 'Project Management and Innovation in the Scientific Instrument Industry', *IEEE Transactions on Engineering Management*, **EM–30**(4): 194–199.

Buijs, J. (1979) 'Strategic Planning and Product Innovation—Some Systematic Approaches', *Long Range Planning*, **12**: 23–34.

Calantone, R. and Cooper, R. G. (1981) 'New Product Scenarios: Prospects for Success', *Journal of Marketing*, **45**: 48–60.

Chohan, S. M. (1979) 'Product Cost, Performance and Technological Innovation, *Proceedings*, ASME, Management Division, Winter Annual Meeting, New York, December 2–7.

Cooper, R. G. (1979) 'Identifying Industrial New Product Successes: Project NewProd', *Industrial Marketing Management*, **8**: 124–135.

Cooper, R. G. (1980) 'Project NewProd: Factors in New Product Success', *European Journal of Marketing*, **14**(5 and 6): 277–292.

Cooper, R. G. (1981a) 'The Myth of the Better Mousetrap: What Makes a New Product Success?', *Business Quarterly* (Spring): 69–81.

Cooper, R. G. (1981b) 'An Empirically Derived New Product Selection Model', *IEEE Transactions on Engineering Management*, **EM–28** (3): 54–61.

Cooper, R. G. (1983) 'A Process for Industrial New Product Development', *IEEE Transactions on Engineering Management*, **EM–30**(1): 2–10.

Cooper. R. G. (1984) 'How New Product Strategies Impact on Performance', *Journal of Product Innovation Management*, **1**: 5–18.

Crawford, C. M. (1980) 'Defining the Charter for Product Innovation', *Sloan Management Review*, (Fall): 3–12.

Crawford, C. M. (1987) *New Products Management*, Irwin, Homewood, IL.

Davies, G. B. and Pearson, A. W. (1980) 'The Application of Some Group Problem-Solving Approaches to Project Selection in Research and Development, *IEEE Transactions on Engineering Management*, **EM–27**(3): 66–73.

Duncan, R. B. (1972) 'Characteristics of Organizational Environments and Perceived Environmental Uncertainty', *Administrative Science Quarterly*, **17**: 313–327.

Emery, F. E. and Trist, E. L. (1965) 'The Causal Texture of Organizational Environments', *Human Relations*, **18**: 21–32.

Ettlie, J. E. and Bridges, W. P. (1982) 'Environmental Uncertainty and Organizational Technology Policy', *IEEE Transactions on Engineering Management*, **EM–29**(1): 2–10.

Ettlie, J. E., Bridges, W. P. and O'Keefe, R. D. (1984) 'Organizational Strategy and Structural Differences for Radical Versus Incremental Innovation', *Management Science*, **30**(6): 682–695.

Ford, J. D. and Slocum, J. W. Jr. (1977) 'Size, Technology, Environment and the Structure of Organizations', *Academy of Management Review* (October): 561–575.

Grotloh, K. and Rothlin, E. (1983) 'Techno-Economic Product Designing', *Design Studies*, **4**(3): 177–182.

Gutman, D. P. and Bennett, A. A. (1979) 'Planned Approach to New Product Development', *Proceedings*, ASME, Management Division, Winter Annual Meeting, New York, (December): 2–7.

Hamilton, H. R. (1974) 'Screening Business Development Opportunities', *Business Horizons* (August): 13–24.

Hamilton, W. H. (1980) 'Encouraging Innovation, *1980 IEEE Engineering Management Conference Record*: 190–194.

Harris, J. M., Shaw, R. W. and Sommers, W. P. (1983) 'The Strategic Management of Technology', *Planning Review* (January): 28–35.

Hubka, V. (1983) 'Design Tactics = Methods + Working Principles for Design Engineers', *Design Studies*, **4**(3): 188–195.

Iyer, E. S. and Ramaprasad, A. (1984) 'Strategic Postures Toward Innovation', *IEEE Transactions on Engineering Management*, **EM–31**(2): 87–90.

Kantrow, A. M. (1980) 'The Strategy–Technology Connection', *Harvard Business Review* (July/August): 6–21.

Lantis, T. (1970) 'How to Generate New Product Ideas', *Journal of Advertising Research*, **10**(3): 31–35.

Lin, G. C. I., Hoang, K. and Kalchbauer, F. E. (1980) 'Value Analysis and Product Redesign',

Proceedings, International Conference on Manufacturing Engineering, Melbourne, Australia, August 25–27: 363–366.

Lorsch, J. W. and Lawrence, P. R. (1965) 'Organizing for Product Innovation', *Harvard Business Review*, **43**: 109–122.

Marquis, D. G. (1969) 'The Anatomy of Successful Innovations', *Innovation Magazine* (November): 29–37.

Martino, J. P. (1972) 'Technological Forecasting, But Haven't I Been Doing That All Along?', *The Futurist* (June): 120–121.

Mathot, G. B. M. (1982) 'How to Get New Products to Market Quicker', *Long Range Planning*, **15**(6): 20–30.

McLellan, R. and Kelly, G. (1981) 'Processes for Developing New Products', *Radio and Electronic Engineer*, **51**(10): 493–496.

Myers, S. and Marquis, D. G. (1969) *Successful Industrial Innovations: A Study of Factors Underlying Innovation in Selected National Science Foundation Firms*, Washington, DC.

New, D. E. and Schlacter, J. L. (1979) 'Abandon Bad R&D Projects with Earlier Marketing Appraisals', *Industrial Marketing Management*, **8**: 274–280.

O'Meara, J. T. Jr. (1961) 'Selecting Profitable Products', *Harvard Business Review* (January–February): 83–89.

Pessemier, E. A. and Root, H. P. (1973) 'The Dimensions of New Product Planning', *Journal of Marketing*, **37**(January): 10–18.

Roberto, E. and Pinson, C. (1972) 'Compatibility Analysis for the Screening of New Products', *European Journal of Marketing*, **6**(3): 182–189.

Segal, M. (1974) 'Organization and Environment: A Typology of Adaptability and Structure', *Public Administration Review*, (May/June): 212–220.

Sherman, R. (1969) 'The Two-and-a-Half Year Man: With New Products, Everyone is an Amateur', *Innovation Magazine* (November): 39–45.

Shocker, A. D., Gensch, D. and Simon, L. S. (1969) 'Toward the Improvement of New Product Search and Screening', *AMA Conference Proceedings* (Fall): 168–175.

Shocker, A. D. and Srinivasan, V. (1974) 'A Consumer-Based Methodology for the Identification of New Product Ideas', *Management Science*, **20**(6): 921–937.

Smith, G. W. and Smallwood, N. W. (1983) 'Preparing for Breakthroughs ... The Rewards of Technology Futuring', *Management Review* (April): 50–53.

Souder, W. E. (1972) 'A Scoring Methodology for Assessing the Suitability of Management Science Models', *Management Science*, **18**(10): B526–B543.

Souder, W. E. (1978) 'Effectiveness of Product Development Methods', *Industrial Marketing Management*, **7**: 299–307.

Staudt, T. A. (1973) 'Higher Management Risks in Product Strategy', *Journal of Marketing*, **37**: 4–9.

Tauber, E. M. (1972) 'HIT: Heuristics Ideation Technique—A Systematic Procedure for New Product Search', *Journal of Marketing* (January): 58–61.

Tauber, E. M. (1975) 'Discovering New Product Opportunities with Problem Inventory Analysis', *Journal of Marketing* (January): 67–70.

Utterback, J. M. (1971) 'The Process of Technological Innovation within the Firm', *Academy of Management Journal* (March): 75–88.

Utterback, J. M. and Abernathy, W. J. (1975) 'A Dynamic Model of Process and Product Innovation', *Omega*, **3**(6): 639–656.

Volkems, R. Jr. (1983) 'Problem Formulation in Planning and Design', *Management Science*, **29**(6): 639–652.

Von Hippel E. (1978) 'Successful Industrial Products from Customer Ideas', *Journal of Marketing* (January): 39–49.

Wilson, T. L. and Hlavacek, J. D. (1980) 'Commercially Successful Project Unshelvings Among Industrial Firms', *Review of Marketing*: 299–303.

15

Successful Industrial Products from Customer Ideas: Presentation of a New Customer-Active Paradigm with Evidence and Implications

Eric von Hippel

Some of the more sophisticated marketing research techniques, such as multi-dimensional scaling, routinely used in the generation of ideas for new consumer products, have not been extensively applied to the generation of ideas for new industrial products. Under the well-founded assumption that there is at least latent demand for improved need search and idea generation methodologies in the industrial sector,[1] research is being conducted by many[2] to explore differences in the consumer and industrial buying situations, which might be preventing straightforward transfer of consumer marketing research tools to that sector.

This article is intended to contribute to the understanding of the essential differences between industrial and consumer buying, and the reasons for the poor utilization of methodologies for generating consumer-product ideas in the industrial-product sector.

The generation of consumer-product ideas is usually 'manufacturer-active' (i.e. the manufacturer plays the active role), rather than 'customer-active'. And it is my contention that the manufacturer-active paradigm (MAP) underlying consumer-need research and product-idea generation methods makes a poor fit with conditions under which ideas for most new industrial products must be generated. Accordingly, I have developed a new 'customer-active' paradigm (CAP), which appears better suited to those conditions under which ideas for new industrial products can, in fact, be generated.

The article describes (and compares) the MAP and the new CAP, and proposes a test which will allow determination of how well each paradigm fits actual conditions in the industrial market.

It goes on to test and analyze the hypothesis that the CAP offers a better fit to current practice in the industrial field than does the prevailing MAP.

I then link the CAP to research findings in industrial buying behaviour and the engineering problem-solving process; and suggest that the new paradigm better fits the inherent requirements of the industrial idea generation process.

Finally, I provide suggestions for further research derived from the customer-active paradigm.

Reprinted with permission from *Journal of Marketing*, January 1978, pp. 39–49.

MAP VS. CAP

Figure 1 shows a schematic representation of both MAP (as actually practiced for consumer-product idea generation) and CAP (as hypothesized and empirically observed in industrial product ideas).

In the MAP, the role of the customer is essentially that of respondent, 'speaking only when spoken to'. It is the role of the manufacturer to select and survey a group of customers to: obtain information on needs for new products or modification of existing products; analyze the data; develop a responsive product idea; test the idea against customer perceptions and purchase decisions.

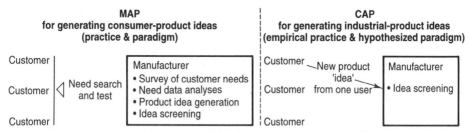

Figure 1. Manufacturer-Active Paradigm (MAP) vs: Customer-Active Paradigm (CA).

In the CAP, it is the role of the would-be *customer* to: develop the idea for a new product; select a supplier capable of making the product; take the initiative to send a request to the selected supplier. The role of the manufacturer in this paradigm is to: wait for a potential customer to submit a request (since, as will be discussed later, potential customers for new products are often not known to product manufacturers until they make a request); screen ideas (not needs) for new products; select those for development which seem to offer the most promise from the manufacturer's point of view.

Clearly, in the instance of consumer products—especially so-called packaged goods—the manufacturer-active product idea generation paradigm has been a strikingly successful one. So, when I hypothesize that this paradigm offers a poor fit to the requirements of industrial product idea generation—and that this poor fit, in turn, is a major reason why consumer product need search and idea generation methodologies are so little used in the industrial product arena—I must provide a strong test of the hypothesis before suggesting even provisional acceptance.

Test of the CAP

Happily, a comparison of the two paradigm schematics presented in Figure 1 suggests a test by which the goodness of fit of each to current *practice* in industrial product idea generation may be probed. The test: can a *customer request* for a new product, containing data sufficient to, in effect, constitute the product 'idea', be found as a triggering event behind most new industrial products? If the answer is *yes*, then clearly the hypothesized CAP offers a better fit to current industrial product idea generation practice than does the MAP. If, on the other hand, the empirical data do not show such a pattern, then the hypothesized paradigm fails. (Note that the test only addresses the fit of the two paradigms to current *practice*; later I will extend the discussion to a consideration of the potential goodness-of-fit of each paradigm in that happy world where practice could be adjusted to the optimum.)

As an aid to clarity, I propose to divide my test of the hypothesis into two segments:

(1) presence (absence) of a customer request;
(2) content of the message when present, and consideration of whether the content observed does (does not) provide the 'idea' for the new product to the product manufacturer.

Presence (absence) of customer requests

In Table 1, I have summarized all the data I can find which bears on the frequency with which innovation requests from customers are associated with the decision to: (a) develop new industrial products; (b) engage in research which ultimately leads to new industrial and military products. (Note that in (b) the 'customer' for the research results solicited was an engineering group.) The exhibit is largely self-explanatory. A more complete review of the methodologies and findings of these studies is available.[3]

It should be noted that all but two of the studies reviewed in Table 1 examined samples of successful innovations only. Obviously, such samples cannot tell us whether innovations initiated in response to customer request are more or less likely to be successful than others. The two studies which did sample both successful and failing innovations, however, give us reason to suspect that innovations requested by customers may in fact be more likely to succeed. Thus:

- Meadows[4] found that, in 'Chem Lab B' project ideas from customers and marketing both show a higher probability of commercial success than do ideas from the laboratory ($P = 0.08$ that customer ideas are not more likely to achieve sales than laboratory ideas).
- Peplow, who reviewed all 94 'creative' projects carried out during a six-year period by an R&D group 'concerned with designing and improving plant processes, process equipment and techniques', reports that 30 of the 48 successfully implemented jobs were started in response to direct request from customers, while failures '. . . lie more with basic [*sic*] jobs started by R&D initiative'.[5]

Taken in aggregate, the studies reviewed in Table 1(a) provide, I suggest, strong support for the hypothesis that manufacturers of new industrial products and processes often initiate work in response to an explicit customer request for the innovation.

Confidence in this finding in the realm of new industrial products and processes is enhanced by data from studies of 'research-engineering interactions' summarized in Table 1(b). In this field too, it appears, succesful interactions between engineering groups, which need research results, and the research teams, which provide these, are characteristically initiated by a request from the research 'customer'.

Does (does not) provide new product idea

Conceptually, it is important to recognize that any statement of a need or problem contains information about what a responsive solution should be. Consider the following statements of need of manufacturing Firm X. All statements address the same need, described in the first statement, but each succeeding statement adds on to those preceding and specifies a desired solution more precisely:

(a) We need higher profits in our semiconductor plant
(b) ... which we can get by raising output
(c)   ... which we can best do by getting rid of the bottleneck in process Step D
(d)   ... which can best be done by designing and installing new equipment
(e)   ... which has the following functional specifications
(f)   ... and should be built according to these blueprints.

A manufacturer must do a lot of work to convert the first need statement, *higher profits*, into a responsive new product. On the other hand, a manufacturer who receives a request containing the maximum amount of product solution data shown in (a)–(f) need only instruct his manufacturing people to manufacture the product according to the customer-supplied engineering drawings.

A reader accustomed to thinking of customers as supplying product 'need' information only, while product manufacturers devise 'solutions'—products responsive to the need—might find the concept of product solution data being conveyed *along with* need data a strange one. In some industries, however, I have found that customers typically do provide a great deal of solution data to manufacturers—field-proven new product designs—as well as need data. (Some 77% of a sample of 111 scientific instrument innovations[6] and 67% of a sample of 49 process machinery innovations[7] have been found to display such a pattern.)

An example from my research may help provide the flavor of the concept. Consider the following case of a product innovation for which a product user did most of the innovation work and provided a great deal of product design data to the manufacturer along with information about his need for a new product.

An example of a user-developed product

'Solderless wrapped connection' is a means of making a reliable, gas-tight electrical connection by wrapping a wire tightly around a special terminal whose sharp edges press into the wire. The system is much faster than soldering and allows much closer spacing of terminals.

The entire system, including a novel hand tool needed to properly wrap the wire around the terminal, was invented and developed at Bell Labs for use in the Bell System in 1947–48. After several years of testing by the Labs, it was given to Western Electric for implementation. Western Electric decided to have the hand tool portion of the system built by an outside supplier, and Keller Tool (now part of Gardner-Denver Company) bid for and won the job in 1952–53.

Keller had other customers who did electronic assembly work and realized that some of these would also find the solderless wrapped connection system useful. It therefore requested and obtained a license to sell the hand tools on the open market. Currently, the system is a major wire connection technique, and Gardner-Denver (Keller) is the major supplier of solderless wrapped connection equipment.

Table 1. Frequency with which manufacturers initiated work on an industrial innovation in response to a customer request

Study	Nature of innovations and sample selection criteria	N	Data available regarding presence of customer requests
(a) Studies of industrial products			
Meadows[a]	All projects initiated during a two-year period in 'Chem Lab B'—Lab of a chemical company with $100–300 million in annual sales in 'Industrial intermediates'	29	Nine of 17 (53%) commercially successful product ideas were from customers
Peplow[b]	All 'creative' projects carried out during a six-year period by an R&D group concerned with plant process, equipment and technique innovations	94	30 of 48 (62%) successfully implemented projects were initiated in response to direct customer request
Von Hippel[c]	Semiconductor and electronic sub-assembly manufacturing equipment: first of type used in commercial production ($n = 7$); major improvements ($n = 22$); minor improvements ($n = 20$)	49	Source of initiative for manufacture of equipment developed by users ($n = 29$) examined. Source clearly identified as customer request in 21% of cases. In 46% of cases frequent customer–manufacturer interaction made source of initiative unclear
Berger[d]	All engineering polymers developed in US after 1955 with >10 million pounds produced in 1975	5	No project-initiating request from customers found
Boyden[e]	Chemical additives for plastics: all plasticizers and UV stabilizers developed post-WW II for use with four major polymers	16	No project-initiating request from customers found
Utterback[f]	All scientific instrument innovations manufactured by Mass. firms which won 'IR-100 Awards', 1963–1968 ($n = 15$); sample of other instruments produced by same firms ($n = 17$)	32	75% initiated in response to 'need input'. When need input originated outside product manufacturer (57%), source was 'most often' customer
Robinson et al.[g]	Sample of standard and non-standard industrial products purchased by three firms	NA	Customers recognize need, define functional requirements and specific goods and services needed *before contacting suppliers*
(B) Studies of research–engineering interaction			
Isenson (*Project Hindsight*)[h]	R&D accomplishments judged key to successful development of 20 weapons systems	710	85% initiated in response to description of problem by application-engineering group
Materials Advisory Board[i]	Materials innovations 'believed to be the result of research-engineering interaction'	10	In 'almost all' cases the individual with a well-defined need initiated the communications with the basic researchers

Table 1. (*Continued*)

References
[a] Meadows, D. 'Estimate Accuracy and Project Selection Models in Industrial Research', *Industrial Management Review*, Spring 1969. Also, 'Data Appendix: Accuracy of Technical Estimates in Industrial Research Planning', M.I.T. Sloan School of Management, Working Paper #301–67.
[b] Peplow, M. E. 'Design Acceptance', in *The Design Method*, Gregory, S. A., ed. (London: Butterworth, 1960).
[c] von Hippel, E. 'Transferring Process Equipment Innovations from User-innovators to Equipment Manufacturing Firms', *R&D Management*, October 1977; see also M.I.T. Sloan School of Management, Working Paper #857–76, May 1976 (revised January 1977).
[d] Berger, A. *Factors Influencing the Locus of Innovation Activity Leading to Scientific Instrument and Plastics Innovations* (unpublished S.M. thesis. M.I.T. Sloan School of Management, June 1975).
[e] Boyden, J. *A Study of the Innovation Process in the Plastics Additives Industry* (unpublished S.M. thesis, M.I.T. Sloan School of Management, January 1976).
[f] Utterback, J. 'The Process of Innovation: A Study of the Origination and Development of Ideas for New Scientific Instruments', *IEEE Transactions on Engineering Management*, November 1971.
[g] Robinson, Farris and Wind, *Industrial Buying and Creative Marketing* (Boston: Allyn and Bacon, 1967).
[h] Isenson, R. 'Project Hindsight: An Empirical Study of the Sources of Ideas Utilized in Operational Weapon Systems', in Gruber, W. and Marquis, D. eds., *Factors in the Transfer of Technology* (Cambridge, MA: M.I.T. Press, 1969), p. 157.
[i] Materials Advisory Board, Division of Engineering, National Research Council, *Report of the Ad Hoc Committee on Principles of Research-Engineering Interaction*, Publication MAB–222–M (Washington, D.C.: National Academy of Sciences—National Research Council, July 1966), pp. 15, 16.

How much solution content?

Perhaps the most appropriate scale upon which to measure the 'amount' of solution content in a customer request is a scale which consists of stages in the product development process. If one were able to measure the solution content of a request on such a scale, one would be able to say:

- For product x, the customer's request supplied the data normally generated by product development process stages, $1 \rightarrow x$, leaving to the manufacturer the performance of the work of stages, $x + 1 \rightarrow N$.

Specifications of linear stages of new product development is somewhat chimerical; researchers in the area have shown that the actual work cannot be said to proceed in clear-cut stages, but for our purposes here, the simple five-stage segmentation shown in Figure 2 will be serviceable.

The Meadows, Peplow, Utterback and Robinson studies reviewed in Table 1(a) do not spell out the solution content of the customer requests they observed. And, on the face of it, the content of those messages could have been anything from a simple 'Give me a new product—any new product' to an explicit, 'Make me some of my compound X according to my process Y'. I would argue that at a *minimum* the solution content of those need messages must have included some functional specifications for the requested new industrial products (indicated in Figure 2 by the solid arrows); and that there is a strong probability that some provided complete product design data to the manufacturer (combined solid and broken arrows).

My argument that, at a minimum, *the need messages must have included implicit or explicit data on the general type of solution* to be embodied in the desired product is as follows: The

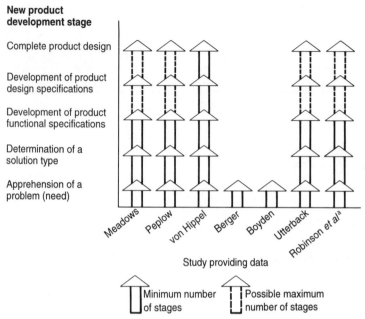

New product development stage

Complete product design

Development of product design specifications

Development of product functional specifications

Determination of a solution type

Apprehension of a problem (need)

Meadows Peplow von Hippel Berger Boyden Utterback Robinson et al[a]

Study providing data

Minimum number of stages

Possible maximum number of stages

Figure 2. New Product Development Data Supplied by Customer to Manufacturer. ([a] Scale valid for new product portion of study sample only.)

need messages observed in the reviewed studies were 'narrow-cast' to specific suppliers—not broadcast to all and sundry. Since different suppliers specialize in different solution technologies, selection of a particular supplier cannot be made until the customer has recognized his need and has envisioned the general type of solution he wants.

For example, if a customer perceives a need to store corporate data, he may make the need known to Kodak envisioning microfilm storage as an appropriate 'type' of solution to the problem. If, on the other hand, he feels physical storage of hard copy is in order, he may contact a manufacturer of file cabinets; or if he feels storage on magnetic tape might be appropriate, he may contact a computer manufacturer; and so on.

My belief that *a customer request must also include some functional specifications* for a product responsive to the need is likewise based on simple logic. It is hard to envision a customer calling up a supplier about a problem and not being able to specify at least some of the functional elements required in a responsive solution. In the instance of the corporate data storage example above, therefore, it seems only logical to assume that, in most instances, such a customer would know roughly how much data had to be stored, how often access was needed etc.

My contention that, at a maximum, *the customer requests* noted in the Meadows, Peplow, Utterback and Robinson studies *could have included complete product design data* for the industrial product requested, is based on the data from my own studies of scientific instruments and process equipment innovations mentioned previously.[8] The data support the notion that product users (customers) in at least some fields are the source of the designs for most of the functionally significant, first-to-market, industrial product innovations in those fields.

Does content mean 'idea'?

Finally, we come to the question: does the solution content observed in the studies reviewed constitute the 'idea' for the new product being sought? Although, as discussed above, most of the studies reviewed indicate only the minimum and maximum, I feel we can safely conclude that the requests did provide the product idea to the manufacturers. Even the minimum solution content of those messages satisfies the definition of a new product idea (a very difficult definition to devise) in the usage of many investigators.

(Rubenstein's working definition of an idea is 'an actual or potential proposal for undertaking new technical work which will require the commitment of significant organizational resources such as time, money, manpower, energy'.[9] Myers and Marquis suggest that 'the idea for an innovation consists of the fusion of a recognized demand and a recognized technical feasibility into a design concept . . . The design concept is only the identification and formulation of a problem worth working on. It is followed by problem solving activity'.[10])

CLOSER FIT OF CAP

There are two possible explanations for our finding that the hypothesized CAP fits more closely with industrial product-idea generation *practice* than does the conventionally assumed MAP:

- MAP is *not* appropriate to the requirements of industrial product idea generation.
- MAP *is* appropriate to the requirements of industrial product idea generation, *but* simply has *not* been extensively applied in that field as yet.

I would like to propose that each explanation applies to the situation—but to different portions of the 'universe' of new industrial products, as a function of these two constraints:

- The CAP can only be applied in situations where the would-be customer is *overtly* aware of his new product need—while methodologies developed in the context of the manufacturer-active paradigm can be applied to either overt (e.g. conjoint analysis) or latent customer needs.
- The MAP can be applied only under circumstances in which the new product opportunity is 'accessible to manufacturer-managed action'.

If we display these proposed constraints and their impact in a two-dimensional table (Table 2), we see the conditions under which the customer-active and/or manufacturer-active product idea generation paradigm will be appropriate.

The logic behind my proposal that the CAP idea generation paradigm can only be applied in instances where the customer is overtly aware of his need is clear: how can a customer send a message regarding a need of which he is not overtly aware? The purpose and logic of my second proposal—on the face of it a near-tautology—is doubtless opaque to the reader at this point. Clarifying it and reasoning that it discriminates well between consumer and some industrial new product opportunities is my next task.

Table 2. Characteristics of new industrial product opportunity appropriate to CAP and/or MAP

	Accessibility of new product opportunity to manufacturer-managed action	
	Low	High
Nature of customer need	Customer-active only	Customer- and/or manufacturer-active
Latent	Neither	Manufacturer-active only

Low accessibility to manufacturer-managed action

The hallmark of the MAP is manufacturer-initiation of the process by which the need for a new product is perceived, manufacturer-initiated analysis of those needs, and a generation of a *responsive* product idea. In contrast, the CAP is characterized by a request, communicated at customer initiative to a customer-selected manufacturer, which contains a customer-generated product idea.

When a customer's need for a new product is overt, I suggest that two characteristics of the new product opportunity determine the paradigm most appropriate to the industrial product idea generation process:

(1) Easy (low-cost) identification of customers sharing a similar new product need via manufacturer-initiated methods (such as surveys) will be favourable to use of the MAP.
(2) Long-duration 'new product selling opportunities' will allow application of either paradigm. These opportunities can be defined as starting when a customer first develops a need for a new product, and as ending when that customer is no longer willing to consider purchase of a responsive product offered by a would-be supplier. Very short opportunities (on the order of a few weeks' duration) will only permit application of the customer-active paradigm.

My reasoning is that a few weeks—at least with current methods—is too short a period to allow a manufacturer the necessary time to accomplish the steps prescribed by MAP: need analysis and generation of a responsive new product idea. On the other hand, a few weeks would seem sufficient if a manufacturer only had to accomplish the step prescribed by CAP: acceptance or rejection of a new product idea proposed by a customer.

How may consumer and industrial new product selling opportunities be seen in terms of these two characteristics?

Consumer product opportunities

In many categories of consumer packaged goods (and in a few categories of industrial products) the following conditions prevail:

- The proportion of all consumers using an existing product in the functional category

being studied (e.g. toothpaste) is sufficiently large and/or well known to allow economical identification of a sample of users via a survey or another manufacturer
initiated technique.

- A sample of current users of many consumer goods is effectively equivalent to a
sample of future buyers—the real category of interest to market researchers—
because the products are frequently repurchased.
- Users/buyers of many consumer goods can be persuaded economically to buy a new
brand if they see it as preferable to their present brand because the switch entails little
adjustment effort/cost on their part.

Economical execution

These conditions suggest an economical execution of the manufacturer-active product
idea generation paradigm because:

- Identification of users with a new product need/dissatisfaction with existing products
via survey or other manufacturer initiative is economical.
- The duration of the new product selling opportunity is sufficient to allow execution of
the MAP. (Since the products are frequently repurchased and since brand switching
involves little change-over costs for the buyer, a 'selling opportunity' remains open to
a manufacturer as long as the need he has identified remains valid.)

Note that the conditions outlined above also hold for *certain* types of industrial products. In the case of electronic components such as resistors, for example, electronics
firms using these components are easily identified, the parts are frequently repurchased,
and their physical and functional characteristics are sometimes so standardized that
customer firms can make a relatively costless switch from one brand to another if they
wish to do so.

Industrial product opportunities

Consider, in contrast, the circumstances which studies of industrial buying and engineering problem solving behavior suggest are characteristic of the selling opportunity for
many or most new industrial goods.

Industrial products (often placed in the categories of materials, components and
capital equipment) are 'needed' and specified largely by engineers. Brand,[11] Robinson,
Farris and Wind[12] and the Research Department of *Scientific American*[13] are unanimous in
concluding that R&D personnel, primarily engineers, within the product buying firms
are the primary decision makers in the key early stages of the buying process in which
the kind of product to be purchased and its specifications are determined.

Such engineers are engaged in 'engineering problem solving', and *derive* their need for
the product from a particular approach to a particular problem. Thus, if you ask an
engineer what he needs in the way of an equipment-cooling fan, his answer may properly
be that it depends *entirely* on the application—the engineer himself has *no* long-term
criteria for what *he* would like to see in a fan. Since engineers are constantly working on
different problems, the result is that an engineer's 'need' for an equipment-cooling fan

may well change from problem to problem. And, even within the context of a particular problem, the engineer's need will very likely change from moment to moment as the work of problem-solving proceeds.

As an example, suppose that an engineer is assigned the problem of stabilizing a circuit whose electrical parameters 'drift' unacceptably because it gets too hot when operating. The engineer may decide to redesign the circuit in such a way as to make it stable at the operating temperatures encountered—in which case he has *no* need for a fan. Or he may decide he will stabilize the circuit by cooling it—in which case he will have a very specific need for a fan, possibly meeting very tight cost, size and performance parameters.

Needs change rapidly because the engineering problem-solving process proceeds rapidly. Studies of the engineering design process by Allen[14] and Marples[15] show that radical changes in preferred solutions—and therefore in needed material and/or process equipment—occur within the span of a few weeks. Allen displays this rapid change in preferred solutions very graphically via 'solution development records' based on data from real-time monitoring of the engineering problem-solving process (see Figure 3).

If the above characterization of needs for new industrial products and the process by which they are generated is correct, one can see that such needs arise quickly within a particular customer firm, and may disappear or change just as quickly. Further, while present, the needs may be very precise, e.g. 'Yesterday I didn't want a fan, but today I want one which must be less than 5⅜ inches in diameter, must cost less than $5 in lots of 10 000'.

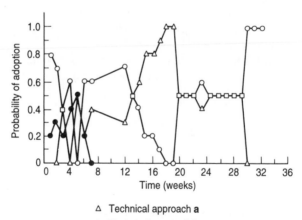

△ Technical approach **a**

○ Technical approach **b**

● Technical approach **c**

Figure 3. Solution Development Record of Engineering Team Designing an 'Antenna Radiation Subsystem' Showing Changes in Probability that Various Solutions Will be Adopted vs. Time. (*Source*: Redrawn from T. Allen, 'Studies of the Problem-Solving Process in Engineering Design', *IEEE Transactions on Engineering Management*, June 1966, p. 75.)

The conditions described above are appropriate for application of the *customer*-active paradigm because:

● *Customers who need the product are difficult to identify through manufacturer-initiated action.* (This assertion is only logical, given that the buyer is a not-very-accessible engineer in the midst of a corporation. He may never before have expressed any interest in the type of product which he now needs. It is a common observation in studies of industrial marketing.[16])

- *The selling opportunity—measured as starting when the customer first develops the need for the new product and ending when the customer selects an initial supplier—is brief (perhaps only weeks).* As we noted above, such an interval is probably too short to accomplish the steps prescribed for the manufacturer in MAP, but it would appear appropriate to the manufacturer's role in CAP.

The selling opportunity noted above is only the *initial* selling opportunity. Such initial selling opportunities are very important to would-be manufacturers of new industrial products, however, for two reasons:

(1) For any given customer, the initial selling opportunity is often the *only* selling opportunity because, after an initial supplier is settled upon, changeover to a new supplier often involves considerable cost to the buyer. Selection of a new supplier to fill repeat orders under such circumstances is unlikely.

(2) A manufacturer who becomes the supplier to the *first* buyer of a new industrial product often has an advantage in obtaining orders from new customers for the same product because (a) he is down the experience curve relative to would-be competitors; and (b) he is a known supplier of the item and thus increases his chances of obtaining 'product requests' from additional customers.

In sum, the CAP appears to fit current industrial product idea generation practice and to offer a good fit to the requirements of such idea generation as well. (Recall here the data from the Meadows and Peplow studies reviewed earlier, which suggest that products initiated via direct customer request tend to be among the commercially *more* successful of all new industrial products.) Perhaps, therefore, CAP offers a useful base on which to build new methodologies for the generation of ideas for new industrial products.

SUGGESTIONS FOR FURTHER RESEARCH

A useful new paradigm should suggest useful new questions. If idea transmission at user initiative is to form the basis for a paradigm describing how manufacturers often acquire ideas for new industrial products, the questions made pertinent for research and practice should be most useful. Among these are the following.

Communications strategy

The manufacturer switches from a paradigm in which his ability to perceive needs is under his control to one in which the customer must see the manufacturer as relevant for his problem and go on to 'narrow-cast' an idea to that manufacturer. Until and unless the customer does this, the manufacturer is unable to see the idea. Thus the question arises: How does the manufacturer get the customer—whom he cannot specifically identify—to see him as a potential supplier for a new product and contact him?

Manufacturers have already worked out many strategies to this end empirically. They advertise the types of technology they are skilled in, e.g. *Brazing problem? Call us'*. They advertise products they have made to solve other's problems, hoping to strike a spark in a customer engineer who may be, even now, solving a problem they could contribute to—but who is, frustratingly, invisible to them until he initiates contact, and so on.

But how is it best done? Studies of what makes a customer engineer see a manufacturer as relevant for his problem are clearly in order. For example, studies of problem-solving behavior by engineers[17] and others show that problem solvers, when faced with a new problem, tend to return to a technique they have previously used successfully. In the present context this finding suggests that customers will tend to transmit their needs to suppliers of old, familiar technologies (e.g. faced with a fastening problem they would tend to turn to a supplier of a familiar hardware-based fastening technology rather than a new, adhesive-based one).

If further study shows this hypothesis to be correct, an interesting strategy implication exists for suppliers of new technology (such as adhesives), i.e. that they should acquire a 'window on need' by buying into an established company which specializes in an older technology of analogous function.

Organizational issues

The manufacturer switches from a paradigm in which he was set up to perceive needs, analyze them and generate product ideas to one in which he must efficiently perceive and screen ideas. Such a change raises major organizational issues for the firm. While, in the CAP, marketing research was the locus of need perception and analysis activity (and was presumably organized and staffed for that role), in the new paradigm, sales becomes the new-need/new-product idea reception area.

How, in detail, do such messages come to sales? In field contacts with the customer? To the firm's central sales office? Are they transmitted orally or in writing? What incentives do sales people have for sensing these requests and passing them on? (Typically, salesmen's commissions are designed to reward large volume sales in the present—not possible sales of new products in the future.) Are salesmen properly trained to understand new product requests? Is there any incentive or organization which will ensure that the salesmen have someone to pass customer ideas along to for evaluation and action? And so on.

Product paradigms

Which classes of industrial product fall under the CAP paradigm and which under the MAP? Do these two exhaustively cover the universe of standard industrial products? As a research hypothesis, I would suggest that at least three paradigms, shown schematically in Figure 4, will be useful in understanding how ideas for new industrial products are acquired by their first-to-market manufacturers.

The first two paradigms are the CAP and the MAP that we have discussed to this point.

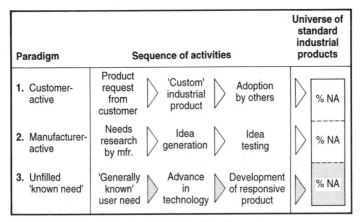

Figure 4. Three Proposed Paradigms for Industrial Product Idea Generation.

CAP we know describes the practice of many industrial-product situations, where a manufacturer, receiving an idea (often in the form of a special order), may decide that the potential payout is attractive enough to merit his working on it—by no means a certainty—and then *may* go on to make it a 'catalog item', a standard industrial product. We do not, however, know how many of these new industrial products, which start out as special order items, go on to become standard products.

MAP, in turn, is conventional wisdom in the consumer product field. I have suggested that *some* proportion of the universe of standard industrial products may appropriately be addressed by it, but, again, we don't know what proportion.

The third and final paradigm which I hypothesize will be found appropriate to some classes of industrial product—and for which I have anecdotal evidence only—is one in which 'everyone knows' what the customer wants, but progress in technology is required before the desired product can be realized. In my work in the computer, plastics and semiconductor industries, I have often been told that new product needs are not a problem: 'Everyone knows' that the customer wants more calculations per second and per dollar in the computer business; 'everyone knows' that the customer wants plastics which degrade less quickly in sunlight; and 'everyone knows' that the semiconductor customer wants more memory capacity on a single chip of silicon.

Under such circumstances, a customer request is not required to trigger a new product—only an advance in technology. And since many of the 'everyone knows' statements are phrased in dimensional terms, a series of new products can be introduced as technology advances, each responsive to the same dimension of need. Thus, computer manufacturers do not stop and rest on their laurels after introducing a faster computer—waiting for a user to approach them with a request for a still faster one. Rather, they continue to move down the clearly defined 'dimension of merit' of greater computing speed as quickly as their advancing technology allows.

I suggest that the absence of explicit need messages directly associated with the samples of engineering plastics and plastics additives examined by Berger and Boyden are the result of such an effect: e.g. that the needs were generally known. Conversations with participants in these industries have lent support to this hypothesis, and further research into the matter should be of value.

NOTES

Readers interested in a further exploration of some of the ideas expressed in this paper may wish to refer to the paper cited in note 3.

1. Empirical research into the industrial goods innovation process has shown that the level of manufacturer 'understanding of user need' co-varies strongly with the level of commercial success attained by an innovative industrial product. See Rothwell, Freeman et al., 'Sappho Updated—Project Sappho Phase II', Research Policy, **3** (1974), 261.
2. Brand, G. The Industrial Buying Decision (New York: John Wiley & Sons, 1972); Choffray, J. M. and Lilien, G, 'Models of the Multiperson Choice Process with Application to the Adoption of Industrial Products', M.I.T. Sloan School of Management Working Paper #861–76, June 1976; Håkansson H. and Östbert, C., 'Industrial Marketing: An Organizational Problem?' Industrial Marketing Management, **4** (1975); Mattsson, L. G., 'Systems Selling as a Strategy on Industrial Markets', Industrial Marketing Management, **3** (1973); Robinson, Farris and Wind, Industrial Buying and Creative Marketing (Boston: Allyn and Bacon, 1967).
3. von Hippel, E. 'A Customer-Active Paradigm for Industrial Idea Generation', M.I.T. Sloan School of Management, Working Paper #935–77, May 1977.
4. Meadows, D. 'Estimate Accuracy and Project Selection Models in Industrial Research', Industrial Management Review, Spring (1969). Also, 'Data Appendix: Accuracy of Technical Estimates in Industrial Research Planning', M.I.T. Sloan School of Management Working Paper #301–67.
5. Peplow, M. E. 'Design Acceptance', in The Design Method, Gregory, S. A. (ed.) (London: Butterworth, 1960).
6. von Hippel, E. 'The Dominant Role of Users in the Scientific Instrument Innovation Process', Research Policy, **5** (1976), 212–239.
7. von Hippel, E. 'The Dominant Role of the User in Semiconductor and Electronic Subassembly Process Innovation', IEEE Transactions on Engineering Management, May 1977; von Hippel, E., 'Transferring Process Equipment Innovations from User-Innovators to Equipment Manufacturing Firms', R&D Management, October 1977.
8. von Hippel, E, notes 6 and 7 above.
9. Rubenstein, A. H., 'Studies of Idea Flow in Research and Development', presented to the New York Chapter, the Institute of Management Sciences, November 1963, p. 2. (As cited in Baker, Siegman and Rubenstein, 'The Effect of Perceived Needs and Means on the Generation of Ideas for Industrial Research and Development Projects', IEEE Transactions on Engineering Management, December 1967, p. 158).
10. Myers, S. and Marquis, D. Successful Industrial Innovations (Washington, D.C.: National Science Foundation, NSF 69–17, 1969), p. 5.
11. Brand, note 2 above.
12. Robinson et al., note 2 above.
13. Scientific American, How Industry Buys/1970 (New York: Scientific American, Inc., 1969).
14. Allen, T. 'Studies of the Problem-Solving Process in Engineering Design', IEEE Transactions on Engineering Management, June, 1966.
15. Marples, D. 'The Decisions of Engineering Design', IRE Transactions on Engineering Management, June 1961.
16. Robinson et al., note 2 above.
17. Allen, T. and Marquis, D. G. 'Positive and Negative Biasing Sets: The Effects of Prior Experience on Research Performance', IEEE Transactions on Engineering Management, December 1964.

16

Do Firms Need a Custom-Designed New Product Screening Model?

Ulrike de Brentani

INTRODUCTION

Applying a systematic and formal management decision approach is closely linked to improved success in the development and launch of new products. Companies using a formal evaluation method, particularly when applied at the front-end or screening stage of the new product process, give serious consideration to fewer new product ideas and spend a greater proportion of their resources on market 'winners' (Booz, Allen and Hamilton, 1982). In spite of these benefits, many firms still do not make regular use of the more sophisticated and more analytical evaluation models that have been proposed in the literature and recommended for screening purposes (Cooper, 1980, 1985; Hopkins, 1980; Souder, 1973).

Why are the new product evaluation models that are currently available not fully used? Some authors argue that managers operate in a company-specific mode, and, therefore, available decision models require substantial fine-tuning to reflect the characteristics of the particular type of firm (Choffray and Lilien, 1980; Lilien, 1975; Little, 1970). However, other evidence—including the findings presented here—indicates that a fairly universal set of new product screening criteria appears to be relevant for most companies (Cooper, 1980). This might suggest that managers could benefit *now* from using some of the new product evaluation models available, without requiring firm-specific adaptations.

Although the issue of model customization has held a relatively important place in the literature, there has been almost no research to determine (1) whether the decision model used for evaluation new product ideas does, in fact, differ in different kinds of companies, and (2) whether customized decision models lead to different, possibly better, new product decisions. This article addresses these issues by investigating the screening decision behavior model of managers under different type-of-firm conditions.

Before describing the findings and discussing the managerial implications in full, the article deals with (1) the importance of a formal new product screening model, (2) the question of model customization and (3) the research design and execution.

Reprinted with permission from *Journal of Product Innovation Management*, Vol. 3, 1986, pp. 108–119

THE NEED FOR FORMAL EVALUATION MODELS

Making new product choices is clearly one of the riskiest and most difficult management decisions. Success in launching new products is increasingly responsible for the growth and profitability of firms (Booz, Allen and Hamilton, 1982), yet the rate of failure and the cost of developing and marketing new products remain high (Booz, Allen and Hamilton, 1982; Crawford, 1979). Furthermore, products that are successfully launched now face a shorter average life, and this makes achieving an adequate profit much less certain. Finally, the decision is a difficult one because companies must usually select the 'right' new product idea from among several development alternatives. Inadequate knowledge about the project, a dynamic new product environment, and opposing points of view regarding a project's feasibility and merit frequently lead to poor development choices.

It is therefore not surprising that managers have begun to search for methods that can help to reduce both the difficulty of the new product decision and its overall level of risk. Booz, Allen and Hamilton (1982) show that, since 1968, companies have shifted toward a formal new product process and have more than doubled the resources they allocate to the early predevelopment stages. Similarly, in Hopkins' (1980) study, about half of the firms used some type of formal screening method. Although these research findings are encouraging, they nevertheless show that many firms still rely on intuitive new product assessments and that managers who use formal models favour the simpler, more subjective checklist approach (Hopkins, 1980).

Recent evidence suggests that some firms are seriously beginning to experiment with the more analytical new product 'scoring'-type models that are usually recommended for screening purposes (Baker and Freeland, 1975; McGuire, 1973; Souder, 1973). The better models are based on the past success/failure experiences of firms. Such models comprise a weighted, empirically derived set of success/failure criteria which, when rated and integrated, provide managers with both important diagnostic capabilities and a prediction of the project's likelihood of success (Cooper, 1985; Freimer and Simon, 1967). Although scoring models do have certain weaknesses (see Baker and Freeland, 1975, for a full discussion) and new product success can certainly never be guaranteed through model use, the research evidence is clear that this type of model can act as an important decision aid.

In summary, although several new product scoring models have been developed (see Baker and Freeland, 1975), few have been applied on a regular basis. Some researchers assert that the models are too general and that decision models should be customized to reflect the new product development environment of the particular company if they are to be viewed as relevant by managers and achieve more widespread application (Urban and Hauser, 1980; Wind, 1982). The issue is should new product decision models be adapted or customized to the industrial type of firm and would such customization lead to more widespread use by managers?

MODEL CUSTOMIZATION

Several authors argue in favour of model customization. According to Little (1970) and Lilien (1975), management decision models, in general, are realistic only when they are adapted to fit the user and the specific use situation. In product development, proponents urge that new product models be customized by taking into account corporate idiosyncrasies and unique situational factors (Choffray and Lilien, 1980; Urban and Hauser, 1980; Wind, 1982). Booz, Allen and Hamilton (1982) summarize this attitude in their call for 'a company-specific, implementation-oriented approach' to the new product development process.

Proponents of customization offer several reasons why evaluation models should be adapted. First, evolution criteria used by different companies might not be the same. The important factors underlying new product choice are, after all, largely derived from company objectives, resources, competitive strengths and management philosophies. Because these characteristics tend to vary for different types of firms, the crucial elements determining the acceptance or rejection of new product ideas could also differ (Choffray and Lilien, 1980; Wind, 1982). Managers who use a generalized screening model, that is, a model that is *not* specific to their firm, might focus on the wrong criteria, and this could lead to poor new product choices.

A second ground for customizing new product evaluation models is the possibility of achieving a more efficient decision process. Research evidence indicates that different companies do not use the same number of criteria when assessing new product alternatives (Choffray and Lilien, 1980; Cooper 1980). A generalized screening model—one that is relevant for all types of firms—would, of necessity, include a broad set of screening factors. Companies that rely on a small number of basic criteria might find using such a model unnecessarily time-consuming.

Convincing managers to make use of a formal screening model when making new product choices is a third reason for proposing company-specific adaptations. According to Little (1970), practitioners respond positively to decision tools that are designed to fit their particular problem environment; hence, customizing the screening model may be essential in achieving more widespread application.

In spite of the arguments in favour of customization, several factors indicate that adapting new product evaluation models to the individual type of firm may not always be necessary. Although decision criteria have been shown to vary for different types of companies (Choffray and Lilien, 1980; Shocker and Srinivasan, 1979), there is little evidence to show that customized models lead to better new product decisions. In fact, in this study of 103 industrial firms, Cooper (1980) found that the factors that underlie the ultimate success of new products are fairly universal. This indicates that a generalized new product screening model might be appropriate. Furthermore, the argument that managers need models that are highly specific to their mode of decision making does not preclude the use of a generalized set of screening factors. An analysis of many of the normative and empirically derived new product evaluation models, as well as the evidence presented here, suggests that managers tend to emphasize, more or less, the same basic criteria (Bradbury *et al.*, 1973; Cooper, 1982).

In conclusion, whether companies actually use or really need customized new product screening models is not a straightforward issue. Ideally, this question should be addressed by identifying the particular evaluation models that companies apply and then determining whether a firm-specific model, as opposed to a more generalized screening model, leads to improved new product choices. This approach is precluded, however, by the fact that many firms do not have formal evaluation methods in place and because the quality of new product decisions generally only becomes evident long after the screening stage. An alternative approach, used here, focuses on the decision behaviour model of the *manager* rather than that of the firm.

Managers can generally be expected to operate within the context of their firm, and we can assume that, on average, their screening behaviour is a realistic representation of the new product evaluation model used by *firms*. By analyzing the decision behaviour of managers in different types of firms, we can determine whether the models actually used are universal or company specific. Dealing with the second part of the question, 'are firm-specific models necessary or desirable?', is somewhat less obvious. Several conclusions can be drawn from the analysis presented here, depending on how we view the quality of the 'average' manager's new product screening decision. This will be discussed at the end of the article.

THE RESEARCH

The research involved two stages. First, a 'general' model, describing the new product screening behaviour of managers from a variety of companies, was presented. In the second step, the analysis turned to investigating how this model might be altered in the case of different types of firms. A brief discussion of the general screening behaviour model is provided below.

A general model of how managers screen new product proposals

In a recent article, Cooper and de Brentani (1984) presented a model that describes how managers make screening decisions, including a list of criteria and the criteria weights. The study involved a large sample of managers from industrial product firms who rated new product proposals, which had recently been evaluated by the firms, in terms of a comprehensive list of 86 screening attributes. Factor analysis was used to reduce the attributes to a smaller and independent set of multidimensional screening factors. Multiple regression (and two-group discriminant analysis) related the factors to the degree of proposal acceptance or rejection. (The Appendix, section A, reviews the research approach.) Table 1 gives a breakdown by industry of the firms that took part in the study.

Table 1. Participating firms: classification by industry

Industry	Number of firms	Percent of total
Electrical, electronics and communications	26	44.1
Chemical	9	15.3
Pulp and paper	4	6.8
Metal products	3	5.0
Industrial equipment apparatus	3	5.0
Construction materials	3	5.0
Avionics	2	3.4
Petroleum	2	3.4
Other	7	12.0
Total no. of firms	59	

The findings, which are presented in Tables 2 and 3, are summarized below:

- A total of 11 multiattribute evaluative factors characterize the new product screening domain of the firms.

Table 2. Screening factors: summary descriptions based on results of factor analysis

Factor		Description
F1	Product differential advantage	Technological leadership achievable through revolutionary innovations or the innovative application of a different technology resulting from a strong in-house new product program; or market dominance achievable through strongly differentiated and clearly superior product offering
F2	Corporate synergy	A new product that fits the firm's current business, its organization, and its managerial skills. Of particular importance is marketing synergy, that is, are current customers a potential market and can present distribution, selling, and research resources be used for launch purposes?
F3	Technological and production synergy	Can the product be developed and produced using current engineering, design, and production skills and resources?
F4	Project financing	What type of financing is required? Both complexity of financing and source of funding (developer, customer, or government) are relevant
F5	Financial potential	Basic quantitative performance criteria, including expected market growth, sales growth, market share, profitability and likelihood of success
F6	Size of market	Does the product have a strong market potential? Dollar sales potential, expected number, and variety of customers, and geographical scope are all relevant
F7	Diversification strategy	Is this product an opportunity for entering a new market, a new technology, and/or a new product class (to the firm?)
F8	Market maintenance strategy	Is the proposal a product replacement or a technological enhancement that can help the firm maintain its strategic position in the market or industry?
F9	Product life	The expected life of the product, its probable development pattern, and its stability with regard to production and market needs and preferences
F10	Rational customer	Do customers understand the product: do they use objective buying criteria, and are they of a commercial versus an institutional nature?
F11	Domestic market	Is the market potential primarily domestic (Canadian) or of a worldwide scope?

- Nine of these factors are highly significant in explaining the decision of managers to accept or reject proposals ($p \leqslant 0.0001$; regression analysis, adjusted $R^2 = 0.567$; discriminant analysis, 86.2% jackknife correct classification).
- Of the nine significant factors, four criteria dominate the new product screening decision (together accounting for 87.7% of the explained variation). A project's expected financial potential (F5), its corporate synergy (F2), and technological and production fit (F3), plus the potential for achieving a differential advantage (F1) play an overwhelming positive role in the acceptance of new product proposals.

Table 3.The new product screening behaviour model—Multiple Regression Results[a]

Screening factors	Regression coefficient	F value	Significance of F	Percent of variation explained
F5 Financial potential	1.398	158.2	0.0001	33.0
F2 Corporate synergy	1.285	134.2	0.0001	60.5
F3 Technological and production synergy	0.931	69.9	0.0001	74.8
F1 Differential advantage	0.880	62.7	0.0001	87.7
F9 Product life	0.576	26.7	0.0001	92.1
F8 Market maintenance strategy	0.426	14.6	0.0002	95.9
F6 Size of market	0.385	12.0	0.0006	98.2
F7 Diversification strategy	0.269	5.8	0.0161	99.3
F11 Domestic market	0.223	4.1	0.0450	100.0
F10 Rational customer	−0.177	2.6	N.S.[b]	100.0
F4 Project financing	0.059	0.3	N.S.	100.0
Constant	0.588			

[a] Adjusted R^2 = 0.567: F of relationship = 54.3: significant at the 0.0001 level.
[b] N.S. = not significant.

- Managers view five additional factors as significant but secondary screening criteria. The project's expected product life (F9), its strategic impact—market maintenance strategy (F8) and diversification strategy (F7)—as well as market size (F6) and domestic potential (F11) are all positively linked to screening outcomes.
- Two factors—project financing (F4) and rational market (F10)—describe new product proposals but are not significant screening factors.

The model describes the screening decision behavior of managers across a large sample of firms and, as such, provides a good representation of both the general criteria that managers use and of the relative importance of these criteria when evaluating new product ideas.

Analyzing firm-specific models

Whether these criteria (or their relative importance) change, depending on the characteristics of the firm, is the next question to be addressed. The research approach first involved identifying those company characteristics that may affect the set of criteria underlying the decision to accept or reject new product proposals.

Seven company dimensions were gleaned from the literature as relevant for customizing new product screening models. These can be classified as (1) firm demographics and (2) company product policies.

Firm demographics. Firm demographics includes company *size*, level of *growth*, the *industry* of the firm, *government involvement* and *foreign control*. First, in large companies, evaluation criteria may differ from those of small firms because screening decisions may be more formalized (Booz, Allen and Hamilton, 1982; Wind, 1982), corporate resources may be less of a constraint (Urban and Hauser, 1980; Wind, 1982), more projects may be carried on simultaneously (Wind, 1982), and large companies are often able to absorb a greater risk (Urban and Hauser, 1980; Wind, 1982). Second, a company's past growth and its industry can affect the criteria used. High-growth firms or companies in technologically dynamic industries may have different expectations regarding techno-logical leadership and market growth than firms in more stable industries (Booz, Allen and Hamilton, 1982; Pessemier, 1982). Finally, two additional firm demographics relate to the national industrial scene (Canada) used for this study: government policies and foreign interests often influence the enterprise (e.g. through ownership or through investment in R&D), their effect on new product screening behavior cannot be ignored.[1]

New product policies. The second category of company characteristics that can affect the screening decision is new product policies. *Firm innovativeness*, or management attitudes about new product development, is often seen as influencing the evaluation (Booz, Allen and Hamilton, 1982; Urban and Hauser, 1980; Wind, 1982). Firms with an innovative or strong technological orientation might worry less about their ability to develop products successfully than companies with a less innovative background. Simi-larly, different *attitudes toward risk* could affect the screening approach (Mansfield and Wagner, 1975). Managers' preference for lower risk, according to some authors, leads to a more conservative attitude with greater emphasis on project 'knowns' (Wind, 1982).

The seven company dimensions used in the analysis, along with their operational measures, are presented in Table 4.

Method

Two methods were employed in analyzing company-specific effects on screening de-cision behavior. Using the screening behavior model described above, all seven com-pany dimensions were introduced, stepwise, in the form of dummy variables (0/1). In this way, the significance of each dimension as a possible moderator to the model could be assessed. Next, each company dimension was introduced separately in order to determine the nature of company-specific new product screening behavior models. Statistical tests were used to assess the effect of the company characteristics on the model, as a whole, and on each of the 11 evaluative criteria. (The Appendix, Section B, provides a detailed discussion of the methodology.)

The following two research questions were addressed:

1. Are the *evaluative criteria* that underly screening decisions the same for different types of companies? For example, do managers in large firms emphasize a different subset (number and type) of factors than do evaluators in small companies?
2. Is the screening decision model that is derived from the evaluation behavior of one type of firm *predictively equivalent* to the model desribing another type of company? In other words, if evaluators rate new product ideas in terms of the 11 factors, does the model that describes screening behavior in large companies, for example, predict significantly different accept/reject decisions from the small-firm model?

DISCUSSION OF RESULTS

Variations in screening behaviour

By introducing each company characteristic separately as a moderator to the overall screening behavior model (all cases/firms), we can compare the decision-making approach of managers in different subgroups of firms. This permits us to answer the first

Table 4. Company characteristics and operational measures

Company characteristic	Operational measure[a]
Firm demographics	
1. Size of firm	Current sales volume (\$)[b]
	Large: sales $\geq$ \$150 million
	Small: sales $\leq$ \$40 million
2. Growth of firm	Average annual sales growth over past 5 years[c]
	High: growth $\geq$ 20%
	Low: growth $\leq$ 14%
3. Industry of firm	Hi-tech vs. 'other'[d]
	Hi-tech: electronics, electrical, communications, chemical
	Low-tech: all others
4. Government support of R&D	Government support of R&D[e]
	High: $\geq$ 20% of total R&D
	Low: 0%
5. Foreign control	Foreign ownership of firm(%) (interview)
	High: $\geq$ 50% foreign control
	Low: 0% (i.e. Canadian owned)
New product policies	
6. Innovativeness of firm	R&D as percent of sales[f]
	High: $>$ 6.5% of sales
	Low: $<$ 4.0% of sales
7. Risk orientation of firm	'Please rate how you see the degree of risk orientation of your firm/division in the new product arena' (interview)
	Very conservative to very risky on a scale of 1–7
	High: self-rating $>$ 5
	Low: self-rating $<$ 5

[a] Notes b–f refer to authors who have used measures in describing/defining the particular company characteristic.
[b] Booz, Allen and Hamilton (1982); Cooper (1980); Pessemier (1982); Wind (1982).
[c] Booz, Allen and Hamilton (1982); Cooper (1980); Pessemier (1982).
[d] Urban and Hauser (1980); Wind (1982).
[e] Urban and Hauser (1980).

research question: do managers in different kinds of companies use different decision behavior models when screening new product ideas? The results, which have been summarized in Table 5, indicate that the decision model underlying new product evaluation does vary somewhat among firms[2] and that companies can be classified as using one of four basic types of screening behavior models: (1) the large or domestic firm model; (2) the maintenance strategy model; (3) the small or low-tech firm model; (4) the innovator or venturer firm model. These are discussed below.

The large or domestic firm model. Of the four model groups, the screening behavior of large companies or of domestic (i.e. Canadian-owned) firms appears to be the most straightforward. Maintaining a stable internal corporate environment seems to be the most important concern when developing new products. These companies focus on five basic factors, of which a clear financial potential (F5) and a good overall corporate fit (both corporate synergy (F2) and technological/production synergy (F3)) are of particular importance. In addition, achieving a differential advantage (F1) and a long product life (F9) are preferred components of 'go' projects.

Table 5. Company-specific screening behavior models[a]

Screening factors	Large or domestic firms			Maintenance strategy firms				Small or low-tech firms			Innovator or venturer firms			
	Large firm	Domestic firm	High govt. support	Low-growth firm	Low-innov. firm	Low-risk firm	Foreign control	Small firm	Low govt. support	Low-tech. ind.	High-growth firm	High-risk firm	High-innov. firm	High-tech. ind.
F5 (financial potential)	*1	*1	*1	*1	*1	*3	*2	*1	*2	*1	*1	*1	*1	*2
F2 (corporate synergy)	*2	*2	*2	*2	*2	*1	*1	*2	*1	*3	*2	*2	*2	*1
F3 (technol. prod. synergy)	*3	*3	*3	*3	*3	*2	*3	*4	*3	*2	*4	*4	*4	*3
F1 (differential advantage)	*4	*4	*5	*4	*4	*4	*4	*3	*4	*4	*3	*3	*3	*4
F9 (product life)	*5	*5	*4	*5	*5	*5	*5	*6	*5	*5	*5	*5	*5	*5
F8 (market maintenance)			†6	†7	†7	†7	†6	†5	†8	†6	†7	†6	†6	†7
F6 (market size)				†6	†6	†6	†7	†8	†6	†7	†6	†7		
F7 (diversification strat.)								†7	†7	†8		†8	†7	
F11 (domestic market)											†8	†8		†6
F10 (rational customer)						Not significant in any of the models								
F4 (project financing)														
No. of significant factors	5	5	6	7	7	7	7	8	8	8	8	8	7	7
Sample size	171	133	134	214	223	195	235	197	234	173	154	173	145	195

[a] Asterisks (*) and daggers (†) represent universal and secondary criteria, respectively: significant at $p \leq 0.05$. Numbers 1–8 represent importance rank of factors in model.

A similar screening attitude is expressed by companies with a high level of government R&D support. Manages emphasize the same five 'basic' criteria as above but, additionally, look for the technological enhancement or innovative update potential in a new product as a way of maintaining its market position (F8, Table 2).

The maintenance strategy firm model. Managers displaying this type of screening behavior tend to operate in companies that have a low sales growth, that are viewed as less innovative, or that have a high level of foreign control. As in the previous model, these firms have a relatively conservative screening attitude. Th_y too emphasize the five basic criteria but, in addition, consider market maintenance strategy (F8) as well as market size (F6) to be important screening factors. This suggests a development programme aimed at maintaining 'cash cow'-type products.

The small or low-tech firm model. Small firms, companies in low-tech industries (see Table 3 for breakdown), or those with low government R&D support are also similar in their screening behavior. They emphasize the five basic criteria but look for three additional factors when making new product choices. These include market size (F6), market maintenance (F8), and diversification strategy (F7). The screening behavior of this group of firms differs from the companies in the previous grouping because they *also* consider diversification as an approach to achieving their new product objectives. In fact, for both the small and the low-tech enterprise, diversifying outside of their current field may be the only way to achieve growth. For example, small firms may not be able to compete with industry giants, and firms in low-tech industries may be faced with low growth. Hence, diversification into new product classes and/or new markets may provide important expansion opportunities.

The innovator or venturer firm model. Venturer firms are accustomed to high sales growth, they are risk-oriented, committed to R&D, or belong to high-tech industries. As with the small firm/low-tech grouping above, these companies emphasize not only the five basic factors, but seek *both* market maintenance (F8) and diversification (F7) when evaluating new product ideas. However, their reasons are probably different. For venturer firms, 'maintenance' is likely to mean keeping up technologically; it entails, simultaneously, a defensive and an offensive new product development strategy in a rapidly changing environment. This dynamic new product environment leads to entirely new product and market opportunities (i.e. diversification).

Because new product proposals often represent advancements along a technological continuum for venturer firms, it is not surprising that market size (F6) for any one proposal is *not* a significant factor. Instead, a reasonably measured domestic market (F11) is important, possibly as a way of lowering the development risk.

In summary, the factors that underlie the new product screening decisions of managers are different, depending on the type of firm. Differences were found both in the number and in the precise set of screening factors used and in the relative importance of these criteria in determining go/no-go decisions.

Similarities in screening behavior

That variations exist in the criteria companies use when they evaluate new product ideas is not surprising and confirms what some researchers have previously found (Choffray and Lilien, 1980; Shocker and Srinivasan, 1979). However, the opinion that such variations significantly affect screening outcomes is not supported. In other words, the findings suggest that the similarities in the screening behavior of firms far outweigh the differences when it comes to predicting the go/no-go decision.

Results of the analysis—relating the 11 screening factors *and* the 7 company dimensions to project acceptance/rejection—show that the company characteristics studied here do not have a significant effect on predictions. The screening behavior model remains virtually unchanged from the original 11-factor model (see Table 3 and Cooper and de Brentani, 1984). The first four predictor variables still account for close to 88% of the explained variation, five additional factors are of secondary importance, and F10 and F4 and all seven company dimensions are not significant in determining the screening decision outcome (i.e. $p > 0.05$).[3]

The analysis of the models that describe the screening behavior of different types of firms leads to similar conclusions. Company-specific models are not significantly different in terms of the accept/reject decision they predict. In other words, using the model derived from the new product screening evaluations made in large firms, for example, on average, predicts similar go/no-go choices for small firms as using a small-firm screening behavior model. For each of the company characteristics analyzed, the stated hypothesis, that pairs of company-type models are predictive equivalent (i.e., coincident, see Appendix, B) was *not* rejected. (See Table 6 for the result of the *F*-tests.)

Table 6. *F*-tests determining the predictive equivalence of company-specific screening behavior models

Model comparisons	*F*-value	Significance[a]
1. Size of firm Large vs. small	0.93	N.S.
2. Growth of firm High vs. low	0.80	N.S.
3. Industry of firm High- vs. low-tech	1.48	N.S.
4. Govt. support of R&D High vs. low	1.32	N.S.
5. Foreign control Foreign vs. domestic	0.74	N.S.
6. Innovativeness of firm High vs. low	0.55	N.S.
7. Risk orientation High vs. low	1.45	N.S.

[a] N.S. = not significant at the 0.05 level.

Further insights regarding similarities in screening behavior can be gained by reexamining the information provided in Table 5. Firm-specific variations in criteria and in relative weightings notwithstanding, it is also clear that the factors that underlie new product choice are fairly universal. Five basic criteria are common to the screening behavior of all types of companies studied, whereas four other factors play a significant secondary role in only some of the firms. This would indicate that the characteristics of the firm have a much smaller impact on screening decision behavior than has traditionally been thought.

CONCLUSIONS

In summary, the findings show that companies do vary somewhat in how they screen new product ideas but that these differences do not significantly affect the predictive character of the decision behavior model. The overwhelming conclusion from the analysis appears to be that the common decision criteria used by all managers far outweigh the firm-specific criteria in importance. The commonalities dominate the differences to the extent that predictions of go/no-go based on the commonalities alone are not significantly different from predictions based on models developed for specific types of firms.

What these research results mean with regard to the issue of model customization is somewhat less obvious. Given that the decision behavior of managers is similar, should companies introduce models that are customized to the particular type of firm or should they think more in terms of a universal or generalized new product screening model?

We cannot argue conclusively from the evidence presented here that new product screening models should or should *not* be customized. No such normative judgment is possible because the models that are derived in this analysis are based on the decision *behavior* of managers, and we do not know for certain whether the choices that were made were good screening decisions. One might argue that had managers applied a properly customized model—one that explicitly reflects the particular type of company situation—they might have made different and, perhaps, better new product development decisions. In fact, the high rate of commercial new product failure might support such a notion.

However, a number of factors, besides choosing the wrong new product idea, have been cited as reasons for new product failure (Cooper, 1975). Hence, we should not assume that it is *necessarily* the screening decision or a poor decision behavior model that is at fault. The essential question becomes do managers, on average, make good or poor decisions? There is considerable evidence that supports the notion that an average behavior model, which is based on many decisions of a certain type, is fairly close to an optimal decision model (Goldberg, 1970). If this is true, then the screening behavior model(s) derived in this study might, in fact, be viewed as reasonably good. This would imply that customized screening models may not be necessary because the models did not vary dramatically from one type of firm to another.

The purpose of the screening process when evaluating new product ideas could also provide some insights about adapting screening models. The analysis shows that some firms use fewer criteria than others and achieve equivalent screening predictions. If the purpose is only to derive a go/no-go decision, these firms could make decisions more quickly and probably at a lower cost by using only the minimum number of factors, particularly when there are large pools of proposals requiring appraisal. On the other hand, the purpose of the screening model may be not only to help companies predict the likelihood of success of a proposed new product but also to provide insights about a project's strengths and weaknesses and about the problems that are likely to arise during development and market launch. In this case, a general model—one that includes a more extensive set of screening factors—may be better because it offers much broader diagnostic capabilities.

Finally, it may be argued that model customization leads to more widespread application of formal screening models. In this study, the decision model underlying new product choices does appear to vary somewhat for different firms and, according to Little (1970), managers are more likely to apply models and make better decisions if the models reflect their particular problem and mode of decision making. Although, in some cases, companies may place particular emphasis on a certain firm-specific criterion, for example, whether a new product idea is enhanced by an already established brand image, the evidence also indicates that customization might not be necessary, especially if prediction of go/no-go is the primary purpose. It seems much more likely that it is the actual application of a formal evaluation model encompassing essential criteria, rather than adaptation of the model to the type of firm, that leads to better management decisions. Thus, if the manager is deciding between waiting for a fully customized evaluation model and taking advantage now of the tools *already* available, we recommend the latter. It can lead to a more systematic and objective decision-making approach, reduce uncertainties, and probably improve screening performance.

ACKNOWLEDGEMENTS

This research was supported by a grant from the Canadian Government, Department of Regional and Industrial Expansion, Office of Industrial Innovation. The author also thanks Dr R. G. Cooper and Dr B. Little for their support and encouragement in the writing of this article.

APPENDIX: RESEARCH METHODOLOGY

A. Deriving the screening behavior model

The study involved a judgmental, geographically convenient sample of industrial product firms with an identifiable new product program.[4] Two data collection phases ensued. In phase I, 45 managers (from 45 firms), responsible for new product development, were interviewed for purposes of (1) exploring the screening attributes companies use and (2) determining company demographics and new product policies. In phase II, the sample was increased to 63 firms; 282 managers selected and rated two new product projects—one accept and one reject decision of the firm in which he/she had recently taken part – in terms of (1) 86 screening attributes (using a 7-point Likert scale from 'strongly disagree' to 'strongly agree') and (2) the degree of acceptance/rejection (ranging from +5 [strong accept] to −5 [strong reject]. A total of 192 managers from 59 firms responded (68.1%), yielding 368 usable rated proposals.[5]

Factor analysis reduced the 86 rated attributes to 11 independent dimensions, explaining 49.1% of the total variation (principal component analysis; varimax rotation). Choice of the 11-factor solution was based on the scree test, Bartlett significance test, factor interpretability (Catell, 1966; Green, 1978), and Cronbach alpha construct reliability (Nunnally, 1978). (See Table 2 for a summary description of the 11 factors.)

Next, the 11 screening factors were related to (1) the degree of project acceptance/ rejection (multiple regression analysis, using a continuous variable) and (2) the go/no-go status (1/0) of the project (two-group discriminant analysis). The two models were virtually identical; both described the average screening behavior model of firms in terms of nine statistically significant factors ($p \leqslant 0.05$) (see Table 3, regression model).

B. Analyzing company-specific models

Whether the characteristics of the firm affect the screening behavior model used by managers was analyzed in three stages. First, using stepwise multiple regression, all seven company dimensions (see Table 4) were introduced as dummy variables (0/1) to the 11-factor model. F-tests ($p \leqslant 0.05$) determined which factors and which company dimensions were statistically significantly related to project acceptance/rejection.[6] (Interaction terms were not included because company/factor correlations were low; i.e. $r \leqslant 0.3$.)

Next, projects were grouped (two groups) according to their rating on each of the seven company dimensions, and company-specific screening behavior models were inferred using multiple regression analysis. F-tests ($p \leqslant 0.05$) determined the statistical significance of each of the factors in the models.

The third stage of the analysis tested pairs of company-type models for significant differences in terms of the go/no-go prediction. The company dimensions were defined as dummy variables (0/1) and introduced, each on an individual basis, to the 11-factor regression model. The following portrays the analysis for each of the company dimensions:

$$D_i = w_0 + \sum_{j=1}^{11} w_j F_{ij} + w_{12}C$$

$$+ \sum_{k=13}^{23} w_k CF_{ij} + \epsilon_i \tag{1}$$

where D_i = project acceptance/rejection rating ($+5$ to -5);

F_{ij} = factor scores for each project i ($i = 1–368$) on j evaluative factors ($j = 1–11$);

C = company characteristic, dummy variable (0/1);

CF_{ij} = interaction terms on j factors;

w_j = unstandardized regression coefficient (weight) of each evaluative factor;

w_{12} = unstandardized regression coefficient of C, when $C = 1$;

w_k = unstandardized regression coefficient of interaction term $CF_{ij} (k = 13 \ldots 23)$;

w_0 = intercept, when $C = 0$;

ϵ_i = error term;

Σ = summation.

Equation (1) can be restated to depict each pair of company-specific screening behavior models. In the case of firm size, for example, new product proposals rated in large firms (where $C = 1$) involve the following equation:

$$D_{i(C=1)} = w_0 + \sum_{j=1}^{11} w_j F_{ij} + w_{12}(1) \tag{1}$$

$$+ \sum_{k=13}^{23} w_k F_{ij}(1) + \epsilon_i \tag{2}$$

which can be restated as

$$D_{i(C=1)} = (w_0 + w_{12})$$

$$+ \sum_{j=1}^{11} \sum_{k=13}^{23} (w_j + w_k) F_{ij} + \epsilon_i \tag{2.1}$$

where $(w_0 + w_{12})$ and $(w_j + w_k)$ represent the intercept and slope of the large-company model.

Similarly, for small-firm projects (where $C = 0$), the following equation applies:

$$D_{i(C=0)} = w_0 + \sum_{j=1}^{11} w_j F_{ij} + w_{12}(0)$$

$$+ \sum_{k=13}^{23} w_k F_{ij}(0) + \epsilon_i \tag{3}$$

which reduces to

$$D_{i(C=0)} = w_0 + \sum_{j=1}^{11} w_j F_{ij} + \epsilon_i \tag{3.1}$$

where w_0 and w_j measure the intercept and slope, respectively.

Testing for significant differences between company-specific models
Linear regression models are *not* significantly different if they have both the same intercept and the same slope. In multiple regression analysis, as used here, models are coincident (predictively equivalent) when both the constant (intercept) and the vector of weights (slope) in one model are not significantly different from those in the other model. Therefore, to determine model coincidence in the company-specific screening behavior models, the following hypothesis was tested:

$$H_1: (w_0 + w_{12}) = w_0$$

and (vector w_j + vector w_k) = vector w_j

which can be restated as

$$H_1: w_{12} = 0 \text{ and vector } w_k = 0.$$

To determine whether the model pairs for each company dimension are predictively equivalent, dummy variable regression models were inferred, as shown above, and the F-test ($p \leq 0.05$) was used to test H_1 (as per Kleinbaum and Kupper (1978).

NOTES

1. During personal interviews with managers, these two characteristics were identified as important for firms operating in Canada because many companies are foreign controlled and because government plays a significant role in supporting R&D. To the extent that these conditions are relevant in other countries, their effect can be viewed in universal terms.
2. Both the number of screening factors and, in some cases, their relative importance differed significantly.
3. The 18-variable model (11 screening factors and seven company dimensions) is not shown because it is almost identical to the 11-factor model.
4. Location: Montreal, Toronto and Ottawa. Source: *Directory of Scientific and Technological Capabilities in Canadian Industry*. Ottawa, Canada: Ministry of State, Science and Technology, 1977. Addendum, 1980.
5. A small number of cases were deleted due to missing data. Also, because ratings involving duplicate projects (i.e. in several instances, two persons rated the same proposal) were not found statistically significantly different from ratings for nonduplicate proposals, all cases were treated as nonduplicates.
6. Because screening involves relatively rough go/kill decisions, two-group discriminant analysis (with a dichotomous accept/reject criterion variable) might be more appropriate. However, because the model was originally presented using multiple regression (with *degree* of acceptance/rejection) and because discriminant analysis produced virtually identical results (Cooper and de Brentani, 1984), the analysis was carried forth using the regression approach.

REFERENCES

Baker, N. R. and Freeland, J. (1975) 'Recent Advances in R&D Benefit Measurement and Project Selection Methods', *Management Science* 21: 1164–1175.

Booz, Allen and Hamilton (1982) *New Product Management for the 1980's*, New York: Booz, Allen and Hamilton, Inc.

Bradbury, F. R., Gallagher, W. M. and Suckling, C. W. (1973) 'Qualitative Aspects of the Evaluation and Control of R&D Projects', *R&D Management*, 3: 49–57.

Cattell, R. B. (1966) 'The scree Test for the Number of Factors', *Multivariate Behavioral Research*, 1: 245–276.

Choffray, J. M. and Lilien, G. L. (1980) *Market Planning for New Industrial Products*, New York: John Wiley and Sons.

Cooper, R. G. (1975) 'Why New Industrial Products Fail'. *Industrial Marketing Management*, 4: 315–326.

Cooper, R. G. (1980) *Project NewProd: What Makes a New Product a Winner*, Montreal: Centre Québecois d'Innovation Industrielle.

Cooper, R. G. (1982) 'New Product Successes in Industrial Firms', *Industrial Marketing Management*, 11: 215–223.

Cooper, R. G. (1985) 'Selecting Winning New Product Projects: Using the NewProd System,' *Journal of Product Innovation Management*. 2(1): 34–44.

Cooper, R. G. and de Brentani, U. (1984) 'Criteria. for Screening New Industrial Products'. *Industrial Marketing Management*, 13: 149–156.

Crawford, M. C. (1979) 'New Product Failure Rates—Facts and Fallacies', *Research Management*, 9(13).

Freimer, M. and Simon, L. S. (1967) 'The Evaluation of New Product Alternatives', *Management Science* B279–B292 (February).

Goldberg, L. R. (1970) 'Man Versus Model of Man: A Rational plus Some Evidence for a Method of Improving Clinical Inferences', *Psychological Bulletin*, **73**(6): 422–432.

Green, P. E. (1978) *Analyzing Multivariate Data*, Hindsdale, IL: The Dryden Press.

Hopkins, D. S. (1980) *New Product Winners and Losers*, Report No. 773, New York: The Conference Board.

Kleinbaum, D. G. and Kupper, L. L. (1978) *Applied Regression Analysis and Other Multivariate Methods*, North Scitvate, MA: Duxbury Press.

Lilien, G. L. (1975) 'Model Relativism: A Situational Approach to Model Building', *Interfaces*, **5**(2): 11–18.

Little, J. D. C. (1970) 'Models and Managers: The Concepts of a Decision Calculus', *Management Science*, **16**(8) (April): 628–655.

Mansfield, E. and Wagner, S. (1975) 'Organizational and Strategic Factors Associated with Probabilities of Success in Industrial R&D', *Journal of Business*, **48** (April): 179–199.

McGuire, E. P. (1973) *Evaluating New Product Proposals*, New York: The Conference Board.

Nunnally, J. C. (1978) *Psychometric Theory*, 2nd ed., New York: McGraw-Hill.

Pessemier, E. A. (1982) *Product Management: Strategy and Organization*, 2nd ed., New York: John Wiley and Sons.

Shocker, A. D. and Srinivasan, V. (1979) 'Multiattribute Approaches for Product Concept Evaluation and Generation: A Critical Review'. *Journal of Marketing Research*, **16** (May): 159–180.

Souder, W. E. (1973) 'Analytical Effectiveness of Mathematical Models for R&D Project Selection', *Management Science*, **19**(8): 907–923.

Urban, G. L. and Hauser, J. R. (1980) *Design and Marketing of New Products*, Englewood Cliffs, NJ: Prentice-Hall.

Wind, Y. J. (1982) *Product Policy: Concepts, Methods and Strategy*, Reading, MA: Addison-Wesley.

17

Concept Testing

William L. Moore

Even a cursory review of marketing literature (Claney and Garsen, 1970; Davidson, 1976; Neilsen, 1971; O'Connor, 1976) reveals that a major problem facing companies today is reducing new product failures and improving the return on funds invested in new product activities. While many factors contribute to the high failure rate, a major factor is the inability to predict consumer response to new products and services (Cochran and Thompson, 1964; Conference Board, 1967; Cooper, 1979; Davidson, 1976; McGuire, 1973).

One way to decrease new product failures is through systematic testing which includes concept testing, product testing (including extended use testing), and market testing. The purpose of this paper is to examine one part of this process, concept testing, with regard to current practices and possible future directions. It is based on a review of the published literature and a number of personal interviews with leading practitioners. (Table 1 gives a list of participants and a discussion of methodology.)

CONCEPT TESTING PROCESS

The primary purpose of concept testing is to estimate consumer reactions to a product idea before committing substantial funds to it. Additionally, concept tests are used to determine the potential target market and how the concept might be improved. There can be some confusion about concept tests because several different tests are called by this name. Also, concept tests are built into a number of sophisticated prediction systems (e.g. Burke's BASES and NPD's ESP®) that use a concept score along with company estimates of spending and distribution in a regression equation to estimate trial. Concepts can be presented in forms that vary from simple statements to finished advertisements, so the line between concept tests and copy tests becomes hazy. Furthermore, concept tests never test concepts. Concepts are ideas; they are in someone's mind. Concept tests measure consumers' reactions to concept statements. Making the distinction may seem like academic squabbling, but it is of great practical interest as it raises the question: 'what is the consumer responding to—concept, positioning or execution?' Obviously, the consumer is reacting to all three.

Reprinted with permission from *Journal of Business Research*, Vol. 10, 1982, pp. 279–294
© 1982 Elsevier Science Publishing Co., Inc.

Table 1. Personal interviews

The following individuals (listed in alphabetical order of company) participated in open-ended interviews that lasted from 45 to 60 min:

Tibor Weiss, AHF Marketing Research
Melvin Harbinger, Bristol Myers Co.
Pamela J. Welker, Burke Marketing Research
Lynn S. Whitton and Stephen K. Zrike, Colgate-Palmolive Co.
Edward M. Tauber, Dancer Fitzgerald Sample, Inc.
Newton Frank, Data Development Corp.
Bernard Ruderman and Steve Roth, Decisions Center, Inc.
Jay Friedland, Guideline Research Corp.
Whitney J. Coombs and Ian M. Lewis, Lever Brothers Co.
Stephen J. Cook, Market Facts—New York, Inc.
Lawrence Newman, Newman-Stein, Inc.
John L. McMennamin, Norton Simon Communications
Neil B. Holbert, Philip Morris, Inc.

Four general questions were asked in each interview: 'How do you perform concept tests?', 'What are the primary problems you see with concept tests?' 'Under what circumstances do concept tests work best and when are they most likely to fail?' and 'What changes over the next few years do you see taking place in the way concept tests will be conducted?' Each of these general questions was followed with a series of more specific questions based on the initial answers. The views expressed in the paper are the author's perceptions of generally held feelings. On any particular point, several of the above-mentioned participates may disagree with the paper.

In order to sort out the differences between types of concept tests, a general concept-testing sequence is described. Each of the practitioners pointed out that the specific test or combination of tests used by a firm depends on a number of factors, including the objectives of the research, what information is already known, the availability of time and money, the number of concepts to be tested, and the type of product or service the concept describes. However, the general description provides a common terminology and a background for discussion.

Concept screening tests

While a test presupposes the existence of an idea, the method of idea generation may have an effect on the number of ideas uncovered and, therefore, on the type of concept tests that are performed initially. Some approaches, such as joint space analysis (Shocker and Srinivosan, 1979) and conjoint analysis (Green and Rao, 1971; Green and Wind, 1975; Gruber, 1970; Wind, 1973), tend to generate a single or at most a small number of concepts per segment. However, a number of other techniques tend to generate a larger number of concepts for a given product class. Examples of these methods include benefit structure analysis (Myers, 1976) and problem detection analysis (Dillion, 1978). Lanatis (1970) suggests several additional ways of generating concepts. Other ideas may come from a variety of sources (McGuire, 1972).

When a large number of ideas (over 10) is generated, it is typically reduced to a more manageable set through screening concept testing (Frank, 1972). In this type of test, usually 10 to 30 (but sometimes up to 50) bland concept statements are presented to

each respondent in sentence or short paragraph form. Typically these concept statements represent only the core idea. They are rated on one primary scale, such as
intention to purchase, interest, or liking and possibly a few secondary scales such as
uniqueness or believability. They are then compared, based on the number of people
rating each concept in the 'top box' (most favorable category). These top box scores can
be weighted by expected usage if the concepts will go into different categories but are
usually unweighted. The concepts are also compared on secondary criteria to choose
between concepts that score similarly on the primary criterion or to determine potential
trouble.

Because this process tends to be reasonably complex, these data are usually collected
through personal interviews using central locations or in-home sampling. Sample sizes
for this stage can vary from 40–50, when few concepts are involved and the analysis is
univariate, to 300–500, when each respondent rates only a subset of the concepts and/or
a multivariate technique such as Q-sort is employed.

The biggest question with regard to concept screening tests is not how but *whether* they
should be done. A significant number of practitioners felt this was a highly unrealistic
task and that managers should determine which four or five ideas were worthy of further
study. However, at least one firm has done some validation research indicating that
concepts scoring well at this stage also score well in subsequent concept tests, and
concepts scoring poorly here also score poorly at a later phase.

Concept generation tests

The next step is usually the concept generation test, the qualitative phase of concept
testing (Frank, 1972) (called diagnosis by Holbert, 1977). According to Holbert (pp. 11–
12), the purpose of this phase is 'to end up with a statement that tells (as clearly and
meaningfully as we know how to present it) all about the product—its physical characteristics and sensory associations—and its benefits to the consumer'. This does not
necessarily mean a long concept statement, or one with lots of execution and 'fluff', but
one that is clear and concise.

Devising a statement is accomplished through one or more focus groups or a series of
individual personal interviews. During interviews, respondents are shown a preliminary
concept statement and asked to respond to it. The researcher is trying to find the
answers to questions such as: 'Is the concept statement clear and forceful?' 'Is there a
better way of stating it?' 'Is it unique and believable?' 'What are its advantages and
disadvantages?' This interactive process can be thought of as concept optimizing, with
consumer reactions on one iteration used to improve the concept statement for the next
iteration. Pietrzak (1975) refers to this phase not as market analysis but as creative work.
This work should be done by the concept statement writers themselves (Holbert, 1977;
Pietrzak, 1975). In practice, time pressure tends to reduce the number of iterations and
push the burden of testing onto someone other than the concept statement writer.

Virtually everyone agrees that concept generation testing is an important step when
used to express the concept in a clear and forceful manner. However, Holbert (1977),
Pietrzak (1975) and Linsky (1975), as well as most of the people interviewed in this
survey, cautioned strongly against the use of this qualitative research in place of the
more quantitative research that should follow.

Concept evaluation, positioning and concept/product tests

The next step is to measure a larger number of consumer responses to the concept statement in a more quantitative manner. If the concept statement does not include a positioning, it is an evaluation test; if it does, it is a positioning test. If the consumers try the product after the concept test, and the reaction to the product and concept are compared, it is called a concept/product test. If a company performs all three tests, they are done in this order. Possibly the most typical sequence is to perform either an evaluation or a positioning test first, and then a concept/product test once the product has been developed.

While these three tests are different, they can be discussed as a group. The primary difference between the first two is the form of the concept statement(s). In an evaluation test, the concept is typically a fairly bland statement typed on a 4″ × 6″ card. Such a statement might read: 'A powdered product that adds considerable nutrition when mixed with milk'. This concept could be positioned as an instant breakfast, a diet or health food, or a snack food. It could be presented in any form from a 4″ × 6″ card to a finished print or television ad. (The concept portion of a concept/product test can also be presented in any of these forms.) Unless different positionings of the same concept are being tested, the distinction between evaluation and positioning tests can become fairly arbitrary. The more important question is usually how much 'sell' or embellishment should be given to the concept statement.

Usually 200–300 people are sampled per concept or per positioning. Concept/product tests may use sample sizes of 300–400. These tests are typically personal interviews at shopping centres or in-home personal interviews, but household mail panels are employed occasionally. The procedure chosen depends on a number of factors, such as the desired amount of dispersion on certain consumer characteristics, the number of open-ended questions, cost, time urgency and whether a focus group discussion is desired after the initial interview.

While the concepts can be presented in a number of designs, the two most popular designs by far are monadic and competitive tests. Competing concepts are not directly compared in either monadic or competitive tests, but comparisons are made using matched samples. Monadic tests are conducted by giving one concept to each respondent. In the competitive design, commonly called competitive environment tests (e.g. AHF Research's CET®), the concept being tested is presented along with concepts written for leading brands in the product class. The CET® is a pre-post design. First, concept statements for the leading brands, which may include price and brand name, are presented to the respondent, who distributes 10 chips across the brands in proportion to expected purchases, preferences, or affect. Then the new concept is presented and the respondent is asked to redistribute the chips. A variation on this basic design is Eric Marder's STEP® test where the old and the new concepts are presented at the same time (i.e. the 'post' only design).

Next, a number of questions are asked. These questions may be divided into four categories: primary criterion, comprehension, diagnostic and classification. One of two questions is usually used as the primary criterion to decide whether to proceed with or to kill the concept. The most popular predictive question with monadic tests is an intention to purchase (ITP) and usually employs a five-point scale. The constant sum scale is used with CET® type designs. Another, less popular prediction method (which is more widely used in concept/product tests and simulated tests markets) is actual choice. Typically, at least one question is asked to determine whether the respondent understood the concept statement. Diagnostic questions are asked to determine why the consumer responded as he or she did, how to improve the concept and how to give additional insight into the possible success of the concept. Finally, some demographic or psychographic questions are included to determine potential market segments.

The responses to the primary criterion question—the percentage of respondents marking the top box or top two boxes on a ITP scale, or the percentage of chips allocated to the new concept on a constant sum scale—are used to evaluate concept tests. These scores can be used three ways. First, they can be compared with what is usually a category-specific norm (because concepts in some categories, e.g. desserts, tend to score higher than others). The norm may be an average or a lower limit of the scores of successful concepts in the past, or it may be the score for a concept written for a brand currently in the category.

The second method is to use the score to predict trial. Although there are some fairly sophisticated systems (e.g. Burk's BASES 1) that incorporate seasonality, distribution build, category and brand development indexes and so forth, most companies use a fairly simple procedure to estimate trial. For example, estimated percent trial is equal to the percentage that marked the top box. This result is adjusted for expected awareness, distribution and the percentage receiving samples or coupons. Frank (1972) cites several other examples of trial estimates derived from top box scores.

The third method is to judge the concept in financial terms. That is, managerial judgment and secondary data are used to make estimates of trial and repeat rates prior to any testing. These estimates are refined through concept and product testing. Therefore a concept should be passed on to the next phase of development if the predicted trial level and best estimate of repeat sales give a prediction of financial success. The estimate of repeat sales can come from managerial judgment, category averages, or responses to an expected usage question on the concept test. The expected usage responses are usually reduced to account for probable overstating (e.g. estimated usage is forecast to be one-half of stated usage). This number may be further reduced by making an estimate of the percentage of triers expected to actually adopt the product.

While the decision to go with a product is based mainly on the answers to these expected trial questions, the answers to other questions such as uniqueness, believability, or need fulfilment are also considered. Typically they are not employed in a systematic fashion but are used as tie-breakers or are compared with some lower limit as an indication of potential problems with the product.

User satisfaction with concept tests

One of the most frequently mentioned limitations of concept tests is that they do not always predict market success. This lack of predictive power may be the result of: (a) the product's not living up to the benefits promised in the concept; (b) changes in the concept, positioning, or physical product between the concept tests and introduction of the product; or (c) changes in the legal or social environment. No amount of improvement in current concept testing practices can remedy these problems. Similarly, Tauber (1975) points out that the success of a frequently purchased product hinges on a number of people adopting it, i.e. using it regularly. Concept testing cannot determine whether this will occur, but, this should not be its objective. Concept testing should be used as an early screening device to obtain some consumer reaction to an idea and to predict the trial rate.

The empirical evidence on the ability of concept testing to perform this more limited role is fragmentary but nonetheless encouraging. Relatively few systematic attempts to validate the predictive ability of concept testing exist, either at the individual or aggregate level. This small number of validation attempts is due partly to the many changes that can occur between concept testing and test marketing or national introduction. However, a few companies have conducted concept tests just prior to market introduction, and the general feeling is that concept tests using an ITP scale reaction to a concept on a 4″ × 6″ card can predict trial rate within 20% (i.e. if the test predicts a trial rate of 50% the actual rate will fall between 40% and 60%) about 80% of the time. Frank (1972) mentioned similar figures for three companies using slightly different projection techniques. One respondent, using print ads and a constant sum scale prior to market introduction, indicated that about 90% of the time the predictions were very good. Another respondent mentioned an explained variance in trial rate of 80% on a series of predictive tests. Several respondents talked about instances in which the results were so good as to be 'uncanny' or 'scary'. These predictions are based almost exclusively on concepts that scored well on concept tests (otherwise they would not be developed further).

However, the question of how many good concepts are screened out through concept testing remains unanswered. Tauber (1973) suggests that this loss may be much greater than that resulting when products are not killed quickly enough. Furthermore, this danger is probably greater with radically new products (Tauber, 1974). However, several respondents mentioned that most any time someone's 'gut feel' overrode the negative results of a concept test, the product did, in fact, turn out to be a failure.

In summary, the evidence to date indicates that properly executed concept tests can do a good job of predicting trial for concepts that are not radically different from products on the market.

PRIMARY DECISIONS TO BE MADE IN CONCEPT EVALUATION TESTS

This section focuses on four specific decisions associated with evaluation or positioning tests: concept statement, test design, questions asked and prediction of success. Whereas the discussion has been separated into four categories, the division is somewhat artificial because decisions made in one area have an impact on other areas. For example, if a tester decides to do a monadic test, he or she can use either a bland or a promotional concept statement, but an ITP scale would be used virtually every time. Similarly, a competitive environment test is usually paired with a constant sum scale and more promotional concept statements.

Concept statement

Virtually all concept statements give a description and list the principal benefits, information that is sometimes called the pure idea. A positioning statement is usually added to compare the product with possible competitors. The primary questions are how much 'sell' or embellishment the concept is given and in what form it is presented. Conventional wisdom suggests that relatively bland concept statements should be used when a large number of concepts is evaluated, as it is quicker and cheaper, and when the concept is radically new, as positioning may limit its appeal. Similarly, promotional concept statements should be used when a concept is going into an existing product class and should be presented in the typical medium for that class.

Many of the people interviewed in this study tended to use almost exclusively either bland or promotional statements. Use of these types of statements enables a company to develop norms and is reinforced by past success with the method chosen. People who usually use only bland statements do so because: (a) they want a reaction to the pure concept; (b) personal experience has found relatively small differences in consumer reactions to bland and promotional concept statements; or (c) it is impossible to tell whether the consumer is reacting to the concept, positioning or embellishment in more promotional statements. Others use promotional statements because of the added realism and because they are ultimately looking for the best combination of concept, positioning, and embellishment and the best pure concept, does not necessarily lead to the optimal combination.

Five pieces of research shed some light on this question. Haley and Gatty (1971) performed an experiment in which three copywriters provided statements for eight positionings of a concept. Their findings indicate that consumer reaction is based not only on the concept, the positioning, and the copywriter but also on the interaction between positioning and copywriter.

Tauber (1972) held the idea, concept and execution constant to test the effect of communication form on respondent ratings. Three concepts were presented in both print ad and paragraph form. He found that scores were much higher for the concept boards than the paragraphs but that the relative scores did not change. Thus the one big idea came through in either form of communication.

Armstrong and Overton (1971) looked at the effect of brief *vs* comprehensive descriptions of a service when testing the intention to purchase a minicar leasing system. They found no significant differences between the two methods of presentation with regard to the respondents' intention to purchase or the price they would pay for the service. In contrast, Pessemier and Wilton (1979a, b) varied the amount and importance of the information given to consumers about electric automobiles and competing products. The type of treatment had a significant effect on perceptions and preferences for the cars.

One related proprietary study compared consumers' responses with rough and finished advertisements. The correlation of the responses was reasonably high, but, as the authors pointed out, this was partly because in a few pairs both scored very high or very low. The finished ads tended to score equal to, or higher than, the rough ones, but there was no systematic relationship between the two scores. In a few cases the finished ads scored lower.

In summary, practitioners agree that great care should be taken in the writing of concept statements. This does not mean writing more promotional concept statements but better ones. We might hypothesize that the amount of positioning and sell is a function of how great the benefit is, how well it is understood, how socially acceptable it is to admit a certain need, and how emotional the benefit is. As a general rule, concept writers should use the minimum amount of sell required. A company would be advised to try to present all concepts for a given category similarly to build up a forecasting track record.

Design of test

No published evidence indicates whether a concept should be presented monadically or in a competitive environment. The primary reason given for using monadic tests is past success with this method. As mentioned earlier, many firms are quite satisfied with the ability of monadic tests to predict trial rate. People using monadic tests argued that the consumer is responding to a new concept in a comparative nature anyway, so a direct comparison is not needed. Most of these people also favored relatively bland concept statements and did not know how realistic consumer reaction to bland, disguised statements for existing brands would be. Reactions to the concept being tested are influenced by competitive concepts, and in some categories (e.g. wine) it is hard to determine the proper competitive products. Some of these people also thought that both the pre-post design in CET®s and the equal prominence given to all competing concepts resulted in decreased realism. The people who favored comparative testing did so because they felt it was more realistic. They tended to use print ads for their concepts and used their competitor's ads for the comparison concepts. So the issue of comparative testing is confounded with that of the amount of 'sell' in the concept statement.

In summary, people have reported considerable success in predicting trials with each method. Apparently, the opportunity exists to conduct research comparing the predictive and diagnostic powers of these two designs. Specifically, it would be valuable to determine under what circumstances each method should be used. In the absence of such research, we might hypothesize that competitive environment tests would be preferable when knowledge of the alternatives is relatively low and there is considerable search prior to purchase. This is the case for many durable goods such as major appliances. Monadic tests would be preferable when it is hard to identify direct competitors or when there is little external search prior to purchase.

Questions asked

While practitioners agree on what questions should be asked, they often disagree on two issues: price and intended usage.

Price

A widely used method of incorporating price into concept tests is to state the price in the concept statements; which may require checking the price of competing products in area stores. Another method used frequently is to ask respondents what they thought the product would cost. A number of practitioners in this survey said that consumers could give the cost accurately when the concept was in a very frequently purchased category, but that accuracy dropped off as purchases became less frequent. However, there seems to be a problem with the interpretation of this question. For example, if a consumer said that he or she would definitely purchase a product but understated its price, should the consumer be counted as a trier or a nontrier? A method similar to Pessemier's dollar metric procedure was occasionally used to determine price elasticity. A person who would purchase at a given price was asked whether he or she would do so at a higher price. Conversely, consumers who would not purchase at a given price, were asked whether they would purchase at a lower price.

Making price part of the concept statement appears to be the best way of incorporating price into the test. The use of multiple questions to estimate price elasticities has considerable face validity, but systematic research is needed to determine its predictive power.

Volume

Although the primary purpose of concept tests is to predict trial, the decision on whether a concept should be advanced to the next stage of development should be based on an estimate of financial success. The trial estimate must therefore be converted into an estimate of cash flow, either implicitly by using category-specific norms or explicitly by estimating sales volume.

A number of companies ask respondents what their expected usage would be or when they might use it (assuming the product was satisfactory). However, several studies (cited in Wind and Lerner, 1979), found a systematic underprediction of the purchases of some brands and overprediction of others, and the total amount in a category tended to be overstated. Whether this percentage of overstating differs substantially across product categories is unknown. How highly correlated are stated and actual usage is also unknown. These two questions need to be answered before respondent estimates of usage are incorporated into concept tests, except as a check on preliminary estimates.

Prediction of success

Aggregate level

Even though the most popular method of evaluating concept tests involves comparison with a norm, several practitioners recommended using an estimate of financial success. This method involves estimating volume from trial based on the concept test and the best available measure of repeat sales.

A number of systems (e.g. BASES and ESP®) use concept/product tests to predict trial and first repeat, which are combined with an estimate of the decay rate to estimate volume. Simulated test markets (e.g. ASSESSOR, LTM and COMP) could also be viewed as fairly similar to concept/product tests in which the respondent purchases a product rather than rates a concept on an ITP scale. Finally, sales waves studies (e.g. Data Development Corporation) can be combined with concept tests to estimate ongoing volume. Examining these tests, which involve consumer contact with the product, is beyond the scope of this paper.

Little empirical evidence exists on the question of using norms or sales estimates to evaluate concepts. In one study, Tauber (1975) shows that the concept with the highest top box score is not necessarily the most successful. Therefore decisions should be based on financial estimates instead of comparisons with norms. In the absence of any track record, testers should use the percentage marking top box adjusted for awareness, distribution and sampling as the estimate of the number of category users that will try the product.

Individual level

Favorable ratings on an attitude or intention-to-purchase scale are positively correlated with trial or usage (Longman, 1968; Stapel, 1968; Tauber, 1977). However, this procedure obscures some predictive problems at the individual level. A frequently cited problem was of 'yea saying'. Two studies shed some light on this problem (Claney and Garsen, 1970; Tauber, 1975, 1979).

DISCONTINUOUS INNOVATIONS

Tauber (1974) has suggested that current new product research techniques, including concept testing, may discourage major innovations because consumer attitudes, upon first exposure to discontinuous innovations, are not good predictors of what their actions will be after a prolonged exposure. This results partly from a lack of knowledge about the product and partly from the social system's influence on adoption decisions. Increased education prior to measuring a reaction helps to reduce part of this problem. Pessemier and Wilton (1979a, b) found that increased levels of information do have an effect on the predicted market share of an electric car. However, there was no way to determine whether the increased information resulted in a better prediction of the level of adoption of the electric car.

Wolpert (1980) has found that the automobile market can be segmented by preferences for style. One segment prefers a conservative functional styling with little change. Another segment prefers nonfunctional, show-type styling. He feels that the second segment may be able to give valid predictions of the acceptance of revolutionary changes in styling. Innovators and early adopters in other categories could also be located. Their reactions to concepts may serve as leading indicators of the acceptance of major innovations.

Behavioral simulations have played a part in the study of various types of decisions. It is also possible that some type of simulation could be devised that would model the word-of-mouth communication that occurs in the diffusion process.

Moving further from concept testing, techniques such as conjoint analysis (Green and Rao, 1971; Green and Wind, 1975) can estimate acceptable tradeoffs between desired characteristics for a product or service without describing the concept except as a bundle of characteristics. With this technique, practitioners may be able to measure the need for some benefit without confounding it with reactions to a product that is very different from ones currently on the market. Howard (1978) is using several concepts from human categorization in an attempt to model extensive problem solving. Some of this work may enable us to predict the response to more discontinuous innovations.

There is lots of room for the creative development of ways to measure consumer reactions to discontinuous innovations. We will probably have to be content with the face validity of these techniques because no norms for products that create their own product classes will be available.

SUMMARY

The purpose of this paper has been to examine current concept testing practices and controversies as reported by the published literature and as seen by some of the leading practitioners. It appears that the basic knowledge of how to conduct good concept tests is available.

A company may gain the most not by developing new techniques but by improving the execution of the different phases of concept testing. Specific suggestions include:

(1) spending sufficient money on idea generation or strategic research to finding concepts that have true benefits;
(2) forcing the concept writer to conduct individual or group interviews to insure that the ideas are communicated clearly and forcefully;
(3) setting the action standards for the quantitative part of the test based on trials needed to meet financial criteria prior to the test;
(4) spending the amount of money required to sample a sufficient number from the proper market segment;
(5) choosing test methodology to suit the nature of the concept (i.e. not testing discontinuous innovations and line extensions in the same manner).

In addition to these suggestions, the paper has highlighted a number of areas for research. An area of prime interest is a comparative study of the predictive and diagnostic ability of the two major methods: (1) monadic design, paragraph form of concept and top box estimate of trial; (2) multiple concept comparison, print ad form of concept and constant sum estimate of trial rate. There are questions regarding each of these general methods, but the greatest difficulty for a practitioner is determining which method is appropriate for the circumstances. A second area of research is improvement of the predictive ability of concept tests at the individual level, primarily to get better estimates of market segments. A final, very large area of interest is the prediction of the success of discontinuous innovations. This issue is the most challenging but ultimately may yield the greatest payoff.

ACKNOWLEDGEMENTS

The author thanks Newton Frank for suggesting a number of the participants in the study, and Noel Capon, Stephen J. Cook, Newton Frank, Neil B. Holbert, Morris B. Holbrook, Ian M. Lewis, John L. McMennamin, Tibor Weiss, Pamela J. Welker and Stephen K. Zrike for comments on an earlier draft.

REFERENCES

Abrams, J. (1969) 'Reducing the Risk of New Product Marketing Strategies Testing', *J. Marketing Res.*, **6** (May): 216–220.

Armstrong, J. S. and Overton, T. (1971) 'Brief vs. Comprehensive Descriptions in Measuring Intention to Purchase', *J. Marketing Res.* **8** (February): 114–117.

Axelrod, J. N. (1964) 'Reducing Advertising Failures by Concept Testing', *J. Marketing*, **28** (October): 41–44.

Batsell, R. S. and Wind, Y. (1979) 'Product Testing: Current Methods and Needed Developments', Working paper, The Wharton School, University of Pennsylvania (May).

Belkin, M. and Lieberman, S. (1967) 'Effect of Question Wording on Response Distribution', *J. Marketing Res.*, **4** (August): 312–313.

Blankenship, A. B. (1966) 'Let's Bury Paired Comparisons', *J. Advertising Res.* **6** (March): 13–17.

Booz, Allen & Hamilton (1968) *Management of New Products*, Chicago.

Claney, K. J. and Garsen, R. (1970) 'Why Some Scales Predict Better', *J. Advertising Res.* **10** (October): 33–38.

Cochran, E. and Thompson, G. (1964) 'Why New Products Fail', *The National Industrial Conference Board Record*, October: 11–18.

Conference Board (1967) *Market Testing of Consumer Products*, New York.

Cooper, R. G. (1979) 'The Dimensions of Industrial New Product Success and Failure', *J. Marketing*, **43** (Summer): 93–103.

Davidson, J. H. (1976) 'Why Most New Consumer Brands Fail', *Harvard Bus. Rev.* (March–April): 117–122.

Dillion, T. (1978) 'Forecasting Wants and Needs of the Consumer', Paper given at the New York Chapter of AMA New Product Conference.

Frank, N. (1972) 'Can We Predict New Product Success from Concept Testing', Paper given at AMA New York Chapter New Products Conference.

Green. P. E. and Rao, V. R. (1971) 'Conjoint Measurement for Quantifying Judgmental Data', *J. Marketing Res.* **8** (August): 355–363.

Green, P. E. and Wind, Y. (1975) New Way to Measure Consumers' Judgments', *Harvard Bus. Rev.* **53** (July–August): 107–115.

Greenberg, A. (1963) 'Paired Comparisons Versus Monadic Tests', *J. Advertising Res.* **3** (August): 44–47.

Greenhalgh, C. (1971) 'Research for New Product Development', in *Consumer Market Research Handbook*, Worster, R. M. (ed.) McGraw-Hill, London: 378–410.

Gold, B. and Salking, W. (1974) 'What Do Top Box Scores Measure?', *J. Advertising Res.*, **14** (March): 19–23.

Golden, H. (1973) 'Concept Tests–Often Used, But How Well', *Marketing Rev.* **27** (September): 20–24.

Gruber, A. (1970) 'Purchase Intent and Purchase Probability', *J. Advertising Res.* **10** (February): 23–27.

Haley, R. I. and Gatty, R. (1971) 'The Trouble with Concept Testing', *J. Marketing Res.* **8** (May): 230–232.

Haller, T. P. (1966) 'Let's Not Bury Paired Comparisons', *J. Advertising Res.* **6** (September): 29–30.

Holbert, N. (1977) *Research in the Twilight Zone*, American Marketing Association Monograph, Series #7, AMA, Chicago.

Howard, J. A. (1978) 'Progress in Modeling Extensive Problem Solving: Consumer Acceptance of Innovation', Working paper, Columbia University, New York.

Johnson, R. M. (1974) 'Trade-Off Analysis of Consumer Values', *J. Marketing Res.* **11** (May): 121–128.

Juster, F. T. (1966) *Consumer Buying Intentions and Purchase Probability: An Experiment in Survey Design*, National Bureau of Economic Research, Occasional Paper 99, distributed by Columbia University Press, New York.

Kassarjian, H. H. and Nakanishi, M. (1967) 'A Study of Selected Opinion Measurement Techniques', *J. Marketing Res.* **4** (May): 148–153.

Lanatis, T. (1970) 'How to Generate New Product Ideas', *J. Advertising Res.* **10** (June): 31–35.

Linsky, B. R. 'Eliminate "Bombs" With A Systematic Approach to Concept Evaluation', Paper presented at 1975 ANA New Product Marketing Workshop, New York.

Longman, K. A. (1968) 'Promises, Promises', in *Attitude Research on the Rocks*. Adler, L. and Crespi, I. (eds), American Marketing Association, Chicago: 28–37.

McGuire, E. P. (1972) *Generating New Product Ideas*, The Conference Board, New York.

McGuire, E. P. (1973) *Evaluating New Product Proposals*, The Conference Board, New York.

Moriarty, M. and Venkatsen, M. (1978) 'Concept Evaluation and Market Segmentation', *J. Marketing*, **42** (July): 82–86.

Myers, J. H. (1976) 'Benefit Structure Analysis: A New Tool for Product Planning', *J. Marketing*, **40** (October): 23–32.

Neilsen, A. C. Co. (1971) 'New Product Success Ratio', *The Neilsen Researcher*, **5**: 1–10.

O'Connor, J. J. (1976) 'R. J. R. Monitors 105 New Brands, Classified 13 as Successful', *Advertising Age* (July 12): 3.

Pessemier, E. A. (1960) 'An Experimental Method for Estimating Demand', *J. Bus.*, **3**: 373–383.

Pessemier, E. A. and Wilton, P. (1979a) 'The Effects of Information on Perceptions and Preferences for New Choice Objects', Institute Paper #683, Krannert Graduate School, Purdue University (February).

Pessemier, E. A. and Wilton, P. (1979b) 'Pretesting the Acceptance of Innovations', Institute Paper #696, Krannert Graduate School, Purdue University (April).

Pietrzak, R. J. (1975) 'Screening and Developing Concept After Idea Generation', Paper presented at ANA New Product Marketing Workshop.

Reibstein, D. J. (1978) 'The Prediction of Individual Probability of Brand Choice', *J. Consumer Res.* **5** (December): 163–169.

Seaton, R. (1974) 'Why Ratings are Better Than Comparisons', *J. Advertising Res.*, **14** (February): 45–48.

Shocker, A. D. and Srinivasan, V. (1979) 'Multiattribute Approaches for Product Concept Evaluation: A Critical Review', *J. Marketing Res.*, **16** (May): 159–180.

Stapel, J. (1968) 'Predictive Attitudes' in *Attitude Research on the Rocks*, Adler, L. and Crespi, I. (eds), American Marketing Association, Chicago: 96–115.

Tauber, E. M. (1972) 'What is Measured by Concept Testing', *J. Advertising Res.* **12** (December): 35–37.

Tauber, E. M. (1973) 'Reduce New Product Failures: Measure Needs as Well as Purchase Interest', *J. Marketing*, **37** (July): 61–64.

Tauber, E. M. (1974) 'How Marketing Research Discourages Major Innovations', *Bus. Horizons*, (June): 24–27.

Tauber, E. M. (1975) 'Predictive Validity in Consumer Research', *J. Advertising Res.* **15** (October): 59–64.

Tauber, E. M. (1975) 'Why Concept and Product Tests Fail to Predict New Product Results', *J. Marketing*, **39** (October): 69–71.

Tauber, E. M. (1977) 'Forecasting Sales Prior to Test Market', *J. Marketing*, **41** (January): 80–84.

Tauber, E. M. (1979) 'The Decision Risks with New Product Concept Testing', Dancer, Fitzgerald, Sample Inc., New York.

Taylor, J. W., Houlahan, J. R. and Gabriel, A. C. (1975) 'The Purchase Intention Question in New Product Development: A Field Test', *J. Marketing*, **39** (January): 90–92.

Wilkie, W. L. and Pessemier, E. A. (1973) 'Issues in Marketing's Use of Multi-attribute Models', *J. Marketing Res.* **10**: 428–441.

Wind, Y. (1973) 'A New Procedure for Concept Evaluation', *J. Marketing*, **37** (October): 2–11.

Wind, Y. and Lerner, D. (1979) 'On the Measurement of Purchase Data: Surveys Versus Purchase Diaries', *J. Marketing Res.* **16** (February): 39–47.

Wolpert, H. W. (1980) 'Why Conventional Automobile Styling Research May Become Obsolete', in *Advances in Consumer Research Vol. VII*. Olson, J. C. (ed.) Association for Consumer Research, Ann Arbor.

Yuspeh, S. (1975) 'Diagnosis—The Handmaiden of Prediction', *J. Marketing*, **39** (January): 87–89.

Part V

Later Stages of the NPD Process

CONTENTS

Introduction to Part V

Susan Hart

During the later stages of the new product development process, market evaluation becomes more precise as the dimensions, characteristics and appeal of the product emerge more specifically. Quite simply, as developers firm up on the nature of the new product, the potential market is presented with a clearer view of the new product to which they can react more reliably. This said, at the end of the introduction to Part IV, the notion that evaluation is a constant and dynamic feature of the new product development process was introduced. In the first article of this section, Mahajan and Wind (Reading 18) introduce the idea of product evaluation occurring throughout the process of new product development. They deal with new product forecasting models, which, they contend, should take place *at each stage* of the NPD process. This article reviews a number of studies of forecasting models and categorizes them into four groups: concept testing models, pre-test market models, test market models and diffusion models. Each category is assessed in terms of their most appropriate use, their output and their ease of use. The article concludes on a research note by suggesting how academic research could help improve the implementation of the models and how they might be improved to better suit the categorization of differing business environments.

Crawford (Reading 19) cogently reinforces this point in his view that new product evaluation is a system, not an act. Crawford takes a holistic view of the NPD process, setting evaluation in a wider, more realistic context. The article is based on exposing four examples of evaluation: that there is *one* important evaluative act—the 'go/no-go' decision; that evaluation only begins after the new product idea has materialized; that the NPD product is made up of discrete stages, each handled by separate units, and that tough early screening can eliminate bad ideas. Each of these stages is explained in detail, and the discussion leads to a number of important conclusions. First, different types of evaluation are suited to different stages in the NPD process and the decisions required at that stage. (A good example of this can be seen in Hart and Baker's article (Reading 9), Table 1.) Second, if the overall corporate strategy and new product strategies are comprehensively formulated, acts of evaluation will have been carried out by the time an idea is forwarded for 'screening'. Third, the information derived from each evaluation should be able to be translated into an aspect of the marketing plan. How the product will be marketed is not something to be left until the 'test marketing stage'. Even as early as the idea screening stage, there should be some assessment of the possible selling proposition. Fourth, evaluations are not stable. The results of a concept or product test may no longer be completely valid by the time the product is ready for launch. Results of evaluation are not written in tablets of stone. At the end of the article, Figure 3 gives an excellent summary of the totally different form of new product evaluation.

The third article in this part (Reading 20) once more reinforces the idea that a plethora of techniques exist which have different evaluative applications. This work, by two practitioners, Greenwald and Ottenfeld, discusses three relatively recent new product research techniques. The first, simulated test marketing techniques, are generally employed *before* actual test marketing takes place. (It should be noted, however, that test marketing is increasingly being seen as an expensive opportunity-cost to companies trying to introduce new products quickly.) Simulated test marketing examines consumer reaction to new product advertising, their experience of the product in home trials, buyer intention and repeat purchase intention. This information can be collected on a smaller scale, more quickly and less publicly than with a full-scale test market. The second technique, using scanners to measure sales, is useful for localized test situations, as the effect of advertising, in-store promotions and pricing can be measured effectively and quickly. The third technique, split cable testing, is more suited to tracking the effect of changes in advertising on purchase patterns, and is less scaled to the new-product evaluation system.

The fourth article in this part, by Thomas (Reading 21) is important because it highlights the particular problems of evaluating demand where a new technology is involved. The subject is at the heart of the big debate regarding the efficacy of market research in NPD, which is based on whether a market—customers—can accurately relate their purchase intentions for a product based on technology they do not understand and whose benefit is not immediately clear. The usual example to cite in support of this question is the Sony Walkman, developed without market research.

Thomas cites four examples of where demand estimation for new technologies went wrong, and goes on to review 29 different methodologies for estimating demand for module radiotelephones. He points out that issues such as the existence of multiple purchasers in any one purchase, a lack of understanding of the concept of demand by researchers and unsophisticated measurement techniques contribute to the inaccuracies in demand forecasting for new technologies. There is little examination, however, of whether more precise techniques of measurement will affect the outcome where buyers themselves are unsure of the potential benefits of the new technology.

The final paper in this part, by Segal and Johar (Reading 22), takes as its subject the choice of location for a test market. As was mentioned by Crawford, there is growing concern for the usefulness of full-scale test marketing phases. The article reports on research which aims to improve test marketing procedures in the issues of identifying representative test sites, and selecting the number and the size of test sites. These questions are essential to test marketing decisions because there is a need to ensure that the test site mirrors the population in general, in order to extrapolate the results accurately. Equally, the size and number of sites have financial implications for what is already a costly endeavour. The research undertaken compares the 46 markets suggested by Dancer Fitzgerald Sample Inc. as those being demographically close to US averages and finds that most of them can be classified into four clusters which are quite distinct from each other on the dimensions used for test site selection, such as number of households, retail sales, average age, levels of unemployment and ethnic grouping. The authors recommend several improvements to selection techniques based on their work.

18

New Product Forecasting Models: Directions for Research and Implementation

Vijay Mahajan and Yoram Wind

1. INTRODUCTION

Forecasting the performance of new products and services is one of the most difficult and critical management tasks. The actual market performance of a new product depends on a large number of factors. Such factors include not only consumer attraction to and satisfaction with the product but also environmental conditions (e.g. economy), the degree of trade support for the product and the nature of competitive actions and reactions. Assessing these uncertainties makes the forecasting of new product performance much more complex than the forecasting of the sales, share and profitability of established products. Yet, accurate forecasting of new product performance is a *must* and constitutes a major input to most business and marketing decisions.

Given the importance of accurate forecasting of new product performance and the intellectual challenge of developing 'better' models, numerous new product forecasting models have been developed over the years both in industry and in academia. These models, as summarized in Table 1, are designed, in addition to estimating long term and short term sales (and market share), to: (a) diagnose the impact of marketing mix variables, competitor's and trade reactions and environmental conditions on the new product's sales estimates; (b) evaluate the impact of the new product introduction on the firm's profitability and the sales of its current products (cannibalization effect).

New product forecasting models vary not only with respect to their objectives and users but also with respect to their data bases. In general, these models use one or more of the following data sources:

(1) Management and expert judgments: management's or experts' subjective estimates are used to forecast new product's likely performance.
(2) Analogous products: a product with similar characteristics to those of the new product under consideration is used to forecast its likely performance.
(3) Consumers: based on consumer responses, likely performance of a new product is derived by estimating its awareness, trial and repeat.

Reprinted with permission from *International Journal of Forecasting*, Vol. 4, 1988, pp. 341–358

Table 1. Expected output of new product forecasting models by user type

| User type | Desired output | | | | | | | | |
| | Sales (market share) estimates | | | Diagnostic impact on sales (market share) of | | | | Impact on the firm's | |
	Long term	Annual	Monthly	Marketing mix variables	Trade reactions and actions	Competitors' reactions and actions	Environmental conditions (e.g. economy)	Financial health	Other products (cannibalization)
Internal stakeholders									
Top management	X			X	X	X	X	X	X
New product manager	X	X		X	X	X	X		X
Procurement/production manager		X	X						
Other brand managers or SBUs				X	X	X	X	X	X
External stakeholders									
Security analysts	X	X						X	X
Firm's competitors (competitive intelligence)	X	X		X	X	X	X	X	X
Stockholders	X							X	
Media	X	X						X	X

The three types of forecasting models, especially the consumer-based models, vary with respect to the stage in the new product development process for which they are most appropriate. Management's subjective estimates and analogy type models are usually used at the idea/concept screening stage, prior to the undertaking of a consumer-based concept evaluation study. If this initial evaluation suggests a 'go' and a concept test is conducted, the next stage often is a forecasting model based on data generated in a concept testing study. Again, assuming a 'go' decision, a product is developed and a simulated test market (or simplified in-home use test) can be designed, the results of which serve as the basis for a pretest market forecasting model. If a *go* decision is reached again and a test market is undertaken, the data from the test market could serve as the basis for a test-market-based forecasting model. Finally, if the product is introduced (regionally or nationally), the early sales results can be used as the basis for an early-sales-based forecasting model.

The various models, despite their close association with the various stages of the new product development process, are not *pure* models. Past experience of marketing managers and their subjective estimates can be incorporated with other, say, concept-testing-based models. Furthermore, a forecasting model structured for test market type data (i.e. requiring, for example, information on awareness, trial, repeat and amount used by regular users) can be used at a simulated test market stage combining actual results of the simulated test market (on trial, repeat and amount of usage, for example) with estimates from previous introductions (e.g. analogy) on the awareness level and its dependency on the advertising, promotion and distribution activities of the firm.

Given the large number of available new product forecasting models, efforts have been made in recent years to compare and evaluate these models. However, these efforts have not been integrated and their scope has been limited to a specific class of models. The objectives of this paper, therefore, are to: (a) briefly assess strengths and weaknesses of the currently available new product forecasting models; (b) outline an agenda enhancing the further development and implementation of these models. Our focus is limited to consumer-based new product forecasting models.

The organization of this paper follows the two objectives. Section 2 briefly provides an overview of the current status of new product forecasting models including summary tables of the major strengths and weaknesses of the various classes of models. Section 3 outlines an agenda suggesting directions for future research and implementation.

2. CURRENT STATUS OF NEW PRODUCT FORECASTING MODELS

Forecasting the potential results (sales, profit and share) of a new product should be undertaken at each stage in the new product development process. In the early development stages, the forecast is tentative and broad. As management narrows its product and marketing options, the forecasting task can and should be done more precisely, narrowing the range of likely results. Consumer-based models are designed to assist management in evaluating concept-product options and forecast their likely performance. A general discussion of such models has been included in a number of recent books (e.g. Urban and Hauser, 1980; Wind, 1981; Wind, Mahajan and Cardozo, 1981). A comparative evaluation of these models has also been provided by several recent review papers. Table 2 summarizes eight such review papers indicating the models compared and criteria used for comparison in the respective papers and briefly commenting on their conclusions. An examination of these review papers, and the actual models reviewed in them, suggests a number of conclusions concerning the current status of new product forecasting models:

(1) There are a very large number of new product forecasting models. The eight review papers include no less than 40 models.
(2) There is no agreement on the criteria that should be used for evaluating these models.
(3) There is no agreement as to the 'best' model(s) within each class of models.
(4) Most of the review papers evaluate the models on their structural characteristics. Little attention has been given to a careful examination of:
   • the external validity of the models and, in particular, their predictive accuracy under various conditions;
   • their implementation costs and problems (e.g. required skills, data, time and cost for model development and maintenance, sensitivity of results to the various assumptions etc.).
(5) There are no published empirical comparisons of the performance of the various models except for a very limited comparison of awareness forecasting models provided in the review paper by Mahajan, Muller and Sharma (1984).
(6) Within each class of models, there is significant variability in terms of marketing mix variables included and the other model features.

   Although the development of new product forecasting models has occupied much of the attention of academic marketing researchers, research suppliers and corporate forecasters, management acceptance of these models could be improved (*Business Week*, 1987; Tauber, 1981; Levine, 1981).
   To better understand the various new product forecasting models currently available to the various users identified in Table 1, Table 3 presents a summary of strengths and weaknesses of the four classes of the models on several key characteristics. Adding to the conclusions from Table 2 mentioned earlier, an examination of Table 3 suggests the following additional observations:

(1) Most of these models are applied under very restrictive conditions and generally lack external validity.
(2) Pretest market and test market models are mostly appropriate only for frequently purchased products in established categories. On the other hand, early sales models are generally appropriate for consumer durables.
(3) Concept test, pretest market and test market models do not project the life cycle of the product;
(4) Other than test market models (and some sophisticated applications of other models), the other models, in their basic form, provide limited diagnostic information with respect to marketing mix variables and competitive actions and reactions.
(5) Most of the models provide limited assessment of the impact of new product on the company's financial health or other product offerings.

Although the above weaknesses of the new product forecasting models suggest avenues for future research for each model type and have been discussed in the review papers summarized in Table 2, the next section outlines a general agenda for directions for research and implementation.

It is important to note, however, that weaknesses identified in Table 3 refer to 'typical' types of models in each of the four types of models. Within each class of models, however, there are specific models that overcome some of these weaknesses.

3. DIRECTIONS FOR RESEARCH AND IMPLEMENTATION

Table 4 highlights 12 areas of future research and implementation, six areas to improve the implementation and utility of the currently available model and six research directions to broaden their scope. These 12 areas are briefly discussed below.

3.1. Improving the utility of currently available new product forecasting models

3.1.1. Model comparison: the M-competition for new product forecasting models

Given the large number of available new product forecasting models, an analytical and empirical comparison of these models is essential to understand the basic differences and similarities among them. Although limited in its scope (providing a comparison of only awareness forecasting models embedded in their respective new product introduction models), the empirical study by Mahajan, Muller and Sharma (1984) was made possible by an active cooperation from the various research suppliers who provided both the data and unpublished analytical details of their models. We echo here the call by Lewis G. Pringle of BBDO, Inc. (Pringle, Wilson and Brody, 1984) that more studies using richer data bases and including other purchase variables such as trial, repeat and sales are needed to further understand the forecasting efficacy of the various models. In that regard, our proposal is in the spirit of the M-competition where 1001 time-series were used by the developers of the various time-series models for forecasting comparison (Makridakis *et al.*, 1982). In the case of new product forecasting models, however, such a comparison is not feasible without cooperation from the various research suppliers and their clients.

To further examine the forecasting efficiency of the various models it will also be fruitful to conduct a meta-analysis (Farley and Lehmann, 1986) within and across the various classes of forecasting models. Such an analysis will assist in isolating variables that seem to cause or relate to consistent differences in the forecasting efficiency of the various models including variables that reflect the differences in the nature of products, marketing mix strategies, market conditions and specific model characteristics.

3.1.2. External validation of the models

In spite of a general trend towards the greater sophistication of new product forecasting models, the percentage of successful new product introductions has not improved in the

Table 2. Summary of review articles

Type of model reviewed	Review article	Criteria used	Specific models included	Remarks
Multiattribute approaches to product/concept	Shocker and Srinivasan (1979)	Methods used to operationalize the following five stages in the concept evaluation and generation framework are evaluated: (1) determination of relevant product markets; (2) identification of determinant attributes; (3) creation of perceptual space; (4) modeling individual or segment decision making; (5) evaluation of/ search for new product concepts	Johnson (1971); Lehmann (1971); Shocker and Srinivasan (1974); Rao and Souter (1975); Hustad *et al.* (1975); Urban (1975); Hauser and Urban (1977)	The article identifies the approaches suggested by Kuehn and Day (1962), Wind (1973) and Myers (1976) as methods which do not explicitly model individual customer decision making, but rather rely on the decisions themselves and on aggregate responses. The comparison is restricted to the various analytical approaches employed by the different concept evaluation/generation models. No best model is identified, and no indication of forecasting efficiency is provided. A simulation comparison of some of these approaches is provided by Sudharshan *et al.* (1987). The industry utilization of these approaches has been questioned by Tauber (1981) and Dodson and Brodsky (1987), who state that the traditional concept testing approaches are still in vogue in industry

| Pretest market models | Robinson (1981) | PURCHASE ACTION (ASI Marketing Research Inc.); ASSESSOR (Silk and Urban, 1978); COMP (Burger, Gundee and Lavidge, 1981); LTM (Yankelovich, Skelly and White, 1981); SPEEDMARK (Robinson Associates); MICRO-MARKET (Tele-Research) | 37 variables related to the following 12 aggregate characteristics are used: (1) scope of test product configuration; (2) scope of test marketing plan; (3) scope of test environmental conditions; (4) measurement of buyer purchase behavior; (5) conditions of exposure environment; (6) competitive context; (7) conditions of measurement; (8) sampling procedure; (9) projectability of results; (10) assumptions used; (11) model specification; (12) operational characteristics | The article does not include several new simulated test market services currently offered in the marketplace such as LITMUS (Blackburn and Clancy, 1983) and BASES (Burke Marketing Services, 1984). The comparison, although very comprehensive, is highly subjective. Clustering analysis results suggest that conventional test markets and limited rollouts are more closely related to each other than to any of the simulated test market procedures. SPEEDMARK is identified as the procedure which approaches this pairing proximity. No indication of the forecasting efficiency of these approaches is provided. Levine (1981) has argued that these approaches need to be validated before they will be accepted by industry |
| Pretest market models | Shocker and Hall (1986) | BASES II (Burke Marketing Services, 1984); ASSESSOR–FT (Information Resources, 1985); LITMUS–II (Blackburn and Clancy, 1983); NEWS/PLANNER (Pringle, Wilson and Brody, 1982) | 14 characteristics are used for comparison: (1) type of model; (2) data sources; (3) product categories; (4) forecast by time period; (5) marketing plan inputs; (6) cannibalization effects; (7) competitive reactions; (8) respondent screening; (9) output; (10) diagnostics; (11) sensitivity/ optimization; (12) average sample size; (13) time to complete; (14) approximate cost | The article provides an overview of pretest marketing models including their historical development, and strengths and weaknesses. A descriptive comparison of four pretest market models on selected dimensions is also included. No best model is identified. |

Table 2. (*Continued*)

Type of model reviewed	Review article	Criteria used	Specific models included	Remarks
Pretest and test market models	Larreche and Montgomery (1977)	(1) Structure: (a) adaptability, (b) completeness, (c) ease of testing, (d) ease of understanding, (e) robustness; (2) expected value; (3) initial cost; (4) usage characteristics; (5) usage context; (6) validation history	DEMON (Learner, 1965); Hendry (Butler and Butler, 1971); STEAM (Massy, 1969); NEWS (Pringle, Wilson and Brody, 1982); NW Ayer (Claycamp and Liddy, 1969); SPRINTER (Urban, 1970)	The models are evaluated as part of a larger Delphi study on the evaluation of marketing models. NEWS and NW Ayer's model scored highest (4) on a 5-point scale of likelihood of acceptance
Pretest and test market models (repeat purchase diffusion models)	Mahajan and Muller (1982)	(1) Model formulation (deterministic vs. stochastic); (2) use of integrated adoption/diffusion framework; (3) model distinguishes between: (a) unaware potential, (b) types of information, (c) depth of repeat; (4) model includes: (a) word-of-mouth, (b) impulse purchase, (c) decay, (d) recycle	Fourt and Woodlock (1960); Parfitt and Collins (1968); NW Ayer (Claycamp and Liddy, 1969); STEAM Nakanishi (1973); NEWPROD (Massy, 1969); SPRINTER (Assmus, 1975); SPRINTER (Urban, 1970); Midgley (1976); TRACKER (Blattberg and Golanty, 1978); Dodson and Muller (1978); Lilien, Rao and Kalish (1981)	The comparison is limited to the adoption/diffusion structure of the models. The article ignores all other important considerations related to the implementation of the models. Although the article does not identify the best model, the comparison suggests that SPRINTER scores highest on most of the selected dimensions
Pretest and test market models (awareness models only)	Mahajan, Muller and Sharma (1984)	(1) Features of models (marketing mix variables considered, word-of-mouth, forgetting, initial awareness, maximum level of awareness); (2) forecasting accuracy	TRACKER (Blattberg and Golanty, 1978); NEWS (Pringle, Wilson and Brody, 1982); LITMUS (Blackburn and Clancy, 1983); Dodson and Muller (1978); AYER (Claycamp and Liddy, 1969)	Using actual data, this article provides an empirical comparison of awareness models included in five new product introduction models. Analytical similarities among the models are derived. All the models are shown to perform equally well with TRACKER marginally leading the compared models

Test market models	Narasimhan and Sen (1983)	(1) Model objective; (2) stages modelled; (3) consideration of marketing; (4) level of model complexity; (5) type of sales data required; (6) diagnostics; (7) number of applications reported at time of publication; (8) degree of commercial acceptance	Fourt and Woodlock (1960); Parfitt and Collins (1968); STEAM (Massy, 1969); SPRINTER (Urban, 1970); Eskin (1973); Nakanishi (1973); NEWS (Pringle, Wilson and Brody, 1982); NEWPROD (Assmus, 1975); TRACKER (Blattberg and Golanty, 1978)	The comparison, although very comprehensive, is subjective. It identifies TRACKER and NEWS as the best test market models on the selected dimensions
Early sales models (first purchase diffusion models)	Mahajan and Muller (1979)	Inclusion of marketing mix variables in: (1) coefficient of internal influence; (2) coefficient of external influence; (3) total number of potential customers	Bass (1969); Chow (1967); Fourt and Woodlock (1960); Mansfield (1961); Hendry (1972); Lackman (1978); Lekvall and Wahlbin (1973); Robinson and Lakhani (1975); Horsky and Simon (1983); Bass (1978); Peterson and Mahajan (1978); Mahajan and Peterson (1978); Mahajan et al. (1979); Dodson and Muller (1980)	The article does not include the models developed in industry although the model developed by Lawrence and Lawton (1981) can be shown as a special case of the Bass (1969) model. No indication of the predictive efficiency of the models is provided. Heeler and Hustad (1980) suggest that the long term predictive ability of these models is questionable in international settings. A state-of-the-art assessment is available in Mahajan and Wind (1986)

Table 3. Key characteristics of new product forecasting models

Characteristics	Type of model			
	Concept testing	Pretest market	Test market	Early sales models (diffusion models)
I. Setting				
1. Product most appropriate for	All	Frequently purchased consumer products	Frequently purchased consumer products	Consumer durables
2. Conditions most appropriate for	These models are generally appropriate for established product categories and are *not* appropriate when: (a) assessment of competitive retailiation and trade support are essential to develop accurate sales or share estimates; (b) product diffusion is highly dependent upon word-of-mouth effect; (c) measurement of depth of repeat is essential to obtain 'loyal' market shares; (d) retail promotion, in-store displays and media can significantly influence product sales; (e) period by period sales estimates are required for financial planning;	These models are *not* appropriate when: (a) product class is new; (b) market for the product category is growing; (c) assessment of competitive retailiation is essential to develop accurate sales or share estimates; (d) it is difficult to measure repeat purchase intentions (e.g. products with longer repeat cycles or products that are used at special or seasonal occasions); (e) it is necessary to ascertain trade support; (f) measurement of the word-of-mouth effect is essential to measure product success; (g) retail promotion, in-	These models are *not* appropriate when: (a) desired results can be obtained from pretest market models; (b) there is a high likelihood of competitors' 'rigging' the test market and hence the results; (c) surprise in results is critical; (d) cost (and time) is prohibitive	These models are *not* appropriate when: (a) new product is a seasonal or a cyclical product; (b) unit of analysis is not an adopter or unit/dollar sales cannot be converted into number of adopters (unless specifically handled by the model); (c) data are contaminated with repeat or replacement sales; (d) situation analyzed is not a monopoly (unless specifically handled by the model)

(f) new product is an innovative breakthrough

store displays and media other than TV or print significantly influence product sales; (h) measurement of depth of repeat is essential to obtain 'loyal' market share

II. Output

3. Sales (market share) estimates

	Short to intermediate term	Mostly annual (first year)	Mostly annual (first year)	Long term
Time period (long or short term)				
Reported validated forecasting accuracy	Limited	Limited	Limited	Limited
4. Diagnostic insights and sensitivity analysis with respect to:				
Changes in marketing mix	Moderate	Moderate	Yes	Limited
Competitive actions and reactions	Limited	Limited	Moderate	Limited
Environment conditions	Limited	Limited	Some	Limited
Market segment responses	Yes	Yes	Yes	Limited
5. Impact on the firm's				
Financial health	Limited	Some	Some	No
Other products	Limited	Some	Some	No
III. Implementation				
6. Required expertise	Moderate	High	High	Moderate
7. Cost of development and maintenance	Moderate	Moderate	Very high	Moderate
8. Ease of understanding	High	High	High	High

Table 4. Directions for research and implementation

I. Improving the utility of existing models

1. A comprehensive analytical and empirical comparison of the models (like the M-competition for the time-series models)
2. External validation of the models
3. Combination of forecasts
4. Combination of models
5. Identification of conditions for skipping forecasts at the various stages of the new product development process
6. Integration with financial criteria of product success

II. Broadening the scope

7. New product models for truly innovative breakthrough products
8. Models based on the newly available data bases
9. Development of models incorporating offensive and defensive strategies
10. Development of forecasting expert systems
11. Incorporation of the concept of marketing hype
12. Models for global markets

---

last two decades. A recent survey by Booz, Allen and Hamilton (1982) indicates that the percentage of new product introductions that met company-specific financial and strategic criteria for success has not improved significantly in the last two decades.

Although several reasons can be put forth to explain this finding by Booz, Allen and Hamilton (Wind and Mahajan, 1988), we believe that external validation of new product forecasting models is a must to further enhance their contribution in picking winners and losers. With the cooperation of various research suppliers and their clients, an empirical study should be undertaken to track the fate of products that were given a go/no-go signal. Such a study would especially track the fate of products that, in spite of a no-go decision by the forecasting models, were still introduced in the marketplace.

3.1.3. Combination of forecasts

The recent literature in forecasting is replete with studies indicating that forecasting accuracy improves when combining results from the various models as compared to forecasting with the individual models. In summarizing results across eight such studies on combining forecasts, Armstrong (1986) found forecast error reductions which varied from zero to 23%. In fact, Makridakis and Winkler (1983) have reported a 7.2% error reduction with as few as two models in combination, with a maximum 16.3% error reduction for five models in combination.

The above trend in the forecasting literature suggests that we need to explore the utilization of combining results for new product forecasting. Such combinations may include results based on judgmental models (e.g. analytic hierarchy process (AHP); see Wind and Saaty, 1980), analogs (see, e.g. Thomas, 1985) and the models based on consumer responses (i.e. Table 2). Forecasts based on combinations will exploit special features of each model and enhance management understanding and confidence in the forecasts.

3.1.4. Combination of models

In addition to the market share that a firm may capture, it is also interested in projecting the rate of penetration of a new product or the time span that will be required to attain a certain level of market share in the marketplace. For example, in evaluating two new products with identical market share estimates, the time period required to attain the market share for each product could impact the no-go/go decision.

In order to obtain such information for a new product it is, however, necessary to integrate concept test, pretest and test market results with diffusion models. For example, concept test studies using conjoint analysis provide results related to the sales or market share that a new product can be expected to capture in the marketplace under conditions of 100% awareness, knowledge and distribution. On the other hand, it has been reported (e.g. Heeler and Hustad, 1980) that forecasts provided by diffusion models are sensitive to the ultimate market share (ceiling) estimates used in these models. Integration of the two types of models, therefore, will enhance the utilization of both types of models providing management forecasting results that are more meaningful and useful.

3.1.5. Skipping stages in the new product development process

Given the competitive environment and shorter life cycles, there is generally a bias towards action. More specifically, our experience with several consumer-packaged companies indicates that there is a bias towards new product introduction as quickly as possible, by-passing several steps of the formal new product development process outlined in Figure 1.

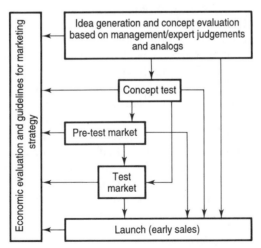

Figure 1. New Product Evaluation Process.

As outlined in Figure 1, a firm could make a 'go' decision to launch a product, skipping the pretest and test market steps or it could make a 'go' decision to launch after pretest market results. Leaving aside the time and financial constraints, the key questions are, how much accuracy in forecasting results does one lose by skipping the various stages in the formal development process? When is it appropriate to skip the various stages before product launch? How much incremental improvement does one obtain from stage to stage in the formal process? Answers to these questions again demand a comprehensive empirical study with the cooperation of research suppliers and their clients. A first study investigating this issue has been reported by Urban and Katz (1983). Their data indicate that products successful in the pretest market have about an 80% chance of succeeding in the test market.

3.1.6. Integration with financial criteria of product success

As outlined in Table 1, top management and external stakeholders are predominantly concerned with the impact of the new product introduction on the firm's financial health. Such an analysis, however, is not feasible unless the sales forecasts can be integrated with the financial commitments and financial gains over time. Such an integration will assist management to evaluate the strategic role of the new product in its product portfolio and develop a mission for the product to protect or gain the desired position in the marketplace.

3.2. Broadening the scope of new product forecasting models

3.2.1. New product models for truly innovative breakthrough products

An examination of Table 2 indicates that the currently available new product forecasting models are predominantly developed for established products in stable markets. Could these models forecast the success of major breakthroughs identified, for example, in the study by Arthur D. Little? (These products include the VHS-format video cassette recorder, 3M Corporation's Post-it note pads, the microwave oven, Federal Express, Tagamet ethical drug, athletic footwear by Nike, exercise machines by Nautilus, Inc.; see Nayak and Ketteringham (1986) for details).

How can consumer-based models be extended or reformulated to forecast success of truly innovative breakthrough products? This is particularly important since the study by Booz, Allen and Hamilton (1982) has indicated that 30% of truly innovative products (either to the company or to the world) accounted for 60% of the 'most successful' new products in the sample examined. Initial efforts in this area by the authors used videocassettes 'educating' the respondents as to the nature and likely impact of the innovations. Following this educational stage a conjoint-analysis-based concept test was conducted, resulting in meaningful responses and valid forecasts.

3.2.2. Models based on newly available data bases

With the exception of early sales models, most of the consumer-based models included in Table 2 are based on some kind of consumer survey data. Recent technological innovations are, however, changing the way we collect data from and on consumers. Examples include people meters (electronic audience measuring devices to profile TV viewing habits) and scanners. The wealth of data provided by these innovations when applied to test market or early sales stage studies offer an emerging opportunity to develop timely and accurate new product forecasting models.

3.2.3. Models incorporating offensive and defensive strategies

Defensive marketing strategies are the strategies developed by a firm to retain its customers (by minimizing brand switching from its brand to competing brands). Offensive marketing strategies are strategies designed by a firm to increase its customer base (by maximizing brand switching from competing brands to its brand). Since the market performance of a new product can be influenced by offensive and defensive strategies designed by a firm and its competitors (Hauser and Shugan, 1983), their incorporation is essential in developing forecasts for a new product.

Consider, for example, the impact of new product-related announcements on consumer purchase intentions. Product-related announcements, whether released prior to the introduction of a new product or during its life span and whether created by design or accident, can influence consumers' perceptions, attitudes, intentions and purchase behavior. For example, a manufacturer may announce a new product well before it is ready for the marketplace hoping to get consumers to wait for its new product rather than buy a competitor's product in the interim. In fact, following Mahajan, Muller and Kerin (1984), in a recent empirical study, Burke et al. (1988) has demonstrated that positive and negative brand-related, product-category-related and industry-related information can be used to influence consumers' purchase intentions for micro-computers. New product announcements are also being used by firms to assess the feasibility and consumer interest in their product concepts.

Recent empirical evidence also suggests that the sales of a new product can also be influenced by its timing of entry into the marketplace as compared to its competitors. Schnaars (1986), for example, has documented case histories of products where pioneers or late entrants gained and maintained dominant position in the marketplace. Empirical evidence for market share pioneering advantage has also been provided by Urban et al. (1986). These studies clearly indicate that the sales or the market share captured by a firm can be influenced by the timing of its entry.

Given the empirical evidence on the influence of offensive or defensive strategies on product sales, it is imperative that such strategies by the firm and its competitors be explicitly considered in developing forecasts for a new product.

3.2.4. Development of forecasting expert systems

Expert systems offer a remarkable technology to capture the expert power and available theory and empirical findings in analyzing and forecasting the impact of marketing decisions. It has been reported that expert systems are currently being used to help design advertising commercials (Rangaswamy et al., 1987), to screen potential customers and their purchases by companies like American Express and to check the quality consistency in canned foods by Campbell Soup (Kupfer, 1987). Expert systems are also being made available to consumers to analyze their product preferences and shop for products like running shoes, washing machines, touring bikes and cars (*Business Week*, 1987).

We anticipate development of expert systems for new product forecasting where a user could interact with a system to develop forecasts for a new product based on rules reflecting cumulative industry experience, company experience and other theoretical or empirical findings relevant to the type of product under consideration.

3.2.5. Marketing hype

Marketing hype is a set of predominately prelaunch activities leading to the creation of a market environment most conducive to the acceptance of a new product (Wind and Mahajan, 1987). This environment includes:

- the distribution channels that stock and promote the product;
- the providers of support products and services whenever these are critical for the acceptance of the product;
- the media, including specialized vertical publications and newsletters as well as the general media;
- the opinion leaders, financial analysts, independent testing and evaluation groups who, through their word-of-mouth and credibility, could significantly affect the perceived value of the product.

The success of a new product in the marketplace, therefore, depends on the support of multiple stakeholders as well as their influence (positive or negative) on each other and the consumer. Consequently, the introductory prelaunch marketing programme of a new product should be geared to all these actors and not just at the consumer. Adapted from Wind and Mahajan (1987), Figure 2 illustrates the difference between a conventional marketing launch and a marketing hype-driven launch.

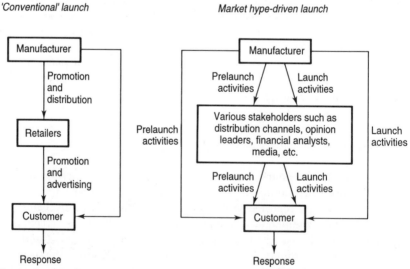

Figure 2. A Comparison of a Conventional and Marketing Hype-Driven Product Launch.

As depicted in Figure 2, in a conventional product launch effort, the manufacturer's key decisions are the selection of a target consumer segment and developing for it a new product with its associated marketing mix programs. In contrast, the marketing hype-driven introductory strategy focuses not only on the target customer segment but also on the relevant segment(s) of each of the key stakeholders and developing for each the most effective prelaunch and launch marketing programs.

The importance of having a receptive market environment for the adoption of a new product has major implications for the development of new product forecasting models. The concept test and pretest models, for example, need to explicitly consider the influence of the various stakeholders (e.g. positive support by key experts) on consumers' purchase intentions and choices. The early sales models, on the other hand, need to develop and empirically validate diffusion models to capture diffusion patterns dominated by the various stakeholders (e.g. distribution channels). Incorporation of marketing hype-driven strategies in the new product forecasting models should make them more realistic and practical.

3.2.6. Models for global markets

In recent years, an increasing number of key industries such as automobiles, motorcycles, agricultural equipment, aerospace, military hardware, telecommunications, electronics and consumer luxury products are becoming global in scope. There has been a consistent trend towards internationalization and integration of markets for many consumer and industrial goods and services. Management consultants like Ohmae (1985, p. 32) have even suggested that given the shorter life cycles for new products and global competition for worldwide markets, a firm should follow a 'sprinkler' model (i.e. introduce a new product simultaneously in all the worldwide markets) rather than a 'waterfall' model (i.e. introduce a new product sequentially in the various markets).

Following the lead of companies like Coca-cola, Marlborough and Levi-Strauss, it has been suggested that the key to worldwide success is the development of global standardized products that will appeal to markets worldwide (Levitt, 1983). On the other hand, in order to take advantage of the idiosyncratic characteristics of each segment and country, it has been proposed (Wind and Douglas, 1987) that companies should develop a portfolio of customized products that tailor the products to the needs of each segment/country and the relevant marketing infrastructure of the various countries, while assuring coordination and integration of efforts across countries.

Irrespective of which of the two strategies is followed by a company in its global market, it is to be recognized that new product introductions overseas by the US companies constitute the largest segment of international business blunders (Ricks, 1984). Although the recent development of global advertising agencies (e.g. Saatchi and Saatchi) may assist companies in better planning their global new product introductions, this trend, however, offers an emerging opportunity to develop new product forecasting models that can assist companies forecast global demand for their products. This will require considerations such as: (a) selection of participants in concept testing and other consumer-based new product forecasting models (consumers as well as other actors as required by the marketing hype concept); (b) evaluation of the comparability across countries of data collection procedures and models in pretest, test market and early sales new product forecasting models; (c) selection of sample of countries to facilitate new product forecasting across countries from a sample rather than from the census of all countries. Like the trend towards globalization, new product forecasting models also need to be 'global' in scope in their data collection and modelling efforts while recognizing idiosyncratic country characteristics and facilitating integration and coordination of efforts across countries.

4. CONCLUSIONS

New products generally constitute a sizeable portion of the total profits of a firm (Booz, Allen and Hamilton, 1982). Rapid technological advances, changing market conditions and global market competition have made it imperative for companies to be more focused and innovative in their search for and development of new products. Each new product is expected to play a key strategic role in the marketplace—either to defend a market share or to gain and maintain a market share. In this context, new product forecasting models have and can play a critical role in reducing the odds against failure in the marketplace.

After briefly reviewing strengths and weaknesses of the various types of currently available new product forecasting models, this paper outlined 12 areas of research and implementation that can help: (a) practitioners improve the existing models to enhance their utilization in evaluating new product decisions; (b) researchers develop models that better meet the needs of users of new product forecasting models.

REFERENCES

Armstrong, J. S. (1986) 'The Ombudsman: Research on Forecasting: A Quarter Century Review, 1960–1984', *Interfaces*, **16**: 89–109.

Assmus, G. (1975) 'NEWPROD: The Design and Implementation of a New Product Model', *Journal of Marketing*, **39** (Jan): 16–23.

Assmus, G. (1984) 'New Product Forecasting', *Journal of Forecasting*, **3** (April–June): 121–138.

Bass, F. M. (1969) 'A New Product Growth Model for Consumer Durables', *Management Science*, **15** (Jan.): 215–227.

Bass, F. M. (1980) 'The Relationship Between Diffusion Rates, Experience Curves, and Demand Elasticities for Consumer Durable Technological Innovation', *Journal of Business*, **53**: S51–S67.

Blackburn, J. D. and Clancy, K. J. (1983) 'LITMUS II: An Evolutionary Step in New Product Planning Models from Marketing Plan Evaluation to Marketing Plan Generation', in Zufryden, F. (ed.), *Advances and Practices of Marketing Science*, The Institute of Management Sciences, Providence, RI.

Blattberg, R. and Golanty, J. (1978) 'TRACKER: An Early Test-Market Forecasting and Diagnostic Model for New-Product Success', *Journal of Marketing Research*, **15** (May): 192–202.

Booz, Allen and Hamilton, Inc. (1982) *New Products Management for the 1980s*, Booz, Allen and Hamilton, New York.

Burger, P. C., Gundee, H. and Lavidge, R. (1981) 'COMP: A Comprehensive System for the Evaluation of New Products', in Wind, Y., Mahajan, V. and Cardozo, R. (eds), *New Product Forecasting: Models and Applications*, Lexington Books, Lexington, MA.

Burke, R. R., Cho, J., DeSarbo, W. S. and Mahajan, V. (1988) 'Assessing the Impact of Product Related Announcements on Consumer Purchase Intentions: An Empirical study', Working paper, Cox School of Business, SMU, Dallas, TX.

Burke Marketing Services (1984) 'BASES: Introduction, Services, Validation, History', Descriptive brochure, Burke Marketing Services, Cincinnati, OH.

Business Week (1987a) 'A Case of Malpractice—in Marketing Research', Aug. 10: 28–29.

Business Week, (1987b) 'The Computer Gives Shoppers Custom-Made Advice', Dec. 7: 127.

Butler, D. H. and Butler, B. F. (1971) *Hendrodynamics: Fundamental Laws of Consumer Dynamics*, The Hendry Corporation, New York.

Chow, G. C. (1967) 'Technological Change and the Demand for Computers', *American Economic Review*, **57** (Dec.): 1117–1130.

Claycamp, H. J. and Liddy, L. E. (1969) 'Prediction of New Product Performance: An Analytical Approach', *Journal of Marketing Research*, **6** (Nov.): 414–420.

Dodson, J. A. and Brodsky, J. B. (1987) 'Commentary on a Simulation Comparison of Methods for New Product Location', *Marketing Science*, **6** (Spring): 202–203.

Dodson, J. A. and Muller, E. (1978) 'Models of New Product Diffusion Through Advertising and Word-of-Mouth', *Management Science*, **15** (Nov.): 1568–1578.

Eskin, G. J. (1973) 'Dynamic Forecasts of New Product Demand Using a Depth of Repeat Model', *Journal of Marketing Research*, **10** (May): 115–129.

Farley, J. U. and Lehmann, D. R. (1986) *Meta-Analysis in Marketing: Generalization of Response Models*, Lexington Books, Lexington, MA.

Fourt, L. A. and Woodlock, J. W. (1960) 'Early Prediction of Market Success for New Grocery Products', *Journal of Marketing*, **25** (Oct.): 31–38.

Green, P. E., Douglas Carroll, J. and Goldberg, S. (1981) 'A General Model for Product Design Optimization via Conjoint Analysis', *Journal of Marketing*, **45**: 17–37.

Hauser, J. R. and Shugan, S. M. (1983) 'Defensive Marketing Strategies', *Marketing Science*, **3** (Fall): 327–251.

Hauser, J. R. and Urban, G. L. (1977) 'A Normative Methodology of Modeling Consumer Response to Innovation', *Operations Research*, **25** (July–Aug): 579–619.

Heeler, R. M. and Hustad, T. P. (1980) 'Problems in Predicting New Product Growth for Consumer Durables', *Management Science*, **26** (Oct): 1007–1020.

Hendry, I. (1972) 'The Three Parameter Approach to Long Range Forecasting', *Long Range Planning*, **5** (March): 40–45.

Horsky, D. and Simon, L. S. (1983) 'Advertising and Diffusion of New Products', *Marketing Science*, **2** (Winter): 1–17.

Hustad, T. P., Mayer, C. S. and Whipple, T. W. (1975) 'Consideration of Context Differences in Product Evaluation and Market Segmentation', *Journal of the Academy of Marketing Science*, **3** (Winter): 34–47.

Information Resources, Inc. (1985) 'ASSESSOR-FT: The Next Generation', Descriptive Brochure, Information Resources, Chicago, IL.

Johnson, R. M. (1971) 'Market Segmentation: A Strategic Management Tool', *Journal of Marketing Research*, **8** (Feb): 13–18.

Kuehn, A. A. and Day, R. L. (1962) 'Strategy of Product Quality', *Harvard Business Review*, **40** (Nov.–Dec.): 100–110.

Kupfer, A. (1987) 'Now, Live Experts on a Floppy Disk', *Fortune*, Oct. 12: 69–82.

Lackman, C. L. (1978) 'Gompertz Curve Forecasting: A New Product Application', *Journal of Marketing Research Society*, **20** (Jan.): 45–47.

Larreche, J. D. and Montgomery, D. B. (1977) 'A Framework for the Comparison of Marketing Models: A Delphi Study', *Journal of Marketing Research*, **16** (Nov.): 487–498.

Lawrence, K. D. and Lawton, W. H. (1981) 'Applications of Diffusion Models: Some Empirical Results', in: Wind, Y., Mahajan, V. and Cardozo, R. (eds), *New Product Forecasting: Models and Applications*, Lexington Books, Lexington, MA.

Learner, D. B. (1965) 'Demon New Product Planning: A Case History', *Commentary*, **7** (Oct.).

Lehmann, D. R. (1971) 'Evaluating Marketing Strategy in a Multiple Brand Market', *Journal of Business Administration*, **3** (Fall): 15–16.

Lekvall, P. and Wahlbin, C. (1973) 'A Study of Some Assumptions Underlying Innovation Diffusion Functions', *Swedish Journal of Economics*, **75**: 332–337.

Levine, J. (1981) 'Pretest Market Research of New Packaged Goods Products—A User Orientation', in Wind, Y., Mahajan, V. and Cardozo, R. (eds), *New Product Forecasting: Models and Applications*, Lexington Books, Lexington, MA.

Levitt, T. (1983) 'The Globalization of Markets', *Harvard Business Review* (May–June).

Lilien, G. L., Rao, A. G. and Kalish, S. (1981) 'Bayesian Estimation and Control of Detailing Effort in a Repeat-Purchase Diffusion Environment', *Management Science*, **27** (May): 495–506.

Mahajan, V. and Muller, E. (1979) 'Innovation Diffusion and New Product Growth Models in Marketing', *Journal of Marketing*, **43** (Fall): 55–68.

Mahajan, V. and Muller, E. (1982) 'Innovation Behavior and Repeat Purchase Diffusion Models', in *Proceedings, American marketing educators' conference*, American Marketing Association, Chicago, IL: 456–460.

Mahajan, V. and Peterson, R. A. (1978) 'Innovation Diffusion in a Dynamic Potential Adopter Population', *Management Science*, **15** (Nov.): 1589–1597.

Mahajan, V. and Wind, Y. (1986) *Innovation Diffusion Models of New Product Acceptance*, Ballinger, Cambridge, MA.

Mahajan, V., Muller, E. and Kerin, R. A. (1984) 'Introduction Strategy for New Products with Positive and Negative Word-of-Mouth', *Management Science*, **30** (Dec.): 1389–1404.

Mahajan, V., Muller, E. and Sharma, S. (1984) 'An Empirical Comparison of Awareness Forecasting Models of New Product Introduction', *Marketing Science*, **3** (Summer): 179–206.

Mahajan, V., Peterson, R. A., Jain, A. K. and Malhotra, N. (1979) 'A New Product Growth Model with a Dynamic Market Potential', *Long Range Planning*, **12** (Aug.): 51–58.

Makridakis, S. G. and Winkler, R. L. (1983) 'Averages of Forecasts: Some Empirical Results', *Management Science*, **29**: 987–995.

Makridakis, S. G., Anderson, A., Carbane, R., Fildes, R., Hibon, M., Lewandowski, R., Newton, J., Parzen, E. and Winkler, R. (1982) 'The Accuracy of Extrapolation Methods: Results of a Forecasting Combination', *Journal of Forecasting*, **1**: 111–153.

Mansfield, E. (1961) 'Technical Change and the Rate of Imitation', *Econometrica*, **29** (Oct.): 741–766.

Massy, W. F. (1969) 'Forecasting the Demand for New Convenience Products', *Journal of Marketing Research*, **6** (Nov.): 405–412.

Myers, J. (1976) 'Benefit Structure Analysis: A New Tool for Product Planning', *Journal of Marketing*, **40** (Oct): 23–32.

Nakanishi, M. (1973) 'Advertising and Promotion Effects on Consumer Response to New Products', *Journal of Marketing Research*, **10** (Aug): 242–249.

Narasimhan, C. and Sen, S. K. (1983) 'New Product Models for Test Market Data', *Journal of Marketing*, **47** (Winter): 11–24.

Nayak, P. R. and Ketteringham, J. M. (1986) *Breakthroughs*, Rawson Associates, New York.

Ohmae, K. (1985) *Triad Power*, The Free Press, New York.

Parfitt, J. H. and Collins, B. J. K. (1968) 'Use of Consumer Panels for Brandshare Prediction', *Journal of Marketing Research*, **5** (May): 131–145.

Peterson, R. A. and Mahajan, V. (1978) 'Multi-Product Growth Models' in Sheth, J. (ed.) *Research in Marketing*, JAI Press, Greenwich, CT.

Pringle, L. G., Wilson, D. R. and Brody, E. I. (1982) 'NEWS: A Decision Oriented Model for New Product Analysis and Forecasting', *Marketing Science*, **1** (Winter): 1–29.

Pringle, L. G., Wilson, D. R. and Brody, E. I. (1984) 'Issues in Comparing the Awareness Component of New Product Models', *Marketing Science*, **3** (Summer), 203–205.

Rangaswamy, A., Burke, R. R., Wind, Y. and Eliashberg, J. (1987) 'Expert Systems for Marketing', Working Paper, The Wharton School, University of Pennsylvania, Philadelphia, PA.

Rao, V. and Souter, G. N. (1975) 'Subjective Evaluations for Product Design Decisions', *Decision Sciences*, **6** (Jan.): 120–134.

Ricks, D. A. (1984) 'Big Business Blunders', Dow Jones Irwin, Homewood, IL.

Robinson, P. J. (1981) 'A Comparison of Pretest Market New Product Forecasting Models', in Wind, Y., Mahajan, V., Cardozo, R. (eds), *New Product Forecasting: Models and Applications*, Lexington Books, Lexington, MA.

Robinson, V. and Lakhani, C. (1975) 'Dynamic Price Models for New Product Planning, *Management Science*, **21** (June): 1113–1132.

Schnaars, S. P. (1986) 'When Entering Growth Markets, are Pioneers Better than Poachers?', *Business Horizons* (March–April): 27–36.

Schnaars, S. P. and Hall, G. (1986) 'Pretest Market Models: A Critical Evaluation', *Journal of Product Innovation Management*, **3** (June): 86–107.

Shocker, A. D. and Srinivasan, V. (1974) 'A Consumer-Based Methodology for the Identification of New Product Ideas', *Management Science*, **20** (Feb.): 921–938.

Shocker, S. P. and Srinivasan, V. (1979) 'Multiattribute Approaches for Product Concept Evaluation and Generation: A Critical Review', *Journal of Marketing Research*, **16** (May): 159–180.

Silk, A. J. and Urban, G. L. (1978) 'Pretest-Market Evaluation of New Packaged Goods: A Model and Measurement Methodology', *Journal of Marketing Research*, **15** (May): 171–191.

Stefflre, V. J. (1971) *New Products and New Enterprises: A Report of an Experiment in Applied Social Science*, University of California, Irvin, CA.

Sudharshan, D., May, J. H. and Shocker, A. D. (1987) 'A Simulation Comparison of Methods for New Product Location', *Marketing Science*, **6** (Spring): 182–201.

Tauber, E. M. (1981) 'The Utilization of Concept for Product Forecasting: Traditional vs. Multiattribute Approaches', in Wind, Y., Mahajan, V. and Cardozo, R. (eds), *New Product Forecasting: Models and Applications*, Lexington Books, Lexington, MA.

Thomas, R. J. (1975) 'PERCEPTOR: A Model for Product Positioning' *Management Science*, **11** (April): 858–871.

Thomas, R. J. (1985) 'Estimating Market Growth for New Products: An Analogical Diffusion Model Approach', *Journal of Product Innovation Management*, **2** (March): 45–55.

Urban, G. L. (1979) 'SPRINTER Mod III: A Model for the Analysis of New Frequently Purchased Consumer Products', *Operations Research*, **18** (Sept.–Oct.): 805–854.

Urban, G. L. and Hauser, J. R. (1980) *Design and Marketing of New Products*, Prentice-Hall, Englewood Cliffs, NJ.

Urban, G. L. and Katz, G. M. (1983) 'Pretest Market Models: Validation and Managerial Implications', *Journal of Marketing Research*, **20** (Aug.): 221–234.

Urban, G. L., Carter, T., Gaskin, S. and Mucha, Z. (1986) 'Market Share Rewards to Pioneering Brands: An Empirical Analysis and Strategic Implications', *Management Science*, **32**: 645–659.

Wind, Y. (1973) 'A New Procedure for Concept Evaluation', *Journal of Marketing*, **37** (Oct.): 2–11.

Wind, Y. (1981) Product Policy: *Concepts, Methods and Strategy*, Addison-Wesley, Reading, MA.

Wind, Y. and Douglas, S. (1987) 'The Myth of Globalization', Working paper, The Wharton School, University of Pennsylvania, Philadelphia, PA.

Wind, Y. and Mahajan, V. (1987) 'Marketing Hype: A New Perspective for New Product Research and Introduction', *Journal of Product Innovation Management*, **4** (March): 43–49.

Wind, Y. and Mahajan, V. (1988) 'New Product Development Process: A Perspective for Reexamination', *Journal of Product Innovation Management*, forthcoming.

Wind, Y. and Saaty, T. L. (1980) 'Marketing Applications of the Analytical Hierarchy Process', *Management Science*, **26**: 641–656.

Wind, Y., Saaty, T. L. and Cardozo, R. C. (1981) *New Product Forecasting*, Lexington Books, Lexington, MA.

Yankelovich, Skelly and White, Inc. (1981) 'LTM Estimating Procedures' in Wind, Y., Mahajan, V. and Cardozo, R. (eds), *Models and Applications*, Lexington Books, Lexington, MA.

19

Evaluating New Products: A System, Not an Act

C. Merle Crawford

New-product managers have perhaps the toughest job in business today. Their assignment:

- Bring out a steady stream of big winners;
- On time, ahead of time, but never behind time;
- With no big failures along the way ... in fact, preferably with no failures at all.
- Meanwhile, deal effectively with hundreds of interface problems while trying to keep a team working together in something that resembles harmony more than chaos.
- Learn to use, but not be overwhelmed by, a steady flow of new techniques, from trade-off analysis to scanner test markets to post-launch tracking and control.
- All the while, increase productivity, cut costs and increase the quality of the new items.

As if this 'impossible dream' of their managements were not enough, several myths about new-product idea evaluation compound the problem and make the job even tougher than it should be.

Along with creativity and learning how to make and sell the thing invented, *evaluation* is at the heart of the new-products process. With efficient, timely and accurate evaluation of the new ideas, concepts and products, we get products on time, selling at profitable levels. Failure in evaluating new ideas leads directly to failure of the products and services marketed.

Evaluation means appraising some aspect of the new product situation. Will people try it? Will they like it when they try it? Will they buy enough of it to make it profitable? Can we make it reliably? Can we market it effectively and efficiently? To evaluate an idea or concept or product means to judge any aspect of it that helps determine its bottom-line payoff.

Reprinted from *Business Horizons*, November–December 1986, pp. 48–55

FOUR MYTHS AND FOUR MYTH EXPLODERS

Four myths needlessly exacerbate the evaluation task. Four aspects of the evaluation process explode these myths.

The four myths

Myth 1. The one real evaluation, and the one that should be done thoroughly and well, is the one we do for the 'go/no-go' decision. Occasionally this is true—when a major manufacturing capability must be built, for example, or when there is no time to run a market test before national launch on TV. But more often than not, things are more gradual than that. It's difficult for a new-products manager to look back and tell exactly when the no-return decision was made.

Myth 2. Evaluation begins when the idea first appears and concludes when the product is marketed. In fact, it begins well *before* ideation. And it goes on for months after marketing.

Myth 3. Product Innovation is like a relay race. First we develop the product itself, and then we hand it off to Marketing. That way we avoid costly and time-consuming back-tracking into the R&D process. This myth is heard less frequently today, but it probably is still the greatest single deterrent to efficient and effective product innovation.

Myth 4. Bad ideas should be weeded out fast. Screen tough and early. Eliminate the losers before we waste a lot of money on them. Maybe, but usually not.

The myth exploders

Several realities lying deep within the product innovation process show these widely held beliefs to be myths:

(1) The evaluation process is continuous.
(2) A product and its marketing plan should evolve simultaneously.
(3) Each evaluation decision is keyed only to the decision or action that immediately follows it.
(4) Newer evaluation techniques are incremental ones.

Let's examine these realities, to see what thinking they substitute for the myths.

The evaluation process is continuous

Odd as it may sound, management is never out of the evaluation mode on a new product. There are several reasons for this continuous process.

(1) First, *some of the most critical and decisive evaluation of new product concepts occurs before the concepts are even discovered.* More and more managements are adopting firm and clear new-products strategy (product innovation charters) to guide their new-products organizations. Strategy narrows company focus and thereby eliminates most new product options.

For example, when Brik Pak decided to concentrate its aseptic packaging technology only on liquids, that decision eliminated yogurts, soups and puddings. Brik Pak's action was evaluation—a deliberate decision that any new concepts in the rejected areas would not be good for that firm. Strategy action such as this is wholesale evaluation—and often very effective. Not that it precedes the creation of a single new product idea.

(2) The second reason why evaluation must be continuous is that *the new-product concept itself is changing*. A product is not born at the time of ideation. An *idea* is, but the manner of its implementation is not. I hold that a new product comes into existence when it is successfully established in the marketplace. Before that, a product is actually only a concept in temporary physical form—and even less than physical form if it is a service. Its form will have to be changed, and changed again, until it succeeds.

This view helps explain the increasingly popular practice of gradually edging a product into the marketplace. The firm is still exploring. Management is not at all sure that the current new product is the one it ultimately wants. Full-scale marketing, which too many people feel is the ultimate act of product innovation, is actually only one step in the evaluation process. Feedback and tracking systems should be built in accordingly.

A good way to test this thesis of gradual product evolution is to take a product your firm marketed about a year ago. Reconstruct the many forms that product took from the time of its original ideation to now. Some firms—for example, computer companies—actually formalize the process and give names to each step: breadboard, preproduction model and so on. And they don't call the current model *final*, regardless of how close they are to selling some of it. They are not finished with development. There probably will be changes in form, in packaging, in service. If they're really lucky, the first shot may be right, but it usually isn't.

(3) The third buttress for the concept that evaluation is a continuous process is *the vague and nebulous nature of the so-called 'go/no-go' decision*. True, there are projects where management must authorize, say, $100 million for a new plant. This is a clear 'go' point, and an abort after that is expensive and unlikely. And firms that launch consumer products with national television advertising probably consider their TV commitment a 'go' decision.

But big showdowns like this are being phased out. For example, a chief argument for the complex simulation test-market models being used increasingly by consumer marketers today is that they permit a firm to move into market-by-market rollouts, rather than a full-scale test market followed by national launch.

The industrial firm is trying to get out of such decisions too. One newly popular tactic is downstream and upstream coupling. By 'renting' the resources of suppliers or potential users, a firm often edges into a new product venture, ascertaining that it will work before making the capital commitment that cuts the umbilical cords of the coupling. In such situations, when was the critical decision made? Surely not at that dramatic but hypothetical time when some general manager intoned with high seriousness, 'OK, folks, this is it'. Managers today try to avoid these decisions.

(4) For a final argument supporting the concept of continuous evaluation, look at how *many firms now view their new product innovation as new business innovation*. Either the new product is just one more in a long stream of items (for example, Sugar-Free Jello), or it takes the firm into a new business (Jello Puddings). In the first example, General Foods has been evaluating gelatin products for more than 40 years. In the second example, the initial product was considered the first in a stream of products based on pudding and associated products (for example, Pudding Pops).

In fact, any really new product should, at the time of launch, have two or three follow-on products moving down the chute right behind it. Why leave those improvement and leap-frog options for the competition? This means that the evaluation of the first product in the stream is really an evaluation of the stream, something that obviously will go on for years.

A product and its marketing plan should evolve simultaneously

People who support the myth that product and marketing planning is a hand-off act in a relay are surprised when they hear that, in the well-managed firm today, several of the most important marketing plan decisions are made before the product idea even appears. In this and several other ways, marketing comes well *before* technical research.

This is not arbitrary nor a mistake. Good product innovation strategy covers more than the area of general focus. It also states the degree of innovativeness sought, and it adds any other parameters important to management at that time.

For example, when Pillsbury introduces a new food product next month, we can be sure that its marketing plan will include, among other things:

- television advertising, with print support in women's and home magazines;
- packaging that carries an important load in shelf identification and promotion;
- distribution through supermarkets and other food outlets;
- promotion of the product on its merits, not on price (which will be value-based, not cost-based).

These marketing tactics are not surprising, to us or to the product innovation team at Pillsbury. Procter & Gamble actually spells them out in printed form so that there will be no mistake.

By coming first, marketing strategy actually helps drive technical innovation. But in firms that want few fetters on the technical function, marketing strategy constraints are carefully avoided. The point is to consider what is best:

- for your product team;
- in your firm;
- at this time.

Whatever the decisions, marketing options are considered first, which is hardly a technical/marketing sequence.

Once technical activity begins, marketing matters are not put away until technical work is finished. The hottest organizational device in new-products work today is the team, a variation on the idea of entrepreneurship. It may be matrix, but less so every day. More likely it is a task force, a venture team, or some other such semi-independent operation. Occasionally it is *very* independent.

Whatever their names, these teams are somewhat separated from the ongoing business for two important reasons:

1. They are free of institutional constraints ('But *this* is the way we do it *here*').

2. The status of 'team' makes certain that any particular department's task is *not* free of influence by the other departments on the team. This frees the team from the firm but knits the functions tightly together.

One valuable payoff is continuous evaluation. For example, a closely knit group guarantees that a decision to change from one gear arrangement to another, during technical development, will not come as a surprise to the technical service group who will have to repair it or to the sales force who will have to sell it. A marketing decision to shift target markets slightly is shared with technical people on the team who, in effect, are helping evaluate the marketing plan. Everyone evaluates everything continuously, just as in a small firm's entrepreneurial setting. As one product developer recently told me, 'No turfs allowed'.

Each evaluation decision is keyed only to the decision or action that immediately follows it

Because new products managers get many shots at evaluating a new item as it comes along, they tailor their evaluation activity to each of those many points. What is good evaluation activity at one stage is quite wrong at another. There are no sacred cows, no 'musts'.

Just as no particular marketing ploy is always right, neither is a test market, a placement test or a trade-off analysis. The firm that insists on a full-scale screening step prior to R&D is either developing extremely similar products (a very narrow innovation charter) or is simply wrong.

What determines the proper evaluation activity is the nature of the decision being made and the immediately subsequent activities it permits. That is to say, what will happen between now and the next time we stop to take a good look at this project? Let's look at some examples:

- *Decision*: whether to license coating technology from du Pont as a starting point in the development.
- *Evaluation*: thorough concept testing, keyed to measuring the acceptance of product attributes that will come from the technology.

- *Decision*: whether to begin production of a chewable vitamin tablet on the current vitamin line.
- *Evaluation*: simple product use-test, using product from the pilot program.

- *Decision*: whether to separate the keyboard from the processing unit on a personal computer.
- *Evaluation*: extensive product use-testing.

The reasons for these evaluations are probably quite clear. In the first case, the coating technology will be the foundation of the entire development process so whatever it will do to the ultimate product needs to be checked out. It can be.

Second, the vitamin product will entail little in the way of start-up costs so the more serious product testing should be held until the production product is available.

Third, the IBM PC Jr. required new learning, which is always dangerous. The decision would in turn drive several other key actions.

Each of these situations could have been changed slightly to make those evaluation recommendations wrong. For example, if the coating technology could be 'rented' from du Pont on an upstream coupling basis, there would be future flexibility and thus less need for decisive data at this time. If the vitamin production line were crowded and required extensive additions to make the new tablets, then the product testing should be done now.

Figure 1 shows the generally accepted curve for cumulative costs of product innovation (curve A). The upsweep is gradual because it is an average. However, individual new product teams often face a curve such as the early expenditures one (E) or the late expenditures one (L). It varies by project, depending on the technical accomplishment required, marketing strategy, and so forth. The early-rising curve would fit a pharmaceutical or bubble memory. The late-rising curve would fit a consumer-packaged good.

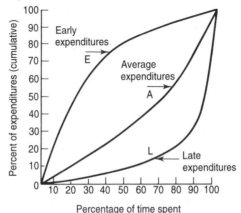

Figure 1. Cumulative Expenditures Curve for a Typical New Product and Two Variations. When X% of the time has been spent on a new product, Y% of the total expenditures will have been accumulated. (*Source*: hypothetical representation based on empirical curve in *Management of New Products*, Booz, Allen and Hamilton, Chicago, 1968, p. 10.)

The consequence is obvious. The evaluation done during the progress of one expenditures curve will be quite different from that of another. The pharmaceutical firm will thoroughly study medical need and the nature of the market. The food company will get to prototype quickly and use very expensive market-testing methodologies—for example, scanner market testing at a minimum of $150 000 per project. Because automobiles have both dimensions, their developers study markets in advance and still continue their prototype concept testing down to the final weeks before announcement.

Some people feel that risk analysis is appropriate here. Any decision involves alternatives, and the various pieces of information to help make that decision have associated costs. The more that rides on the decision, the greater the worth of good data. But the opposite is also true. If nothing big follows, there is no need to belabour the evaluation.

The result of this line of reasoning is shown in Figure 2, which depicts several decay curves that match the expenditure curves in Figure 1. A decay curve is the pattern of project or concept rejection as work proceeds. The firms that spend early need a decay curve like E, cleaning out all doubtful projects before very expensive work is done on them. Once these projects get well down the road, they are rarely stopped. Why stop them? There is little left to be spent.

Projects in late-spending firms, on the other hand, will be kept alive much longer, though they will begin dropping like flies when they get closer to the big dollar phases (curve L).

Again, there is nothing sacred about a particular decay curve. If a firm's new product work customarily blends different types of projects, there should be a mix of decay patterns. This is one reason for using teams. Let them develop their own particular pattern of evaluation, appropriate to their project.

There is one complication to all this—opportunity costs. One cost of going ahead on a project is the lost time or dollars on another project that would be activated if the current one is aborted. If a firm has more good ideas standing by than resources to pursue them, evaluators should cut bait earlier than the expenditure pattern would call for, and vice versa.

Newer evaluation techniques are incremental ones

Creative work in the area of evaluation techniques is almost totally concerned with techniques that do only part of the job. They evaluate understanding of the concept, or willingness to try, or likelihood of repeat use, or reaction to the trial supply, or ability to get distribution, or competitive price reaction.

Take test marketing, for example. Historically, the test market was thought to be the final exam, the dress rehearsal, with everything on go. Sales and profits would be projected, and the managers have their answer.

Today this is rarely so. Some firms still use test marketing in its traditional form and purpose, but for most it is far too expensive (in many ways) for a final exam. More can be learned by new variations on the tool.

Simulations. For example, where appropriate, pre-test market simulations are growing rapidly. They don't predict actual success or failure, but they do measure a few variables that are critical to success—for example, understanding of the concept and willingness to try. (Simulated test markets use simplified shopping mall settings and are sold under such names as BASES, ASSESSOR, COMP and LTM.)

Scanner market testing. Another new market-testing approach, also only a partial one, is the one-city minimarket test based on in-store scanner devices. Called 'scanner market testing', these services are sold under such names as BehaviorScan, Scan-America and Testsight. They have controlled advertising and controlled distribution, but they do test the willingness of people to buy under given circumstances, how the product is used, what it replaces and how long usage continues.

This approach provides a tool for situations where only part of the total answer is needed. If a firm knows pretty well that it can get distribution on a new item, why pay the price for a full-scale test market to prove it? If prior research has demonstrated a strong customer acceptance of the item when tried, further testing can concentrate on duration of use, or on the rate at which given levels of awareness generate various levels of trial.

Other partial evaluation devices in wider use today are early concept testing, early prototype testing, employee product placement testing and gradual market rollouts. The

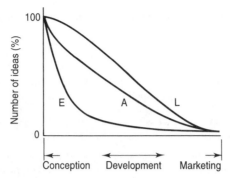

Figure 2. Mortality of New Product Ideas.
At any point of time in the development process, *Y*% of the original number of ideas are left from the number it takes to develop one of them for marketing. (*Source*: hypothetical representation based on empirical curve in *Management of New Products*, Booz, Allen and Hamilton, Chicago, 1968, p. 10.)

manager is building a case, and many little tests make more sense than one big test, particularly for a development process in which the product itself is never set until it succeeds in the marketplace.

Evaluation surrogates. Product developers are also making more use of what I call evaluation surrogates. They substitute a measurement for something that cannot be measured. Managers have long done this at the screening stage. In fact, most screening lists are surrogates. For example, if management wants to know in advance whether it will be able to produce an item at a competitive cost, it asks such questions as, does the technology fit our manufacturing setup? Are special people skills required? Are there complex chemical problems? Who will we be competing against? The answers to these surrogates yield a conclusion on the real question.

Today the use of surrogates is expanding. As an example, what if a manager cannot safely say early in the process whether users actually will give the new item a try? In times past, the procedure was to prepare the product, put it into test market and see. Today, managers are more likely to ask, What produces trial in this market? A state of dissatisfaction? Low cost of the trial? Ease of trial (without disrupting things)? Past evidence of willingness to try new things?

Measuring these factors is somewhat 'iffy' early on, but experience increases the skill. And doing this early cuts costs and is conducive to wise use of R&D monies.

A HYPOTHETICAL EVALUATION SYSTEM

Evaluation is a continuing flow of decisions, assessments and measurements, all designed to lead ultimately to a successful product being established in the marketplace. There is not just one evaluation. Evaluations are made before and after the actual development period. They are made during development and during marketing, and they intensify at particular times, depending on the cost/decision situation.

Table 1 offers a highly abbreviated hypothetical evaluation system for a team of people assigned the task of making commercial cleaning devices and systems for use in industry and commercial settings. It is easy to find the places where changes would have to be made to make this system fit other types of products.

Table 1. Hypothetical evaluation system for a new-product program (commercial cleaning devices and systems)

Phase	Procedure
1. Preconceptualization	Evaluate the firm, its people, its technical capabilities. Evaluate the marketplace. Spell out product innovation charter, narrow the focus, evaluate innovation options, communicate and instruct. Generally speaking, we will use technological focus, commitment to true innovation and early market precedence
2. Concept testing	As ideation begins, use concept testing appropriate to each concept. Concepts precede technology and relate primarily to customer applications. No R&D until concept has support of the marketplace. Exception: if low-cost prototype is needed for the evaluation
3. Screening	Depending on predicted technical cost accumulation, screening may come early or late. The screen will predict the likelihood of our technical accomplishment (both in R&D and in manufacturing), and the likelihood of successful marketing. Screening ends with a statement of the performance attributes required of the product, agreed to by all parties
4. Early product testing	As concepts begin to take technical form, there will be early in-house and then customer application. Meanwhile, more market analysis will be done on those concepts that give early positive feedback
5. Field product testing	Phase 4 work merges into Phase 5, where we ascertain whether the item has the required performance attributes agreed to at the screening stage. This testing is to be of impartial, typical users who form the target market. During this testing, verify product positioning statements
6. Market testing	Put the product and the marketing plan together for the first time. Interview potential customers to get their opinions and attitudes on our new product, set in a commercial (selling) mode. Then begin offering it for sale. Delivery may be delayed until there are sufficient purchases to warrant production. Start with friendly customers, especially those we have talked to earlier, and then move to more neutral ones. Resolve pre-agreed critical issues, usually (1) understanding of the final product concept, (2) willingness to lay out the money for a trial supply and (3) mode and success of uses
7. Rollout	Unless regular customers won't wait, market introduction will be by rollout: regional, customer by customer, or application by application, whichever seems appropriate. Rollout will generally take six months to a year and will speed up if there is early indication of success. Track precise target on concept acceptance, trial rate and successful application

IMPLICATIONS FOR TODAY'S NEW-PRODUCT MANAGERS

How can these concepts be applied to a particular company situation? Here are some general applications:

- Discard company-wide or division-wide evaluation systems, unless there is only one, homogeneous new-product operation involved. Demand that every new-products team stipulate the specific system it will use for its assignment as early as possible, preferably before ideation begins.

- Try very hard to avoid go/no-go situations. Break them down. Dilute the focus and the drama.
- Put new product strategies into place. Provide a product innovation charter for every new product program, covering the focus (technology, user target, application), specific goals of the program and any constraints deemed essential, such as whether to be first, second or whatever to the market, and which function of the firm probably will have to be the driver.
- Organize a multifunction team for each major new-products program. See that the members operate as a team. Because the very idea of matrix management is to share obligation between function and program, matrix teams are only a last-ditch option when really innovative new products are sought.
- Erase all barriers between technical and marketing people. See that any and all evaluations are done by both groups in cooperation. Never allow one side of this pair to make important evaluation-based decisions without the other one's knowledge and participation. Business is no democracy, and urging involvement does not mean voting; but the best new product decisions allow for all relevant inputs.
- Allocate more dollars to early-on evaluations. Research has shown that more than 20% of the total costs of the average new product's development are spent *prior* to R&D. Thorough market analysis and concept testing are vital.

   Be sure that the marketing strategy for a new product begins to take shape early, before technical work. True, it often will change, as will product form, and parts of the marketing strategy cannot be known early. But what *can* be known *should* be.
- Don't let participants—particularly top managements—get in the habit of seeking the 'true' situation, the 'actual' profits, 'accurate' market feedback. Accept today's evaluations for what they are: estimates of what we will be able to do, later, in a changing environment, with the advantage then of information yet to surface, and with the option to change much of what we currently plan to do. You are sculpting with clay, not marble. What ultimately should be an excellent product income statement is being formed, bit by bit, with much back-tracking, iteration and change.

Above all, don't let thinking on product characteristics come to closure prior to marketing the new product. It is still a concept in temporary physical form. The act of marketing is actually just one more step in the evaluation process, and the firm should be ready (if possible) to alter the product further as findings from the marketplace dictate.

20

New Product Testing: A Review of Techniques

Patricia Greenwald and Marshall Ottenfeld

New product testing and introduction is the most difficult challenge faced by any consumer products company and advertising agency. Across the years, new techniques have been developed. These techniques are designed to reduce the risk of new product introduction by increasing the controls on testing, thereby improving the reliability, validity and sensitivity of data used in decision making.

This article discusses three new product research technologies. It is intended that they serve as an introduction to these approaches and how they function. Discussed are: (1) simulated test marketing techniques; (2) split-cable testing services; (3) the use of scanners to measure sales. In discussing the simulated test market, the question is raised whether such approaches are truly alternatives to traditional test marketing. The split-cable testing portion compares traditional matched test marketing with split-cable systems while the discussion of scanners provides an update on the state-of-the-art of scanner technology.

PRE-TEST MARKET RESEARCH TECHNIQUES

Are they really alternatives to traditional test marketing?

The introduction of new products and services has been—and will continue to be—a costly, risky, but essential, marketing function for any corporation to survive and thrive in this world of change. However, few new products eventually become successful in-market despite the care taken by the corporation in the development and test marketing of these products. Enormous effort, time and money are expended on test marketing only to find, after six months or a year, that the product hasn't 'made it' with the consumer.

Are there ways to reduce this risk? Many corporations answer in the affirmative. Their experience has shown that a key to risk reduction is a means whereby success—or the lack thereof—can be predicted before test marketing, including the capability to identify the strong and weak elements of the proposed marketing plan so that adjustments can be made before it is fully implemented in the marketplace. This is test market simulation.

Reprinted with permission from *Applied Marketing Research*, Vol. 29 No. 3, 1989, pp. 17–24

There exists a number of simulation techniques commercially available to the manufacturer, some dealing primarily with new product success prediction based on a single marketing strategy (simulation labs); others, through simulation and mathematical modelling, are designed to project the relative performance of the proposed new product (or existing brand) under varying marketing mix conditions. In addition, several independent research suppliers offer customized 'sales wave' testing, a simple technique whereby repeat buying is measured. Each of these types has its 'place in the sun' under certain conditions, and each will be briefly discussed.

Simulation labs

Below is a list of commercially available simulation labs for new product prediction based on consumer response to a single marketing strategy encompassing a predetermined marketing mix:

- Laboratory Test Market (LTM) (Yankelovich, Skelly & White, NY, NY);
- Assessor (Management Decisions Systems, Inc., Waltham, Mass., Division of Information Resources Inc.);
- COMP (Elrick & Lavidge, Inc., Chicago, Ill.);
- Simulator (Operations Research/Management Science Dialogue, Inc., Cambridge, Mass.);
- Bases (Burke International Research Corp., Cincinnati, Ohio);
- ESP (NPD Research, Inc., Floral Park, NY);
- RAM (DM&M/Chicago);
- Adopter (Data Development Corp., NY, NY);
- Critique (Custom Research, Inc., Union, NJ).

While there are some minor methodological differences between these simulation labs, they encompass the following basic steps:

- exposure to a commercial or ad for the new product;
- 'shopping', during which the consumer has the opportunity to buy or not to buy the product in a real or simulated supermarket;
- reactions to the product under in-home use conditions;
- repurchase intention;
- opportunity to further repurchase it over time ('sales wave' option).

This procedure permits the development of estimates for initial trial and repeat purchase projected to potential share of market and volume, as well as providing an understanding of the elements underlying predicted short-term success or failure *vis-à-vis* competition. In arriving at final projections, estimates of brand awareness, distribution and advertising/promotion plans are included in the calculations.

- Requirements: advertising stimulus; at minimum, silk screened packages; realistic pricing;
- Timing: typically three months (without sales waves);

- Estimated costs: customarily $50 000–$150 000 per product, depending on options.

These labs are traditionally used as screening devices for new products. Based on their prediction of the degree of success or failure for the new product—including identification of areas of weakness—marketing managers will go to test market as is, go to test market with improvements indicated, or stop the project. Therefore, they are not widely used as a replacement for test marketing. Most advertisers contend that since the results of simulation reflect product performance under ideal conditions, test marketing must still be executed to measure:

- awareness level actually accomplished;
- distribution level actually accomplished;
- actual results of promotion;
- effect of any defensive or offensive moves on the part of competitors;
- trade acceptance;
- long-term consumer response.

Most lab techniques are claimed by their sponsors to correlate highly with actual test market results, with case histories—unidentified as to brand—available. So far the only published validated system is that of ASSESSOR.

In April 1982, with the cooperation of its clients, Management Decisions Systems, in conjunction with the Alfred P. Sloan School of Management at M.I.T., published validation encompassing 44 separate new products. In the process, original prediction factors (awareness, distribution and sampling) were adjusted according to actual in-market accomplishment—where they deviated significantly—and the model run again. The correlation between simulated and actual brand shares of market improved still more. The implications of this are clear:

- Original estimates of market share from the simulation were highly predictive (in 'pass/fail' terms) in most cases.
- It is extremely important that original awareness, distribution and sampling input be as realistic as possible.
- In cases of resounding simulation success, there may not be a need for test marketing (although most users will initiate it nonetheless).
- In cases of clear simulation failure, all elements of the marketing mix must be carefully reviewed before proceeding further, if at all.
- In cases where product success is predicted after a less than optimal test marketing experience, indicated adjustments/improvements in the plan that were fed back into the model from test market results can be made before national roll out.

Positives and negatives

Positives:

- 'Pass/fail' predictable (in most cases);
- acceptable length of time for results;
- confidential.

Negatives:

- cannot predict competitive response;
- cannot predict trade response;
- cannot predict long-term performance;
- not geared to evaluate alternative plans;
- not sensitive enough to predict effect of change in marketing mix for an established brand;
- based only on supermarket purchasing, and therefore not fully representative of total market performance.

Mathematical models

These models differ from simulation labs in that they do not employ real or simulated 'shopping'. Their prediction is based on understanding of the dynamics of consumer brand choice (via a market study or simulation lab) tied in with a mathematical program. Below is a list of the major models available:

- Scimitar (The Beaumont Organization, Ltd., NY, NY);
- Hendry (The Hendry Corp., Croton-On-Hudson, NY, NY);
- Litmus, in conjunction with Laboratory Test Market (Yankelovich, Skelly & White, Inc., NY, NY).

These models are traditionally used as initial strategic planning devices for new products, and generally furnish the following via different scenarios:

- effect of alternative product positionings;
- effect of varying price levels;
- effect of varying advertising and promotion plans;
- source of potential consumer business;
- effect of competitive reaction.

They are often used in conjunction with—and as an extension of—a simulated lab (a la Litmus with LTM) to predict the likely effects of changes in strategic and tactical input on potential sales and market share.

As with simulation labs, each model claims a high degree of correlation with real-world performance.

Positives and negatives

Positives:

- ability to forecast effect of multiple variables in the marketing mix;
- fast;
- confidential;
- can be used to explore effect of marketing mix changes for established brands as well as new products.

Negatives:

- unless used in conjunction with a simulated lab (based on consumer response), can be considered too 'black box', too theoretical;
- cannot predict trade response;
- only allows for quantitative market factors (e.g. size of budgets), not the nature of the communication or competitive response (e.g. defensive advertising, coupon drop, discounting etc.).

Custom 'sales wave' testing

Several research suppliers offer customized 'sales wave' testing to manufacturers who have products or market targets which do not 'fit' the typical simulation model and/or when a product is suspected of having a 'novelty' effect, since its primary use is for estimation of repeat purchase. This method is most commonly employed with:

- products with important sales outlets other than the supermarket (e.g. candy, cigarettes);
- children's products;
- 'image' products supported with 'soft sell' advertising for which one exposure to a commercial or ad is not considered enough to cause a change in consumer attitude or behaviour.

Custom 'sales wave' tests are generally used in place of commercially available simulation labs or in conjunction therewith when the conditions mentioned above exist. The decision to employ customized sales waves is typically made when the marketing or research manager is of the opinion that commercially available labs cannot logistically 'do the job' to their satisfaction, or when repeat purchase measurement is the primary or sole objective.

Custom 'sales wave' tests are usually employed to measure one pre-determined marketing mix (as are simulation labs) and are set up according to specific needs; e.g. simulated shopping in more than one retail outlet-type environment; recruitment of children for the test; built-method for multiple exposure to the advertising etc.

Extended 'sales waves' (beyond those traditionally offered by commercially available labs) are also feasible for measurement of repeat purchase over several product purchase cycles.

Since they are customized by the buyer, results are proprietary. It is said, however, that 'sales wave' tests are used for screening, and those which 'pass the test' are then test marketed as well.

Positives and negatives

Positives:

- permits customization according to specific needs;
- fast—in some cases faster than commercially available labs depending on product purchase cycle and objectives;

- confidential.

Negatives:

- cannot predict competitive response;
- cannot predict trade response;
- cannot predict extended long-term performance;
- not geared to evaluate alternative plans;
- not geared to assess individual impact of variables in the market mix on market share;
- not sensitive enough to predict effect of changes in marketing mix for an established brand;
- customizing can result in extremely high cost ($100 000 or more, depending on objectives).

MEASURING SALES WAVE SCANNERS

Why is marketing management so excited?

Interest in, and experimentation with, scanners began in the early 1970s. A. C. Nielsen and the Newspaper Advertising Bureau were pioneers in this endeavour. Nielsen worked with the Kroger Company in their initial Kenwood Plaza experiment in 1972–73.

There are two types of scanners:

- those which read and computer-record the UPC code—adopted primarily by super-markets;
- the OCR (optical character recognition) scanner which employs the use of a 'wand'—adopted by some department stores, mass merchandizers and a few specialty stores.

To date, compatibility between the two scanner types has not been achieved due to resistance from non-food store product manufacturers toward UPC coding.

Growth of scanners

Early adoption of supermarket scanners was inhibited by three basic factors:

- slow acceptance of UPC coding by manufacturers;
- the cost of scanner installation at all check-out counters incurred by retailers;
- resistance on the part of the consumer to the elimination of individual item price

marketing (which, in effect, becomes unnecessary with scanners since continuously updated prices are entered into the computer daily, as needed).

With widespread adoption of UPC coding and chain store management's gradual recognition of retail scanning volume and extensive consumer education, concerns about the elimination of item pricing were minimized and scanners are now showing steady and exceptional growth.

An important consideration, however, is the proportion of total US grocery store all-commodity volume for which these scanning installations account. Even if all 12 000 stores were to be converted today, they would still only represent roughly 27% of grocery store AVC.

Retail scanning advantages

At the outset, the installation of scanner equipment was positioned primarily to the retailer as a means of increasing his operating efficiency. (Benefits to the advertiser as a market research tool were hypothesized, but not emphasized.)

Some of the benefits to the retailer were (and are):

- daily movement of products off the shelves;
- exact, up-to-the-minute inventory of all items in each store using the scanner system;
- overall inventory for all outlets served by the central computer;
- elimination of individual item price marking (since prices are stored in the computer and can be changed quickly, as necessary);
- quick information on the effectiveness of in-store promotions, alternative shelf allocations, stock locations, etc.;
- determination of sales dollar amount handled by each clerk;
- determination of exactly how much money should be in cash registers at any given time;
- increased customer check-out speed.

Advertiser advantages

As retailers gained experience and accepted scanners, software programmes became available for handling the tons of data generated, and advertisers (and market research firms) became convinced of the benefits of scanning to them. As opposed to traditional test marketing measured by traditional sales audits, scanning can afford more accurate measures of marketing mix variables in local test situations:

- promotion (short-term and long-term effect on test product and competition);
- displays;
- POP;

- in-ad coupons;
- flyers;
- store signs.

SPLIT-CABLE TESTING

Advertisers with significant television budgets are often faced with business decisions such as these:

- 'I want to strategically reposition my product from a cleaning strategy to a softening strategy. I don't feel my strategic study and copy tests alone provide enough proof that I should make this change. How can I find out?'
- 'My agency tells me I should flight my media and I want strong evidence to back up that recommendation before I'll change my year-round schedule. What can I do?'
- 'Faced with a significant ad budget cut next year, how can I find out, in advance, what it will do to my brand's sales and share?'

The answer to these questions is often 'Let's go to test market ...'.

For testing strategic repositioning, 'matched' markets will be selected; one or two will run the new (softening) strategy via cut-ins and one or two will continue with current (cleaning) strategy. The same will be done for:

- flighting vs. year-round media schedules;
- reduced budget vs. current budget.

The market research department will typically set up tracking studies to measure relative changes in brand and advertising awareness, trial and purchase. The brand group will set up store audits or obtain SAMI warehouse withdrawal measurements and track shipments to the test and control areas.

Sounds good, doesn't it?

Well, not necessarily.

What are the problems involved in traditional 'matched' test marketing? Separate test and control markets can seldom, if ever, be precisely matched on all—or even most—of the following conditions:

(1) Consumer variables:
- consumer demographics;
- consumer awareness, trial and usage of your brand and competitive brands;

- consumer attitudes toward your brand *vis-à-vis* competitive brands.

(2) Competitive variables:
- competitive brands in the markets;
- relative strength of competition;
- advertising and promotion (strategy forms, budgets and timing);
- new brand introductions (should such occur);
- offensive/defensive actions/reactions on the part of competitors (should such occur).

(3) Media variables:
- inability to efficiently 'cut out' national control advertising in test markets;
- exposure to competitive advertising;
- spill-in.

(4) Retail variables:
- retailer acceptance (distribution);
- in-store treatment (depth of distribution, shelf-facings, retailer promotions, displays etc.);
- out-of-stock conditions;
- pricing.

(5) Sales force variable:
- special attention given to test/control markets in numerous ways.

(6) Market environment variables:
- product category development and trends;
- the general economy in the markets;
- unemployment rate;
- weather.

Any number of variable conditions—individually or in combination—can cause a significant bias or inequity in the markets, thereby obfuscating the effect of the single variable the test is designed to measure (i.e. strategic repositioning, alternative media schedules, alternative budget levels etc.).

While no technique exists which permits a perfect match on all these factors, split-cable testing within one or two markets significantly minimizes test/control variables thus increasing sensitivity in isolating the objective variable is increased.

Split-cable systems available

- Ad Tel (Div. of Burke Marketing Research, Chicago, Ill.);
- Behavior Scan (Information Resources, Inc., Chicago, Ill.).

Both systems offer a number of markets in which test/control conditions are automatically built into a split-cable TV system in each. Alternating cable homes are randomly assigned to either the test panel or the control panel, these panels being matched demographically. The panels are 'checkerboarded' throughout the city (not, for example, the northern half vs. the southern half). This method of household assignment furnishes controls for many of the variables inherent in a geographical split within a given market.

The technology

Cut-in capability over all sources of TV commercials—network, local or 'imported'—rests with the system's central computerized cut-in facility. Cut-ins executing the test variable can only be made over client-owned time, with the media buying responsibility remaining entirely with the advertiser or its agency.

If a test brand is cut-in over the client's other brands' commercials, the loss to those other brands is minimal since it is limited to cable subscribers only. (To protect the integrity of other client tests which may be going on simultaneously, cut-ins that conflict with other tests are obviously not permitted.) Cut-in accuracy is reported to be virtually 100% in both systems.

Depending on the system, measurements are made by either diary panels or scanner-recorded sales. Typical measurements are:

- trial;
- repeat purchase over time;
- buying rate;
- loyalty;
- purchase cycles;
- brand switching and source;
- demographics of buyers.

Since the systems are designed for campaign measurement, both recommend that tests be scheduled for one year with the option of stopping after six months, depending on the product's purchase cycle and other marketing considerations.

For a typical one-year test, split-cable costs range between $130 000 and $140 000. Placed in perspective with traditional test marketing costs—typically including store audits, consumer panels, controlled distribution and spot media—split-cable tests can cost up to 50% less.

A comparison of Ad Tel and Behavior Scan points out similarities, as well as important differences (Table 1).

Table 1. Comparison of Ad Tel and Behavior Scan

	Behavior Scan	Ad Tel
Method of splitting panels	Data bank available on *individual homes* for maximal matching of panels, household by household. In addition to demographics, matching can be done on: • product category usage; • test brand and competitive brand usage; • exposure to promotions; • in-store variables. Individual targeting permits more than one test cell (plus control), e.g. two test strategies or two test budget levels. Number of cells dependent only on sample size requirements	Only two cells available (test vs. control) matched on demographics
Markets	Pittsfield, MA Marion, IN Eau Claire, WI Midland, TX	Charleston, WV Quad Cities, IA/IL Bakersfield, CA Orlando, FL Evansville, IN Portland, ME
Method of purchase measurement	Scanner-recorded purchases in supermarkets in each city, plus option of chain drug stores, if applicable. (ID cards presented by panelists at checkout counter; *all* purchases recorded)	Scanner-recorded purchases in Orlando, Evansville, Portland; traditional purchase diary panels in Charleston, Quad Cities & Bakersfield
Panel sample size	3000/market	2600–3400/market
Data generated other than purchases	Coupons and promotions related to purchase	Coupons and promotions related to purchase Awareness and attitudinal information available at extra cost in diary markets via one-page 'disguised' mail questionnaires to sub-sample of panel members
Availability of two-way cable system	Permits Behavior Scan to know if TV set is on, to what channel and at what time	No
Other optional services offered	FASTRAC, a controlled store testing service, encompassing product placement and four months of media and promotion support in test stores	None

CONCLUSION

Reviewed here are three test marketing technologies that have served marketers well by increasing and improving a firm's abilities to make new product decisions. While research into the effectiveness of these techniques is primarily financial, the database is subjective. At best, one can make the statement that these technologies have reduced the expense and time commitments involved in new product marketing research.

21

Problems in Demand Estimation For a New Technology

Robert J. Thomas

INTRODUCTION

There may be serious consequences for firms that experience substantial inaccuracies in prelaunch estimates of demand for new products over a planning period. Consider the following cases reported in the business press in which demand was much lower than expected:

- RCA launched a new videodisc player in March 1981. They expected sales of 200 000 units by year end and invested in plant and equipment to be capable of producing 500 000 units by December 1981. At year end, only half of the projected sales were realized. In addition to production, inventory, marketing and other costs, a major consequence of this shortfall in demand was reportedly reduced credibility among distributors and investors. The product was finally terminated in April of 1984 with a total estimated loss of $580 million (*Business Week*, 1984).
- In the 1960s, AT&T top management approved the development of 'Picturephone', which allowed callers to see each other on small screens while talking. Picturephone was launched in 1969 on the basis of demand projections that would grow to annual sales of $1 billion by 1980. The demand did not materialize. After considerable investment, the service was taken off the market (*Business Week*, 1983a).

Actual demand can also be much greater than expected, as indicated in the following cases:

- During 1983, Wang Laboratories, Inc., apparently underestimated demand for their word processors and minicomputers in the European market. Wang's management,

Reprinted with permission from *Journal of Product Innovation Management*, Vol. 3, 1985, pp. 145–157

customer service and customer support were unable to keep pace with the growth in demand. Reportedly, customers complained of failure to honour hardware and software delivery promises and of poor technical support people, the effects of which could eventually translate to the bottom line (*Business Week*, 1983b).

• In mid-1982, Sony introduced a $350 hand-held TV, called the 'Watchman', patterned after the successful 'Walkman'. Management felt that due to the relatively high price of the small set and the difficulty in watching it while walking, demand would be slow to develop. Some 2000 units per month were scheduled for production. Actual demand however, far outstripped production. Reportedly, Sony's error in estimating the rapid growth in demand enabled aggressive competitors to develop less expensive, smaller models that could threaten their competitive advantage (*Business Week*, 1983c).

What models and methods did the managers in these situations have available to develop prelaunch estimates of demand and demand growth? For new *repeat purchase* products, a wide variety of prelaunch models are available, and recent experience with them reveals reasonably good results in comparing predicted with actual market shares (Pringle *et al.*, 1982; Urban and Katz, 1983). Unfortunately, models for other kinds of new products are not as well developed—managers in these situations may be relying more on judgment than on systematic methods to arrive at demand estimates.

THE PROBLEM OF DEMAND ESTIMATION FOR NEW TECHNOLOGIES

The difficulty of securing data on actual market response before launch for new technologies makes it especially hard to develop prelaunch demand estimation models. Although test markets can solve this problem for *repeat purchase* products, they do not help in the case of new technologies. The value of information from a test market for a new technology product may not be worth its cost (Urban and Katz, 1983). This is due, in part, to the substantial cost of setting up a production line or whole technology systems to conduct the test market. Test-market data for other than repeat purchase products therefore provide an impractical option for developing prelaunch models of demand estimation. Managers must rely on other data sources and modelling approaches.

Marketing research studies, historical analysis of analogous products and markets, simulated test markets and expert judgment comprise alternative data sources available to managers of new technologies for demand estimation. The models and approaches that might be formulated using these sources for prelaunch demand estimation are, at best, in their early stages of development. For example, Wilton and Pessemier (1981) describe a sample survey approach in which the acceptance of an innovation (as described with selected information) might be predicted from respondent perceptions and preferences. Choffray and Lilien (1984) and Thomas (1985) provide examples of models based on diffusion theory and data from analogous products to estimate growth in market demand. These approaches and others (Pessemier, 1982; Urban and Hauser, 1980; Wind, 1982) are exploratory, however, and require additional development, testing and validation.

Some knowledge about the problems facing managers involved in formulating pre-launch estimates of demand would seem to be important input for the continued development of improved models and methods in this area. The opportunity to acquire some of this knowledge recently became available with the development of a new telecommunications technology and the published data base of methods used to estimate demand for this innovation. The objectives of this paper, therefore, are to describe the procedures used to estimate demand for this new technology and, based on a review of these procedures, to identify and discuss major problems needing attention.

CASE STUDY OF DEMAND ESTIMATION FOR A NEW TELECOMMUNICATIONS TECHNOLOGY

On June 7, 1982, the Federal Communications Commission (FCC) accepted applications for cellular mobile radiotelephone licenses in the top 30 US markets (SMSAs). Briefly, the cellular mobile radiotelephone is a combination of microwave technology, solid-state electronic switching and computerization, which provides an improved mobile telephone service to users. It overcomes problems of existing mobile telephone services by substantially improving voice-transmission quality and increasing user and usage capacity in the system. The technology is implemented as a honeycomb of geographically contiguous cells that facilitate rapid switching of signals across cells. It will eventually permit subscribers of the service to place and receive calls anywhere in the world without being tied to a wire. Young (1979) describes the basic concepts of cellular technology in greater detail.

To encourage competition and efficiency in the provision of this new mobile telephone service, the FCC ruled that one firm (designated a 'non-wire-line' carrier) would be selected in a comparative hearing process to be the sole competitor in a specified geographic area to a 'wire-line' carrier (essentially, one of the Bell operating companies). There were 142 non-wire-line applications for the competitive position in the first 30 markets designated for licensing by the FCC. There were anywhere from two to 15 non-wire-line applicants per market.

In anticipation of multiple applicants per market area, the FCC required each party to submit a comprehensive application that was to be judged against a set of 'comparative criteria'. In addition to basic financial and technical capability, the FCC was clearly concerned about market demand for the new service.[1] More specifically, they were concerned about: (1) the size of the proposed area to be served as it related to expected demand for the service; (2) the applicant's ability to expand the service to meet expected growth in subscriber demand over time; (3) the rates and charges for the service, as indicated by demand. To meet these concerns, very specific estimates of annual demand over a planning period were required.

Various industry sources considered the market for these new services to be substantial, although specific reliable estimates were not generally available. The average cost of preparing an application was considered to be quite high but so, too, were the potential gains. Therefore, it could be assumed that applicants would put their 'best foot forward' in submitting an application, particularly with respect to estimating market demand. Not only should there be a presumed concern about the overall size of the market but, importantly, the expected annual growth in market demand. This would be important input to the engineering design of the proposed cellular system and to the proposed rates. Consequently, a review of these applications will provide a glimpse at the pre-launch methods for estimating market size and growth, at least among a narrow sampling of firms in a specific industry.

DATA BASE AND RESEARCH APPROACH

An overview of the 142 non-wire-line applications revealed that multiple firms applied in more than one of the top 30 markets; furthermore, some used the same consultant or research firm to prepare demand estimates. For example, one firm applied in all 30 markets with virtually an identical methodology in each market. In other cases, different firms applied in different markets using the same research or consulting firm, resulting in identical methodologies being employed. Almost all firms utilized an outside consultant or marketing research firm to provide demand estimates. Consequently, the designated unit of analysis in this study was the demand estimation methodology rather than the applicant.

After reviewing the 142 applications, 29 independent methodologies were identified. The 142 applications represented approximately 47 companies applying in the 30 market areas. To survey the 29 methodologies, a research instrument was developed that listed key topics related to market potential estimation, annual demand growth estimates, and specific research methods relevant to the conduct of market research (e.g. sampling, data collection and data analysis). Data were collected by reviewing each application at the FCC offices thoroughly and recording the appropriate information.

To obtain a more in-depth view of prelaunch demand estimates, methods and problems, two additional sets of data were obtained. The first was a detailed analysis of a specific market area with five competing applicants. Each methodology and the resulting demand estimates for the same basic market area were compared for convergence. The second involved a comparison of two identical methodologies used by the same firm in two separate studies in each of the 30 market areas. The focus was on the correlation of two identical survey questions used to estimate the proportion of respondents intending to subscribe to the new service.

The methodologies are presented in the following three sections according to three aspects of the data base. The first section is a description of the prelaunch demand estimation methods used, the second is an analysis of different methods in the same market and the third is an analysis of the same method across different markets.

PRELAUNCH DEMAND ESTIMATION METHODS

Of the 29 methodologies reviewed, two did not present any prelaunch estimates of market demand to support the design of their cellular system. The extent to which the remaining 27 applications included formal market-based estimates of market potential and annual growth is summarized below:

- Provided market potential and growth estimates   10
- Provided market potential estimates only   8
- Provided market growth estimates only   5
- Provided neither   4

Total   27

Therefore, 23 of the 27 (85.2%) applications provided some form of market-based estimate for market potential or growth. Of the 27 applications, 18 (66.7%) provided an estimate of market potential, primarily based on a survey of purchase intention. However, of the 27 applications, 12 (44.4%) provided no systematic development of demand growth estimates—a key set of measures for cellular system design. In reviewing these 12 applications, it became apparent that system designs were generated by engineering assumptions about demand, rather than market-based estimates of demand.

Of the 15 applications that provided subscriber growth estimates over a planning period (usually 5–10 years), two presented methods based largely on historical analogies with radio-paging service market growth and one presented a method based on a model of growth with respect to selected demographic market factors. The majority (12 of the 15, or 80.0%) estimated growth based on judgment or some type of heuristic. This usually took the form of an assumed constant annual growth rate, but in some cases, the growth rates changed from year to year, often in inexplicable patterns.

Profile of methodologies

As noted above, all 27 applications included a market survey. Four of these 27 surveys were not used to develop estimates of demand but, rather, were informational. In Table 1, a summary of the methods used in the 27 market surveys is presented. The items listed were included in the research instrument that were developed to evaluate the applications. Note that the proportions presented in Table 1 merely indicate whether or not a method was used—not how well the method was implemented or whether it was even appropriate for the situation.

Table 1 reveals that research objectives were specified in nearly all of the methodologies. With regard to sampling, single respondents from organizations were the primary units of analysis in the studies. These were most often drawn as simple, stratified and systematic random samples. Notably, 88.9% of the studies did *not* appear to use statistical estimation procedures in determining sample size, and 66.7% did not consider non-response issues with respect to their samples.

Although the majority of methodologies included their research instruments, it was surprising, given the open comparative nature of the FCC hearing process, that 22.2% of the studies did not. Furthermore, 70.4% did not provide any indication of a questionnaire pretest. With regard to data analysis, a large proportion of the sample (70.4%) did *not* present frequency distributions for all data; only selected results were presented. In particular, cross tabulations were used to depict the relationship between intention to buy at various prices and, usually, a demographic variable.

Relatively few methodologies employed multivariate analysis (17.4%) or used statisti-

Table 1. Summary of methods used in surveys of market demand for a new telecommunications service

Method	Proportion ($n = 27$)	
	Percent	No.
Research objectives		
Specified	92.6	25
Not specified	7.4	2
Sampling		
Unit of analysis: business organizations	88.9	24
occupations	11.1	3[a]
household	37.0	10
Respondent: single person	100.0	27
multiple persons	—	—
Sampling method: nonrandom	7.4	2
simple random	40.8	11
stratified random	25.9	7
cluster random	3.7	1
systematic random	22.2	6
Statistical estimation of sample size: used	11.1	3
not used	88.9	24
Discussion of nonresponse issues: yes	33.3	9
no	66.7	18
Data collection		
Inclusion of questionnaire in report: yes	77.8	21
no	22.2	6
Stated questionnaire pretest: yes	29.6	8
no	70.4	19
Method used: mail	14.8	4
telephone interview	81.5	22
personal interview	3.7	1
Specified fieldwork procedures: yes	48.2	13
no	51.8	14
Data analysis		
Presented frequency distributions for all data: yes	29.6	8
no	70.4	19
Used bivariate analysis: yes	66.7	18
no	33.3	9
Used multivariate analysis: yes	17.4	4
no	82.6	23
Used statistical confidence intervals: yes	33.3	9
no	67.7	18
Used intent translation model: yes	22.2	6
no	77.8	21

[a] Does not add to 100% because eight studies used multiple sampling units.

cal confidence intervals with respect to their demand-related results. Finally, six of the 27 methodologies applied some form of 'intent translation' probabilities to the purchase potential scale to model expected behavior. Typically, these were judgmental estimates of the probability that 'most likely' and 'somewhat likely' responses would subscribe.

Questionnaire quality

The actual questions used to measure 'intention to subscribe' to the new service in 19 methodologies are presented in the Appendix. From our subjective evaluation, there appears to be considerable complexity and unevenness in the quality of wording in these questions. Of the 19 questions, nine used *dichotomous* response formats.

Other important parts of the purchase potential question were the scale measures and the concept description. Of the 19 questions in the Appendix, seven used the variable 'interest' in the concept as the basis for their demand measure. Clearly, being *interested* in the new service and being willing to *subscribe* to it are measuring two different concepts of demand. Although too lengthy to present here, the concept descriptions varied widely in quality of wording. Common problems, such as leading the respondent, confused wording, overly lengthy descriptions and unusual demands on the respondent, were evident.

SAME MARKET/DIFFERENT METHODS ANALYSIS

To provide greater insight into the effects of different methods on demand estimates, five applications from a single market area were selected and compared. Tables 2 and 3 include the estimates of market potential and annual demand growth for each of the five applicants. Also included are key assumptions used in the development of the estimates.

Table 2. Comparative estimates and assumptions of market demand for a new telecommunications service in the same market area

			Firm		
	A	B	C	D	E
Market potential	91.0	14.2	32.8	23.0	39.6
Key assumptions in methodology					
Price	NS[a]	$40–$60/mo. service only	$100+/mo. service and equipment	NS	$150–$200/mo. service and equipment
Unit of analysis	Pop.	Org.	Org.	Pop.	Household
Data collection	NA[a]	Tel.	Tel.	NA	Mail and tel.
Sample size	NA	462	1001	NA	Mail = 885 Tel. = 255

[a] NS, not specified in application; NA, not applicable.

Market potential estimates for the new service varied from approximately 14 000 to 91 000 subscribers. Firms B, C and E used market surveys to derive these estimates. Firm B's estimate of some 14 200 subscribers at a price of $40–$60 per month is considerably less than firm E's estimate of some 39 600 subscribers at a price of $150–$200 per month. This somewhat contradicts what might be expected, i.e. the lower price should generate higher demand. These differences in estimates could, however, be due

Table 3. Comparative estimates and assumptions of market growth for a new telecommunications service in the same market area

| | Firm | | | | | | | | | |
| | A | | B | | C | | D | | E | |
Year	No.	%GR[b]	No.	%GR[b]	No.	%GR[b]	No.	%GR[b]	No.	%GR[b]
1	15.0	—	NS[a]		NS		3.4		3.8	
2	18.0	20	NS		NS		4.6	35	4.4	16
3	7.6	−58	NS		NS		5.7	24	4.9	11
4	13.4	55	NS		NS		4.6	−19	5.2	6
5	18.8	40	NS		NS		4.6	0	5.0	−4
5-year total	72.8		NS		NS		22.9		23.3	
Cum. % of market potential	80		NS		NS		100		59	
Key assumptions in market growth estimates	Demographic predictors and S-shape growth curve related to similar products		NA[a]		NA		Judgment		Based on diffusion growth of similar product and survey demand factor	

[a] NS, not specified in application; NA, not applicable.
[b] Number of new subscribers and annual growth rate (%GR).

to the price used in the market survey, seeing that the lower price does not include equipment costs and the higher price does. That is, firm B's estimate might have been higher if prices for service and equipment were bundled.

Convergence or divergence of estimates

Differences in estimates could also be due to differences in sampling unit and data collection method. Firm B uses a telephone survey of individual organization members, whereas firm E uses a mail and telephone survey of individual *household* members. Insofar as there are likely to be potential subscribers in the universe of households who are not in the universe of organizations, one might expect firm E to generate a higher estimate than firms B or C. Consequently, the three different estimates of market potential, based on a survey of intentions, tend to show some directional convergence when the different methods used in the surveys are taken into account.

Although firms B, C and E derive their estimates from a survey of market demand, firms A and D use alternative methods based on a market level analysis. Firm A, which reports the highest market potential, bases the estimate on a regression model, using selected demographic variables found to be significant in an analysis of similar products (existing mobile phones and paging devices). Firm D uses another methodology (not clearly described in their application) that is based on the determination of a demand factor in a national level analysis and is subsequently applied to the population of the area under study. The magnitude of the difference in estimates from these two methods (some 91 000 vs. 23 000 subscribers) is considerable. Since the details of firm D's methodology is not clearly described, it is difficult to compare them for convergence. However, there appears to be no basis for claiming convergence between the regression-based estimate of firm A and the survey-based estimates of firms B, C or E.

A comparison of the annual growth in demand (number of new subscribers) reveals that of the three firms reporting these data, firm A differed considerably from firms D and E. Although the details of firm A's growth methodology were not presented, the approach was apparently similar to that used to derive its market potential estimate; however, an 'S-shaped' diffusion curve was incorporated into the estimation process. Firm E also used a diffusion curve, based on the growth of a similar product (paging services) to model growth of the new product. The growth rate from year 1 to year 2 is somewhat comparable between firm A and firm B, but after that, there is considerable divergence. Firm D's estimates, which are apparently based on judgment, grow over twice the rate of firm E's year-to-year estimates for the first three years; however, beyond year 3, there is considerable divergence in the patterns of growth. Since clear descriptions of specific methods used were not provided by all firms, there is no basis for establishing convergence (or lack of it) among these three growth estimation methodologies.

DIFFERENT MARKETS/SAME METHODS ANALYSIS

As noted earlier, one firm applied for a cellular licence in all 30 market areas. In support of the application, two different studies were conducted that were identical in methodology. Both were telephone surveys to individuals within organizations who were screened for their input into the purchase decision for a telecommunications service. Both studies used the same questionnaire and, hence, the same question to develop a measure of demand. The question used is the last one listed in the Appendix. The only differences in the two studies were that: (1) one was used as part of a national stratified sample and the other was not; (2) they were both probably conducted at different times (although this is not known). It is assumed that the two samples were drawn independently. The sample sizes for each of the two methods varied from 60 to 112 organizations. The average difference in the two sample sizes for each pair of studies was 14 organizations.

Of the 30 market studies, paired data for 26 were available in the FCC offices. The results of each study were only presented as the weighted number of organizations responding to the various questions. Figure 1 shows two plots of the estimated volumes from the two studies. The data in the top plot are volumes derived from the number of respondents, indicating that their establishment was 'very likely' to use a mobile telephone if it was available at $110 per month. The data in the bottom plot are volumes derived from the number of respondents who indicated their establishments were 'very likely' *and* 'probable' to use a mobile telephone if it was available at $110 per month.

The simple correlation of the two estimates of demand are 0.70 for the top plot and 0.86 for the bottom plot. Both correlations are significant ($p < 0.01$). If this were broadly interpreted in a test-retest reliability sense, it suggests that the 'intention to buy' scale used in this case tends to be reliable. Since raw data were not provided describing the

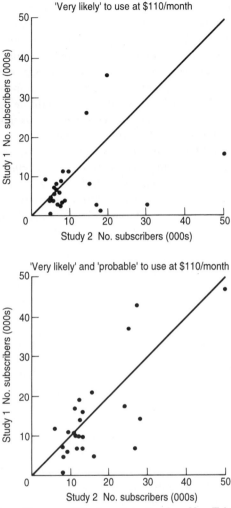

Figure 1. Plots Comparing Same Measures of Purchase Intention for a New Telecommunications Service in 30 Major Market Areas. Plots do not include two outliers with extremely large volumes; however, they are computed in the reported correlation coefficients in the text.

composition of each sample, it is difficult to evaluate this finding further in terms of the comparability of each pair of samples.

THE NEED FOR IMPROVEMENT

Analysis of the methods and models used in the applications, relative to frequently purchased products, suggests that estimating demand for new products is in need of additional development. Although this cannot be generalized beyond this limited sample and case study, the finding is consistent with observations in the marketing literature on product development (Urban and Hauser, 1980; Wind, 1982).

More specifically, 66.6% of the market-based surveys of buyer intentions was used primarily to estimate market potential. However, only three of the 27 applications provided any systematic modelling attempt to estimate demand growth. Twelve of the 27 relied primarily on judgment. Consequently, methods and models to improve the measurement of *growth in demand* for new products prior to launch are needed.

For example, the heavy use of judgment in estimating demand growth suggests that the use of a decision calculus (Little, 1970) approach might be appropriate and a logical next step in the development of such models. However, securing additional relevant data sources on expected market response to the new product or service to complement or replace judgment maybe difficult. One promising avenue of development may be the use of historical data on analogies to model growth of new products (Choffray and Lilien, 1984; Lawrence and Lawton, 1981; Thomas, 1985). Hauser and Urban (1982) present a 'value priority' approach for modeling demand for new products, which relies on survey data. Clearly, the creative use of survey data, simulations, laboratory experimentation and other procedures will be needed to improve demand growth methodologies for new products.

Purchase intentions

Although the need to develop prelaunch growth models is clear, the need to improve surveys of purchase intention to estimate market potential is subtle, but critical. The review of telecommunications studies above suggests that the methods used are predominantly simplistic in nature. For example, the statistical estimation of sample size and the use of statistical confidence intervals around demand estimates were used in relatively few cases. Furthermore, the issue of nonresponse was generally ignored, and data analysis was generally inadequate. This is surprising, because these are areas that have been satisfactorily developed in the research methodology literature. Better communication between the academic community and practitioners would seem to be called for on these issues. Other key issues that require additional basic methodological development and testing include the demand unit of analysis, purchase intention measures, and the general issues of reliability and validity.

A number of the mobile phone studies reviewed above used the organization as the unit of analysis, with a single person from each organization as the respondent. However, demand for technological, durable products, such as mobile phones, may be subject to interpersonal influence processes more than repeat purchase products. This would be particularly true for new industrial products marketed to organizations. Research has shown that the use of single individuals without consideration of the preferences of others may lead to estimation difficulties (Phillips, 1981; Silk and Kalwani, 1982; Thomas, 1982). Consequently, methodological developments in accurately assessing the demand of a 'buying center' (Wind, 1967), whether in organizations or in families, will be needed for progress in the area of estimating demand for new products.

The finding that a large proportion of the purchase intention questions presented in the Appendix relied upon dichotomous response formats as the measure of market potential at various prices indicates a different view of the optimal number of response alternatives than that recommended by Cox (1980). Cox (1980, p. 420) concludes that 'scales with two or three response alternatives are generally inadequate in that they are incapable of transmitting very much information and they tend to frustrate and stifle respondents'. In fact, all but one of the telecommunication studies use four or less response alternatives. Kalwani and Silk (1982) review this issue and conclude that the 'relative merits of longer vs. shorter intention scale remain an unresolved question'. Clearly, additional research is required not only on this issue of the optimal number of response alternatives but on the wording of the purchase intention question, the concept description and the time frame of the question.

The structure of the purchase intention question in a survey designed to estimate market potential also raises issues of reliability and validity. In the demand estimation procedures used in the mobile telephone applications, there was minimal concern for reliability and validity of the concept and measures used. The findings from the analyses of different methods in the same market and the same methods in different markets reveals the importance of these issues. First, the finding that the use of a purchase intention measure may generate reliable measures is encouraging and consistent with the finding by Kalwani and Silk (1982); however, it should be noted that the finding in this study was not based on a strict test–retest interpretation of reliability.

Second, the finding that there was a tendency toward convergence of the demand estimates when selected methodological differences were accounted for tends to support the contention that the concept of purchase intention may possess convergent validity. That is, the use of different research methods (e.g. sampling, data collection) in the survey designs produced different estimates of market potential, however, in ways that could explain these differences (Campbell and Fiske, 1959). This tendency toward convergence enhances the belief that the results are valid and not a methodological artifact.

Validity of the concept of demand

However, the finding that the regression-based methodology and the buyer intention survey of demand (two very different methods) resulted in considerably different estimates of market potential in the same market raises concerns about the overall validity of the concept of market potential and demand. It is one thing for purchase intention measures of demand incorporated in surveys to be reliable, and it is another for the concept of demand (market potential etc.) to be valid. Do purchase intention measures really measure what is meant by 'market potential', or 'demand'? Or is it really one operationalization of the concept?

Progress in establishing the validity of the concept of demand will depend on a clarification of the definition of demand and related concepts. For example, considering its 'content' validity, should demand be defined strictly in economic terms (the relationship between price and quantity sold), or should it be expanded to include other marketing mix and environmental variables and their effects on quantity sold? The concern about 'construct' validity, in terms of convergent validity expressed above, should be expanded to consider both discriminant and nomological validity. Importantly, for practitioners, 'predictive' validity for the concept should be investigated. The work by Morrison (1979) and Kalwani and Silk (1982) in the area of purchase intentions are excellent examples of the type of progress needed with respect to other concepts and measures of demand.

GUIDELINES TO BETTER RESEARCH

Implications for methodological research on demand estimation were considered throughout the discussion section of this paper. Some tentative guidelines for practitioners are suggested below; however, they must be considered in light of the limitations of the analyses performed. First, the application for a new telecommunications technology should not be construed to represent how all of industry measures demand. The sample is narrowly defined by the industry and a specific new product within it. Second, the analyses of different methods in the same market and the same method in different markets were flawed by the lack of complete raw data from which to conduct the analyses and from a complete description of all methodologies involved. Third, the innovation discussed in this case has a durable product component (the telephone hardware) *and* a service component (monthly usage charges of the system). Therefore, it is not purely a 'durable' product in the sense that a television might be. Fourth, the FCC's competitive process may provide an atypical setting for evaluating demand estimation methodologies. For example, second-guessing about the FCC's criteria among the applicants may have affected the demand estimation process or the demand estimates. However, it can also be argued that the presence of the FCC would have stimulated greater concern for more accurate demand estimates, as evidenced in part by the use of outside consultants and research firms. Despite these limitations, the general findings were somewhat consistent with those of others.

What to measure

Carefully defining the concept of demand to be measured is a first, and often overlooked, step in estimating demand. Will it be for an idea, a new concept, or a prototype? Will it be an individual purchase or a buying centre purchase? Which of the marketing mix variables will be allowed to vary or be held constant during the measurement? What will be competitive, economic and other environmental assumptions? Will the focus be on interest in the new product, knowledge or understanding, preference, intention to buy, anticipated usage, or demand for similar products? The importance of this step is that the concept of demand defined will have implications for the methodologies employed.

Multiple measures

To the extent possible, use multiple methods and measures of the concept defined. Each measure should be produced by a well-defined and different methodology. For example, consider the use of judgmental estimates from experts in the field as one measure (perhaps through a Delphi approach), a survey of buyer intentions as a second measure and, perhaps, a marketing decision model based largely on managerial input for parameterization as a third measure. Using an approach known as 'triangulation' (Jick, 1979), differences in demand estimates generated by the various approaches may be explained by the differences in methodologies. The attempt to reconcile differences may lead to a convergence among estimates or to a re-examination of the definitions, methods and assumptions employed. In either case, a better understanding of the demand estimation problem is obtained.

Finally, in conducting surveys of buyer intention, it is recommended to follow basic marketing research principles in a systematic and objective approach. Carefully define all concepts, sample multiple respondents from the same organization or family where necessary, follow basic recommendations on scale construction for the purchase intention measures (e.g. Cox, 1980), use multiple measures within the same study to the extent possible, and develop clear statements or descriptions of the concept or product being measured. Greater attention to, and specification of, methodology is not only important to improve accuracy but also to defend estimates when called upon to do so.

A PRIORITY PROBLEM

Accurate prelaunch estimates of market demand for new technologies are critical input for strategic planning and marketing decisions. The constant pressure for innovations and profitable new products should make the concern for accurate demand estimation a priority in the new product development process. However, demand estimation for new products is a difficult and complex set of problems. These problems include, but are not limited to, such issues as multiple person buying situations, validity and reliability of the concept of demand and specific measures of it, and difficulties in modeling the growth of a new product when market response data are not practically obtainable prior to launch.

Unfortunately, in the marketing literature, relative to repeat purchase products, little attention has been devoted to developing models and methods to resolve demand estimation problems for new technologies. This is reflected, in part, in the findings based on the analysis of 29 applications for a new mobile telephone service, in which demand estimation was a key basis for being selected a 'winner' in a comparative hearing process. Clearly, considerable methodological and modelling work is in need of development. This should be the basis for progress in estimating demand for new technologies in the future.

APPENDIX: QUESTIONS USED TO MEASURE INTENTION TO SUBSCRIBE TO NEW TELECOMMUNICATIONS SERVICE

Question wording	Scale measure	Response alternatives (no.)
The actual cost of providing mobile telephone service is not yet precisely known. However, if the total monthly cost to your organization was in the range of $175–$200, do you think that you would be interested in the service, either now or in the future?	Interest	2
If the mobile or portable phone was available next year for $40–$60 per month, would you subscribe?	Subscribe	2

Question wording	Scale measure	Response alternatives (no.)
If a carrier in the ____ area was to offer such a service beginning in 1982 at a rate of $65 per month for basic service and equipment rental, plus $0.50 per local 1-minute call, with toll calls as an extra charge, do you think you would be likely to subscribe to this service?	Subscribe	2
If this mobile telephone service was available within the next year or two at a total cost of $75 per month, including the equipment and service usage fees, would you subscribe? (Definitely to Definitely not)	Subscribe	4
You will be able to use this new phone service by either paying a monthly fee of $____ or by purchasing the phone equipment for $____ and paying a monthly fee of $____. These fees include local phone call charges but do not include long-distance charges. At these prices how interested would you be in using this service?	Interest in use	4
If ____ monthly charge for service was between $45 and $65 (excluding toll charges and equipment costs), would you subscribe (Yes/No)	Subscribe	2
This new mobile car or portable telephone service will probably cost $150 per month for each unit. This cost includes the first 100 minutes of talking time. It would be an additional $0.40 a minute thereafter. How likely would you be to subscribe to this service when it becomes available? (Very likely, Somewhat likely, Somewhat unlikely, or Very unlikely)	Subscribe	4
Not including long-distance charges, if the cost of portable or mobile phone service, including the equipment lease, was $60 per month, how interested would you be in using this service? (Very interested to Not interested at all)	Interest in use	4
Let's suppose the lease or rental cost of such a mobile telephone, not including long-distance charges, is ____. At that price, would you or your company get such a mobile telephone within the next 60 days? (Likely/Unlikely)	'Get'	2
I realize that you would need more information to make a definite decision about getting the Cellular Mobile Telephone Service, but I'd like to know how likely you would be to subscribe to the service if it was available. Considering the cost of the equipment and this monthly service charge, would you subscribe? (Definitely to Definitely not)	Subscribe	5
How interested would you be in leasing a car telephone if the monthly cost to you, excluding long-distance charges, was $200? The cost would cover leasing and maintenance of the equipment and local telephone service. Would you be interested? (Very interested to Not interested at all)	Interest	4
If the cost of service was in price categories below, would you subscribe? (Yes/No)	Subscribe	2
If the average monthly bill for phone calls was approximately $70 per unit, do you think your company would be interested in having these mobile phone units? (Yes/No)	Interest	2

Question wording	Scale measure	Response alternatives (no.)
If this service was available for a monthly charge of $____, would you be interested? (Extremely interested to Not interested at all)	Interest	4
If this service, which includes equipment rental, maintenance, and basic service, cost $____ a month per unit, would you buy it? (Yes/No)	Buy	2
If the cost of the service, including the equipment lease but excluding long-distance charges, was $____ per month, how interested would you be in subscribing to the service? (Very interested to Not interested at all)	Interest	2
Let's assume that the average rental charges for this improved mobile service was set at $____ a month, including equipment rental, or $____ a month if you purchased the equipment, would your (office/company) be likely to subscribe to this service? (Yes/No)	Subscribe	2
If the cost of this new mobile phone service was $____ per month, would you be likely or unlikely to use this service? (Very likely/unlikely or Somewhat likely/unlikely)	Use	4
How likely is it that this establishment would use a mobile telephone mounted in a car if this service was offered for $____ per month for each unit, including the telephone equipment? (Very likely, Probable, or Unlikely) Use Very likely, Probable, Uncertain and Unlikely to record responses	Use	4

REFERENCES

Business Week (1984) 'Behind AT&T's Change at the Top' (November 6): 115.
Business Week (1983a) 'Big Time for Tiny TV's' (April 18): 73.
Business Week (1983b) 'Where Wang Wants Slower Growth' (May 30): 45.
Business Week (1983c) 'The Anatomy of RCA's Videodisc Failure' (April 23): 89.
Campbell, D. T. and Fiske, D. W. (1959) 'Convergent and Discriminant Validation by the Multitrait-Multimethod Matrix', *Psychological Bulletin*, **56**: 81–105.
Choffray, J.-M. and Lilien, G. L. (1984) 'Strategies Behind the Successful Industrial Product Launch', *Business Marketing* (November): 82.
Cox, E. P. III (1980) 'The Optimal Number of Response Alternatives for a Scale: A Review, *Journal of Marketing Research*, **17** (November): 407–422.
Hauser, J. R. and Urban, G. L. (1982) 'Prelaunch Forecasting of New Consumer Durables. Ideas on a Consumer Value Priority Model'. Working paper, Sloan School of Management, Massachusetts Institute of Technology.
Jick, T. D. (1979) 'Mixing Qualitative and Quantitative Methods: Triangulation in Action', *Administrative Science Quarterly*, **24** (December): 602–611.
Kalwani, M. U. and Silk, A. J. (1982) 'On the Reliability and Predictive Validity of Purchase Intention Measures', *Marketing Science*, **1** (Summer): 243–286.
Lawrence, K. D. and Lawton, W. H. (1981) 'Applications of Diffusion Models: Some Empirical Results', in *New Product Forecasting*, Wind, Y., Mahajan, V. and Cardozo, R. (eds) Lexington, MA: Lexington Books: 529–541.
Little, J. D. C. (1970) 'Models and Managers: The Concept of a Decision Calculus', *Management Science*, **16** (April): B466–B485.

Morrison, D. G. (1979) 'Purchase Intentions and Purchase Behavior', *Journal of Marketing*, **43** (Spring): 65–74.

Pessemier, E. A. (1982) *Product Management*, 2nd ed. New York: Wiley.

Phillips, L. W. (1981) 'Assessing Measurement Error in Key Informant Reports: A Methodological not an Organizational Analysis in Marketing', *Journal of Marketing Research*, **18** (November): 395–415.

Pringle, L. G., Wilson, R. D. and Brody, E. I. (1982) 'NEWS: A Decision Oriented Model for New Product Analysis and Forecasting', *Marketing Science*, **1** (Winter): 1–31.

Silk, A. J. and Kalwani, M. U. (1982) 'Measuring Influence in Organizational Purchasing Decisions', *Journal of Marketing Research*, **19** (May): 165–181.

Thomas, R. J. (1985) 'Estimating Market Growth for New Products: An Analogical Diffusion Model Approach', *Journal of Product Innovation Management*, **2** (March): 45–55.

Thomas, R. J. (1982) 'Correlates of Interpersonal Purchase Influence in Organizations', *Journal of Consumer Research*, **9** (September): 171–182.

Urban, G. L. and Hauser, J. R. (1980) *Design and Marketing of New Products*, Englewood Cliffs, NJ: Prentice-Hall.

Urban, G. L. and Katz, G. M. (1983) 'Pre-test-market Models: Validation and Managerial Implications', *Journal of Marketing Research*, **20** (August): 221–234.

Wilton, P. C. and Pessemier, E. A. (1981) 'Forecasting the Ultimate Acceptance of an Innovation: The Effects of Information', *Journal of Consumer Research*, **8** (September): 162–171.

Wind, Y. (1982) *Product Policy*, Reading, MA: Addison-Wesley.

Wind, Y. (1967) 'The Determinants of Industrial Buyer Behavior', in *Industrial Buying and Creative Marketing*, Robinson, P. and Faris, C. (eds) Boston: Allyn & Bacon: 151–180.

Young, W. R. (1979) 'Advanced Mobile Phone Service: Introduction, Background, and Objectives'. *The Bell System Technical Journal* (January).

22

On Improving the Effectiveness of Test Marketing Decisions

Madhav N. Segal and J. S. Johar

INTRODUCTION

Before a product is introduced nationally, many companies require that it be test marketed. Test marketing lets the marketer gain experience with marketing the product, find potential problems and learn where more information is needed before going to the great expense of full introduction. The basic purpose of test marketing is to test the product itself in real market situations. But test marketing also allows the company to test its entire marketing programme for the product—its positioning strategy, advertising, distribution, pricing, branding and packaging, and budget levels. The company may also use test marketing to learn how consumers and dealers will react to handling, using and repurchasing the product. Test marketing results can also be used to make better sales and profit forecasts. Therefore, a good test marketing can provide a wealth of information about the potential success of the product and marketing programme. Because a majority of new products fail, test marketing can provide a necessary safeguard against product failures through the evaluation of marketing plans prior to implementation.[1,2]

Despite its enormous potential benefits, and the revitalized emphasis on it, excessive test marketing may be very expensive—the average standard test marketing costs more than $3 million.[3] In addition to the high cost, a major concern among researchers and practitioners is the ability of test marketing to produce reliable and projectable estimates of the national performance of a new product.[1,4,5-7] Some companies today have shifted towards quicker and cheaper controlled and simulated testing methods for improving test marketing-based predictions. Even though simulation approaches are increasingly used,[8] it seems that they are not a substitute for 'real market' experience. Such methods are a precursor to test marketing and, consequently, can provide help in the pretesting stage of product introduction and serve to reduce the uncertainty/risk prior to test marketing. Thus, standard test marketing is still the most widely used approach for major testing.

The issue of projectability/prediction from test marketing may be examined from the

Reprinted with permission from *European Journal of Marketing*, Vol. 26 No. 4, 1992, pp. 21–33 perspective of test market selection. The problem of where to test a product and the number of markets to use appears to be the most difficult aspect of test marketing for researchers. Rao and Winter[6] very appropriately pointed out, 'this aspect of test marketing remains very much an art and seems to be guided by many rules of thumb that lack both analytical rigour and documentation as to their validity'. This article proposes methodological improvements in the traditional test marketing procedure by providing guidelines for: (1) the number of markets to use; (2) the size of markets to use; (3) the identification of markets with representative demographics, retail-wholesale, and media characteristics. The general purpose of this study is to suggest, use and empirically validate a numerical procedure for segmenting and matching prospective test markets on the basis of a large variety of key market characteristics. It appears that this approach, though not a panacea for all problems associated with test marketing, will help to improve the selection of matched markets for test marketing by reducing undesired variability among test market areas. The section following discusses the problems associated with the test market selection before the research methodology and empirical results are presented and discussed.

BACKGROUND: TEST MARKET SELECTION

For several decades now, the most popular and professional approach to test market selection has involved the search for an 'average' America. In the 1947 film, *Magic Town*, James Stewart played a pollster who discovered an American town which precisely reflected the demographics and attitudes of the entire country.[9] Likewise, a New York company, Dancer Fitzgerald Sample (DFS), Inc., publishes a list of 46 best markets which it considers demographically close to US averages (see Table 1 for a sample list).

Times Publishing Company also publishes a list of most frequently used test markets which are selected and evaluated based on key demographics, media, retail sales and other variables. Its publication in the past had included three best-matched markets: Erie (PA), Fort Wayne (IN) and Tucson (AZ) (1982). Another marketing research organization, Behavior Scan (Information Resources, Inc.), cites eight favourite test cities which are believed to match the country's averages as closely as possible with respect to city size, income, and age of the household head. These cities are identified through almanacs, atlases and demographic directories, and this process may take 12 people working for up to six months. Behavior Scan attempts to track the buying habits of the 'average' consumer in a controlled setting.[2]

While some cities/markets can replicate aggregate national market characteristics better than others, one cannot assume that a single city or group of cities may be a perfect miniature replica of an entire country. However, DFS, Behavior Scan, and most other practitioner researchers do base their test market selection on such a premises. Nevertheless, there is a growing awareness that 'The United States isn't a bland, homogeneous glob of humanity'.[10] Garreau's theory states that a host of economic, social, cultural, political, typographical, and natural-resource factors have worked to create nine distinct 'nations' in North America. Some of these differences can have a great impact on attitudes and behaviours in certain parts of the country. Studying these differences can provide marketers and researchers with valuable clues about consumers and their values.

Table 1. Dancer Fitzgerald Sample's list of recommended test markets

Albany/Schenectady/Troy, NY	Lexington, KY
Boise, ID	Little Rock, AK
Buffalo, NY	Louisville, KY
Cedar Rapids/Waterloo, IA	Minneapolis, MN
Charlotte, NC	Milwaukee, MI
Chattanooga, TN	Nashville, TN
Cincinnati, OH	Oklahoma City, OK
Cleveland, OH	Omaha, NB
Colorado Springs/Pueblo, CO	Orlando/Daytona Beach, FL
Columbus, OH	Phoenix, AZ
Des Moines, IA	Pittsburgh, PA
Erie, PA	Portland, OR
Evansville, IN	Roenoke/Lynchburg, VA
Fargo, MD	Rochester, NY
Fort Wayne, IN	Sacramento/Stockton, CA
Green Bay, WI	St. Louis, MO
Greensboro/High Point/Winston/	Salt Lake City, UT
Salem, NC	Seattle/Tacoma, WA
Greenville/Spartanburg, SC	South Bend/Elkhart, IN
Indianapolis, IN	Spokane, WA
Kalamazoo/Grand Rapids/Battle	Springfield/Decatur/Champaign, IL
Creek, MI	Syracuse, NY
Kansas City, KS	Tulsa, OK
Knoxville, TN	Wichita/Hutchinson, KS

Source: *Marketing News*,[9] p. 15.

The selection of markets for test marketing is a critical undertaking especially if reliable comparisons among markets are to be made. Companies interested in evaluating the effectiveness of particular marketing programmes/subprogrammes (specific promotion or pricing levels) will frequently use a 'matched market' strategy. In this case, two or more markets are chosen for their similarities on several market characteristics. Of course, a larger number of markets selected will allow more reliable results, and a greater number of variations of marketing mixes can be tested. The geographical markets are presumably selected so that they are not only similar to each other on a variety of key characteristics, but they also resemble as nearly the larger geographical market (regional or national) in which the marketing offering will ultimately be made. Therefore, the success of a test marketing programme ultimately rests on the basic assumption or the ability to project results to a larger geographical area.

Therefore, this study proposes a cluster analysis approach for segmenting cities as an aid in choosing an appropriate set of cities for testing marketing programmes. It is based on the premise that the nation as a whole is very diverse regionally, and any attempts to discover an 'average' city are not going to be very useful. The methodology of this research effort is somewhat similar to the one outlined in an earlier article by Green, Frank and Robinson.[11] Since their pioneering work in this area, there has been a complete absence of any studies reported in the marketing literature either replicating or improving on their basic approach to city segmentation. Our study builds on the approach suggested by Green *et al.*[11] However, it differs in that more recent data are used because the market situation is very different in the 1990s from that in the 1960s.

Further, unlike their study, a methodology for validating the city segmentation results from cluster analysis is suggested; even as a replication effort, the study is expected to enhance understanding of the current state of the art in standard test marketing and city/market dynamics of the nation in the 1990s.

THE RESEARCH APPROACH

There are many criteria and key market characteristics which must be considered when selecting a test market, and the possible combinations and permutations can be enormous. In addition, several marketing professionals—researchers and practitioners— have suggested different lists of generalized criteria for the test market selection (see, e.g. *Sales and Marketing Management* or *The Wall Street Journal*). However, most would agree that the test market selection should ideally involve the selection of cities where market and demographic characteristics most nearly resemble the national profile. An informal survey of major marketing research companies compiling test cities lists reveals that the following key characteristic categories are generally essential for test market selection:
(1) demographic elements—population, age, income, education etc.;
(2) purchasing and buying patterns (as revealed by retail sales);
(3) distribution elements (retail and wholesale outlets);
(4) advertising media availability (broadcast and print media coverage).[12]

These four broad categories have been translated in terms of the 13 key market characteristics used in this study. Table 2 lists these characteristics along with the sources of data. Not only are these market characteristics consistent with industry practices, but they also exhibit a large overlap with the variables used by Green *et al.* in their earlier study.[11] An attempt was made to gather information on these characteristics for 100 US cities (standard metropolitan areas).

Since complete data were available for only 94 cities, cluster analysis was applied to this set to identify groups of cities based on the 13 characteristics. Discriminant analysis was used as a way of validating the segmentation/clustering scheme, and the empirical and validation results of the study are presented below.

MAJOR FINDINGS AND DISCUSSION

Cluster analysis results

Cluster analysis refers to a set of multivariate techniques used to develop mutually exclusive groups based on the similarities of characteristics possessed by the entities. The primary contribution of cluster analysis lies in the preclassification of data as suggested by natural groups of the data themselves.[13, 14] This empirical study used a clustering procedure to segment 94 cities based on 13 key market characteristics.[15] Table 3 presents the initial results of applying the cluster analysis procedure.

Cluster 4, for example, consists of Boston, Dallas, Houston and Nassau-Suffolk; the results from the cluster analysis indicate that these four cities are more similar to each

Table 2. Market characteristics/variables used in cluster and discriminant analysis[a]

Variable number	Description	Measurement units	Data source
1	Population	Thousands of persons	Sales and Marketing Management
2	Number of households	Thousands of households	Sales and Marketing Management
3	Retail sales	Dollars (billions)	Sales and Marketing Management
4	Effective buying income	Dollars (billions)	Sales and Marketing Management
5	Median age	Number of years	US Census
6	Proportion male	Percent	US Census
7	Proportion non-white	Percent	US Census
8	Education[b]	Number of years	US Census
9	Proportion of labour force unemployed	Percent	Labor Department, Employment and Training Report of the President
10	Retail outlets	Number of outlets	US Department of Commerce, Bureau of Census
11	Wholesale outlets	Number of outlets	US Department of Commerce, Bureau of Census
12	Newspaper circulation	Thousands of papers	Editor and Publisher Market Guide
13	Television coverage	Thousands of homes reached	Standard Rate and Data Service, Inc.

[a] All cities are defined in terms of the SMSAs (standard metropolitan statistical areas).
[b] Median school years completed for persons 25 years old.

other, in terms of a composite of all 13 variables, than they are to any other cities in the whole group of 94 being segmented.

For test marketing purposes, one could select cities from this segment/cluster or within other clusters because they are best matched in terms of the 13 composite market characteristics. These results can help an analyst to decide to use one city as a control city and another as a test/treatment city. Thus, the performance of a variation of a market offering in a test city can be evaluated and compared with that of the control city. However, if researchers are interested in differences among cities which are quite distinct from each other, they could perform matched pair tests by selecting a pair of cities from several different clusters. Further, within cost constraints, the cities selected should be large enough to give a reliable reading. Therefore, researchers can elect to include cities from a cluster so that collectively their sum represents 2% or 3% of the total population.

Depending on the test marketing objectives, such an approach offers a logical way of dealing with the problem of representativeness. In addition, segments of cities which can be viewed as the most typical of the whole sample can also be identified. This should further add to compiling a list of the most typical cities to be used for test marketing in the 1990s.

Because of the smaller number of entities in clusters 4, 5 and 6, and their geographic proximities in a multidimensional space, they were collapsed into one cluster. Therefore, final results from the cluster analysis include four clusters only. The obvious question

Table 3. Cluster analysis—initial results

Cluster No.	Cities
1	Albany (NY), Birmingham, Nashville, Oklahoma City, Greensboro, Dayton (OH), Norfolk (VA), Toledo, Honolulu, Orlando, Tulsa, Allentown, Akron, Charlotte (NC), Syracuse, Northeast Pennsylvania, West Palm Beach, Greenville (SC), Jersey City, Hartford, Rochester, Salt Lake City, Memphis, Louisville and Jacksonville
2	Bridgeport, El Paso, Knoxville, Las Vegas, Lansing, Albuquerque, Harrisburg, New Haven, Worcester, Gary, Richmond, Grand Rapids, New Brunswick, Springfield (MA), Omaha, Austin, Tucson, Oxnard (CA), Raleigh (NC), Youngstown, Wilmington, Fresno, Flint, Long Beach (NJ), Baton Rouge, Tacoma, Mobile, Patterson (NJ), Johnson City (TN), Chattanooga, Columbia (SC), Wichita (KS), Bakersfield (CA), Canton (OH), New Bedford (MA) and Charleston (SC)
3	Kansas City (MO), San Jose (CA), Portland, Buffalo, Riverside (CA), Phoenix, Cincinnati, Milwaukee, New Orleans, Indianapolis, Columbus (OH), San Antonio, Fort Lauderdale, Sacramento (CA) and Providence (RI)
4[a]	Boston, Dallas, Houston and Nassau-Suffolk (NY)
5[a]	Washington, DC, St. Louis and Pittsburgh
6[a]	Baltimore, Minneapolis (MN), Atlanta, Anaheim (CA), Tampa-St. Petersburg, Newark (NJ), San Diego, Cleveland, Miami, Denver and Seattle

[a] Combined to form cluster 4, because of the smaller number of entities in clusters 4, 5 and 6, and their geographical proximities in a multidimensional space.

which a researcher would like to ask is: 'Are these cluster/groupings really distinct and different from each other?' Given the ill-defined nature of the classification problem and the atheoretical basis of many cluster analysis algorithms, this is indeed an appropriate question. Discriminant analysis can be used to examine the resultant clusters[13] and should prove to be a useful part of the assessment process. Therefore, a discriminant analysis was done to provide a validity check on results from the clusters.

Discriminant analysis, as a multivariate technique, allows a researcher to test the significance of any differences among the average profiles of the four clusters uncovered through cluster analysis. In addition, a determination can also be made about which city characteristics (in a multivariate setting) account most for observed intercluster differences. The empirical results from the discriminant analysis using city clusters as the dependent and 13 city characteristics as independent variables are presented first. Next, the results obtained by discriminant analysis by using a split-half analysis-prediction procedure are validated.

The following variables were determined to be statistically significant in terms of differentiating among the four clusters of cities: retail outlets, households, TV coverage, population, retail sales, effective buying income (EBI), wholesale outlets and newspaper circulation (Table 4).

Based on their absolute F-values and discriminant loadings, this list also indicates the relative importance of the city characteristics in differentiating among the four clusters. Table 5 displays the overall results from discriminant analysis.

These results suggest it is safe to conclude that test city selection decisions may not be affected by the city characteristics of median age, proportion of males, proportion non-white, education levels and the rate of unemployment in a given city. Overall, it appears

Table 4. Univariate significance-of-difference tests between city clusters

	Means				
Variable	Cluster 1	Cluster 2	Cluster 3	Cluster 4	F
Population	772.732	552.092	1239.773	2258.061	162.60[a]
Households	276.480	183.561	454.460	818.361	184.40[a]
Retail sales	3.362	2.327	5.637	10.758	132.20[a]
EBI	6.208	4.236	10.609	20.528	116.10[a]
Age	30.264	29.297	30.300	30.939	1.99
Male (%)	48.344	48.703	48.340	48.430	0.91
Non-white (%)	17.692	16.911	15.220	17.478	0.21
Education	11.904	12.031	12.087	12.183	1.33
Unemployment (%)	6.640	7.272	6.653	5.806	2.15
Retail outlets	5839.680	3535.611	9192.867	16197.833	235.90[a]
Wholesale outlets	1326.640	698.472	2030.467	4062.111	108.00[a]
Newspaper	470.180	266.886	715.713	1329.739	105.40[a]
TV coverage	270.556	179.344	443.667	801.050	182.90[a]

[a] Significant at 0.01 level.

Table 5. Discriminant analysis—overall findings

	Standardized discriminant function coefficients		
Variable	Function 1	Function 2	Function 3
Population	−1.727	−0.108	2.946
Households	6.998	−14.804	−14.698
Retail sales	−0.688	0.984	0.125
EBI	−0.271	0.683	0.003
Age	0.244	0.113	0.796
Male (%)	0.294	0.487	0.466
Non-white (%)	0.136	−0.388	0.297
Education	−0.085	0.121	−0.362
Unemployed (%)	0.084	0.299	−0.243
Retail outlets	1.072	−1.238	−0.277
Wholesale outlets	0.159	0.585	0.417
Newspaper	−0.003	−0.517	0.882
TV coverage	−4.582	14.975	11.140
Group centroids	Function 1	Function 2	Function 3
Group 1	−1.092	−0.407	0.389
Group 2	−2.839	0.337	−0.091
Group 3	1.385	−0.503	−0.579
Group 4	6.040	0.310	0.123

that media and distribution factors are relatively more important in differentiating among clusters than are general demographic variables.

Under the assumptions that a priori probabilities are equal for membership in any of the four city clusters, Table 6 gives the confusion matrix for the 13-variable discriminant analysis for the sample of 94 cities. Entries on the main diagonal of the matrix (in italics)

Table 6. Confusion matrix for 13 variables (sample A)

Actual group memberships	Predicted group membership[a]				
	Cluster 1	Cluster 2	Cluster 3	Cluster 4	Total
Cluster 1	*21*	4	0	0	25
Cluster 2	2	*34*	0	0	36
Cluster 3	1	0	*14*	0	15
Cluster 4	0	0	0	*18*	18

[a] Predicted cluster membership was based on the discriminant functions reported in Table 5, adjusted for the prior probabilities of group membership.
Note: Total correct predictions = 92.55% (87/94). This is significantly different from the maximum chance prediction at 0.01 level.

denote correct classifications or hits, while the off-diagonal elements represent misses. This confusion matrix indicates that discriminant functions were successful in correctly assigning 92.55% of cities to the four city segments, and these predictions were significantly different (at 0.01 level) from the maximum chance prediction. The normalized confusion matrix in Table 7 represents the probabilities that a city which is actually allocated to a cluster group will be so classified. Based on the diagonal entries (in italics), it appears to be safe to assume that all four clusters exhibit a fairly distinct profile.

Table 7. Normalized confusion matrix for 13 variables (sample B)

Actual group memberships	Predicted group membership[a]				
	Cluster 1	Cluster 2	Cluster 3	Cluster 4	Total
Cluster 1	*0.84*	0.16	0.00	0.00	1.00
Cluster 2	0.06	*0.94*	0.00	0.00	1.00
Cluster 3	0.07	0.00	*0.93*	0.00	1.00
Cluster 4	0.00	0.00	0.00	*1.00*	1.00

Validation of results

Even though discriminant results appear to be significant and encouraging, they still need to be validated. As shown by Frank *et al.*,[16] bias can occur in discriminant analysis if the discriminant function is applied to the same data which are used to estimate the function. The discriminant results were validated using a double crossover validation procedure. The sample was divided into approximately equal subsamples, termed samples A and B. A four-way discriminant analysis was then conducted on the data from sample A. The results of this analysis were used to classify the cities in sample B. The procedure was then reversed, with the results of a discriminant analysis conducted on sample B being used to classify the cities in sample A. Although the results (Table 8) show a drop in the percentage of correct classifications when the discriminant functions are applied to new data, they are still significantly different from what one would expect by chance.

These results lend support to the overall segmentation/clustering scheme and indicate that the four city clusters uncovered are indeed distinct and quite different from each other on the 13 characteristics included in this empirical study.

MANAGERIAL IMPLICATIONS

If the research results are reliable, then the efforts of marketing researchers to find the 'Middletowns' or 'Magic Town(s)' or 'Middle America' or 'Mr and Mrs Average' are futile. The 46 test market cities from the DFS list (Table 1) were fitted into their appropriate clusters based on this study (see Table 9).

Whereas the DFS list is supposed to represent 'Middletowns', most of these can be classified into four clusters which are distinct and quite different from each other on dimensions commonly used for test market selection.

If we are to accept the notion that the US is not a homogeneous market, and we are to allow some credence to Garreau's theory of 'Nine Nations of North America', then marketers must not develop a universal strategy for the coast-to-coast US market. More basic is the false assumption of some researchers that a 'Middle America' exists. Since brand preferences for most product categories have been found to vary across regions, it is difficult to understand the logic behind the search for the average American and the practice of a national marketing strategy. Automotive manufacturers now build and advertise cars to match regional tastes. They feel that responding to regional attitudes is crucial to the successful launch of a new car line.[17] Likewise, Campbell, which has for decades used a marketing policy of standardization and national brand identity, has revised its marketing strategy to tailor its products, advertising, promotion and sales efforts to fit different regions of the country—and even individual neighbourhoods within a city.[18]

This study has shown that cluster analysis leading to segmentation of the US towns and cities is an important first step in identifying similarities and differences among different regions *and* their populace. After such groupings are identified, based on the characteristics relevant to the product under test, marketers can decide which groups to use for market testing based on their market introduction/penetration goals. Each grouping would offer a homogeneous set of markets from which test and control markets may be selected. This not only results in selection of matched markets but, very importantly, permits marketers to develop tailor-made test marketing strategies for each market group. Under the present procedure by research practitioners (e.g. DFS), the market test goal is to measure the acceptance of one or more marketing strategies among a very diverse set of populations (test towns). This is counter to the basic tenets of the 'marketing concept', that is, offering the same marketing mix to different markets.

The argument presented here is to test different marketing strategies on a homogeneous populace to measure their acceptability of the most desired strategy. In this way the regional differences of the vast US or any other large market can be better identified, and strategic adaptations can be made to fine tune a company's offerings most effectively to each unique regional target. From this perspective, the approach presented here is

Table 8. Results of discriminant validation tests

Analysis–prediction combination:	Percentage correctly classified			
	Sample A		Sample B	
	A–A	A–B	B–B	B–A
Cluster 1	92.30	75.00	100.00	61.53
Cluster 2	94.40	77.77	100.00	88.88
Cluster 3	100.00	28.57	100.00	75.00
Cluster 4	100.00	62.50	100.00	90.00
Total	95.92	66.66	100.00	79.59

Table 9. The DFS test market list classified into segments based on city clusters developed in this study

Segment 1	Segment 2	Segment 3	Segment 4
Albany	Chattanooga	Buffalo	Pittsburgh
Nashville	Knoxville	Kansas City	Minneapolis
Oklahoma City	Springfield	Portland	Cleveland
Greensboro	Omaha	Phoenix	Seattle
Orlando	Wichita	Cincinnati	
Tulsa		Milwaukee	
Charlotte		Indianapolis	
Syracuse		Columbus	
Greenville		Sacramento	
Rochester			
Salt Lake City			
Louisville			

also directly applicable to test marketing products in Europe, especially starting this year, 1992—the year marking the inauguration of the Single European Market. As the similarities in consumer behaviour across national boundaries in Europe increasingly outweigh the differences, it is quite possible that many European marketers are also likely to err and look for an 'average' Europe for test marketing. Instead, we recommend that the city segmentation approach outlined in this study can be quite effective for developing homogeneous sets of European cities from which test markets may be selected for control and testing purposes.

The cluster analysis approach is not without its limitations. Rice,[19] in applying cluster analysis to the problem of store selection for test marketing, found different solutions based on the use of different clustering algorithms. He recommended close interaction between the researcher and the marketer to decide on the choice of the appropriate methodology and the resulting outcome. Next, there does not yet exist a single method to select the optimum cluster solutions. Researchers may find two or more cluster solutions equally appropriate. The marketer's input and decision may be also necessary here. Selection of characteristics on which to conduct the cluster analysis is another key decision which the marketer and researcher need to decide based on the company's marketing objectives. Since characteristics for the analysis are generally measured in different units, the achievement of their equivalence is worthy of consideration.

CONCLUSION

By addressing the issues related to the city selection process, methodological improvements in the traditional test marketing procedure have been suggested. Cluster analysis was used as an operational procedure for grouping cities which exhibited similarities on 13 different key characteristics. An effort was made to validate the segmentation scheme via discriminant analysis. Furthermore, the discriminant analysis results, themselves, were validated via a double crossover procedure. These empirical findings enhance confidence in the basic clustering approach. If used appropriately, this approach can help to make the test-city selection process more effective and efficient. While an inherent weakness may be that it is too generalized, additional improvements in clustering procedures[13, 20, 21] and appropriate selection of relevant market characteristics for specific product and marketing situations are likely to further enhance its strengths.

Future researchers working in this area should try improved numerical taxonomic techniques, in conjunction with discriminant techniques, for more efficient ways of handling test-city selection problems. Additional factors (for example: stability of year-round sales, availability of retailers who will co-operate, availability of media willing to co-operate, availability of research and audit service companies, level of competitive activity etc.) affecting the city selection should also be examined. Efforts in this direction of test market selection should prove to be helpful in reducing the risk of new product failures in the marketplace.

NOTES AND REFERENCES

1. Giges, N., 'Test Marketing Alternatives Are Expected Soon', *Advertising Age*, 9 January 1984, 41.
2. Norris, E., 'Product Hopes Tied to Cities with the "Right Stuff"', *Advertising Age*, 20 February, M10, 39, 40.
3. Kotler, P. and Armstrong, G., *Principles of Marketing*, 5th edn, Prentice-Hall, Englewood Cliffs, NJ, 1991.
4. Dulin-Salkin, B., 'The Dancer List: A Guide Turned Media Event', *Advertising Age*, 20 February, M14–M18.
5. Gold, J. A., 'Testing Test Market Predictions', *Journal of Marketing Research*, **1**, 1964, 8–16.
6. Rao, V. and Winter, F., 'A Bayesian Approach to Test Market Selection', *Management Science*, **27** (12) 1981, 1351–1369.
7. 'To Test or Not to Test', *The Nielsen Researcher*, **30**(4), 1972, 3–8.
8. Edel, R., 'Lab-to-Rollout Becoming More Traveled Test Path', *Advertising Age*, Special Report (20 February), 1984, M–11.
9. 'Magic Town Doesn't Exist for Test Marketers', *Marketing News*, **19**(5), 1985.
10. Garreau, J., 'The Nine Nations of North America', *Marketing News*, **17**(2), 1983.
11. Green, P. E., Frank, R. and Robinson, P. J., 'Cluster Analysis in Test Market Selection', *Management Science*, **13**(8), 1967, 387–400.
12. Companies and sources surveyed include: Burgone, Inc.; Dancer Fitzgerald and Sample Advertising; Market Audits, Inc.; Marketest (a division of Market Facts, Inc.); Paratest Marketing, Inc.; and SM&M Standard Markets.

13. Klastorin, T. D. 'Assessing Cluster Analysis Results', *Journal of Marketing Research*, **XX** (February) 1983, 92–98.
14. Funkhouser, G. R., 'A Note on the Reliability of Certain Clustering Algorithms', *Journal of Marketing Research*, **XX** (February) 1983, 99–103.
15. Six cities (New York, Chicago, Los Angeles, Philadelphia, Detroit and San Francisco) were dropped after the very first run of cluster analysis as each formed a separate cluster and was considered an outlier.
16. Frank, R. E., Massy, F. and Morrison, D. G., 'Bias in Multiple Discriminant Analysis', *Journal of Marketing Research* (2 August), 1965, 250–258.
17. Seamonds, J. A., Dworkin, P., Mutts, D. and Welch, R., 'America's Favorite Cars for the Road', *US News and World Report* (19 January) 1987, 52–53.
18. Dugas, C., Vamos, M., Levine, J. B. and Rothman, M., 'Marketing's New Look', *Business Week* (26 January) 1987, 64–69.
19. Rice, J. M., 'Statistics and Data Analysis—Art or Science?' *European Research* (July) 1980.
20. Arnold, S. J., 'A Test of Clusters', *Journal of Marketing Research*, **XVI** (November) 1979, 545–551.
21. Day, G. and Heeler, R., 'Using Cluster Analysis to Improve Marketing Experiments', *Journal of Marketing Research*, **VIII** (August) 1971, 340–347.

FURTHER READING

Cooley, W. W. and Lohnes, P. R., *Multivariate Data Analysis*, John Wiley & Sons, New York, NY, 1971.
'Special Test Marketing Section', *Sales and Marketing Management*, 14 March 1983, p. 84.
'A Survey of Market Research Directors on Their Practices, Plans and Perceptions', Special Report, *Data Development Corporation*, November 1982, 15.

Part VI

The Developmemt of New Services

CONTENTS

Introduction to Part VI

Susan Hart

Parts I–V in this volume have featured articles dealing with one or more aspects of the development of new *physical* products. The NPD process is conceptualized on the basis of physical product developing, functional and market testing of physical products, and the need to integrate marketing functions with those immediately concerned with manufacture: R&D, engineering and production. Until recently, very little research was carried out to investigate and improve practices in the development of new services. However, mirroring the increasing attention being paid to services marketing in general, researchers have begun to turn their attentions to new service development (NSD). The articles in this part have been chosen to provide a flavour of the issues addressed by this nascent body of literature.

The first, by Shostack (Reading 23), is a good introductory account of how and why the design and development of services has suffered in comparison to that of physical products. Citing issues such as the intangibility, perishability, variability and simultaneity of production and consumption, she argues that designers of services have concentrated on service management techniques such as time–motion engineering, process coding and procedures and PERT/GANTT charting to the detriment of analysing the consumer's relationship to and interaction with, services. The article goes on to propose that designing a service blueprint, by identifying the process, isolating the fail points, establishing a time frame and analysing profitability, will allow a company to explore all the relevant issues. Other issues germane to service quality are incorporated, such as attention to the tangible (physical) evidence associated with services marketing as well as investment in training employees.

Although the article is wider in scope than new service development, it contains many of the practical issues included in delivering good services. These issues are picked up and expanded upon by the next two articles which focus more explicitly on NSD.

The second article, by de Brentani (Reading 24), is a detailed study of what factors lead to success and failure in new service development. The study is firmly set within the context of 'how services differ' and integrates the salient concepts with much of the insights and conceptual frameworks to be found in the NPD literature. The research methodology parallels previous work by investigating how service firms view the success and failure of NSD and by relating the ensuing 'outcomes' to descriptors of the NSD

391

process in companies. The methodology used a two-phase approach: first, interviews with managers in 95 firms, followed by a mail questionnaire to 148 managers in 115 firms. The level of analysis was the individual projects, some 276 were investigated in total. In the comprehensive discussion of the findings, the following points are most striking. First, many of the factors in NSD that have a positive impact on success mirror those in the NPD literature, including: synergy, market potential, project innovativeness, synergy and proficient development and launch procedures. Second, the newness of the service to the firm had a negative impact on the performance of the new service. Third, the extent to which a new service entered a new market did not affect the performance (positively or negatively).

The final article in this part by Johne (Reading 25) also based on research, focuses on five issues in the insurance sector: the type of services developments generally pursued (incremental *vs* radical); the key activities which form the service development process; the organizational mechanisms used to handle the NSD process; the contribution of marketing to NSD; and the contribution of top management to NSD. The methodology used was personal and telephone interviews with managers in 20 insurance companies. The key findings, discussed in detail by Johne *et al.* are: most NSDs are incremental; an increasing amount of attention is being paid to finalizing NSD processes; a wide variety of organizational mechanisms for NSD is employed, from new product committees to using product managers; marketing specialists are making increasing contributions to NSD, whilst the involvement of top management is generally low. This article does not relate these findings to the relative performance of the companies interviewed. It does, however, give interesting insights and explanation of the key issues of importance in developing new insurance services. One issue tackled by Johne *et al.*'s research is the organizational mechanisms used by firms for NSD, an issue largely neglected by research in this field. The wider issues involved in organizational design for new product development are covered by the articles in Part VII.

23

Designing Services that Deliver

G. Lynn Shostack

We're all familiar with the symptoms of service failure. Your shirt comes back from the laundry with a broken button. Within a week of paying an outrageous repair bill, that ominous rattle reappears in your car's engine. A customer service representative says he'll get back to you and doesn't. An automatic teller swallows your card.

Examples of poor service are widespread; in survey after survey, services top the list in terms of consumer dissatisfaction. Ideas like H&R Block's approach to tax preparation, the McDonald's formula for fast-food service and Walt Disney's concept of entertainment are so few and far between that they seem to be the product of genius—a brilliant flash that can never be duplicated.

Faced with service problems, we tend to become somewhat paranoid. Customers are convinced that someone is treating them badly; managers think that recalcitrant individual employees are the source of the malfunction. Thinly veiled threats by customers and managers are often first attempts to remedy the problem; if they fail, confrontation may result.

But these remedies obscure the basis for a lasting 'cure'. Even though services fail because of human incompetence, drawing a bead on this target obscures the underlying cause: the lack of systematic method for design and control.

The development of a new service is usually characterized by trial and error. Developers translate a subjective description of a need into an operational concept that may bear only a remote resemblance to the original idea. No one systematically quantifies the process or devises tests to ensure that the service is complete and rational, and that it fulfills the original need objectively. No R&D departments, laboratories or service engineers define and oversee the design. There is no way to ensure quality or uniformity in the absence of a detailed design. What piecemeal quality controls exist address only parts of the service.

There are several reasons for the lack of analytical service systems designs. Services are unusual in that they have impact, but no form. Like light, they can't be physically stored or possessed, and their consumption is often simultaneous with their production.

People confuse services with products and with good manners. But a service is not a physical object and cannot be possessed. When we buy the use of a hotel room, we take nothing away with us but the experience of the night's stay. When we fly, we are

Reprinted with permission from *Harvard Business Review*, January–February 1984, pp. 133–139 transported by an airplane but we don't own it. Although a consultant's product may appear as a bound report, what the consumer bought was mental capability and knowledge, not paper and ink. A service is not a servant; it need not be rendered by a person. Even when people are the chosen means of execution, they are only part of the process.

Outstanding service companies instill in their managers a fanatical attachment to the original service idea. Believing that this product of genius is the only thing they have going for them, they try to maintain it with considerable precision. They bring in methods engineers to quantify and make existing components more efficient. They codify the process in volumes of policies and procedures. While the outline of a great service concept may be reflected in these tools, the procedures are only fragmented views of a more comprehensive, largely undocumented phenomenon. Good and lasting service management requires much more. Better service *design* provides the key to market success, and more important, to growth.

The operations side of service management often uses work flow design and control methods such as time-motion engineering, PERT/GANTT charting, and quality-control methods derived from the work of W. Edwards Deming. These procedures provide managers with a way to visualize a process and to define and manipulate it at arm's length. What they miss is the consumer's relationship to, and interaction with, services. They make no provision for people-rendered services that require judgment and a less mechanical approach. They don't account for the service's products that must be managed simultaneously with the process. And they don't allow for special problems of market position, advertising, pricing or distribution.

We can build on the strength of these operational systems, however, to come up with a more comprehensive and workable framework for addressing most issues of service development. We can devise a blueprint for service design that is nonsubjective and quantifiable, one which will allow developers to work out details ahead of time. Such a blueprint gives managers a context within which to deal with the management and control of the process.

DESIGNING A BLUEPRINT

A service blueprint allows a company to explore all the issues inherent in creating or managing a service. The process of designing a blueprint involves the consideration of several issues.

Identifying processes

The first step in creating such a blueprint is mapping the processes that constitute the service. Figure 1 maps a shoeshine parlor. As the service is simple and clear-cut, the map is straightforward. For more complex services, identifying and defining the processes involved may be difficult and result in a large, complicated diagram. Tax-return preparation or health care, for example, involves many decision points, alternative courses of action and variable methodologies. Portfolio management, care repair and even tailoring require contemplation and observation before diagramming.

Even within the simplest process, further definition is beneficial; in shoeshining it

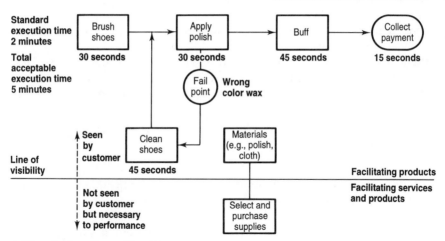

Figure 1. Blueprint for a Corner Shoeshine.

might be useful to specify how the proprietor will perform the step called 'buff'. Definition doesn't mean you must mechanize all procedures. But identifying the components of a step or action reveals the inputs needed and steps covered, and permits analysis, control and improvement. For example, a doctor or a lawyer would do well to break down the 'problem diagnosis' step.

It is important to watch out for parts of the service that the consumer does not see, like purchasing of supplies. Though invisible, these processes are important because changing them may alter the way consumers perceive the service. If, for example, a bank redesigns a computer program so that it produces a different account statement for customers, the bank may affect its image or other consumer perceptions of value. These subprocesses are integral to the success of the service.

Isolating fail points

Having diagrammed the processes involved, the designer can now see where the system might go awry. The shoeshiner may pick up and apply the wrong color wax. So the designer must build in a subprocess to correct this possible error. The identification of fail points and the design of fail-safe processes are critical, The consequences of service failures can be greatly reduced by analyzing fail points at the design stage. When designers and managers think through potential problems together in advance, the quality of service execution is invariably higher.

Establishing time frame

After diagramming a service profile, identifying processes and vulnerabilities, and building-in fail-safe measures, the designer must consider the execution.

Since all services depend on time, which is usually the major cost determinant, the designer should establish a standard execution time. As a blueprint is a model, the design should also allow for deviation from standard execution time under working conditions. The amount of latitude necessary in the time frame will depend on the complexity of the delivery.

In the shoeshine example, the standard execution time is two minutes. Research showed that the customer would tolerate up to five minutes of performance before lowering his or her assessment of quality. Acceptable execution time for a shoeshine is then five minutes.

Analyzing profitability

The customer can spend the three minutes between standard and acceptable execution time at the corner parlor waiting in line or during service, if an error occurs or if the shoeshiner does certain things too slowly. Whatever its source, a delay can affect profits dramatically. Table 1 quantifies the cost of delay; after four minutes the proprietor loses money.

Table 1. Shoeshine profitability analysis

		Execution time (minutes)		
		2	3	4
Price ($)		0.50	0.50	0.50
Costs ($) Time @	$0.10 per minute	0.20	0.30	0.40
	Wax	0.03	0.03	0.03
	Other operating expenses	0.09	0.09	0.09
Total costs ($)		0.32	0.42	0.52
Pretax profit ($)		0.18	0.08	(0.02)

A service designer must establish a time-of-service-execution standard that precludes unprofitable business and maintains productivity. Such a standard not only helps measure performance and control uniformity and quality, it also serves as a model for distribution of the service to far-flung locations.

DELIVERING THE SERVICE

Recruiting, training and general management are important considerations in services rendered by people, and for complex professional occupations such as legal, consulting or medical services these factors are of paramount importance. But some services can be rendered mechanically, as banks have demonstrated with automatic tellers, and some can be performed by customers themselves, as at salad bars.

Implementation constantly evolves. Schools, for example, once depended entirely on teachers to render the service of education; today computers and television have an important function in the classroom. A service designer must weigh alternative means of execution, for example, by considering the merits of using a buffing machine in the process of shoeshining. The productivity and profit margin increases must be weighed against a customer's perception of lower quality. A blueprint facilitates the analysis of cost-benefit trade-offs and can be used to test the appeal of different designs to prospective customers.

A blueprint can help the service developer with other problems. For the pricing department, it provides a basis for a thorough cost analysis; for distribution, a map to be duplicated; for promotion, tangible evidence it can manage and control.

Highlighting tangible evidence

To maintain credibility, the service must select and manage products with care. In some cases, products are optional—a consultant may not have to present a written report for instance. Consumers, however, often deduce the nature of the service from this type of circumstantial evidence. The design of a service should therefore incorporate the orchestration of tangible evidence—everything the consumer uses to verify the service's effectiveness. The setting, including color schemes, advertising, printed or graphic materials, and stationery, all proclaim a service's style. The design should not be carelessly delegated to outsiders or left to chance.

Airlines have learned this lesson. The interior and exterior decor of the plane, flight attendants' uniforms, the appearance of the reservation desk, ticket folders, baggage tags and advertising graphics all tell the customer what kind of service to expect. They either reinforce or contradict personal experience with the airline.

Making people special

To the customer, people are inseparable parts of many services. The presence of people, however, brings a higher risk that service quality will vary. At the design stage, the developer must plan and consider every encounter between consumer and provider. The good manners and attentiveness customers associate with good personal service must be made part of the hiring, training and performance standards of the company. Indifferent or surly execution can devalue the service.

Both the Disney organization and IBM offer outstanding examples of superior people management to provide uniform service. Airlines and fast-food chains 'package' services personnel in clothes that proclaim and reinforce an overall service identity. These companies invest heavily in training and retraining at all levels.

At the beginning and end of the design cycle lies the marketing goal to which all service organizations aspire: benefiting customers. For the customer, a good shoeshine is 'shiny shoes', 'clean shoes' or 'preservation'. It goes without saying that market research throughout the design cycle is the best control mechanism to ensure that the service meets the goal.

MODIFYING A SERVICE

Market research during a service's operating life enables managers to measure quality and identify needs for redesign.

Figure 2 shows how the designer may add a repeat of steps 2 and 3 in the shoeshine service to create a two-coat shine, and justify a 20-cent price increase, thus increasing the profit margin by nearly 30%. Moreover, the shoeshiner might decide to add a receipt or a sample of shoepolish as tangible evidence of good care. Such service reminders (the shoeshiner could print his or her name and address on the shoepolish sample) could lead to a premium price for a premium service.

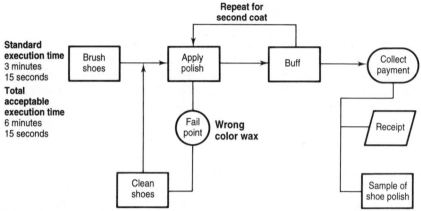

Figure 2. Modified Shoeshine Blueprint.

A designer can use a blueprint to engineer new market products or services (see Figure 3). A designer can do much at the drawing board, well before expensive formal market introduction of the service.

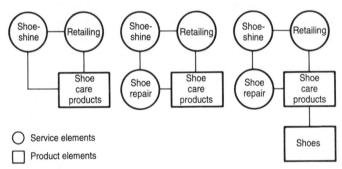

Figure 3. Blueprint for More Complex Shoe Products and Services.

APPLYING THE PRINCIPLES

Service blueprint methods can be applied in the development of a discount brokerage service in a large money-center bank (see Figure 4). Very little of this service is visible to customers. In fact, customers have virtually no conception of the processes that underlie most services.

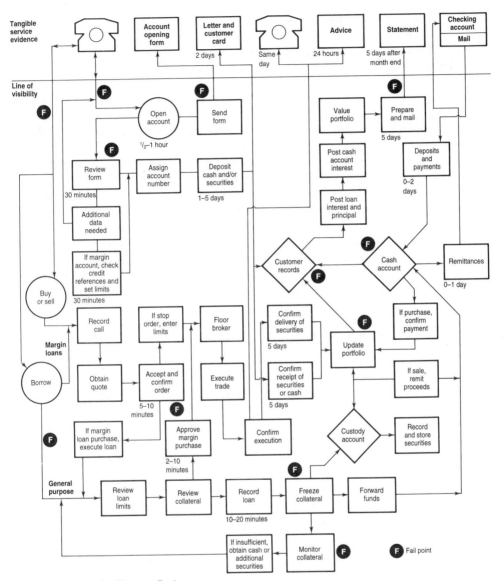

Figure 4. Blueprint for Discount Brokerage.

Discount brokerage is not particularly complex, but the blueprint condenses and simplifies the service and omits many minor steps. For example, the step 'prepare and mail statements' includes more than 12 activities, such as printing statements and stuffing and sealing envelopes.

The important fail points (F) show where the service may experience quality or consistency problems. Telephone communication, for example, is a component that is not only critical and difficult to control but also one of the most powerful influences of customer perception, since it provides the only personal contact. To deal with this potential fail point, management decided to script dialogues for various situations, to train staff thoroughly in communication and response techniques, to establish procedures making certain that calls never went unanswered, and to ensure accuracy by logging, recording and confirming all customer instructions. While the blueprint doesn't show these processes, the system designer has diagrammed and controlled each one.

The design shows execution time standards that can be easily monitored and quantified. They allow the measurement of capacity and productivity through volume and throughput relationships. In telephone communication, for example, the brokerage set a broad time limit for opening accounts (one-half to one hour). Execution standards can be tightened as operating experience increases.

Although the superficial aspects of services may seem the same, the design particulars involve so many alternatives and choices that no two services will have exactly the same design. Services differ from competitor to competitor in the sum of particulars. Individual aspects allow consumers to discriminate between companies offering the same product.

In its complete form, Figure 4 permits the analysis of competitive differences. The designer can then respond to unfavorable comparisons with appropriate changes. As new processes or products are added, or enhancements made, they can be mapped on the blueprint and analyzed for their impact on operations, profitability, and reliability.

CREATING BETTER SERVICE

A blueprint is more precise than verbal definitions and less subject to misinterpretation. It illustrates the dictum of W. Edwards Deming that workers are never to blame for flaws in a process. Process design is management's responsibility.

A service blueprint allows a company to test its assumptions on paper and thoroughly work out the bugs. A service manager can test a prototype delivery on potential customers and use the feedback to modify the blueprint before testing the procedure again.

A blueprint encourages creativity, pre-emptive problem solving and controlled implementation. It can reduce the potential for failure and enhance management's ability to think effectively about new services.

The blueprint principle helps cut down the time and inefficiency of random service development and gives a higher level view of service management prerogatives. The alternative—leaving services to individual talent and managing the pieces rather than the whole—makes a company more vulnerable and creates a service that reacts slowly to market needs and opportunities. As the United States moves to a service economy, companies that gain control of the design and management process will be the companies that survive and prosper.

24

Success Factors in Developing New Business Services

Ulrike de Brentani

What factors lead to success and failure in the development of new 'goods and services?' This question has been addressed in depth for manufactured goods, but almost totally ignored for services. Innovation has been shown to be costly, yet vital to the continued prosperity of firms. In the manufactured goods sector, researchers and practitioners have contributed to lowering the risk associated with new product development by helping firms to implement more highly focused and more sophisticated new product development processes.[1] Yet services, which form a major part of our modern economy and account for most of its recent growth, have not seen the same kind of in-depth research and management emphasis on the issue of new service development (NSD) and on what are the causes of success and failure in this important endeavour.

That services and the marketing of services differ(s) from physical products is well established. The literature on services marketing, as well as the small number of articles that deal specifically with new service development, concentrate almost exclusively on the four factors that distinguish services from manufactured goods. Since differences between goods and services, however, are often a question of degree—for example, services are more intangible-dominant or more variable than their physical product counterparts—many established marketing concepts are relevant to both the goods and the services sector. It is surprising, therefore, that of the writings which deal with new service development, few incorporate the conceptual and research paradigms that have evolved from studies of new manufactured goods. This article reports on such a study. It describes the results of a major empirical investigation of success and failure in new service development in the business-to-business services sector. By integrating the two literatures on new physical product development and services marketing, the author reports on what factors companies must look to for ensuring new service success.

Previous Research

Zeithaml *et al.*[2] effectively summarize the substantial literature that has developed over the years on how the four factors commonly viewed as distinguishing services from

Reprinted with permission from *European Journal of Marketing*, Vol. 25 No. 2, 1991, pp. 33–59 physical products (intangibility, inseparability of production and consumption, variability and perishability of the service offering) create unique problems that call for different kinds of marketing solutions. Very little, however, has been written about the development of new services and even less has been done in the way of broad empirical research to probe the question. What makes new services successful and what causes failure?

Previous to 1980, only a tiny fraction of product innovation articles addressed services (see [3]) and only one of these focused specifically on the development of new services within the firm.[4] Perhaps in response to this groundbreaking article on the need to treat new services differently, some authors started to look more closely at the issue of new service development. During the early 1980s, most of these writings were of a conceptual nature, usually concentrating on one specific element of the NSD problem (e.g. new service design[5,6], modelling the service operation[7] of the delivery system[8], concept testing and business analysis[10], importance of the frontline[11], and the corporate culture in NSD[12]. Studies in the latter half of the 1980s took on a somewhat broader and more empirical view. Authors started tackling multiple NSD issues and began to use empirical evidence as a basis for conclusions. Thus, Langeard and Eiglier[13] studied a typology of new services, the design process and development strategy of 43 European consumer and business service organizations; Bowers[14] analysed the process, structure and organization of new service development in 253 US banks, insurance firms and hospitals; Reidenbach and Moak[15] also looked at US banking by relating NSD practices and activities to overall bank performance; and Easingwood[16] based his study of new service development—its strategic role, organization and process—on a cross-section of 31 UK firms. Furthermore, rather than concentrate exclusively on the factors that make services distinct, a small number of studies began to incorporate theoretical concepts derived from research on the development of manufactured goods, taking into account that services often have marketing characteristics that are similar to goods (see 14–17]).

Taken together, the past decade of research on new service development offers a qualitative base of concepts on how the process of service development might be handled, given the distinctive character of services, and some preliminary empirical findings that support or deny these concepts. Certain limitations, however, are also apparent:

- Only a tiny fraction of articles on new service development incorporate concepts from both the services marketing and the new physical product development literatures. Moreover, the number of NSD variables analysed in these studies tend to be small (e.g. five and 23 items) and limited to the firm's organization and the stages of the new service development process.[1]
- The small number (four only) of empirical studies with samples that permit statistical inference offer only limited insights about new service development. One study provides a qualitative assessment; two others offer relatively simple quantitative results (frequencies, means).
- Since past studies of new service development tended to concentrate on consumer services or on a specific service sector (e.g. retail banking), their conclusions may not be generalizable to a broader service context and specifically to the important and growing business services sector.

It is these gaps in new services research that the current article addresses. It reports on a major empirical study that identifies a broad set of factors which distinguish successful from unsuccessful new services. The research incorporates a wide spectrum of business service projects, companies and industries and synthesizes in its research framework concepts from both the new physical product development and services marketing literature. (Table 1 provides a summary of the companies and industries taking part in the research.)

Table 1. Firms taking part in study: classification by industry

Industry	Number of firms	Percentage of total
Financial		
Banking and Trust	18	15.7
Insurance	10	8.7
Other Financial	8	7.0
Management services		
Computer and Systems	18	15.6
Marketing and Advertising	17	14.8
Management Consulting	14	12.2
Accounting	6	5.2
Transportation and communication		
Shipping and Transportation	16	13.9
Communications	5	4.3
Other services	3	2.6
Total number of firms	115	

THE RESEARCH FRAMEWORK

Past studies of new physical product development and services marketing underlie the structure of the current research. The two literatures combined provide a rich source of research variables, hypotheses and methodologies for an objective study of new service development.

How services differ

Differences between goods and services has been the continuing theme in the services marketing literature. By focusing specifically on the factors that distinguish services from physical products, researchers have offered insights about how intangibility, inseparability, variability and perishability affect the marketing of services. These articles, together with the small number of studies that focus on business services and on new service development, form the service-specific basis for the current research. A large number of attributes that describe services and which might be hypothesized as affecting new service development were included in the study. A discussion of how differences between services and manufactured goods might affect new service development follows.

Intangibility in new services

Services are more intangible than tangible. In other words, although services are often associated with certain physical elements (for example, a cargo carrier with airplanes or trucks), for the most part, customers must risk buying an eventual outcome and/or an experience which they cannot fully asses prior to purchase[4,18]. In the industrial sector, this inability to examine and evaluate a planned purchase is of particular significance since services frequently play a critical role in the client's operations[19]. To successfully market a new service, therefore, particularly one that is highly innovative or new-to-the-world, the company must place special emphasis on helping clients to conceptualize and evaluate the service[13,20]. The recommended solution to this problem is usually in the form of providing a tangible representation of the service in order to make it less abstract for buyers. Companies should incorporate physical clues or 'evidence', such as a brochure, a logo, or factual information, into the design of the service[5,21,22]. Also, special efforts during the launch of new service, to connect it in some way to the company itself, its reputation for expertise and performance, can help to overcome the problem of intangibility[23,24].

Another implication of the intangibility aspect is that new services are usually developed much more easily and more quickly than their physical product counterparts[6,21]. Designing and launching a new or modified service generally does not involve physical prototypes, patent applications, or major investments in raw materials, plant or equipment. Hence, NSD for many firms becomes an on-going, relatively informal, process where 'new' services tend to evolve over time in response to changes in client needs or competitive offerings[25]. Particularly in the industrial sector, where a specific client need is often the impetus for offering a new or changed service, the fact that firms can respond quickly and at relatively low cost means that 'new' product development efforts in service companies are more likely to entail modifications of augmentations to existing offerings rather than completely new services[24,26,27].

Ease of development, however, also has its negative side. Since services are not patentable and usually require little up-front investment, innovative ideas can be quickly imitated. This often leads to a proliferation of highly similar services, where a reasonable market share can be difficult to achieve[16]. Moreover, service companies have much less incentive than physical product firms to undertake costly and time-consuming pioneering development since attaining a long-term competitive edge is often impossible[28]. A second negative effect of the apparent ease with which new services can be created is that firms tend to use too casual an approach for the development process and this can lead to failure in new services. In reality, even the simplest service is a highly complex process, involving many operations, experiences, outcomes and customer perceptions. Companies that move too quickly often experience problems, such as a poorly researched service concept, a haphazard design process, inadequate testing and too little planning for an effective market launch[6,14,16,29].

The effect of simultaneous production and consumption

Of equal importance in distinguishing services from physical products is the concept of simultaneous production and consumption. Many services are produced and delivered in the presence of customers (e.g. executive travel or operating services for the office/ plant) or they require substantial interaction with the client at the time the service arrangement is first established as well as at later stages in the relationship as circumstances change (e.g. share issue services, pension fund administration). As with intangibility, the simultaneity (or inseparability) characteristic has certain implications for the development of new services.

Direct consumer contact with the firm's service process means that customer satisfaction is linked both to the outcome of the service and to the process by which it is produced and delivered[30,31]. In other words, while for manufactured goods, the production and distribution systems tend marginally to only influence how new products are perceived by customers, in services, production and delivery become critical components in the successful design of the new service offering. This has certain implications for new service development. First, as suggested by Shostack[6], to design a new service successfully, is likely to require active involvement from a much broader set of functional specialities (such as systems design, product specialists and frontline personnel) than in the manufacturing sector. Second, because production and delivery are so essential to the success of a service, companies need to guard against inadvertently ignoring market needs by concentrating too exclusively on operations[13,17,29]. Inseparability of production and consumption, however, also means regular customer contact and this should make service firms more cognizant of client problems and offer the opportunity to respond more precisely to customer needs[24]. In the business services sector, where customer expectations are usually more clearly communicated and where on-going relationships tend to be the norm, successful NSD projects are likely to involve: more customized than standardized services, flexible offerings that can be adjusted to specialized needs, and individual services as well as service lines that evolve over the life of the company-client relationship[19,24,27]. In fact, because business service relationships are often initially forged on the basis of the firm's ability to satisfy the client's long-term needs, developing a complete line of services is often an important strategic objective in the development of new services[23].

Service variability

Because services typically depend on input from company personnel for their production, the actual service outcome and the customer's experience when consuming the service can vary at each purchase occasion. This can have both positive and negative implications. Since, as noted, business clients frequently demand services that are customized, the potential for variability offers opportunities for responding more effectively to customer needs and for developing services that are different from competitive brands. A service company might decide to position itself as an expertise-based operation and design services that emphasize the heterogeneity inherent in both customer and service provider[13,16,32].

Variability, of course, can also mean a lack of consistency or poor service quality. Services that provide a different outcome/experience each time they are purchased and that are not in line with buyer expectations are likely to be perceived as unreliable. Implications for new service development are obvious. In cases where reducing customer uncertainty is essential for success, companies should focus on offering a more standardized service (for example, a courier service with very reliable pick-up and delivery times)[32,33]. In some situations, firms can meet an added objective—that is, lowering customer uncertainty *and* reducing costs—by developing presassembled packages of services[23]. For example, a small number of standardized insurance packages for different types of small businesses was a major success for one of the firms taking part in this study. Levitt[34] recommends that companies go even further and 'industrialize' their services by substituting capital for labour and by introducing planned work systems for previously highly variable operations.

NSD and the perishability factor

A fourth factor usually cited as distinguishing services from physical products is perishability. Because services cannot be produced in advance and then be inventorized, and since demand often fluctuates during the business cycle, companies can incur high costs associated with supporting underused capital or human resources (during purchase lulls) and lost revenue when they cannot meet peak demand levels[35]. Implications for new service development are in the form of: faster, more efficient services; line additions that make use of existing operating systems during periods of low demand; and offering alternate, peak load, versions of a service when the organization is strapped to capacity[21].

RELEVANT NEW PRODUCT STUDIES

In planning the conceptual framework of the current study, the new goods development literature also played a key role. While it is important to understand how services differ from physical products, several authors have addressed the issue of developing and marketing new services by concentrating on what is similar to manufactured goods or by treating services as an integral part of the 'goods and services' mix. These researchers argue that marketers can and should learn from theories derived from the study of innovation in manufacturing so long as the theories are modified to fit the specifics of new service development[17,28]

New product success and failure

Of particular importance in the research underlying the current investigation of new services are the success/failure studies carried out in the physical product sector. The best known studies are the broad empirical investigations by Myers and Marquis[36], Rothwell[37,38], Cooper[39,40], Booz *et al.*[1], and Maidique and Zirger[41] which looked at the new product successes and failures of a large number of firms in order to identify the factors that are related to winning new products. Although these research efforts differed in the methods used for data collection and analysis, the type of products studied (industrial/consumer), and the locus of the study (USA, Canada, UK), the findings are often similar and consistent. For example, product superiority, understand-

ing the market, and proficiency of the marketing operation are factors which are prominent in explaining success in almost all of the studies. A close second in importance in
determining new product performance is the degree of business-project fit (particularly
technological synergy), while effective interaction between R&D and marketing/produc-
tion, an innovative and supportive management environment, and effective project
management are additional key factors accounting for new product success. These
explanatory factors, or determinants, of new product success, derived from the literature
on new manufactured goods and adjusted to account for services, comprise the physical
product basis of the current study on new service development. In particular, the studies
by Cooper[39,40], Cooper and de Brentani[42], and de Brentani[43,44] were used as a
basis due to their broad range of variables and their industrial focus.

Also closed related to what causes success and failure is the question of how firms
measure new product success. Some of the more recent studies of new manufactured
goods show that companies gauge new product performance using multiple criteria and
that different factors are associated with achieving different types of new product
success[45,46]. Several measures of new product success/failure suggested in the literature include financial measures such as profits, sales, growth and costs[1,47] and non-
financial indicators—such as 'technical success' (creativity and innovativeness) and
'market success' (competitive uniqueness)—that measure customer perception of
success relative to competitive products[45,48]. A set of 17 cRiteria was used in the study
to measure new service performance, incorporating the most common criteria used for
new manufactured goods with adjustments introduced to account for services.

THE RESEARCH PROJECT

The objective of the research project was to investigate success and failure of new
services in the business services sector. Past studies of new product development and
services marketing provided a large pool of variables which could be used not only for
measuring new service performance, but also for characterizing the project itself, the
nature of the new service development process, the market and the internal corporate
NSD environment. A previous analysis of the research data (see [49]) focused on how
service firms *measure* the success/failure of NSD projects. Four composite measures,
labelled as sales performance, competitive performance, cost performance and 'other
booster', were identified and found to be similar to the new product performance
measures used by other researchers[45,46,48]. Analysis of the four measures showed
that they were fairly reliable and highly significant, although of variable importance, in
describing how firms measure new service success (see Table 2 for a summary of the
measures and their relative importance).[2] Taking these performance measures as given,
the questions singled out for investigation in the current analysis include:

- What underlying composite dimensions or factors describe new service projects?
- Which of the descriptive factors are related to each measure of new service success/
  failure?
- How are the findings relevant for managers in successfully developing new business
  services?

Table 2. Measures of new service performance: a review

1. Sales performance (70.0%)	Exceeds market share objective Exceeds sales/customer use level objectives Exceeds sales/customer use growth objectives High relative sales/customer use level High overall profitability Positive impact on corporate image/reputation
2. *Competitive performance* (13.4%)	Buyer perceives superior service 'outcome' Buyer perceives superior service 'experience' Unique benefits: perceived as superior to competitors Gives firm important competitive advantage
3. *Cost performance* (8.3%)	Substantially lowers costs for the firm Performs below expected cost Achieves important cost efficiencies for firm
4. *'Other booster'*	Enhances sales/client use of firm's other products/services Enhances profitability of firm's other products/services

Summary of analysis: Principal component analysis (varimax rotation) of 16 individual performance measures suggested four independent composite factors (eigenvalue ≥ 1) explaining 71.1% of the variance, prior to rotation. Cronbach alpha (reliability) for each factor ranged from 0.52 to 0.94, with reliability of the linear combination (all four factors together) = 0.78. Multiple regression analysis of the projects' overall success/failure rating (dependent variable) with the four performance measures (independent variables) suggested the relative importance of the four measures as shown above (%), and showed that 83.6% of the service projects analysed have their overall performance gauged by managers in terms of one or more of the four measures described here (see de Brentani, 1989[49], for details).

Methodology

A research population of 184 companies known to be active in new service development and comprising 12 business service sectors were contacted. Managers responsible for NSD were asked by telephone to take part in one or in two research phases. Phase one involved personal interviews with managers in 95 firms exploring such topics as: the strategic role of new service development, internal and external factors that drive or hinder NSD, the new service development process and its management, and the innovation orientation and NSD performance of the firm. These interviews provided a basis for designing and testing the questionnaire used in the second phase of the study. In phase two, the original sample was expanded to 184 companies and the unit of analysis became the individual new services these firms had introduced in the past five years. The managers each selected two projects—one success and one failure. Definitions of what are 'new', 'successful' and 'unsuccessful' services were provided. 'New' services could range from modifications, to major innovations, to services that were new only to the firm; 'successes' were defined as ventures that had met or exceeded the overall goals for which they were developed, while 'failures' or unsuccessful services had clearly fallen short of their objectives or had been aborted late in the development process (as in [39,40]). Respondents rated the projects on each of 121 items: 104 items characterized the nature of the service itself and the NSD project, corporate fit, the market and internal environment, as well as the new service development process used by the firm; and 17 items gauged managers' perception of the extent to which the project had succeeded or failed in terms of one global and 16 specific performance measures. Project descriptors and performance indicators were measured in the great majority of cases using seven-point, agree/disagree (Likert) scales. The data were collected in three waves: a personally addressed mailing to all managers in the 184 firms who had agreed to take part in the study; a follow-up mailing after six weeks to all non-respondents of the first wave; finally, a telephone call to encourage response. In total, 148 managers in 115 firms completed the questionnaire (company response of 62.5%), yielding 276 rated projects: 150 were successes; 126 had failed.[3]

THE RESULTS

New service descriptive factors

What are the underlying dimensions that describe new business service projects? Due to the large number of variables included in the study, several iterations of factor and reliability analyses were undertaken to determine a reduced set of composite dimensions. Principal component analyses (varimax rotation) and Cronbach alpha reliability analyses were used to 'purify' the dimensions by removing variables with low item-to-total correlations (as in [50,51]) and certain variables which were purely descriptive.[4] As shown in Table 3, a final run reduced the remaining 75 variables to 17 independent factors which accounted for 60.1% of the total variation, prior to rotation. Choice of the 17-factor solution was based on the criteria of factor interpretability, eigenvalue ≥ 1, and Bartlett significance test[52].

The constructs derived of this study appear to describe the success/failure domain of new business services rather well. Reliability of the 17 factors, as measured by Cronbach alpha, ranged from adequate to very good,[5] suggesting internal consistency of the constructs. As expected, many of the factors are similar to dimensions previously identified by researchers of new physical products. This reflects both the breadth of the research framework as well as the argument that the development and marketing of goods and services share many concerns. At the same time, the characteristics which make services distinct are also accounted for. At least ten of the factors derived in this study are clearly associated with service concepts. The 17 new service descriptive factors, which could be further classified into four broad categories of dimensions (proficiency in new service development, project synergy, market characteristics and nature of the new service offering) are discussed below and summarized in Table 3 together with factor loadings, alpha coefficients and appropriate references from the two branches of theory.

Proficiency in new service development

Two factors describe the firm's proficiency in marketing new services. The first, a *Detailed/formal NSD process (F1)*, describes the quality of the activities used for creating and launching new services. Projects strong on this dimension entail a number of up-front activities, including in-depth market studies, customer researched concept descriptions, idea screening and financial analysis, as well as a 'drawing-board' design

Table 3. New service project descriptive factors

Factor name	Variables loading on factor	Factor loading	Selected references[b]
F1: Detailed/formal NSD process ($\alpha=0.8520$)[a]	Design: used detailed 'drawing board' approach	0.72768	P1, 39, 40, 45,
	Design: incorporated in-depth market study	0.71177	12.36.41
	In-depth 'financial analysis' preceded design stage	0.70034	
	Concept descriptions customer researched before design	0.62088	
	Design: considered alternative means of rendering service	0.60996	S5, 6, 13, 14, 16, 18, 22, 24, 55
	Formal 'Idea screening' used	0.59744	
	Market Launch: documented and highly detailed program	0.58728	
	Service fully tested before final launch	0.56462	
	Formal post-launch evaluation procedure used	0.50640	
	Market launch: extensive training of production personnel	0.49353	
	Market launch: formal promotion (7) vs word-of-mouth (1)	0.42857	
F2: Overall corporate Synergy ($\alpha=0.8360$)	Fit: managerial skills and preferences	0.78707	P1, 39, 40, 42
	Fit: company 'expertise'/human resource capabilities	0.76431	44, 45
	Fit: current service delivery system	0.73027	
	Fit: in line with financial resources	0.65746	S4, 16, 17, 20
	Fit: sales and promotional capabilities and resources	0.62667	22, 23, 24, 35 36
	Fit: sales and promotional capabilities and resources	0.62667	
	Fit: current, behind-the-scenes, production facilities	0.61001	
F3: Market competitive-ness ($\alpha=0.8003$)	Extremely aggressive competition	0.79638	P1, 39, 45
	Intense price competition	0.75592	
	Market has frequent service introductions/modifications	0.71927	S13, 16, 18, 20, 23, 24, 55
	Very similar competitive offerings	0.65372	
	One or two dominant competitors with large market share	0.51168	
F4: Product-market fit/attractiveness ($\alpha=0.7433$)	Satisfies clearly identified customer/client need	0.70518	P1, 35, 36, 39 40, 42, 44, 45
	Responds to important changes in customer needs/wants	0.69139	
	Consistent with existing customer values/operating systems	0.60609	
	Solves important customer problem	0.57088	S13, 17, 20, 24 26, 27, 56,
	High growth rate market	0.45942	
	Large dollar volume market	0.33103	

Table 3. (*Continued*)

F5: 'Expert'-people-based service ($\alpha=0.7930$)	Frontline: highly skilled (7) vs unskilled (1)	0.85818	
	Production: trained/skilled (7) vs unskilled personnel (1)	0.80791	S16, 19, 23, 32, 33, 53
	Frontline: experts/professionals perform judgmental tasks	0.77538	
	Experts/professionals important in creating service	0.54805	
F6: Equipment-based service ($\alpha=0.7111$)	Production: highly equipment-intensive process	0.73255	P37, 57
	Installed new capital equipment at delivery level	0.65536	
	Delivery: Customer contact equipment – (7)/people-based (1)	0.65068	S4, 17, 21, 33, 56
	Production: (Not) people-intensive process	−0.55785	
	Quality of Delivery: improved equipment character (e.g. user friendly)	0.50453	
	Source of Idea: Technology (resources, new technology)	0.44044	
F7: Service innovativeness ($\alpha=0.6833$)	Highly innovative service; replies vastly inferior alternative	0.72327	P1, 39, 40, 42, 45
	Strategy: 'follower' (7) versus 'innovator' (1)	−0.69571	
	Subtle (7) versus radical differences from competitor (1)	−0.68185	S13, 16, 20, 23, 24
	Service concept difficult for clients to evaluate/understand	0.48248	
F8: Service quality evidence ($\alpha=0.6363$)	Tangibles added which clients use to judge quality	0.70753	
	Developed 'high quality' image for service	0.59422	S6, 13, 16, 19 20, 23, 32, 56
	Quality of Delivery: improve personal character (e.g. appearance, expertise)	0.57529	
	Tangible 'peripherals' used to enhance customer perception	0.56285	
F9: Service newness to the firm ($\alpha=0.6682$)	Class of service totally new to firm	0.69038	P1, 39, 42
	(Not) Improvement/modification of existing service	−0.67771	
	Service production process totally new to firm	0.56122	
	Exploited technology totally new to firm	0.55480	S13, 20, 23, 28, 30, 55
	(Not) 'Core' or primary service of firm	−0.45506	
F10: Effectiveness of NSD management ($\alpha=0.7482$)	NSD process (did Not) suffer from poor communication among functional areas	−0.67201	P1, 37, 41, 45
	Top management did not play strong enough role in NSD (Reverse)	−0.66064	S6, 16, 17, 21
	Employee involvement in planning, design and launch not adequate (Reverse)	−0.65934	

Table 3. (*Continued*)

Factor name	Variables loading on factor	Factor loading	Selected references[b]
	Top management created highly innovative environment	0.52447	
	Did good job in marketing service to frontline	0.38000	
F11: Service complexity/ customness (α=0.5442)	Complex service: many intricate parts	0.69591	P39, 40
	Consider 'high cost' service (by customers)	0.64709	
	Quality: more customized (7)/more standardized (1) than before	0.50031	S13, 16, 19, 20, 23, 26, 32, 34
F12: Quality of service experience (α=0.8024)	Quality: faster or more efficient service	0.79448	S16, 20, 22, 23,
	Quality: more reliable service (fewer failpoints)	0.74892	26, 32, 34, 56
F13: Standardization of service process (α=0.5530)	Standardized the behind-the-scenes production process	0.66845	S21–23, 29, 32– 34, 56
	Customer contact (delivery) made more uniform	0.63312	
	Marketing approach (e.g. customer contact promotion) totally new to firm	0.41570	
F14: Market newness to firm (α=0.5468)	Customers/clients totally new to firm	0.71997	P28, 39, 40, 42–45
	Customers (Not)) similar to ones already served	−0.60539	
	Competitive environment totally new to firm	0.54193	
F15: Specialized initial market (α=0.4195)	Service initially aimed at one or two clients	0.67535	P57
	Source of Idea: customer contact personnel	0.52798	
	Firm reputation played major role in trial of service	0.38892	S5, 16, 18, 20, 24, 23
	'Auxilliary' service: facilitates sale of primary product/service	0.36381	
	(Not) a large dollar volume market	−0.31298	
F16: Responds to demand cycle (α=0.6789)	Role: uses firm's excess (or off-season) capacity	0.81291	P1
	Role: responds to variations in demand conditions	0.78075	S16, 19, 21, 33, 35
F17: Market segment adjustments (α=0.5001)	Fit: marketing research capabilities and resources	0.45100	S13, 16, 18, 20, 23, 32, 34
	Service tailored to well-defined market segments	0.39467	

[1] Numbers in parentheses: Cronbach alpha (α) construct reliability coefficients.
[b] References in the new product (*P*) or the services marketing (*S*) literatures in which similar constructs or attributes are noted.

procedure that systematically identifies and plans for specific service elements and processes. The new services undergo pre-launch testing to determine customer response and to rehearse the service production and delivery procedure. During commercialization, a deliberated programme is directed at both the market and the firm's service personnel, while formal post-launch evaluation is used for gauging the extent to which the new service met planned objectives.

The second NSD proficiency factor describes the company's *effectiveness in NSD management (F10)*. New services rated high on this dimension successfully exploit the different types of expertise available within the firm; that is, good communication and a procedure that actively involves employees from different specialities (e.g. computer systems, customer service and marketing research) in the development and launch processes have been established. Management additionally plays a key role in creating an innovative corporate environment and in planning, implementing and internally marketing the new service project.

Project synergy

Three factors (overall corporate synergy, service newness to firm, and market newness to firm) measure the project's synergy with the firm's existing resources and experiences. *Overall corporate synergy (F2)* describes project fit with several company skills and resources including: managerial capabilities and preferences, company 'expertise', sales and promotional capabilities, service delivery and production facilities, and financial resources. In contrast, *services newness to the firm (F9)* describes a *lack* of synergy; that is, the project introduces the firm to a new class of services and to a production process and technology with which it is unfamiliar. Similarly, services with high *market newness to the firm (F14)* require that the company deal with a new type of client and competitive environment.

Market characteristics

A third category of dimensions describes the characteristics of the market for the new service. These are:

- *Market competitiveness (F3)*: a high rating means aggressive competition, one or two dominant competitors and price sensitivity. Also, frequent new service introductions and highly similar service offerings are the market mode.
- *Product-market fit/attractiveness (F4)*: the new service responds to a clearly identified customer need/problem and is consistent with existing client operating systems; the market exhibits a good potential for revenue and growth.
- *Specialized initial market (F15)*: some expert 'auxiliary' services are aimed at a specialized market segment (one or two key clients), their purpose being to promote the company's *primary* service offerings. Company reputation and close customer contact play a key role in defining this factor.
- *Responds to demand cycle (F16)*: the new service uses the firm's excess/off-cycle capacity and/or responds to variations in market demand.

Nature of the new service offering

A final group of eight dimensions identified in this analysis describes the nature of the new service developed by the firm. Two of the factors portray the people-versus-equipment character of the service. For new services that are strongly *expert-/people-based (F5)*, professional or highly skilled personnel play a critical role in producing and delivering the service to clients. Conversely, *equipment-based (F6)* services involve significant investment in capital facilities and concentrate on reducing the people-intensive nature of services. Service production and the customer interface are made more equipment-intensive, and service quality is sometimes enhanced through improvements in hardware (e.g. more user friendly, faster etc.).

Another three factors deal with the *quality of the service* offering. First, development projects with a high degree of *service innovativeness (F7)* are perceived by customers as truly unique, replacing vastly inferior alternatives. Firms developing such a service are often on an 'innovator' strategic track, being first to introduce a very different new service offering. Second is *service quality evidence (F8)*. Companies whose projects rate high on this factor succeed in creating a 'high quality' image for their service. They also incorporate tangible evidence of quality as well as improvements to the delivery system with which customers interface (e.g. appearance, expertise etc.). A third quality dimension is *quality of the service experience (F12)*: that is, a new or changed service that offers clients a faster, more efficient and more reliable service process.

Factors that define the nature of the new service also concern the extent to which companies *customize or standardize* the new service offering. *Service complexity/customness (F11)* characterizes costly and highly tailored service features designed to meet the individual requirements of client firms. A second factor in this subcategory is *market segment adjustment (F17)*: the market has undergone detailed analysis and the new service has been adjusted to respond to one or more specific customer groups. Finally, *standardization of the service process (F13)* concerns NSD efforts that incorporate highly standardized mechanisms with which to produce and deliver the service.

VALIDITY OF THE FACTORS

The 17 new service factors (classified as new service development proficiency, project synergy, market characteristics and nature of the new service offering) are in many ways similar to the descriptive dimensions suggested in studies of new manufactured goods. As such, they adequately reflect what is relevant for services in the new physical product literature. Cooper[39], for example, identified 18 factors (grouped as production versus market orientation, innovativeness of the venture, nature of the project, market factors, and the company and its proficiencies) that define winners and losers in the industrial new product sphere. Similarly, Maidique and Zirger[41] offer ten index variables (categorized as environmental factors, corporate skills and resources, and the corporate and product strategy) that distinguish between successful and failed new product ventures. Table 3 provides these and other references that relate to the physical product character of the new service projects analysed in this study (see 'P' references).

The factors describing new business services also capture their service-specific character. Table 3 provides references gleaned from the services marketing literature ('S') for services) for ten of the factors which can specifically be linked to the distinctive character of services. For example, the need for a detailed and formal new service development process and using a 'drawing-board' approach to design services (F1)[6,16], and offering physical evidence to help characterize the quality of the service (F8) are clearly related to the intangibility attribute[4,21,22,30]. Similarly, NSD factors which emphasizes the customer experience and the service delivery system (F5) reflect the inseparability of service production and consumption[20,21,30,53]. The question of service variability is addressed by factors that deal with degree of customization (F11, F17)[13,16,21,32] and standardization (F13)[32,33,34], and with service quality as reflected by the reliability of the service experience (F12)[29,34]. Finally, the perishability characteristic is partly dealt with by new services that introduce equipment-based processes (F6)[33,34] and that respond to variations in market demand (F16)[22,35].

DETERMINANTS OF NEW SERVICE PERFORMANCE

Identifying a set of descriptive factors that underlie new business service projects, as above, was the first objective of this analysis. The second question deals with which of these dimensions are related to new service success. As noted above and summarized in Table 2, business service firms use at least four approaches to measuring NSD performance. Hence, the next question in the analysis concerns: which of the factors that describe new service projects are critical to each form of NSD success? Four separate multiple regression analyses (stepwise) were used: one for each performance criterion with the new service project factor scores on each of the 17 descriptive dimensions as independent variables. In other words, for each measure of new service performance (sales performance, competitive performance, cost performance and 'other booster') a model of 'success factors' was derived. The results for all four regression models are statistically, highly significant and explain a fair proportion of the variance in the level of performance that was achieved (α for the model ≤ 0.001, with the cut-off criterion for the entry of variables at $\alpha \leq 0.05$). The results are presented in Table 4 and Figure 1; a discussion follows.

Achieving high sales performance

Of the 17 factors that describe new service projects, nine were found to be related to the most important measure of success, achieving high sales performance. The market characteristics of the new service and the firm's proficiency in new service development are the groups of factors with the greatest explanatory value (40.0 and 31.2% of the explained variance, respectively). Project synergy and nature of the new service offering also play a significant, although less important role (see Table 4; Figure, 1).

Of major importance for achieving high levels of sales performance is the product-market fit/attractiveness (F4) of the new service. New or improved services that respond to clearly identified customer needs and problems and that are aimed at broad markets with volume and growth potential (F4, F15) are obvious candidates for success in this regard. But market potential is not enough. Success in achieving high sales is also

Table 4. Determinants of new service performance: results of regression analyses[a]

New service factor	Sales performance	Competitive performance	Cost performance	'Other booster'
I. *NSO proficiency*	(31.2%)	(8.1%)	(42.3%)	—
F1: Detailed/formal NSO process	6.6*	4.5[+]	10.6[+]	—
F10: Effective NSO management	14.6**	3.6[+]	31.7**	—
II. *Project synergy*	(15.2%)	(6.1%)	(39.1%)	(69.1%)
F2: Overall product synergy	7.2*	6.1*	26.7**	47.1*
F9 : Service newness to firm	−80*	—	−12.4*	22.0[+]
F14: Market newness	—	—	—	—
III. *Market characteristics*	(40.4%)	(16.5%)	(18.6%)	(30.0%)
F3: Market competitiveness	—	−4.4[+]	—	—
F4: Market attractiveness	35.4**	12.1**	—	—
F15: Specialized initial market	−5.0[+]	—	—	30.0[+]
F16: Responds to demand cycle	—	—	18.6*	—
IV. *Nature of service offering*	(13.2%)	(68.8%)	—	—
F5: Expert-/people-based service	6.1*	14.7*	—	—
F7: Service innovativeness	—	26.7**	—	—
F8: Service quality evidence	—	13.3*	—	—
F12: Quality of service experience	—	14.2**	—	—
F11: Service complexity/ customness	−3.0[+]	—	—	—
F17: Market segment adjustment	4.1[+]	—	—	—
Number of factors in equation	9/17	9/17	5/17	3/17
Adjusted R^2	0.34	0.30	0.14	0.06
F-value (equation)[b]	14.186	12.293	9.799	5.831

[a] Numbers in table stand for % of total R^2 in each equation; **, * and [+] stand for 0.001, 0.01 and 0.05 levels of significance respectively.
[b] Significant at $\alpha \leqslant 0.001$ for all four equations.

greatly affected by the company's proficiency in implementing its NSD process. A detailed/formal NSD process (F1) and effective NSD management (F10) are two factors that are critical for developing successful new services for volume markets. In other words, ideas for new services need to be well thought out and tested before being offered to clients, and should involve promotional efforts directed at both customer and frontline personnel. Of particular relevance for a proficient NSD effort is management's ability to harness its specialized functional resources (F10). Designing and marketing the right new service requires a supportive and innovative new product environment; one in which the diverse resources of the firm, such as information technology, service concept and process design, as well as customer interface skills, are all committed to creating and launching the new service.

Also significant for delivering high level sales are two of the project synergy factors.

For the business service firm, focusing on services with which the company is familiar and for which it is known in the market (i.e. *not* a new service for the firm—F9) is a preferred strategy. In other words, companies that develop modifications and improvements of existing services, or additions to the 'core' offering, are more likely to succeed not only because they are already proficient at producing and marketing such services, but also probably because clients can more easily associate the new service with the firm's established reputation. Similarly, new service projects that fit management preferences and that benefit from the firm's production/delivery facilities, marketing skills and financial resources (i.e. overall corporate synergy—F2) are likely to have a more successful launch and gain customer acceptance more quickly than new services that do not have these advantages.

Finally, three factors that describe the nature of the new service offering affect sales performance. Using expert personnel to interface with clients (F5) and offering new services that provide for market segment adjustments (F17) are factors which positively impact on the rate of success. On the other hand, offering a highly complex/customized service (F11) understandably is a barrier to achieving a high level of sales in a broad volume market.

Determinants of competitive performance

Sometimes, a new service is a 'success' because it achieves a differential advantage in the market. Competitive performance was the second most important performance indicator and measures success in qualitative terms, based on customers' perception of the new service: its superiority to competitive offerings both in terms of *what* customers receive (i.e. the outcome) and the type of experience they have during the service encounter (as in [30,48]) (see Table 2). What factors lead to this form of NSD success? Although as for the sales performance measure, nine factors in all four categories of dimensions play a significant explanatory role, the key factors responsible for achieving a competitive market edge are different. In particular, factors that describe the nature of the new service offering—that is, its innovativeness, quality and expert/people character—are by far the most important and account for 68.9% of the variation explained by the entire model (see Table 4, Figure 1).

The finding that service innovativeness (F7) is of primary importance in gaining a competitive edge is not surprising. Service intangibility and the fact that services are frequently viewed as generic, means that developing a new service and company from competitors. For example, containerization in shipping and the cash account pioneered by Merrill Lynch, are two well-known departures from traditional services where companies, first to launch an innovative offering, gained an important market edge.

The research also confirms the importance of quality in new services. A strategy to incorporate tangible clues (F8) which makes services more visible and highlight quality features—for example, a promotional package that describes the services, a strong image and company logo, or the enhanced appearance of the frontline—is more likely to succeed in competitive terms. Similarly, focusing on improvements in the quality of the service experience (F12) (i.e. providing greater reliability, a faster and more efficient process) and using experts or trained personnel (F5) for the customer encounter are both linked to the simultaneity characteristic of services and are essential for competitive success.

The market characteristics of a new service is a second category of dimensions that influences competitive performance. New services with a high rating on product-market fit/attractiveness (F4) (i.e. solve important client problems and cater to a defined target group of buyers), particularly when combined with being first in the market, are strong candidates for success. Conversely, an aggressive competitive environment (F3) tends to have a detrimental effect. Since services are not patentable, yet easily and quickly imitated, sustaining an edge in a highly competitive market—one with many similar services and frequent new service introductions—is understandably difficult to accomplish.

The two other categories of dimensions, NSD proficiency and project synergy, have only a moderate effect on competitive performance. New services that fit well with the firm's capabilities and resources (F2) and that benefit from a proficient NSD function (F1 and F10) are likely to have a better design, be more meticulously launched, blend in better with the firm's reputation and, as a result, are more likely to be perceived as competitively superior by buyers.

Cost performance

Perishability and the people-intensive nature of many business and professional services makes the achievement of cost efficiencies an important new service development objective. Table 4 and Figure 1 reveal that a relatively small number of dimensions (five factors in three categories) are of particular relevance in accomplishing this end.

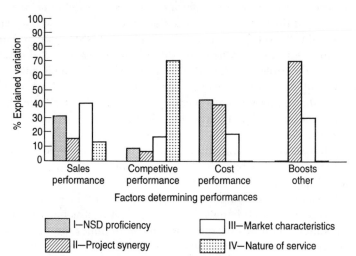

Figure 1. Determinants of New Service Performance by Type of Performance: Results of Regression Analysis.

Fundamental to realizing savings through new service development is the firm's proficiency in the NSD function. Companies must have both an effectively managed (F10) and a formal NSD process (F1). Successfully exploiting the specialized pool of resources in various functional areas of the firm and creating a supportive environment for innovation is essential for developing cost effective solutions through the NSD process. For example, many firms have improved cost performance by streamlining and computerizing the behind-the-scenes processes without detrimentally affecting the service outcome for clients (e.g. media selection by advertising agencies). Additionally, companies with a formal and detailed new service development process are more likely to identify optimum design alternatives (which satisfy customers *and* provide savings for the firm) and to avoid costly errors during launch and delivery of a new service.

Project synergy is the second major concern for achieving cost efficiencies. According to the findings, new service projects that produce savings tend to include:

(1) modifications or additions to the company's 'core' offerings (i.e. *not* a new class of service (F9));
(2) new services that leverage the production/delivery facilities and/or the expert and marketing resources that are already in place (i.e. overall corporate synergy (F2)).

Finally, since high costs often result from a combination of fluctuating demand and service perishability, the finding in this study that new services which respond to this problem (F16) prove to be effective cost reducing agents was clearly anticipated.

Boosting the performance of other services

New services are sometimes introduced in the hope that they will boost the sales/profits of the firm's other, already existing, products or services. An advertising firm, for example, might offer its clients special lunchtime seminars on current topics in media planning as a route to fostering customer loyalty. NSD projects that lead to this form of success are characterized by efforts to reach a small number of key clients (market characteristic factor F15) and by services which, although not previously offered by the firm, fit well with its specialized skills, facilities and financial capabilities (project synergy factors F2 and F9).

Non-significant factors

Three of the 17 descriptive variables, namely market newness to the firm (F14) (a project synergy factor) and two factors that define the nature of the new service offering (that is, equipment-based service (F6) and standardized service process (F13)) were not significant determinants of success. These are discussed in the conclusion section.

IMPLICATIONS FOR BUSINESS SERVICES FIRMS

One of the findings in this study is that many of the dimensions that describe and impact on the success of new business service projects relate not only to services but also to the development of physical products. Factors such as market potential, project innovativeness, synergy, and the implementation of a formal development and launch procedure have been identified by several researchers as significant indicators that lead to new product success.[6] These results reflect the rationale of integrating both the services marketing and new product literatures in the theoretical framework and, at the same time, confirm that some of the paradigms which have emerged in the new product arena appear to be applicable also to services. But does service distinctiveness matter? Considering the volume of literature on this subject, an important question driving this study was whether the distinguishing features of services (intangibility, inseparability of production and consumption, variability and perishability) are relevant for companies when developing and marketing new business services? Several conclusions are presented and discussed below.

IMPORTANCE OF PROJECT SYNERGY IN SERVICES

A key factor in the success of new business services is the question of project synergy. The findings substantiate that new service offerings which feature a strong fit with existing services and which benefit from the firm's operating strengths and facilities, have a greater chance for success. Understanding the nature of services helps to explain part of this phenomenon.

Overall corporate strategy

This which concerns whether companies can leverage their existing proficiencies and resources, is by far the most important determinant of success in new industrial services. Although this factor has its physical product counterpart, research has shown that it plays a somewhat less dominant role in the goods sector and is primarily concerned with technological synergy[36,37,39,41]. For the new services analysed in this study, overall corporate synergy—that is, project fit with a broad set of capabilities and resources of the firm—appears to be an underlying *requirement* for success. The importance of this factor on all four forms of NSD performance is very likely the result of three of the features that make services unique. Intangibility, for example, explains why overall corporate synergy is so important for sales and competitive performance. Since new services can be difficult for customers to evaluate and to differentiate from competing services, it is often the firm's expertise and facilities for performing the service that become the essence of the service being purchased. Hence, a good fit (or conversely incompatibility) with the firm's image and known capabilities becomes a key ingredient for success (or failure). Similarly, the finding that new services which fit the firm's demand cycle *and* existing expertise/resource base affect cost performance is very likely the result of the inseparability and perishability of services. Companies with huge capital facilities (e.g. airlines or cargo carriers) and/or with expert personnel that must be retained during periods of low demand (e.g. high-tech systems companies or consulting firms), can rationalize costs by adding new services that are synergistic in this regard.

Service newness to the firm

This is a second project synergy factor that impacts on the outcome of new services, but in a negative sense. In other words, introductions which modify or closely fit the 'core' offerings of the firm, rather than completely new service classes, are more likely to succeed. This finding is similar to what has been found in the physical product sector where companies are generally reluctant to incur the high risks associated with developing products with which they are unfamiliar[1]. Added to this risk averseness is the fact that services are much easier to adjust (than goods) and that custom modifications are frequently required to maintain long-term business client relations. As a result, service firms enhance sales performance by concentrating on service evolutions rather than on the development of entirely new classes of services. In addition, in services, a high quality outcome can often depend on the satisfactory performance of a 'sequence' of independently produced transactions. For example, a typical sequence in shipping might involve pick-up service, air transport, custom brokerage, in-transit storage and courier delivery. Firms often try to extend their control over the final outcome clients receive, and therefore over the quality of the service, by adding new services that complement and facilitate the successful completion of their primary service[33].

Introducing service improvements and modifications are also related to the cost performance measure of success. This is understandable considering the high costs associated with such features as client contact, customization and expertise/human resource-intensity. Service firms devote at least some NSD efforts to modifications that make existing services more cost efficient. Levitt's[34] call, however, to 'industrialize' services—that is, to introduce capital equipment and planned work systems to fully rationalize the production and delivery process—was not supported by this study. The two factors, an equipment-based service and a standardized service process, were not significant (negative) codeterminants (with service newness to the firm) of success on the cost performance dimension. Likely reasons include: that highly standardized services have limited utility in the business services sector; and that industrial service firms may not yet fully appreciate the cost reduction potential inherent in systems- and equipment-based service processes[23].

Market newness to the firm

This was not a significant success/failure ingredient for new industrial services. This outcome was unexpected, since in some of the physical product studies, market diversification or, conversely, having a good understanding of the market has been shown to have a major impact on new product success[37,40,41]. Two reasons, both related to the special character of services, might account for this finding. First, because the firm's reputation is so essential for the success of a new service, companies tend to avoid entering new markets in which they are unknown to clients. Conversely, since satisfying divergent customer needs is indigenous to the business services sector (inseparability, variability), the findings might reflect a greater flexibility on the part of service companies to respond to different types of customers and that, therefore, market newness to the firm is a less relevant issue.

PRODUCT-MARKET FIT IS A KEY TO SUCCESS IN SERVICES

Aside from the synergy factors, identifying and responding to market needs is a second underlying ingredient in the new service success equations of firms. Companies with a strong market orientation when developing new services are superior on both the sales and the competitive performance dimension. This finding, which has consistently also been noted as a primary success factor for new manufactured goods, is highly relevant for services due to the frequently expressed concern that service firms are too exclusively operations-oriented[16,22]. Clearly, service companies must and should be market-driven in their NSD efforts. The close proximity of firms to their customers, coupled with the ability to develop and imitate new services quickly, offers opportunities to: minimize the detrimental effect of competitive innovations; make more timely responses to changed needs and market conditions; and use the frontline as a key source of ideas for new services.

Innovativeness and service quality

Studies of manufactured goods emphasize product uniqueness and superiority as the most important factors explaining new product success[39–41,45]. This emphasis on innovativeness and quality is also partially substantiated in the study of new service development. First, the thesis that service firms must focus both on what buyers receive and on what they perceive when purchasing a service was supported[4,21,30]. New services that concentrate on the client interface by providing a superior service experience and that incorporate service quality evidence to help buyers make evaluations, had a significantly greater success rate. Only competitive performance, however, and not sales performance, as one might expect, was affected by quality and innovativeness. Intangibility, as well as the relatively more long- versus shorter-term nature of the two NSD success measures, might hep to explain this finding. As Wind[28] has pointed out, non-patentability in services reduces the incentive for creativity by firms since success in terms of increased sales performance is often dissipated quite quickly through imitation. As shown above, most companies therefore concentrate on low cost/risk modifications and improvements as a way of achieving short-term sales results. Nevertheless, the findings also show that some firms use service innovativeness and quality in NSD for affecting sales in the long-run, via the competitive performance dimension. In effect, since it is the firm's reputation, rather than the service itself, that often determines buying decisions and since a superior image in the market can only be developed over time, some companies focus their new service development efforts on this longer-term objective of gaining a reputation for innovativeness and quality as a route to NSD success.

PROFICIENCY IN THE NEW SERVICE DEVELOPMENT PROCESS

A final, although no less important, conclusion in this study is that companies need to be proficient in how they go about developing new services. According to the exploratory interviews carried out during the initial research phase one, as well as the findings of other researchers[6,14,16], most service firms do not use a highly detailed NSD process (F1). Yet, the analysis of successful and unsuccessful new services indicate that a formal and planned approach to NSD leads to better performance on at least three success measures. The implications are clear. Instead of operating in what traditionally has been a relatively haphazard fashion, managers responsible for new service development should establish a system that incorporates: a formal procedure for generating and evaluating new service ideas, a 'drawing-board' approach for identifying and designing the necessary service elements and processes, testing new services with customers and with the frontline in order to eliminate potential failpoints, and a documented launch plan to ensure the proper marketing of new services.

Aside from using a detailed NSD process, success in new service development depends on getting the necessary commitment and interaction from management and from the different functional specialities within the firm. Similar to the communications gap that often prevails between marketing and R&D in the manufacturing sector, service companies have difficulties getting their technical, systems and marketing personnel to combine their respective points of view and proficiencies. As summed up by the manager in a trust company: 'harnessing the technical resources of the firm and effectively combining these with the company's marketing and customer-oriented skills is the single most important factor in bringing about new service success'. This concern over effective NSD management(F10), as a key ingredient in the success of new services, was clearly supported by the findings in this study.

Three of the four measures of new service performance were affected by the NSD management factor. In each case, the fact that services differ from physical products offer some insights. For sales performance, the fact that services are complex and operations-intensive requires that all the functions concerned with planning, developing and marketing the service (including international marketing to the frontline) be fully involved in the project. Similarly, for cost performance, internal resource management is an essential ingredient for new service success. Since, for service companies, information technology has been the key technology underlying past efforts to make service more cost efficient, the findings confirm the continued efforts by business services companies to harness these specialized resources for successfully reducing costs.

A third concern of effective NSD management is gaining a competitive market edge. During the interviews, managers had indicated that, although systems capabilities were initially directed at reducing costs, today it is primarily the effective applications of this technology that embody the most innovative and competitively superior services. The finding, therefore, that NSD management plays only a marginal role in the competitive performance model was surprising. The experiences of the trust company manager also provide some insights here. According to him, systems people often 'don't have a customer or market-oriented attitude and generally don't think in terms of how the different capabilities (of the firm) can be combined to create new services' while marketing personnel tend to have a poor understanding of the systems side and 'don't fully appreciate the potential that information technology offers for creating completely new and innovative services'. This problem of effectively harnessing information technology for the purpose of new service development was echoed by several managers and is analogous to the communication difficulties that manufacturing firms experience between R&D and marketing. But for service companies, the problem can be more extensive since the expertise and points of view of a larger number of functional areas and personnel (e.g. information systems, process specialists, service concept designers, frontline and marketing personnel) are all directly responsible for creating superior services. The conclusion we should draw from the research results, therefore, is *not* that effective NSD management is relatively unimportant, but that business service firms are probably not as proficient as they should be in using their diverse resources to create successful, new-to-the-world services.

SUMMARY AND CONCLUSION

Developing successful new services is critical for many companies. Past studies of this phenomenon have been concerned almost exclusively with physical goods, although a small number of articles have looked at how the factors that distinguish services from physical products affect new service development. The investigation reported here studied success and failure of new services in the business-to-business services sector and responds to calls from the literature to:

(1) integrate theoretical concepts from various disciplines—in this case, new goods development, and services marketing in the industrial sector;
(2) move from the traditional case or small sample and industry-specific approach to empirical research that permits generalizations about many types of service firms across different service sectors;
(3) provide empirical evidence that substantiates or refutes services marketing concepts.

More particularly, this study makes several important contributions. It identifies a comprehensive and fairly reliable set of 17 independent factors that describe the problems and issues relevant for managers concerned with developing and marketing new business services. Moreover, since companies create new services to achieve different performance objectives, the results show which of these descriptive dimensions are responsible for accomplishing each form of new service success. Finally, the findings speak to managers of business services about how some of the distinguishing characteristics of services impact on the successful development of new services. Responding to market needs with new or changed services they offer clients both functional and experiential quality, that are innovative and truly superior to competitive offerings, and that fully benefit from a formal and well-managed new service development process and from the unique strengths and proficiencies of the firm are key requirements for creating and marketing winning new service products.

ACKNOWLEDGEMENT

This research was supported by grants from the Social Sciences and Research Council of Canada, Ottawa, Canada, and from Shell Canada, Ltd.

NOTES

1. Easingwood's (1986) study of 67 variables is an exception in this regard, but has a limited sample size of 31 firms.

2. Principal component analysis (varimax rotation) of 16 measures of performance on which each project was rated accounted for 71.7% of the variance prior to rotation and suggested four independent, composite success/failure dimensions. Cronbach alpha reliability coefficients ranged from 0.52 to 0.94 and reliability of the linear combination of factors (scale reliability) was 0.78. Multiple regression analysis relating the four independent performance measures to the project global success/failure rating was highly significant (adj. $R^2 = 83.6\%$, $\alpha \leqslant 0.001$ for all factors together and for each factor separately). See Methodology section in text for details of the data collection.
3. Several multidivision firms provided more than one response. Brief project descriptions provided by respondents show no duplicates. Several cases involved *both* industrial and consumer services (e.g. airlines). Consumer-only services firms were not included.
4. Several variables which were of a purely descriptive nature (e.g. whether the service was a 'pure' service) and planned for use in future analyses were also omitted from the analysis.
5. Cronbach alpha for 16 of the factors ranged from 0.50 to 0.85 which is in the minimum range suggested by Nunnally[54]; one factor (F15) was rated somewhat lower at $\alpha = 0.42$.

REFERENCES

1. Booz, Allen and Hamilton (1982) *New Products Management for the 1980s*, Booz, Allen and Hamilton, Inc., New York.
2. Zeithaml, V. A., Parasuraman, A. and Berry, L. L. (1985) 'Problems and Strategies in Services Marketing', *Journal of Marketing*, **49** (Spring): 33–46.
3. Glazer, R. H. and Montgomery, D. B. (1980) *New Products Innovation—An Annotated Bibliography*, Stanford University, Graduate School of Business, Palo Alto, Ca.
4. Shostack, G. L. (1977) 'Breaking Free from Product Marketing', *Journal of Marketing*, **41** (April): 73–80.
5. Shostack, G. L. (1982) 'How to Design a Service?' *European Journal of Marketing*, **16**(1): 49–63.
6. Shostack, G. L. (1984) 'Designing Services that Deliver', *Harvard Business Review*, **62** (January–February): 133–139.
7. Chase, R. B. (1983) '*Modelling Services Process*', in Berry, L. L., Shostack, G. L., and Upah, G. D. (eds), Chicago: 137–138.
8. Beckwith, N. E. and Fitzgerald, T. J. (1981) 'Marketing of Services: Meeting of Different Needs', in Donnelly, J. H., and George, W. R. (eds), *Marketing of Services*, American Marketing Association Proceedings, Chicago: 291–302.
9. Murphy, P. E. and Robinson, R. M (1981) 'Concept Testing for Services', in Donnelly, J. H. and George, W. R. (eds), *Marketing of Services*, American Marketing Association Proceedings, Chicago: 217–220.
10. Robinson, R. K. (1983) 'New Service Development: The Cable TV Connection', in Berry, L.L., Shostack, G. L., Upah, G. D. (eds), *Emerging Perspectives on Service Marketing*, American Marketing Association Proceedings, Chicago: 73–76.
11. Schneider, B. and Bowen, D. E. (1985) 'New Services Design, Development and Implementation and the Employee', in George, W. R. and Marshall, C. E. (eds), *Developing New Services*, American Marketing Association Proceedings, Chicago: 82–101.
12. Schwartz, H. (1985) 'Developing a Climate for Innovation of New Services', in George, W. R. and Marshall, C. E. (eds), *Developing New Services*, American Marketing Association Proceedings, Chicago: 1–8.
13. Langeard, E. and Eiglier, P. (1983) 'Strategic Management of Service Development', in Berry, L. L., Shostack, G. L. and Upah, G. D. (eds), *Emerging Perspectives on Services Marketing*, American Marketing Association Proceedings: 68–72.
14. Bowers, M. R. (1986) 'The New Product Development Process: A Suggested Model for Banks', *Journal of Retail Banking* (Spring/Summer): 19–24.
15. Reidenbach, R. E. and Moak, D. L. (1986) 'Exploring Retail Bank Performance and New Product Development: A Profile of Industry Practices', *Journal of Product Innovation Management*, **3** (3): 187–194.

16. Easingwood, C. J. (1986) 'New Product Development for Service Companies', *Journal of Product Innovation Management*, **3** (December): 264–275.
17. Lovelock, C. H. (1984) 'Developing and Implementing New Services', in George, W. R. and Marshall, C. C. (eds), *Developing New Services*, American Marketing Association Proceedings, Chicago: 44–64.
18. Thomas, D. R. E. (1978) 'Strategy is Different in Service Businesses', *Harvard Business Review*, **56** (July–August): 158–165.
19. Morris, M. H. and Fuller, D. A. (1989) 'Pricing an Industrial Service', *Industrial Marketing Management*, **18**: 139–146.
20. Besson, R. M. (1973) 'Unique Aspects of Marketing Services', *Arizona Business* (20 November): 8–14.
21. Berry, L. L. (1980) 'Services Marketing is Different', *Business*, **30** (May–June): 24–29.
22. Lovelock, C. H. (1981) 'Why Marketing Management Needs to be Different for Services', in Donnelly, J. H. and George, W. R. (eds), *Marketing of Services*, American Marketing Association Proceedings, Chicago: 5–9.
23. Easingwood, C. J. and Mahajan, V. (1989) 'Positioning of Financial Services for Competitive Advantage', *Journal of Product Innovation Management*, **6** (August): 207–219.
24. Gummesson, E. (1981) 'The Marketing of Professional Services: 25 Propositions', in Donnelly, J. H. and George, W. E. (eds), *Marketing Services*, American Marketing Association Proceedings, Chicago.
25. Rushton, A. M. and Carson, D. J. (1985) 'The Marketing of Services: Managing the Intangibles', *European Journal of Marketing*, **19**: 19–40.
26. Jackson, R. W. and Cooper, P. D. (1988) 'Unique Aspects of Marketing Industrial Services', *Industrial Marketing Management*, **17**: 111–118.
27. Lynn, S. A. (1987) 'Identifying Buying Influences for a Professional Service: Implications for Marketing Efforts', *Industrial Marketing Management*, **16**: 119–130.
28. Wind, Y. J. (1982) *Product Policy: Concepts, Methods and Strategy*, Addison-Wesley, Reading, Ma.: 550–553.
29. Booms, B. H. and Bitner, M. J. (1982) 'Marketing Strategies and Organization Structures for Services Firms', in Donnelly, J. H. and George, W. R. (eds), *Marketing of Services*, American Marketing Association Proceedings, Chicago: 47–51.
30. Grönroos, C. (1982) 'An Applied Service Marketing Theory', *European Journal of Marketing*, **16**: 30–41.
31. Grönroos, C. (1990) *Service Management and Marketing: Managing the Moments of Truth in Service Competition*, Lexington Books, Lexington MA.
32. Shostack, G. (1987) 'Service Positioning Through Structural Change', *Journal of Marketing*, **51** (January): 34–43.
33. Maister, D. H. and Lovelock, C. H. (1983) 'Managing Facilitator Services', *Sloan Management Review*, **23** (Summer): 19–31.
34. Levitt, T. (1976) 'The Industrialization of Service', *Harvard Business Review*, **48** (September–October): 63–74.
35. Sasser, Jr. W. E. (1976) 'Match Supply and Demand in Service Industries', *Harvard Business Review*, **48** (November–December): 133–140.
36. Myers, S. and Marquis, D. C. (1969) 'Successful Industrial Innovation', *National Science Foundation*, Rep. NSF 67–17.
37. Rothwell, R. (1972) 'Factors for Success in Industrial Innovations', in *Project SAPPHO—A Comparative Study of Success and Failure in Industrial Innovation*, University of Sussex, Science Policy Research Unit, Brighton, Sussex.
38. Rothwell, R. *et al.* (1974) 'Updated: Project SAPPHO Phase II', *Research Policy*, **3**: 258–291.
39. Cooper, R. G. (1980) *Project NewProd: What Makes a New Project a Winner?* Centre Quebecois d'Innovation Industrielle, Montreal.
40. Cooper, R. G. (1984) 'New Product Strategies: What Distinguishes the Top Performers?' *Journal of Product Innovation Management* **1** (June): 151–164.
41. Maidique, M. A. and Zirger, B. J. (1984) 'A Study of Success and Failure in Product Innovation: The Case of the US Electronics Industry', *IEEE Transactions in Engineering Management*, **EM–23** (August): 116–123.

42. Cooper, R. G. and de Brentani, U. (1984) 'Criteria for Screening New Industrial Products', *Industrial Marketing Management*, **13** (August): 149–156.
43. de Brentani, U. (1986) 'Do Firms Need a Custom-Designed New Product Screening Model?' *Journal of Product Innovation Management*, **3** (June): 108–119.
44. de Brentani, U. and Dröge, C. (1988) 'Determinants of the New Product Screening Decision: A Structural Model Analysis', *International Journal of Research in Marketing*, **5** (Fall): 91–106.
45. Cooper, R.G. and Kleinschmidt, E. J. (1987) 'Success Factors in Product Innovation', *Industrial Marketing Management*, **16** (August): 15–23.
46. Yoon, E. and Lilien, G. L. (1985) 'New Industrial Product Performance: The Effects of Market Characteristics and Strategy', *Journal of Product Innovation Management*, **3** (September): 134–144.
47. Crawford, M. C. (1980) 'Defining the Charter for Product Innovation', *Sloan Management Review* (Fall): 3–12.
48. Nyström, H. and Evardsson, B. (1982) 'Product Innovation in Food Processing: A Swedish Survey', *R&D Management*, **12**: 62–72.
49. de Brentani, U. (1989) 'Success and Failure in New Industrial Services', *Journal of Product Innovation Management*, **6** (December): 239–258.
50. Churchill, G. A. (1979) 'A Paradigm for Developing Better Measures of Marketing Constructs', *Journal of Marketing Research*, **16** (February): 64–73.
51. Peter, J. P. (1979) 'Reliability: A Review of Psychometric Basics and Recent Marketing Practices', *Journal of Marketing Research* **16** (February): 6–17.
52. Green, P. E. (1978) *Analyzing Multivariate Data*, The Dryden Press, Hindsdale, Ill.
53. Lovelock, C. H. (1983) 'Classifying Services to Gain Strategic Marketing Insights', *Journal of Marketing*, **47** (Summer): 9–20.
54. Nunnally, J. C. (1978) *Psychometric Theory*, 2nd ed, McGraw-Hill, New York.
55. Meyers, P. W. (1985) 'Innovation Shift: Lessons for Service Firms from a Technological Leader', in George, W. R. and Marshall, C. E. (eds), *Developing New Services*: 9–22.
56. Levitt, T. (1972) 'Production-line Approach to Services', *Harvard Business Review*, **44** (September–October): 41–52.
57. Von Hippel, E. (1978) 'Successful Industrial Products from Customer Ideas', *Journal of Marketing*, **42** (January): 39–49.

25

Insurance Product Development: Managing the Changes

Axel Johne

INTRODUCTION

Both life and general insurers in Britain are today under pressure to strengthen their market offerings. This is a direct result of deregulation, which has brought with it increased competitive activities and will continue to do so under ongoing legislative changes within the European Community. Product innovation is also being stimulated by heightened customer expectations, advances in enabling technology, and by new forms of competition.

Traditional players now poach each other's customers. Not only this, but they themselves are vulnerable to new styles of competition from entrants like banks and building societies. In many insurance markets, old-style combative marketing is being supplemented by new style competitive marketing in which companies fight for business in radically changed ways (McKenna, 1991; Peters, 1990). These competitive changes have powerful implications for established insurance companies which now face urgent decisions as far as the management of product development is concerned.

WHAT IS SUCCESSFUL PRODUCT DEVELOPMENT?

It is commonly assumed that a product development is successful if it meets objectives set by the supplying company. But, because companies have differing objectives and use different methods for measuring financial performance, there is disagreement over how product development success can be measured. There is also disagreement over what constitutes a product development. Some have argued that the tasks faced by suppliers define the nature of a development. This has led to the suggestion that there are two main types of product development—product improvement and new product development. Product improvement being concerned with updating existing products and new product development being concerned with quite new offerings (Johne and Snelson, 1990). We can call this approach the supply-based approach.

Reprinted with permission from *International Journal of Bank Marketing*, Vol. 11, No. 3, 1993 pp. 5–14.
© 1993 MCB University Press

Other writers stress that the true nature of product development and whether it is successful can only be understood from the viewpoint of the market. The argument runs that it is customers' preferences which determine how offerings are received: appropriately targeted offerings are likely to be successful, while poorly targeted offerings are likely to be unsuccessful. Proponents of this viewpoint stress that what needs to be analysed is not the challenge with which a particular product development presents a supplier, but how different a development is in meeting the preferences of customers (de Bruicker and Summe, 1985; Mathur, 1992; Quinn *et al.*, 1990). We can call this latter approach the market-based approach.

Fundamental to the market-based approach is the concept of the offering—that is to say, what has been developed for a target market. An example will bring this concept alive. Insurance offerings are made up of merchandise (cover) and support (service). Proponents of the market-based approach argue that it will be the mix of both which determines the level of demand. Market segments will respond differently. Some segments will want support and will be prepared to pay for it. Others will just want the basic cover.

In the case of many insurance offerings it has been left to brokers to add the support element. However, increasing numbers of companies now usurp the broker's function by selling direct. This is often the practice of new entrants, such as banks, which use their own distribution networks. A key question facing suppliers who do this is how much support to provide for the basic merchandise. If too little support is provided, inexperienced customers will feel hesitant in dealing direct. If too much support is provided, resources are wasted which could be applied to strengthening other elements in the marketing mix.

The market-based approach provides an effective method for assessing product development success. It is in specific markets that suppliers win or lose business, and therefore it is in markets that explanations for success or failure are to be found. Measuring success in target markets is, of course, quite different from the supply-based approach which uses internal measures. The distinction is important because frequently the internal hurdles used ignore market potentials.

We have deliberately spent time on the issue of product development success and how it might best be measured. Much academic research continues to rely on self-assessment by managers for classifying developments as successful or unsuccessful. Few researchers include controls to ensure that managers were aiming to fulfil similar objectives. The issue is important because reluctance on the part of analysts to state the objectives against which developments were undertaken can cause successes to be classified as failure and vice versa. For example, a company with high market or profitability hurdle rates will classify a product development as a failure if it fails to meet these, while another company with low hurdle rates will classify a similar performing development as a success.

Market-based measures of product development success are powerful. An associated external measure of success is the degree to which a company is creating a market for itself on its own terms, rather than just competing on terms laid down by established industry players. This latter type of success can be achieved by destabilizing and reshaping an established market or, perhaps, even by opening up a completely new market, as was done by providing low-cost private motor insurance to customers direct through telesales (Johne, 1992).

While market share success registers that customers are responding positively to new offerings, it nonetheless represents an incomplete measure of success. The market-based measure tells us nothing about whether a supplier is managing to meet customers' preferences profitably (as opposed to doing customers a great favour). For this reason both measures must be considered together: the market-based measure to appraise the extent to which market potentials are being exploited; the supply-based measure to appraise whether internally determined targets are being met in the quest to maintain and develop the business.

The two measures of product development success pose marketing specialists with considerable challenges. Marketing specialists should, by virtue of their skills in accessing relevant information, be able to assist in developing offerings which have positive market appeal. Not only this, but marketing specialists have a responsibility to identify markets affording maximum opportunities. Additionally, they have responsibility in working together with other specialists to ensure success in terms of internal profitability. The extent to which marketing specialists can and do get involved in both these operational aspects depends on the extent to which marketing has been accepted in a company. It is this topic to which we turn next.

THE ADOPTION OF MARKETING IN INSURANCE COMPANIES

Table 1 shows different stages which one American author (Kotler, 1991) has suggested are typical in the slow learning of marketing in US banking. We shall see, later, that the adoption of marketing in British-based insurance companies appears to be following a similar pattern. Probably all British insurers now embrace marketing in the form of advertising, sales promotion and publicity. In companies at this first stage, marketing managers do just that—they are responsible for advertisements, sales promotions and publicity. Similarly, most insurance companies, and especially those which deal direct with customers (as opposed to relying on brokers), have now progressed through this second stage in adopting marketing—the smiling and friendly atmosphere stage—typified by Commercial Union's message: 'We won't make a drama out of a crisis'.

Table 1. Five stages in the adoption of marketing

1. Marketing is advertising, sales promotion, and publicity.
2. Marketing is smiling and a friendly atmosphere.
3. Marketing is innovation.
4. Marketing is positioning.
5. Marketing is marketing analysis, planning and control.

Source: Kotler (1991).

Greatly increased competition from established competitors and also from new entrants is forcing more and more suppliers of insurance to progress to the third stage in adopting marketing, where emphasis falls on developing new products. An internal slogan which typifies this stage is: 'We must innovate in response to market changes, or we shall be overtaken by competitors'. All insurers approached in our study have now reached this stage in adopting marketing.

The next, higher, stage is the use of marketing expertise to position product developments in an optimal way. In this fourth stage, emphasis is on developing offerings (in terms of merchandise and support features) which are preferred above those offered by competitors. In the field of personal general insurance, some British insurers have now become skilled at applying this type of marketing to destabilize and reshape traditional markets. An example is provided by Direct Line, a new supplier established in 1985, which is a wholly owned subsidiary of the Royal Bank of Scotland. Direct Line was one of the first motor insurance companies to cut out the traditional broker middleman to operate direct with customers using telesales techniques. In its first five years of operation it created over 300 000 new policyholders.

The fifth, and highest stage of marketing is when a company has installed effective systems for marketing analysis, planning, implementation and also control. When this has happened, marketing expertise is used to: (1) collect relevant marketing data; (2) analyse it for the purpose of positioning offerings appropriately; and (3) implement product change programmes profitably through planning and control. It is, of course, in this highest stage that marketing experts contribute not only to designing better positioned offerings, but also to their profitable introduction and management.

SAMPLE OF COMPANIES

There are literally hundreds of companies in Britain authorized to transact insurance business. Not all are active in the major areas of insurance. However, rivalry is increasingly tense, especially as a result of completely new entrants into the market. From the population of authorized companies identified from the *Insurance Directory & Year Book* (1992) a convenience sample of ten general insurers and ten life companies based in London and the south-east of England were selected. Both large and small companies were included.

Initial contact was made by letter addressed to the chief executive of the relevant part of each company followed by a telephone call to amplify the objectives of the study. The purpose of the telephone call was to obtain the company's co-operation and to identify the names of appropriate managers to interview. Fourteen general insurers were initially approached, of which 10 agreed to take part in the study. In the case of life companies the numbers were 12 and 10. The names of the co-operating companies are given in Table 2.

The main data were obtained through face-to-face interviews conducted at the relevant operating site. It was not possible to control strictly for the job title of respondents. In some companies the chief executive was interviewed, in others less senior managers were interviewed holding a variety of titles, such as assistant general manager, business development director/manager, product development manager, marketing actuary. All respondents were, however, directly involved in product development decision taking. A tape recorder was used during interviews, with objections being raised by only two respondents to this form of data collection. When objection was raised, written notes were made of the responses. Each face-to-face interview lasted, on average, one-and-a-half hours.

Table 2. Companies which co-operated in the research

Life insurers	General insurers
Barclays Life	Cornhill
Clerical Medical	Eagle Star
Confederation Life	Iron Trades
Colonial Mutual Life	Legal & General
Crown Life	London & Edinburgh
CCL Assurance	Minster
Eagle Star	Norwich Union
Equitable Life	Provincial Insurance
Prudential	Royal Insurance
Manufacturers Life	Sun Alliance

THE FOCUS OF THE STUDY

Prior analysis of theoretical and practical writings in the area of product development led us to focus data collection on five key issues. Because questions were not plucked out of the air, we were able to underpin them with hypotheses built up from the product and service development literature (Cooper and de Brentani, 1991; de Brentani, 1991; Easingwood, 1986; Johne and Snelson, 1990). The questions asked of respondents related to one or more of the following five key issues.

Issue 1   What types of development are currently being pursued? Our hypothesis was that there would be a preference for pursuing low-risk, incremental types of product development.

Issue 2   What are the key activities in the development process during which important decisions are made? Our hypothesis was that it is difficult to identify key activities because development is pursued in an informal and unsystematic manner.

Issue 3   What formal organizational arrangements are in place to handle development activities? Our hypothesis was that insurers do not adopt formal organization structures to deal with the development of new offerings.

Issue 4   What is the contribution made by the marketing specialists? Our hypothesis was that marketing specialists play a minor role in the development of new insurance offerings.

Issue 5   What contribution does top management make? Our hypothesis was that top management fails to take on the role of 'envisioning, energizing and enabling the innovation programme'.

DISCUSSION OF FINDINGS

Data were collected in 1990 and in 1992. The findings for the general insurers are based on personal interviews conducted in 1990 and updated by follow-up telephone interviews in 1992. The data from suppliers of life insurance were collected in personal interviews in 1992. Findings are presented under the headings for each main issue. To respect confidences, responses are not ascribed to individual company sources.

It must be stated at the outset that a common feature shared by all the sample companies (10 general insurers and 10 suppliers of life insurance) was that each was currently undergoing changes in its business operation and orientation. Not surprisingly, these changes were more pronounced in some companies than in others. All companies co-operating in our investigation have now recognized the need to become more market oriented. A marketing manager in a large company offering general insurance explained the background to the current situation as follows:

In the 1980s we just could not cope with business that came to us through overall growth in the market. This has led some people even today to ask: 'Why change to a customer orientation when we have been successful in the past without it?'. What these people can't see, is that past success is no guarantee for future success.

The follow-up interviews with general insurers indicated that there has been increased acceptance of the importance of marketing. It is true that in some companies marketing has become heavily involved in pruning product lines, rather than in adding to them, but both in large and small companies there is now clear evidence of increased responsibilities having been given to marketing specialists for the purpose of exploring and exploiting product development opportunities. Further, in many companies top management is now prepared to involve itself in checking product development progress. These changes are going on now, and so we were not surprised to find control procedures in place in several general insurers which are now far more formal than in 1990.

In 1990 traditionalism and functional specialization were mentioned time and time again by general insurers as barriers to change. The issue was described boldly by the product development controller in a small company providing general insurance:

The main problem has to do with attitude. It's about trying to persuade technical experts, such as underwriters who have traditionally wielded all the clout around here, that their way is not the only way, and certainly not the most effective way for preparing for the future.

Overall, we found the approaches to and systems for managing product change to be more developed in companies offering general insurance. Three general insurers within the sample of 10 have now taken very considerable steps in tightening their product development procedures. In one small company, in which top management involves itself fully, marketing and underwriters now co-operate closely from initial brainstorming sessions for identifying new product opportunities right through to launch. In this company development times have been reduced considerably from approval of an idea to launch.

There was also clear evidence in several general insurers of far more sophisticated approaches to analysing markets. A few companies are making extensive use of marketing maps in which target markets have been identified through careful segmentation analysis. These more sophisticated approaches had in some companies been introduced by consultants, while in others they had been developed internally. Increasing use of project or venture teams was also reported in general insurers, though in a number of companies these were obviously being used by top management as a mechanism to drive changes within and between traditional functional fiefdoms.

In the 10 life insurers we again found a situation of flux. While still predominantly led by the underwriting function, product development is increasingly being influenced by marketing inputs. This is happening as a by-product of strenuous attempts within companies to become more marketing oriented. To effect heightened market orientation new staff have been recruited. In most companies in the sample these new marketing specialists have not, as yet, been able to assume responsibility for driving product development. Instead, they are expected to work closely with underwriters when asked by them to do so, in order to ensure that developments are promoted appropriately on completion. In several companies actuaries involved in product development work have been given the new title of 'marketing actuary', to reflect their widened responsibilities.

Types of developments being pursued

In companies supplying general insurance, as well as those supplying life cover, the predominant types of development currently being undertaken concern the updating of existing products. At its most limited the updating of existing products involves changing aspects of the rating structure or altering the promotional mix. The director of operations and marketing in a small company offering general insurance summarized the situation in 1990 as follows:

Most of our product development is revamping/repackaging of existing products. Half of what we do is pure reaction to competitor's moves. Most of the other half is us trying to steal an edge in the short run. We do devote time and resources for the longer run. That's the futuristic bit—worrying about the sort of products we are going to need in five years' time. Unfortunately, this gets quite low priority, because we have limited resources which tend to get drawn into immediate fire-fighting activities.

A number of factors were suggested as contributing to the predominant emphasis on incremental product developments. First, copying is a low-risk, inexpensive activity. Second, because of the heavy reliance placed on selling though brokers, many companies perceive there to be little room for improving products apart from lowering the price. The frustration of the constraints imposed by selling through brokers was summed up by a marketing manager as follows:

If you sell through intermediaries as we do, you have the problem of having them between you and the end customer all the time. So we often ask ourselves: 'What's the advantage of coming up with something new, when there is always this filter between us and the customer?'

In the constrained circumstances in which companies selling through brokers perceive themselves to be operating, development initiatives frequently focus on targeting more accurately the preferences of specific socio-economic groupings, or types of business customers. A marketing manager expressed this rather neatly by saying: 'Really, anything we do is a spin-off from an existing product range into another market niche'. A product manager for general products went further:

In terms of new lines of business, there are very limited opportunities in the insurance industry. True innovation in terms of a new kind of product are few and far between. Because of this, we concentrate on segmenting the market, rather than segmenting the products.

In 1990 not one respondent in general insurance would admit to us that their company had a regular programme of product development involving both updating existing lines and developing new lines. At that time the emphasis was on *ad hoc* initiatives. No evidence of programmes which involve making fundamental changes to the merchandise content or the support content was found. The situation was particularly marked in small companies, which all emphasized the need to continue to sell through the established broker network.

We found the situation markedly different in 1992. Three general insurers in the sample have now established classical marketing departments staffed predominantly by outsiders. Such departments are headed by a marketing director or manager supported by marketing specialists, especially including product managers. Product managers then typically assume responsibility for product improvement. For more radical product development, use is being made of business development managers whose job is to head teams of specialists from different internal business functions.

As one would expect, there is wide divergence in the way general insurers approach product development, and within the limited sample we cannot claim to have captured the total span. However, whereas in 1990 we found a situation in which reactive product development was the rule, in 1992 there is clear evidence in some companies of a far more systematic approach to progressing product developments. While we did find evidence of monitoring product development systematically in certain life insurers, the trend within these companies appears less advanced.

We must emphasize that our findings in this area need to be rated with caution, especially as far as the larger companies are concerned. In large companies, major initiatives such as selling direct, rather than through an established broker system, are not taken by those charged with day-to-day product improvement. However, despite the fact that our respondents were first and foremost concerned with managing improvements, they did express quite strong views on the subject of more fundamental product change. Indeed, there were marked differences in opinion on whether it was better to focus predominantly on copying competitors, as opposed to becoming more proactive in developing new offerings. Some felt it wasteful to develop new products continuously which could be readily copied. Others argued that leading with new and better offerings on a continuous basis represented the essence of competing successfully in the long term.

In a general insurer, a company which clearly appreciates the advantages afforded by product development, we heard the following statement:

We reflected on what each of our products was offering customers, and decided that the best way to create sustainable competitive edge was through beefing-up the support we provide. Accordingly, we have decided that we are no longer going to be a low cost supplier. We are going to ensure that our customers get better treatment from us than they do from our competitors. We feel that's the way we can differentiate ourselves. Product features can be copied quickly. It's in providing superior services we'll make sure we stay ahead.

It is clear that personnel in this company—a medium-sized one—have adopted a much wider view of product development opportunities. In this company, clearly articulated views exist on how offerings can be improved to stay in tune with changing market preferences. Not only this, but certain officers in this company see that by making radical changes to the way their offerings are delivered to customers, considerably greater shares of business can be captured. At the present time, management in this company is locked into detailed discussions with a range of technical specialists on how this can best be done.

Overall, as far as Issue 1 is concerned, we found that the emphasis was on low-risk, incremental types of product development in all the sample companies. This confirms our hypothesis. In large measure top management is responsible for this skewed approach to product development, which would appear to stem directly from a short-term orientation to investment. More radical product developments require larger and longer-term investment and, typically, involve higher risks, which most top managements approach with utmost caution.

Key activities in the development process

All serious research in the product development area has shown that completing a new offering successfully does not happen instantaneously. Typically, a number of supporting activities need to be undertaken. For example, first there may be a need to sift out ideas for possible new developments against objectives; thereafter, exploratory research may be needed prior to projecting profits and comparing alternatives. Often, it is only then that development work starts in earnest, and even thereafter the new product might not be launched before a test market exercise has been completed.

A large number of development models have been advanced in the area of manufactured products (Booz, Allen and Hamilton, 1982; Cooper, 1988; Crawford, 1987; Johne and Snelson, 1990). Researchers in the area of services development have advanced similar models (Donnelly, Berry and Thompson, 1985; Johnson, Scheuing and Gaida, 1986; Scheuing and Johnson, 1989). Of the services development models the normative model advanced by Scheuing and Johnson (1989), shown in Table 3, is the most comprehensive.

Table 3. Scheuing and Johnson's model of service development

1. Formulation of objectives and strategy
2. Idea generation
3. Idea screening
4. Concept development
5. Concept testing
6. Business analysis
7. Project authorization
8. Service design and testing
9. Process and system design and testing
10. Marketing programme design and testing
11. Personnel training
12. Service testing and pilot run
13. Test marketing
14. Full-scale launch
15. Post-launch review

Source: Scheuing and Johnson (1989).

Many researchers have argued that systematic attention to development tasks contributes to success, or at least to the avoidance of failure. Yet whether development tasks should be attended to in sequential order, as opposed to some being undertaken simultaneously, remains open for debate. Several authors (Dumaine, 1989; Smith and Reinertson, 1991; Takeuchi and Nonaka, 1986), have stressed that while simultaneous or parallel working is wasteful of resources (because some tasks are duplicated), it allows developments to be completed faster. They show, for example, that faster, less efficient development can be profitable, especially in markets in which early adopters are prepared to pay a premium price.

As well as deciding how much parallel working to countenance through teamwork, companies need to decide whether one standard way is appropriate for the different types of offering which can be developed. The issue here is whether different organizational arrangements are needed for completely new offerings as opposed to making improvements to existing offerings. In this respect, in accordance with the contingency approach to management, some analysts have argued that completely new product development is best managed differently from making ongoing improvements (Johne and Snelson, 1990).

Whereas, in 1990, in general insurance companies, there had been limited evidence of the use of formal guidelines for progressing individual developments, we found the situation changed in 1992. Three general insurers have now introduced formal monitoring systems, while in others the merits of so doing are under active discussion at the present time. In life insurers, only very rudimentary systems were in evidence, but several companies are currently actively contemplating changes in this area of their operations.

For the purpose of analysing the systems currently being used, we focused attention on the following five key activities:

(1) planning product changes;
(2) idea exploration;
(3) screening and evaluation;
(4) physical development;
(5) launch.

Our aim was to ascertain how systematically each separate activity is undertaken. This issue is important, for previous research has suggested that systematic attention to key product development tasks is strongly associated with success (Booz, Allen and Hamilton, 1982; Cooper and de Brentani, 1991; Cooper and Kleinschmidt, 1986; Edgett and Jones, 1991; Johne and Snelson, 1990).

As far as planning product changes are concerned there is evidence of increasing attention being paid to this within the context of overall planning systems. In both life and general insurers were found important changes under active consideration. The situation was particularly changed in certain general insurers compared with the situation in 1990. Most life companies and general insurers now undertake what is commonly referred to as 'fundamental reviews of the product portfolio'. Such ongoing monitoring and analysis against broader market opportunities is most commonly conducted annually, either by the corporate planning department or by representatives of marketing.

Responses concerning the second key activity—idea exploration—provided further important insights. A common reply was that there are no really new insurance products and that product development is merely a matter of putting together different policies with a few frills to make them attractive to different market segments. A product manager responsible for general insurance used the following words:

> In insurance terms there are very few new products. So what we tend to find ourselves doing is segmenting the market.

The sentiments behind these words illustrate the limited way in which ideas are often considered. In most of our discussions emphasis was placed predominantly on the merchandise element of the offering, with little or no attention being paid to how this can be supported differently for specific market segments. In the case of companies which sell through brokers, it was not uncommon to find great reliance on these for ideas. However, some life insurers and some suppliers of general insurance are now taking important independent initiatives in reading markets. We found this to be the case predominantly in companies selling direct. A number of such companies are now taking part in joint market research programmes with other suppliers into end-user attitudes and behaviour. As a result, some respondents claimed that they had made some very interesting and surprising discoveries about how existing markets might be reconceptualized and served better.

The third key activity—screening and evaluation—was found, in 1990, in general insurers, to be undertaken in an *ad hoc* fashion. In 1992, in several general insurers, as well as in a few life companies, this activity is now undertaken far more systematically. There is, however, a reluctance on the part of most companies to use explicit formal criteria for evaluating developments. To a large degree this is to be expected when developments are of the incremental, or 'me-too' type, which are commonly undertaken without a formal feasibility study. One respondent explained the reasons for this in racy terms:

> For developments where we are responding to competitive action in the market, the proper routine will often be ignored. In such cases—and it's all too frequent for my liking—we are responding to cries of anxiety from the front line. So we have to make very quick decisions.

In 1990 we found that screening and evaluation criteria were poorly defined in most general insurance companies. When assessment criteria existed their form and content were frequently not shared across the company. In 1992 we found that in several general, as well as in some life companies, it is marketing departments which are making strenuous efforts to rectify this situation.

While there is clear evidence of greater involvement by top management in some companies, there is still widespread non-involvement in screening decisions. We would venture to comment that non-involvement on the part of top management in screening makes a pretty dangerous cocktail with regard to future business prosperity. Under a *laissez-faire* regime, marketing criteria frequently takes second place to financial considerations and also to the level of technical and systems synergy looked for. The dominance of the latter factors can lead to the development of low risk, incremental product improvements. While this can give the illusion of active product development, it can spell long-term disaster if some competitors undertake more radical product developments (Foster, 1986; Gluck and Foster, 1975).

As far as the fourth key activity is concerned—physical development—we found that, while in all traditional insurance companies co-ordination is still undertaken by underwriters, the situation is changing in favour of marketing, or at least to include marketing. In two general insurers we found sophisticated product management software systems in use which enable development tasks to be attended to sequentially. In all companies which adopt a co-ordinated team approach to development, we found that the core team was responsible for physical development, with extra specialists brought in as and when required.

The fifth key activity—launch—was found to be formally and tightly controlled in the majority of life and general insurance companies. Companies typically launch on a national basis because of a widespread belief that test marketing is uneconomic because it gives the game away to competitors. The importance of involving others in the company for gaining commitment was stressed using the following words:

Promotional campaigns are given a high profile so that everyone knows what's happening in advance. A third of what you do in product development is promoting to your own people. If the sales force are not on your side, then it's never going to get into the marketplace successfully.

Overall, as far as Issue 2 is concerned, we are able to confirm the hypothesis that it is, indeed, difficult to identify key activities. Most developments are still pursued in an informal and unsystematic manner. Yet, there are clear indications that this situation is changing. More systematic development processes and more rigorous methods for monitoring progress are currently being introduced by consultants in a number of companies. In other companies staff with experience of marketing fast-moving consumer goods have been recruited for assisting in this area.

Formal organizational arrangements

Companies have widely differing organizational mechanisms at their disposal for developing offerings. A commonly used method is to ascribe responsibility for product development to product managers. However, as many companies have found to their cost, these managers are usually so busy fighting fires with present products, that they have little time for new products. To overcome this problem, some companies have created permanent new product managers. New product committees may also be used as semi-permanent organizational devices to review and approve proposals. While committees serve an important co-ordinating role, they can seriously slow down decision making, especially when departmental representatives seek to preserve sectional interest, rather than focusing on exploiting market opportunities fast. Despite their disadvantages, we found committees to be the predominant organizational mechanism for progressing developments in both life and general insurance companies.

To overcome problems associated with subordinating functional interests to business interests, some companies have established interdisciplinary new venture teams. Their purpose is to force important developments through the bureaucracy. We found evidence of such new venture teams in both life and non-life companies, but frequently their remit was wider than product development. In some companies their purpose included process innovation. We found this to be the case particularly in companies in which top management preferred to delegate responsibility for innovation.

We found no real evidence of new-style organizational arrangements, such as self-managing teams. One life company is currently going through the traumas of introducing matrix-based structures which simultaneously accommodate specialist functional inputs, geographical sales and distribution territories, as well as target markets. Overall, however, the picture remains one of functional structures built on rigid hierarchical lines of control.

When one considers the dominant culture of the companies in the sample, and the types of developments most frequently undertaken (improvements as opposed to completely new offerings), it is not surprising that terms such as 'product champion' were but rarely heard. In the majority of companies in the sample, changing the offering was seen as a process requiring a methodical and routine approach. Once the broad parameters had been agreed between underwriting and marketing, individuals were drawn in to contribute on the basis of their position and specialist skills, rather than any distinct personal qualities such as enthusiasm or creativity. This was stressed by the business development manager in a large company:

I will use the systems manager and underwriting manager, the reason being that if they are going to run their own subgroups, then they need to have the authority to pull that subgroup together and make it work. Therefore, it's not really a team brought together for its expertise, it's a "power team" which can make things happen and get the job done.

Our findings overlap with those of Easingwood (1986) who found that few service suppliers adopt radical organizational structures, because it is comparatively rare for them to be involved in the development of really new offerings. Overall, as far as Issue 3 is concerned, our hypothesis about the lack of formal organizational arrangements was not supported by the findings. In our sample a clear presence emerged in favour of managing developments through permanent new product committees comprising a mix of functional specialists.

Contributions by marketing specialists

The traditional skill base of insurance companies has been underwriting. In the past it has been excellence in underwriting as well as investment in expertise which has been the key to sustained profitability. As has already been stressed, in almost all companies underwriters retain their traditional power as far as initiating product development is concerned. This has serious implications for the types of development which are being undertaken, or perhaps put more accurately: the types which are not being undertaken.

In large part, the failure to envisage more radical amendments to the offer is a direct result of poor market information usage. In small companies, in particular, marketing information systems and the use of formal market research is still underdeveloped. The corporate planning manager of a small general insurance company explained the situation in the following way:

We are in the early stages of using market research. This is an innovation in itself. In the past we tended to design products based on what we thought customers need, rather than finding out what they really want.

The marketing actuary of a medium-sized life company stated:

Our understanding of the market basically comes from conventions and meetings that we go to within the industry, and we do receive information regularly from the insurance press.

It would be inaccurate to give the impression that all companies lack formal market research information. At least one life company in the sample has now established a strong department dedicated solely to collecting and disseminating market research information internally. In this company extensive use is made of salesforce feedback. As far as salesforce feedback is concerned, it is again dangerous to generalize. In some companies marketing and sales co-operated actively in identifying opportunities for new products, in others there is enmity between 'newfangled' marketing and old-established sales.

Overall, as far as Issue 4 is concerned, our hypothesis concerning the role played by marketing specialists is not supported. Marketing specialists were found to make increasing contributions to product development in many life insurers and in general insurance companies, even if they did not take the leading role. Unfortunately, marketing expertise is not being used to its full effect. Often, marketing's contribution is restricted to merchandise amendments and promotional amendments aimed at particular market segments. In the absence of greater demands from top management for contributions aimed at exploiting market potentials more purposefully, it is unlikely that full use will be made of the marketing expertise which is now in place.

Contributions by top management

Our hypothesis concerning top management involvement was supported by the findings. We found such involvement low in the case of the predominant type of development undertaken—product improvements. As a general rule, this type of product development is left to underwriters or product managers to get on with as part of their normal duties.

We must emphasize, however, that our investigation concentrated on updating offerings, rather than new offering development. It may be that top management is more closely involved in completely new developments, which may in some companies be pursued through separate organizational mechanisms, such as new business development departments. The extent to which this is the case requires further research.

It was stressed to us by several respondents that when aims were articulated by top management, these are typically expressed in terms of sales targets over what had been achieved in the past. The issue was highlighted by a new product manager in a life company as follows:

Our corporate strategy is based on sales projections. We work backwards from these. Our task becomes one of reflecting on the type of new products needed to meet particular targets. Our strategy, therefore, is grounded in the past rather than in the future.

As far as we were able to judge, few top managers in the companies we sampled, provide the sort of top management support that Tushman and Nadler (1986) speak of in 'envisioning, energizing and enabling' an innovation programme. Hence, as we have indicated, initiatives are most commonly left to technical specialists. Unfortunately, mainly because of the lack of interest and direct involvement by top management, marketing specialists who get involved in the later stages of product development are not able to lead in suggesting ways to which market opportunities might be exploited to the full. This problem is particularly acute in companies—the vast majority—in which underwriters and systems specialists continue to have a dominating influence over the types of products to be developed.

DISCUSSION

It has been argued that the financial loss from failed product development in financial services is low (Davison, Watkins and Wright, 1989). However, such a suggestion assumes that development costs can be ascertained accurately. Although not specifically commented on in this article, many respondents stressed difficulties in accurately attributing costs to products, let alone to specific product developments. We can, therefore, confidently assume that the true costs of managerial time wasted on less than successful product development is rarely known precisely.

During the 1980s many insurance companies in the UK enjoyed high returns on capital as a result of buoyant equity and property markets. In many cases, investment gains offset any insurance losses handsomely, meaning that sometimes insufficient attention was paid to operating efficiencies. The early 1990s have seen a dramatic fall in returns on capital. Further, the UK equity market is no longer buoyant and property prices have also declined. With anticipated new competition from abroad following the Single European Market in 1993, all insurance companies now operate in a far more abrasive competitive climate. Today, operating costs do matter, and far greater importance is attached to efficient product development.

In order to understand the nature of the changes now under way in companies, it is necessary to look behind the trappings for evidence of substantive changes. A critical factor determining the nature of change in organizations is top management. On the basis of the data collected it appears that top insurance management still remains reluctant to articulate strategies which spell out clearly to organizational members expectations as far as product development is concerned. In the absence of clearly communicated competitive game plans it is questionable whether the grafting on of efficient product development practices from other industries will achieve anything but limited success. Our interviews indicated that in many companies individuals are now well aware of the type of changes needed. But, what is not at all clear is the order in which changes can best be introduced, and the way in which changes can best be managed within environments still dominated by technical experts and controlled on a hierarchical basis.

CONCLUSIONS

The increasing competitiveness of the insurance marketplace now requires companies to change their offerings more frequently than before. Ideally, companies will need to adopt both a proactive and an innovative approach to developing new products. This will entail a change of emphasis away from exploiting asset strengths to exploiting market opportunities. It will almost certainly require assets to be used differently than before. This type of change—to higher risk and higher investment activities—will require emphatic support from top management. Further, the successful implementation of innovative strategies will almost certainly require far more formalized systems for control purposes.

In many companies, particularly in the case of new entrants like banks, the quest for sustainable competitive advantage will centre on developing offerings which cannot readily be copied in their entirety. Quinn (1985) has argued that innovative companies anchor their visions of what is possible to the practical realities of the marketplace and ensure that this is achieved through two main mechanisms. First, a strong market orientation at the very top of the company. Second, an organization which forces purposeful interaction between technical and marketing specialists. While technical systems problems are likely to continue to feature strongly in insurance product development, greatest long-term payoff is likely to result from innovative interpretations of market opportunities (Easingwood and Mahajan, 1989). Achieving these types of changes will require insurers to make increasingly challenging alterations to their operations.

REFERENCES

Booz, Allen and Hamilton (1982) *New Products Management for the 1980s*, Booz, Allen and Hamilton, New York, NY.

Cooper, R. G. (1988) 'The New Product Process: A Decision Guide for Management', *Journal of Marketing Management*, **3** (3): 238–255.

Cooper, R. G. and Kleinschmidt, E.J. (1986) 'An investigation into the New Product Process: Steps, Deficiencies and Impact', *Journal of Product Innovation Management*, **3**: 71–85.

Cooper, R. G. and de Brentani, U. (1991) 'New Industrial Financial Services: What Distinguishes the Winners', *Journal of Product Innovation Management*, **7** (2): 75–90.

Crawford, C. M. (1987) *New Products Management*, Irwin, Homewood, IL.

Davison, H., Watkins, T. and Wright, M. (1989) 'Developing New Personal Financial Products— Some Evidence on the Role of Market Research', *International Journal of Bank Marketing*, **7** (1): 8–15.

de Brentani, U. (1991) 'Success Factors in Developing New Business Services', *European Journal of Marketing*, **25** (2): 33–59.

de Bruicker, F. S. and Summe, G. L. (1985) 'Make Sure Your Customers Keep Coming Back', *Harvard Business Review*, **63** (1): 92–98.

Donnelly, J. H., Berry, L. L. and Thompson, T. W. (1985) *Marketing Financial Services*, Irwin, Homewood, IL.

Dumaine, B. (1989) 'How Managers Can Succeed through Speed', *Fortune*, **13** (February) 30–35.

Easingwood, C. J. (1986) 'New Product Development for Service Companies', *Journal of Product Innovation Management*, **4**: 264–275.

Easingwood, C. J. and Mahajan, V. (1989) 'Positioning of Financial Services for Competitive Advantage', *Journal of Product Innovation Management*, **6**: 207–219.

Edgett, S. and Jones, S. (1991) 'New Product Development in the Financial Service Industry: A Case Study', *Journal of Marketing Management*, **7**: 271–284.

Foster, R. N. (1986) *Innovation: The Attacker's Advantage*, Macmillan, London.

Gluck, F. W. and Foster, R. N. (1975) 'Managing Technological Change: A Box of Cigars for Brad', *Harvard Business Review*, **53** (5): 139–150.

Insurance Directory & Year Book (1992), I and III, Buckley Press Ltd, London.

Johne, F. A. (1992) 'New Style Product Development', *Management Decision*, **30** (2): 8–11.

Johne, A. and Snelson, P. (1990) *Successful Product Development: Lessons from American and British Firms*, Basil Blackwell, Oxford.

Johnson, S. C., Scheuing, E. E. and Gaida, K. A. (1986) *Profitable Service Marketing*, Irwin, Homewood, IL.

Kotler, P. (1991) *Marketing Management: Analysis, Planning, Implementation and Control*, Prentice-Hall, Englewood Cliffs, NJ.

McKenna, R. (1991) 'Marketing Is Everything', *Harvard Business Review*, **91**(1): 65–79.

Mathur, S. S. (1992) 'Talking Straight about Competitive Strategy', *Journal of Marketing Management*, **8**: 199–217.

Peters, T. (1990) 'Get Innovative or Get Dead'. *California Management Review*, **33**(1): 9–36.

Quinn, J. B. (1985) 'Managing Innovation: Controlled Chaos', *Harvard Business Review*, **63**(3): 73–84.

Quinn, J. B., Doorley, T. L. and Paquette, P. C. (1900) 'Beyond Products: Service-based Strategy', *Harvard Business Review*, **90**(2): 58–67.

Scheuing, E. D. and Johnson, E. M. (1989) 'A Proposed Model for New Service Development', *Journal of Services Marketing*, **3**(2): 25–34.

Smith, P. G. and Reinertson, D. G. (1991) *Developing Products in Half the Time*, Van Nostrand Reinhold, New York, NY.

Takeuchi, H. and Nonaka, I. (1986) 'The New Product Development Game', *Harvard Business Review*, **64**(1): 137–146.

Tushman, M. L. and Nadler, D. A. (1986) 'Organizing for Innovation', *California Management Review*, **28**(3): 74–92.

Part VII

Organizational Interfaces in New Product Development

CONTENTS

3469PARTS   00   000001254   0213   00111

Introduction to Part VII

Susan Hart

The readings in the volume thus far have generally related to the *activities* in the process of new product development. These activities implicate employees from several different functional specialisms within the company. Equally, the success articles indicate that the effective integration of these functional specialisms is a prerequisite for successful new product development. Integration is one factor in organizing for successful innovation. Other factors include the overall culture of the company and how it encourages the acceptance of change, the ability to learn constantly, the overall structure of the organization. Issues such as these remind the reader of how the subject of NPD is closely linked with wider managerial issues of strategy, structure, human resources management as well as the technical and marketing inputs necessary to develop new products. Three articles have been selected for this final section of the book, which try to reflect this variety of issues tangential and central to the study and understanding of innovation. The first, by Tushman and Nadler (1986) (Reading 26) begins by illustrating how the nature of innovation changes over time and takes place within the context of the need to manage current businesses. The optimal structures for this variety may be many, encapsulating the management of stability without sacrificing the ability to experiment and learn. Indeed the authors argue that success over an extended period of time tends to increase organizational complexity and eclipses the ability to learn. They build a 'congruence model of organizational behaviour' based on four fundamental components: the task, the individuals, the organizational arrangements and the informal organization. Thus, where the task is organizing for today's business, the four components become increasingly contingent, engendering the risk of being unable to change. Where the task is organizing for tomorrow's business, a number of factors related to individuals, the informal organization and organizational arrangements are listed and explained. The factors encapsulated by these three headings are wide ranging, from recruitment and socialization practices, through alternative innovation mechanisms to the values, norms and reward structures within the company. The article is important because it addresses the hierarchical interfaces in NPD and it shows how the creativity of any particular NP project will depend on a wide range of organizational factors that have little to do with the specifics of the project itself.

The article by Gupta, Raj and Wilemon (Reading 27) backs up this last point, based on research. Although their focus is how to manage the interface between marketing and R&D—an interface widely accepted as critical in NPD—they situate this interface within a broader context of wider organizational factors such as the wider structure and senior management support. Based on interviews with 109 marketing and 107 R&D directors involved in NPD, the authors measured the levels of integration between marketing and R&D during the innovation process. This examination allowed them to classify the companies into two groups, those with high levels of marketing–R&D integration (39) and those with low levels of integration. They then compared these groups on four sets of issues: the quality of R&D–marketing relations; the organizational structure; support from senior management and the structures used for NPD. The most significant results were found in the quality of R&D–marketing relations and support for senior management.

The third and final paper in this part, by Larson and Gobeli (Reading 28), focuses on measuring the success of different approaches to new product project management structure. They begin the article with a review of issues relating to project management, from which it is quite clear that research has been widely inconclusive regarding the most appropriate form of structure for R&D projects. The authors argue that this confusion is largely as a result of the failure to incorporate relevant contextual factors such as the complexity of the project and resources into the research design. In their study of 547 individuals, listed in the Canadian and American Project Management Institute, they found that projects using a traditional functional organization had the lowest level of success followed by those using a functional matrix (where a project manager co-ordinates the project, but where the functional managers are 'in charge'). Projects using other forms of structures where functional managers do not dominate in terms of responsibility and authority were more successful. Of the contextual variables the authors studied, the most important influence was the extent to which objectives were clearly defined.

This paper is an interesting contribution on a number of counts. First, its perspective is slightly different from the 'business and marketing' articles in the volume, in that the sample surveyed were project managers. Second, it is concerned with a popular, if somewhat berated form of management, namely matrix management. Third, its findings do not support the view that matrix management structures are ineffective, thus contradicting the view popularized by Peters and Waterman. Fourth, the findings dispute the view that 'project teams' or 'task forces' are the most effective vehicles for product development. This contrasts, to some extent, with the view of Gupta, Raj and Wilemon, who suggest that venture teams are the most effective method of achieving R&D–marketing integration. The two studies, however, are measuring different phenomena; Larson and Gobeli relate project organization to success measures while Gupta, Raj and Wilemon relate project organization to achievement of R&D–marketing integration.

The three articles included in this part provide some insight into the many and complex issues involved in organizing for new product development. In this sub-area above all, the richness of knowledge is due to the research work being carried out in a number of disciplines. Future research in the topic should attempt to get away from the 'base' discipline of the researcher and consolidate knowledge across the relevant academic fields and functional areas.

26

Organizing for Innovation

Michael Tushman and David Nadler

In today's business environment, there is no executive task more vital and demanding than the sustained management of innovation and change. It sometimes seems that every aspect of business is in a state of flux—technology, government regulation, global competition. These rapid changes in the marketplace make it increasingly difficult, and essential, for business to think in terms of the future, to constantly anticipate tomorrow's definition of value—the right mix of quality, service, product characteristics and price. To compete in this ever-changing environment, companies must create new products, services and processes; to dominate, they must adopt innovation as a way of corporate life.

Sustained innovation is both important and tremendously difficult. Consider these brief examples:

- For more than 30 years General Radio dominated the market for electronic test equipment. While new competitors took advantage of computers, systems technology and innovative approaches to working with customers, General Radio remained committed to the technologies and marketing practices that it knew best. During the 1960s, market share and profits declined. It took a complete transformation of the organization, driven by mostly new managers, to bring about product, market and production innovations.

- Technicon Corporation created the automated clinical diagnostic instrument industry. Technicon initially prospered by successfully producing a number of product innovations based on their expertise in hydraulics technologies. While Technicon led with product innovation, other firms entered the market leading with process innovation (i.e. cost and quality) and with a broadened view of the clinical market. Technicon's response to the external threat was increased reliance on its old winning formula. Market share and relative performance declined. It was not until Technicon was acquired by Revlon that the organization was able to successfully develop product, process and market innovation.

- Biogen is known world-wide as an organization doing excellent basic research in genetic engineering. While science flourishes at Biogen, marketing and product development have been ignored. Nobel laureate Walter Gilbert no longer runs Biogen. A new management team has been brought in to create the conditions for enhanced product, market and process innovation.

The common theme is obvious: in all three cases, once highly innovative organizations became trapped by their own success. These examples are not unique. In one industry after another, the same factors that create a successful innovative company often plant the seeds of complacency and failure as competitive conditions change.

Nevertheless, many exceptional firms have demonstrated that sustained innovation, though difficult, is certainly attainable. Large corporations (such as IBM, 3M, Citicorp, American Airlines, GE, Merck and Philip Morris) as well as smaller firms (such as Rolm, Wang, Charles River Breeding Labs, Federal Express and Dunkin' Donuts) have been highly innovative over long periods. They have simultaneously managed the dual challenges of innovating for the markets of both the present and the future.

What are the organizational factors which enhance innovation? The most innovative organizations are highly effective learning systems. Organizations that can be self-critical—and can learn to keep improving on today's work while aggressively preparing for tomorrow's—will be more successful than those organizations that evolve towards greater stability and complacency. Sustained innovation, somewhat paradoxically, requires both stability and change: stability permits scale economies and incremental learning, while change and experimentation are necessary for advances in products, processes and technologies.

TYPES OF INNOVATION

Innovation is the creation of any product, service, or process which is new to a business unit. While innovation is often associated with major product or process advances (e.g. xerography, transistors, float glass), the vast majority of successful innovations are based on the cumulative effect of incremental change in products and processes, or in the creative combination of existing techniques, ideas or methods. Innovation is not just R&D; just as important are marketing, sales and production. Effective innovation requires the synthesis of market needs with technological possibility and manufacturing capabilities.

At the most basic level, there are two kinds of innovation: *product innovation*, or changes in the product a company makes or the service it provides; and *process innovation*, a change in the way a product is made or the service provided. Within each of these two categories, there are three degrees of innovation—incremental, synthetic and discontinuous (see Figure 1). Some illustrations help clarify these differences.

Product innovation

Most product innovations are *incremental* changes. They provide added features, new versions or extensions to an otherwise standard product line. Obviously, such innovations occur all the time, and large numbers of incremental innovations related to customer requirements can add up to a significant competitive advantage.

A second type of product innovation, *synthetic*, involves the combination of existing

	Product	Process	
Incremental	Incremental product change	Learning by doing	Small
Synthetic	Dominant designs: DC-3, Boeing 707, IBM 360	Major process improvements	↑
Discontinuous	Vacuum tubes → Transistor Piston → Jet Steam → Diesel locomotives	Individual wafer → Planar process	↓
		Continuous grinding and polishing → float glass	Substantial learning requirements

Figure 1. Types of Innovation

ideas or technologies in creative ways to create significantly new products. For example, the DC–3 incorporated existing airplane innovations which, together, resulted in a single airplane which combined speed, efficiency and size. Similarly, the 707 and 747 and Merrill Lynch's Cash Management Account were important synthetic product innovations which dominated their respective industries. These product innovations didn't require any new technology. Rather, each represented a creative combination of existing technology which, when linked with marketing and production skill, resulted in a product which set the standard in its product class—until the next major product innovation came along.

The third category, *discontinuous* product innovations, involves the development or application of significant new technologies or ideas. Examples include the shift from piston airplanes to jets, the change from steam to diesel locomotives, or the move from core to semiconductor memory. These major innovations required new skills, processes and systems throughout the organization. Each required wholesale changes in those firms moving from old to new product technologies.

As innovation moves from incremental to discontinuous, there are higher risks and greater uncertainty. It becomes increasingly important for organizations to function as effective learning systems, benefiting from both failure and success.

Process innovation

Process innovations change the way products and services are made or delivered. Process innovation may be invisible to the user except through changes in the cost or quality of the product.

As in product innovation, most process innovations are *incremental* improvements which result in lowered costs, higher quality, or both. Learning curve efficiencies and learning-by-doing produces small process innovations that incrementally improve upon existing production processes.

Synthetic process innovations involve sharp increases in size, volume or capacity of well-known production processes. For example, the rotary kiln in cement manufacturing or Owens' process in glassware production were significant innovations, but they were basically larger, faster and more efficient versions of well-known existing processes.

Discontinuous process innovations are totally new ways of producing products or services. For example, the float-glass process in glass manufacturing, planar processes in semiconductors and the use of robots in auto plants are fundamentally different ways of making established products. Major process innovations reduce costs and increase the quality of the product or service, but they require new skills, new ways of organizing and, frequently, new ways of managing. As with product innovation, the greater the degree of process change, the greater the uncertainty and the greater the required organizational learning.

The strategic role of product and process innovation

Both product and process innovation are important, yet their relative importance changes over time. Studies in multiple industries find predictable patterns in the amount and degree of innovation over the product life cycle (see Figure 2). In the introductory stage, there is a substantial amount of product innovation as several forms of the same product compete for dominance. For example, during the early stages of the automobile industry, at least four automobile types (internal combustion, battery, wood and steam-powered) competed for the relatively small market. This period of product competition leads to the emergence of a dominant design, representing industry standardization in the product's basic configuration and characteristics. For example, the DC-3, IBM 360, Smith Model 5 typewriter, the Fordson tractor and VHS design in video cassette recorders all represent dominant designs which shaped the evolution of their respective product classes for years.

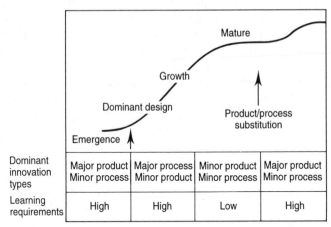

Figure 2. Types of Innovation Over Product Life Cycle.

In the next stage, major product variation gives way to competition based on price, quality and segmentation—in other words, process innovation rather than product innovation. Thus, major process innovation, combined with incremental product innovation, allows firms to enhance the product and open the market to a more diverse customer base. In the mid-1970s, for example, personal computers were sold mainly to customers with substantial computer expertise; standardization of the Apple and IBM PCs permitted the development of customized software and services for small businesses, homes and schools.

During the mature stage of a product life cycle, this pattern of incremental product and major process innovation continues until the product and its associated production processes are so intertwined that only incremental product and process innovation are possible. This period can be very profitable, since small changes in the product or processes can lead to significantly decreased costs or higher quality. The mature phase of product life cycle, with its emphasis on incremental innovation, lasts until some external shock such as deregulation, technological change or foreign competition triggers a new wave of major product innovation. For example, Ford's Model T was enormously profitable until fully-enclosed cars were made possible by advances in steel. Thus, product innovation initiated by General Motors forced Ford to reinitiate major product and, in turn, major process innovations.

Consequently, innovation is a complex and uncertain endeavour which shifts over time and requires the close collaboration of R&D, marketing, sales and production. Effective organizations create conditions that allow today's work to be done well while simultaneously generating tomorrow's innovations. The challenge is to optimize today's work while producing the uncertainty and chaos so essential to tomorrow's innovation. Only those organizations which can manage stability and, at the same time, nurture the capacity to experiment and learn will be able to master both product and process innovation. Those organizations that get stuck in a single mode of operation will be incapable of producing different kinds of innovation as product life cycles evolve.

ORGANIZING FOR TODAY'S WORK

This formula for innovation—managing for today while building the infrastructure for tomorrow—involves a basic dilemma: building the systems and processes for the short run often undercuts the innovative process.

The general manager has two basic tasks. The first task is strategy formulation: making fundamental decisions about markets, products and competitive basis in the context of a larger environment, a set of resources, and organizational history. The second task is organizing. This involves creating, building and maintaining the organization—a mechanism which transforms strategy into output.

One way of thinking about organizing is that there are four major components to any organization:

- *task*: the basic work to be done;
- *individuals*: the members of the organization;
- *organizational arrangements*: the formal structures and processes created to get individuals to perform tasks;
- *informal organization*: the unwritten, constantly evolving arrangements—including 'culture'—which define how things get done.

In the short to medium term, organizational effectiveness is greatest when two conditions are met. First, the four components are designed and managed so that they are congruent; in other words, they fit well together. Second, the pattern of congruence of the four components matches the basic requirements of the strategy.[1] (See Figure 3.)

When strategy fits environmental conditions, congruence is associated with

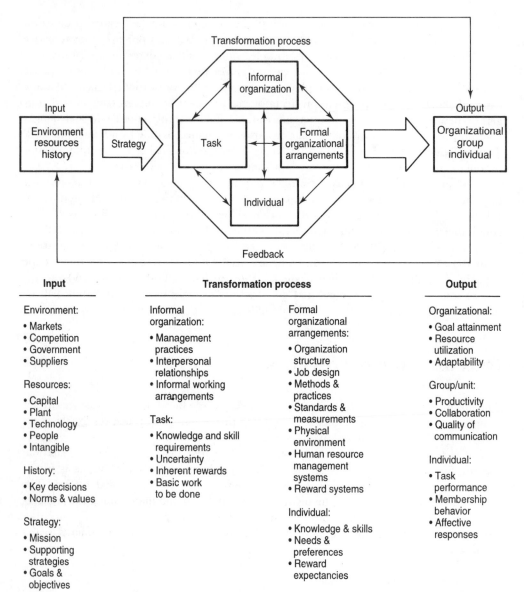

Figure 3. A Congruence Model of Organizational Behaviour. (*Source*: Nadler and Tushman, 1979.)

organizational effectiveness. Since organizations are never totally congruent, part of management's job is to initiate incremental changes to more fine-tune the organization. Incremental change is relatively easy to implement and builds increasing consistency among strategy, structure, people and processes. Increasing congruence, however, can be a double-edged sword. As organizations grow and become more successful, they develop internal pressures for stability. Organizational structures and systems become so interlinked that they allow only compatible changes. Further, over time, employees develop habits; patterned behaviors begin to take on values (e.g. 'service is our number one goal') and employees develop a sense of competence in knowing how to get work done within the system. These reinforcing norms, values and patterns of behavior contribute to increased organizational stability and, over time, to a sense of organizational history epitomized by common stories, heroes and standards.

This organizational momentum is profoundly functional as long as the organization's strategy is appropriate. At Technicon, Biogen and General Radio, the culture, structure and systems, and associated internal momentum were critical to each organization's success. However, when a new strategy is called for, this momentum cuts the other way. The organizational history—which can be a source of tradition, precedent and pride— can also be an obstacle to alert problem solving and organizational learning. When faced with an environmental threat, highly inertial organizations either may not register the threat due to organizational complacency and/or stunted external vigilance (e.g. the automobile or steel industries) or if the threat is recognized, the response, very often, is more rigid conformity to the status quo and an increased commitment to keep doing 'what we do best'. For example, when faced with a technological threat, dominant firms frequently have responded with even greater reliance on the obsolete technology (e.g. telegraph/telephone; vacuum tube/transistor; core memory/semiconductor memory). A paradoxical result of long periods of success may be increased organizational complacency and a stunted ability to learn.

To summarize, long periods of success can easily result in organizational complacency and tunnel vision: the longer the success lasts, the greater the internal forces for stability, and the less the system is able to learn and innovate. This pattern is accentuated in business units that dominate a product class (for example, Polaroid or Caterpillar), in historically regulated organizations (AT&T, GTE or financial service firms) or in organizations that have been traditionally shielded from competition (universities, not-for-profit organizations and government agencies).

ORGANIZING FOR TOMORROW'S WORK

Successful organizations innovate for today as well as for tomorrow. Managing this duality is an immensely difficult task. Each company described in our previous examples was a once-innovative firm which had become trapped by its own success. Put in the context of our organizational model, congruence and internal consistency, taken to extremes, diminished learning and discouraged major innovation. But firms such as 3M, Lilly, IBM and Citibank manage to produce for the short run while keeping close to customers, competitors, technologies and internal competence. This sensitivity to external opportunities and internal possibilities provides the stimulus for organizational learning and sustained innovation.

The most innovative organizations are effective learning systems; they maximize both their ability to acquire information about customers, competitors and technology, and their ability to process that information. They gather diverse input and involve multiple actors in processing these data. While costly, chaotic and potentially disruptive, this process of generating ideas and solving problems provides the foundation for tomorrow's innovation.

What are the key elements of designing for tomorrow's work? Research on innovative organizations has begun to shed some light on this question.[2] Using our organizational model, we can identify some approaches and practices related to the major components (Individual, Organization Arrangements and Informal Organization) that can be used to manage a new Task, preparing for tomorrow's work (see Figure 4).

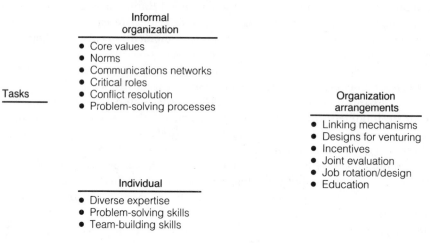

Figure 4. Critical Factors in Managing Innovation.

Individuals

Because innovation requires multiple disciplines and in depth expertise, management's challenge is to hire, train and develop a set of individuals with diverse skills and abilities, and the capacity to innovate. But in-depth and diverse expertise is not sufficient. Because organizational learning and innovation is a group and intergroup phenomenon, individual contributors rarely produce the creative ideas or solutions required for complex or discontinuous innovation. Thus, strong individual specialization must be bolstered by skills in problem solving, communication, conflict resolution and team building. Those skills which broaden an individual's ability to communicate with other professionals and to appreciate multiple perspectives can be developed in the organization through recruitment, training and socialization practices. For example, IBM managers must spend 40 hours per year on managerial education. This programme, which gathers individuals from different disciplines and/or divisions for up to three weeks, continually reinforces the importance of communication, collaboration and problem solving.

The general manager has to build a top team to help provide direction, energy and enthusiasm for the organization. These are the role models who create the conditions for learning and innovation throughout the organization. This senior team needs skills and abilities which match environmental demands; it requires individuals who are respected for their disciplinary competence, and who are well-linked to external sources of information and expertise. This senior team not only manages for today, but is alert to external opportunities and threats. As competitive conditions change, so too must composition of the executive team.

Group problem-solving skills are particularly important if the senior team is to take advantage of its collective expertise to develop and communicate its vision of organizational objectives and core values. This executive team needs to develop internal processes that work against both the complacency so common in dominant organizations and the 'group-think' (i.e. stunted problem solving) that often accompanies crisis conditions. The tasks of the general manager are to build a top team that has the required functional expertise and to develop the group's problem-solving processes so that it can effectively manage both today's work and tomorrow's innovation.

Formal organizational arrangements

Formal organizational arrangements provide structures, systems, and procedures which direct and motivate behaviour. Consequently, these arrangements exert an important influence on organizational learning and innovation. Formal organizational arrangements include the following key elements:

Formal linking mechanisms

The choice of basic organization form (e.g. product, market, functional, geographic) focuses resources on critical strategic contingencies. No single organization form is inherently more conducive to innovation than the next: each can either stimulate or retard innovation. Whatever the basic form chosen, organizations must develop formal internal linking mechanisms, which are important vehicles for creativity and innovation. These links—bridges connecting disparate functions—encourage collaboration and problem solving throughout the organization. For example:

- *Teams, committees or task forces* bring together individuals from diverse areas to work on common opportunities or problems. At Lilly Research, for example, where the laboratory was organized by disciplines, research teams organized by therapeutic area pooled the expertise of scientists and managers from different disciplines. At Xerox, an innovation board brought a diverse group of marketing, production and R&D executives together to evaluate and provide early funding for corporate ventures.
- *Project managers* play a formal linking role which brings a general management perspective deep in the organization. A project manager works to achieve integration and coordination for new product and/or process development.
- *Formal meetings* provide a regularly scheduled setting for individuals from different areas to share information and trade ideas. These meetings also have the added benefit of building informal relationships which further facilitate cross-organization problem solving and collaboration. For example, NCR has 'show and tell' meetings in which R&D, marketing, and manufacturing individuals unveil their latest ideas. At Union Carbide's product fairs, the various divisions present new products and ideas to each other. At Tetra-Pak, cross-functional teams regularly visit customers and then return to generate new product/process ideas.

Organization designs for venturing and entrepreneurship

Linking mechanisms are most effective when the nature of required learning and innovation is relatively small. When major innovation is required, working across the existing organizational structure may not be effective. A series of organization forms, all outside the core organization, can stimulate major corporate innovation. These major innovation forms include venture capital, joint ventures, licensing, acquisition, internal venturing and independent business units. Some of these forms are much more closely tied to the core organization than others; venture capital, for example, is the most distant form of venturing in that it only provides a window on new technologies and markets, while internal venturing builds on in-house expertise.

The more dissimilar the required technology or markets, the greater the required organizational learning and the greater the use of the more independent venture forms. When both required technology and markets are unfamiliar, the most appropriate vehicles might be licensing, joint ventures or venture capital. On the other hand, when organizations want to take advantage of internal expertise yet still produce major innovation, corporate venturing or independent business units may be most effective.

Independent business units or corporate venture units are separated from the core organization. These units are small and made up of individuals from all important disciplines and functions. These teams tend to be self-selected, and operate as independent ventures. Their business plans may be evaluated by a board of directors made up of corporate executives who have some interest in the venture; they act as venture capitalists, providing funding and overall review. The venture teams are not evaluated by traditional corporate yardsticks (e.g. profit, ROA), but rather on the basis of criteria more relevant to ventures—growth in sales or market share, for example. Similarly, the entrepreneur's compensation is pegged to performance against long-term targets and may involve stock or paper ownership in the new venture. The basic idea is to build in risk/return relationships that are similar to those encountered by outside entrepreneurs.

Corporate ventures are vehicles to marshall dedicated resources for major new products and/or process development. These entrepreneurial units can move rapidly and get quick feedback from the market. Corporate venturing and independent business units are important vehicles for organizational learning. These high-risk/high-return organizational experiments may fail nine times out of ten. Yet, they are relatively low-cost ventures and, when they fail, provide new information about technologies and markets. Further, these successes can be highly profitable and strategically important for the firm in the long run (e.g. IBM's PC business or Dupont's Nylon venture in the 1930s). Those ventures that succeed are either folded into existing divisions (e.g. IBM's PC independent business unit) or set up as distinct divisions. IBM, 3M, Dupont, Tektronix and Control Data, among others, have had considerable success with venture units.

Incentives

Incentives and rewards have a major impact on individual and group behavior. Organizations get what they reward. If organizations only measure and reward short-term performance, or if everyone is rewarded equally, then innovation suffers. To encourage innovation, organizations must base rewards on actual performance and make innovation an important dimension of individual and group performance. Bonuses, stock options, salaries and promotions can be linked to innovation and new product/process development. For example, at Biogen, as long as scientists are evaluated solely on the quality of their pure science and marketing people strictly on the basis of sales, the firm will never enjoy sustained innovation and collaboration from these critical groups.

Management can bolster formal incentives with special recognition and rewards for particularly innovative employees. For example, the Watson awards at IBM or innovation prizes at H-P and 3M provide special status to innovative individuals and teams. At Intel, highly innovative teams may go to trade shows where their products are introduced. Formal and informal rewards are an important managerial lever to stimulate innovation. Innovative individuals and groups can clearly see the benefits of innovation; non-innovators can just as easily see the consequences of clinging to the status quo.

Joint evaluation, staffing and appraisal

As innovation necessarily involves individuals from different disciplines and departments, management can use joint problem-solving teams to maximize ownership and coupling between areas. Together, such teams can develop priorities, direction, and emphasis on new products and processes. These teams can then sell their innovations to their more local colleagues and greatly improve internal technology or product transfer. Further, these problem-solving teams can evaluate their successes and failures. Such joint evaluation helps the organizations learn and reduces finger pointing and the 'not-invented-here' syndrome which together reduce learning and innovation. The most innovative organizations create these joint problem-solving teams early in the product development cycle; thus, problem solving comes to be perceived as part of the normal process, rather than a bureaucratic intrusion. For example, at Pharmacia, joint problem solving and evaluation have been institutionalized throughout the corporation and are given much credit for this firm's extraordinary innovation record.

Job design, job rotation and careers

Innovation depends on motivated employees who are willing to experiment and be creative. The design of jobs, job rotation and career paths all have important effects on the creativity of managers and their employees. Jobs with substantial autonomy, variety, and individual involvement offer intrinsic motivation to perform well. Jobs with low involvement and autonomy cannot capture an employee's enthusiasm; motivation comes only from extrinsic factors (e.g. pay). Larger jobs involve more of the individual and create greater internal drive for learning innovation.

Career paths also play an important role: individuals who spend an entire career in a single functional or product area will be more narrowly focused and less innovative than their colleagues with broader career experiences. Employees with experience in multiple areas and functions will have a more balanced view of the organization's strengths and weaknesses and a broader set of contacts from whom they can learn. Similarly, within many R&D organizations, scientists and engineers have the opportunity of pursuing either managerial or technical career tracks. Such dual ladders, when effectively implemented, can encourage innovation and specialization along both tracks.

Though an organizational structure that discourages job diversity can inhibit innovation, it is also true that a human resource system that produces too many promotions, and too quickly, can have the same effect. Firms that lead employees to expect a promotion every two years only encourage short time frames. Innovation and change take time; individuals must expect to stay in jobs long enough to influence both short- and long-term performance indicators. Thus, career-planning systems must find the right balance between the complacency bred by narrow career mobility, and the short-run mentality of job-hopping.

Education

Education programmes are also an influential tool in effecting innovation. Education and training programmes expose managers from different areas of a firm to the other disciplines and functions in the organization, to the nature and importance of innovation and change, and to skills in communication, problem solving and conflict resolution. IBM, Control Data, GTE and Pepsico all have programs in managing innovation that involve cross-sections of the corporations in joint work on innovation-related problems.

Quite apart from their substance, these educational programs provide a relaxed setting in which individuals meet and get to know a range of different individuals from throughout the organization. These informal contacts provide a valuable informed infrastructure which nurtures both individual and organizational learning and innovation. IBM's three-week innovation program, for example, provides substantial content on innovation and change; but, even more importantly, it provides an opportunity for 50 managers from around the corporation to become much better acquainted with each other and their respective areas. IBM is not alone; the most innovative firms invest substantially in the training and education of their managers.

Informal organization

Innovation is disruptive and complex work which requires close collaboration between actors who are usually quite separate. A competent set of individuals and the correct formal organization are not enough to deal with the complexities and uncertainties inherent in innovative work. The informal organization must bolster and complement the formal system. While formal organization arrangements facilitate corporate learning and innovation, individual creativity springs from a healthy informal organization. Several dimensions of the informal organization are particularly important in managing innovation.

Core values

Core values provide the basic normative foundation of a business unit. Core values are beliefs about what is good or bad, right or wrong in a particular firm. For example, IBM core values are the importance of individuals, service and excellence; Tandem's are quality, personal excellence and teamwork. A clear set of core values helps focus and motivate behavior. The most innovative firms have clear core values that provide focus in a sea of diversity, and a common objective to which disparate professionals and divisions can agree.

Some examples of core values that facilitate innovation:

- developing technology that meets users' needs;
- individual autonomy and organizational identification;
- risk taking and tolerance of failure;
- informality in problem solving;
- disciplinary and organizational effectiveness;
- high performance standards for short and long run;
- an emphasis on human resources and the importance of individual growth and development.

As these examples suggest, core values in highly innovative firms emphasize the duality so important to the innovation process. Also, core values in innovative firms are broad enough to be meaningful across a diverse organization. Thus IBM's trilogy of service, individuals and excellence is broad enough to fit a highly decentralized organization, yet is also pointed enough to guide and focus behavior. Though any organization can publicly espouse a set of core values, most innovative organizations have effectively infused their value system throughout the company.

Norms

While core values (for example, service or excellence) have no clear behavioral referents, norms do; they elaborate and specify the meaning of core values in a particular firm. Norms are expected behaviors: if they are violated, the individual or group is informally censured. For example, norms help specify dress codes, language, work standards and hours, decision-making processes, boss–subordinate relations, inter-unit communication, conflict resolution processes and the degree of risk taking and playfulness in the organization.

In general, highly innovative organizations have norms that stress informality in behavior, dress and boss–subordinate relations; high work standards and individual/group performance expectations; flexibility in decision making, problem solving and conflict resolution patterns; and strong informal linkages within and outside the organization. This informality, high work standard and exposure to multiple sources of information facilitate collaboration, learning and innovation. Less innovative firms, on the other hand, have norms which emphasize formality, standardization and operating 'by the book'.

Rewarding risk

Highly innovative organizations deftly manage the subtleties of reward and punishment. Paradoxically, they provide highly visible rewards for success but often downplay the punishment for failure. This approach may seem contradictory, but many companies have made it work. In essence, they make decisions regarding promotions, job assignments and careers with an eye toward strengthening the informal system's support for innovation and risk taking.

The cornerstone of this approach is that those who perform well—and in particular, the successful innovators—receive rapid promotion or successively more challenging assignments. It becomes clear to others in the organization that outstanding performance is the surest path to success.

On the other extreme, there is little tolerance for those whose performance falls short of the organization's standards. Those who perform poorly are encouraged to leave and, if necessary, are forced out.

We have just described a highly performance-oriented organization culture which is not particularly unique. But some very innovative organizations take the added step of creating conditions that tolerate failure—and sometimes even support it. They apply this approach to employees with an established record of performance, when their failure is the result of risk taking or experimentation, rather than incompetence or dereliction.

This attitude emboldens potential innovators: they see the likely prospect of tangible rewards for success and relatively few risks for trying something new and failing. As the belief spreads throughout the organization, the entire environment becomes increasingly innovative. An organization that has worked hard to nurture this culture is Citibank—one of the nation's most innovative corporations—where many senior executives have tried new things and 'failed'. Failure often results in assignment to the 'penalty box', or a job with less responsibility. But after spending time in a 'penalty box' assignment, people can return to a position comparable to—or even more responsible—than their 'pre-failure' job.

Innovation occurs when organizations function as effective learning systems, and learning comes through experimentation and failure. Truly innovative organizations are those where people can take risks, reap the rewards of success and survive constructive failures.

Communication networks

Informal communication networks are vital to innovation. For new products and processes, direct feedback and problem solving is much more effective than formal bureaucratic procedures. The most innovative organizations have diverse informal communication networks; people know who to call. And the calls generally solve problems, if the participants share a common set of core values and language. These informal networks are important both within the organization as well as between the organization and customers, vendors, suppliers and external professional sources. Direct contact is an effective way of keeping close to customers, competitors and technology.

Critical roles

Several informal roles are critical in the innovation process:

- *Idea generators* are those key individuals who creatively link diverse ideas. These individuals see new approaches to linking technologies to markets, products with new processes, etc. Without idea generators, organizations have very few breakthroughs.

- *Champions or internal entrepreneurs* take creative ideas (which they may or may not have generated) and bring the ideas to life. These individuals have the aggressiveness, energy and risk-taking personalities to actively champion their causes. Without internal entrepreneurs, organizations may have many ideas but few tangible innovations.
- *Gatekeepers or boundary spanners* link their more local colleagues to external information sources. They acquire, translate and distribute external information within the organization or steer their colleagues to the right sources. Without gatekeepers, organizations are deaf to outside sources of information so vital to innovation.
- *Sponsors, coaches or mentors* are senior managers who provide informal support, access to resources, and protection as new products or ventures emerge. Without sponsors and mentors, new products and processes get smothered by organizational constraints.

Each of these roles is critical; if any fails to emerge informally, innovation suffers. Formalizing these roles seems to make them disappear. While these roles cannot be formalized, they can be diagnosed, developed and nurtured. Management can develop each role through job rotation and design, formal and informal rewards, educational programs and personal encouragement.

Conflict resolution and problem-solving practices

Innovation is an inherently disruptive phenomenon; it creates conflict among various parts of the organization, each with its own perceptions and priorities. For innovation to succeed, the informal organization must value conflict and provide constructive ways to resolve it. IBM's contention management system engenders such conflict, while relying on its deeply embedded norms and values to deal with it at low levels in the organization. At Pharmacia, a shared problem-solving framework is used to diagnose the causes of conflict and to adjudicate it in ways that benefit the company.

Clearly the informal organization is critical to innovation. Informal processes can encourage risk-taking, experimentation and learning. Management must shape different informal processes in different parts of the organization (e.g. R&D vs. production), while providing informal linkages between these areas.[3] In the most innovative organizations, the informal organization allows individuals to be creative and learn, and promotes creative problem solving both within and outside the organization. While formal organization arrangements are relatively more important in high-volume, low-innovative settings, the informal organization is more important for tasks that require learning and innovation; the greater the required learning, the greater the importance of the informal organization.

Executive leadership and innovation

Beyond making choices concerning strategy, structure, individuals and the informal organization, leaders also face the crucial, personal task of infusing their organizations with a set of values and a sense of enthusiasm that will support innovative behavior. Without a clearly committed executive team which consistently emphasizes the importance of innovation, organizations inevitably become slaves of the status quo. At the first, middle and senior managerial levels, the management team must send a clear and consistent set of messages about the importance of short-term management and long-term innovation.

Several aspects of executive leadership behavior can help (or hinder) innovation:

- The executive team can develop and communicate a clear image of the organization's strategy and core values and the role of innovation in meeting the organization's strategy. If objectives are unclear and the role of innovation ambiguous, individuals and groups will focus on the status quo. The executive team must clearly and consistently articulate the importance of innovation and reinforce the necessary behavior.
- The executive team can be a role model for subordinates. Executive behavior, actions and statements send important messages to subordinates about the importance of learning and innovation. Inconsistent signals about the importance of innovation confuse subordinates; if faced with ambiguity, they will stick to the safest course, the status quo. For example, though the CEO of a large advertising agency talked a lot about creativity and innovation, his actions spoke eloquently about the importance of safe, non-controversial ad campaigns. Innovation and creativity floundered. On the other hand, Jack Welch's obsession with innovation at GE sends clear messages about the importance of new product and process innovation.
- The executive team can use formal and informal rewards to reinforce innovation. Innovative individuals and groups must receive recognition, attention and support as well as formal rewards from the executive team. If mediocrity is rewarded, or if everyone is equally rewarded by the executive team, then excellence will disappear. The management team must use all the formal and informal rewards at its disposal to consistently reinforce behavior consistent with strategy and core values.
- Organizational history has an important impact on today's innovation. Key crises, events, prior executives, organizational myths and heroes all shape and constrain current behavior. Highly stable organizations may have no tradition or precedent that fosters innovation. For example, both AT&T and General Radio had proud 75-year histories which glorified the role of engineers and minimized the relevance of marketing. For these organizations to be innovative in the 1980s, management must create new heroes, new visions and new histories.

  Executive leadership can seize upon innovative aspects of an organization's history and build new stories, myths and heroes consistent with current competitive conditions. For example, management's challenge at Xerox is to take advantage of a proud history of innovation while trying to build a new tradition that emphasizes quality and technology transfer.
- The senior executive (CEO, general manager, functional manager etc.) cannot manage the organization alone. As stated earlier, senior executives must build executive teams with appropriate technical, social and conceptual skills to accomplish diverse tasks. As the required innovation changes, so too must the nature of the executive team. Executive succession and promotion are powerful tools in innovation management. At General Radio, as noted earlier, the move to marketing and process

innovation was driven by a new management team made up of both old-line General Radio engineers and new executives skilled in marketing and manufacturing.

The senior executive must also develop effective problem-solving processes in the top team. The team must be alert to external opportunities and threats, and possess the internal dynamics to effectively deal with uncertainty. Once the decisions are made, the executive team must implement these decisions with a single voice. Publicized dissension within the top team can bury innovation in organizational politics.

• Managing innovation requires visionary executives who provide clear direction for their organizations and infuse that direction with energy and value. Observation and research indicate that such executives frequently display three types of behavior: first, they work actively on *envisioning* or articulating a credible yet exciting vision of the future. Second, they personally work on *energizing* the organization by demonstrating their own excitement, optimism, and enthusiasm. Third, they put effort into *enabling* required behaviors by providing resources, rewarding desired behaviors, building supportive organizational structures and processes, and by building an effective senior team.

SUMMARY

Organizations cannot stand still. In ever more global markets, effective performance depends more and more on the successful management of innovation. Organizations can gain competitive advantage only by managing effectively for today while simultaneously creating innovation for tomorrow. But, as we have seen, success often breeds stagnation; in dominant companies, the challenge is to rekindle the innovative spirit that led to past success.

The challenge for executives is to build congruent organizations both for today's work and tomorrow's innovation. Organizations need to have sufficient internal diversity in strategies, structures, people and processes to facilitate different kinds of innovation and to enhance organization learning.

There is perhaps no more pressing managerial problem than the sustained management of innovation. There is nothing mysterious about innovation: it doesn't just happen. Rather, it is the calculated outcome of strategic management and visionary leadership that provide the people, structures, values and learning opportunities to make it an organizational way of life.

NOTES

1. For an in-depth discussion of this congruence approach to organizational effectiveness, see D. A. Nadler and M. L. Tushman, 'A Congruence Model for Diagnosing Organizational Behavior', *Organization Dynamics (1980)*.
2. See W. Abernathy, *The Productivity Dilemma* (Baltimore, MD: Johns Hopkins Press, 1979); T. Allen, *Managing the Flow of Technology* (Cambridge, MA: MIT Press, 1983); R. M. Kanter, *The Change Masters* (New York, NY: Simon and Schuster, 1984); P. R. Lawrence and D. Dyer, *Renewing American Industry* (New York, NY: The Free Press, 1983); D. A. Nadler and M. L. Tushman, *Strategic Organization Design* (Homewood, IL: Scott, Foresman, 1986); M. L.

Tushman and W. Moore, *Readings in The Management of Innovation* (Marshfield, MA: Pitman Publishing, 1982).
3. For a detailed discussion of shaping informal processes, see Nadler and Tushman (1986), op. cit.

27

Managing the R&D–Marketing Interface

Ashok K. Gupta, S. P. Raj and David Wilemon

Whether a company is seeking consumer applications of its technologies or is developing a new product on the basis of a perceived market need, innovation success to a great extent depends on the vital link between R&D and marketing. Too often, the failure to integrate R&D and marketing in the new product development process can result in over-designed, over-priced and either obsolete or radically-advanced products with little customer value.

Building an integrated R&D–marketing effort is, however, a difficult and demanding task. Numerous problems arise in the process of mixing creativity with the reality of the market. For instance, there is R&D's notion that no one from the outside should direct their efforts, that 'managing innovation' often means stifling creativity and that R&D cannot be programmed. On the other hand, marketing may feel that R&D should be able to 'create on demand'. Moreover, a marketing group often believes that only they can understand the 'real needs' of the market.

In light of such attitudes, what can management do to achieve a high degree of integration between R&D and marketing? We conducted an empirical investigation to identify the management practices that distinguish companies achieving high and low levels of R&D–marketing integration. We found that four factors separated the high-integration companies from the low-integration ones:

- The quality of R&D–marketing relations.
- Organizational structure.
- Senior management attitudes.
- Methods used to organize new product activity.

These findings emerge from our study of the experiences of 167 high-technology companies in managing the critical R&D–marketing interface. The conclusions are based on a survey of more than 200 marketing and R&D directors from these companies. These managers were asked to identify the degree of R&D–marketing integration their organizations were able to achieve and the management practices their companies followed in managing new products.

Reprinted with permission from *Research Management*, March–April 1987, pp. 38–43

Not every factor was found in every high-integration company; nor were companies with a low level of integration found totally lacking in all respects. Nevertheless, high-integration companies generally scored high in these four areas (Tables 1 and 2). Although these factors were not perceived equally important by R&D and marketing managers, there was general agreement between them.

HOW WE CONDUCTED THE STUDY

The data for this study come from 109 marketing and 107 R&D directors involved in new product development activity in 167 high-technology firms. Companies with 1981 sales between $20 million and $1 billion, and with R&D expenditure of at least 2% of sales, were selected from the chemical, electrical, electronics, information processing, instrumentation, semiconductors and telecommunications industries. This industry classification is based on *Business Week*'s survey of Corporate R&D Expenditure, July 5, 1982. Aerospace and drug industries were not included because the heavy involvement of the federal government in these industries makes comparison with other industries difficult.

Questionnaires were mailed to R&D and marketing directors from 331 companies selected according to the above criteria. A total of 167 companies responded. Profiles of non-responding companies in terms of sales, number of employees and R&D to sales ratio were similar to the responding firms. Industry representation in R&D and marketing responses was also similar.

Both R&D and marketing managers were asked to indicate the extent of their involvement and information sharing in the new product planning and development process in their organizations. The extent of involvement and information sharing was measured by a six-point scale on 19 activities involving R&D and marketing during the innovation process. Those companies which scored an average of more than 3.5 on our 19-item integration scale were classified as high-integration companies.

Respondents were also asked to indicate the management practices of their organizations employed to manage R&D–marketing interface such as organization structure, reward systems, top management's attitude, and methods used to organize new product activity. Some managers also were interviewed to probe further into the problems of R&D–marketing coordination and how it was handled in their organizations.

R&D–MARKETING RELATIONS

The quality of the relationship existing between the R&D and marketing groups had the greatest impact on the degree of integration achieved by a company. High-integration companies were characterized by: a give-and-take relationship between R&D and marketing; an early involvement of both groups in the new product development process; and quick resolution of conflicts between R&D and marketing at the operating levels. Harmonious R&D–marketing relations also were achieved as a result of various organizational design factors and by senior management's attitudes.

Table 1. How R&D directors rate factors contributing to high integration between R&D and marketing[a]

Factors	High-integration firms, $N = 39$	Low-integration firms, $N = 68$	Level of significance[b]
R&D–marketing relations			
Give-and-take relationship exists between R&D and marketing	4.79	4.19	0.01
R&D and marketing are involved early in the new product development process	4.87	3.88	0.0003
Early resolution of conflicts between R&D and marketing	3.28	2.85	0.10
R&D perceives that marketing information lacks credibility	3.20	4.05	0.0008
Organizational structure			
Performance appraisals are based on written standards	3.87	3.71	NS
Roles, authorities, and responsibilities are clearly documented	3.87	3.65	NS
Very few actions are taken without the approval of a superior	3.43	3.42	NS
Even small matters have to be referred to someone higher up for final answer	2.33	2.67	NS
Employee participation is encouraged in the decisions related to:			
– new product development	4.46	3.97	0.02
– product modification	4.74	3.85	0.0001
Support from senior management			
Values cooperation and collaboration between R&D and marketing	5.13	4.42	0.001
Provides incentive to work on new ideas despite uncertainty of their outcome	3.95	3.70	NS
Initial failures in new product development don't reflect on individual manager's competency	4.23	3.95	NS
R&D and marketing share equally in the rewards from a successfully commercialized new product	4.05	3.39	0.01
Credit for success and blame for failure given to the group that deserves it	4.64	3.68	0.0003
Provides opportunities for R&D and marketing to communicate and understand each other	4.02	3.36	0.009

[a] Numbers represent mean scores on a scale of 1 (strongly disagree) to 6 (strongly agree) on each factor for each category of firms. Differences in the mean scores were tested for statistical significance by *T*-test. Responses from marketing managers are similar.
[b] NS means that the difference is not significant at 0.10 level.

Table 2. How companies organize their new product activities

	Percent use in	
Method	High-integration companies	Low-integration companies
Through venture teams	80	20
Through temporary task forces	72	28
Through product, project, or matrix managers	69	31
Through separate new product departments	69	31
Marketing manager runs complete new product show	60	40
Through standing committees	58	42
R&D manager runs complete new product show	50	50
Company president runs complete new product show	36	64

Give-and-take relationship

We found that in high-integration companies there was a high level of give-and-take between the R&D and marketing groups. Each group was able to challenge and confront the other in a constructive manner and each was interested in understanding the other's point of view. When conflicts did develop they were not brushed aside, ignored, or denied. A major effort was made to resolve them. Various tradeoffs such as cost, design and feature tradeoffs, for example, were weighed in an effort to ascertain if there was a common understanding of important issues. As one marketing manager stated:

We try to understand the 'pulse' of the technical people in these meetings. You simply don't do what R&D says without some questioning and probing. At the same time, we have to make certain that they understand our needs and concerns. We expect honest, frank discussions with the R&D people and they know that's how we operate.

This give-and-take attitude helps build trust and solve problems. As a result, in the high-integration companies there was a sense of integrity in their communications, and both groups felt free to disagree and discuss opposing viewpoints. In low-integration companies, R&D perceived marketing's input as lacking credibility.

We also found that in high-integration companies there were less sociocultural differences among R&D and marketing managers. This helped in achieving harmonious relations between them. Specifically, we found that more marketing managers had a technical background, they were more eager to substantiate their claims with hard data, and a larger number of R&D managers had exposure to business courses—some of them even had an MBA degree.

Early involvement

One of the key differences between those companies which achieved high-integration and those which did not was that a conscious effort was made to involve both R&D and marketing from the earliest stages of the new product development process. As one vice-president of marketing in a California-based high-tech company puts it:

Product planning, priority setting, product selection, and most functions of this type are performed jointly by our marketing group and the product development team at the initial stages in the new product development process. This facilitates communication and avoids misunderstanding later. Those activities which are clearly marketing functions or clearly design functions are handled independently, but each group is sensitive to the needs of the other group.

Another marketing manager from a laser equipment manufacturer stated that, 'R&D is brought in during the earliest stages of the product conception. We start off with a "position paper" of where we are and where we want to go. This helps us communicate with R&D about proposed new product opportunities'.

Early involvement helps reduce development delays, assists in mutual understanding of the customers' real needs and, consequently, develops products to match customers' needs.

Conflict resolution

In high-integration companies, R&D–marketing conflicts were resolved sooner and at lower organizational levels. Typical conflicts were due to personality differences, disagreements over market needs, unclear product priorities, or different views over development schedules. The senior management of high-integration firms were seldom involved in these conflicts since they were handled by the managers at lower organizational levels.

ORGANIZATIONAL STRUCTURE

Our research indicates that the organizational design of high-integration firms differed from the low-integration companies in four respects: they had clearer role definitions; more decision-making autonomy; a high degree of organizational participation in new product decisions; and minimum geographic separation between R&D and marketing.

Clarity of roles

In high-integration companies, the responsibilities of the managers were clearly articulated via policies, new product development procedures, and job descriptions. Many of these companies also had written performance standards. Nevertheless, these organizations did not appear too 'structured' in their product development approaches. As one R&D manager from a Texas-based electronics company noted, 'clear policies and procedures help us know what is expected. They remove much of the ambiguity and stress'.

Another marketing manager from a semiconductor device company commented that, 'in our organization we do not have to deal with a lot of ambiguity in terms of reporting relationships. We know who is in-charge of what activities'.

Another manager in a high-integration firm made this comment: 'The most important thing we did to increase R&D–marketing integration was to first create an informal communication process. This laid the groundwork which then helped us establish a more formal approach'.

Thus, the high-integration firms 'formalize' the need for R&D–marketing integration in their new product planning and development process. We did not find that these procedures dampened an organization's capacity to innovate.

Decentralized decision-making

High-integration companies were characterized by a high degree of decentralization, where managers were delegated authority to make 'important' decisions. On the other hand, in the low-integration companies, very few actions could be taken without approval—even small matters often had to be referred to a superior for a final answer. One R&D manager commented on the impact of having to continually seek approvals on the R&D–marketing interface this way:

We are so tightly controlled that we have to get approval from our bosses to do anything. The marketing people face the same constraints. So, when we need to make a design change we have to get the approval of our bosses and sometimes even the corporate product review committee. Our boss will often have to consult and negotiate with the marketing manager. Sometimes they will make changes we don't want or even worse they will sit on it for weeks while we are grinding our teeth for some action.

Decentralized decision-making facilitates communication between the various groups contributing to the new product development process. There is less tendency to screen unfavourable information or withhold information, as is often the case in many centralized, hierarchically-structured companies.

Increased participation

We found that high-integration firms encouraged participation at all levels within R&D and marketing regarding new product development. The increased involvement, along with the power to make decisions, helped create a climate that resulted in high creativity. Greater participation also increased the commitment to working through tough problems throughout the entire new product development process.

Physical proximity

'Out of sight, out of mind'. This phrase characterized the low-integration companies, where R&D people were usually far apart from their marketing counterparts, sometimes even a couple of hundred miles! In high-integration companies, the R&D marketing groups were often in the same building, even on the same floor.

Proximity facilitates communication, creates understanding and trust, and can reduce product development time. All this helps a company target the right product to its customers at the right time. As one marketing manager remarked:

It's just a lot easier working with R&D when their key people are just down the hall. When you have a problem or a question you don't need to fly to the West Coast or call twenty people together and have a formal meeting. You simply walk down there and say, 'Frank, my group has a problem with the design and we need to talk with you about it.' Such accessibility makes the whole development process work so much more effectively.

We found that there is a real sensitivity to close, direct communication between marketing and R&D in many of the high integration companies.

SUPPORT FROM SENIOR MANAGEMENT

Our research findings indicate that senior management plays a crucial role in creating a climate and culture conducive to a collaborative R&D–marketing effort. Senior managers in high-integration companies could be characterized as interested in promoting the need for R&D–marketing integration and tolerant of failure. They also established joint rewards for R&D and marketing's new product development efforts; and they provided opportunities for R&D and marketing to meet and discuss mutual concerns. Senior managers also took personal interest in the development of new products, were committed to innovation, and were able to balance the long and short-run interests of the company.

Promoting integration

We found that in the high-integration companies senior management valued and supported cooperation between R&D and marketing. These values were an essential part of their corporate cultures. They also emphasize the need for collaboration in their public statements, departmental reorganizations, and by personal visits to customers. Senior management in high-integration companies clearly understand that technology alone won't make successful new products. They realize that brilliant scientists can only take a company so far.

Tolerance of failure

We discovered that senior management in the high-integration companies understood that you may fail when you try something new. Moreover, senior management provided enough incentives for R&D and marketing to work on new ideas, despite the uncertainty of their outcomes. Initial failures in the attempt to develop new products were not perceived as reflecting the ultimate competence of those involved. Rather, failure was often viewed as one step in a long process toward innovation success.

Senior management also takes a long-term view of R&D and has patience and courage to wait. They usually do not cut back on R&D and product development to relieve short-term pressure on earnings.

Joint reward system

Both R&D and marketing managers in high-integration firms felt that they shared equally in the rewards from successfully commercializing a new product. They did not feel that marketing was given credit for product successes while R&D was blamed for failures, or vice versa. R&D and marketing were jointly held responsible and were jointly rewarded or blamed for the success or failure of a new product.

On the other hand, R&D managers in low-integration companies complained that they received little credit for commercial success of a new product. These managers also believed that marketers were rewarded for taking risks while they were not, and that marketing's performance measures don't facilitate R&D–marketing integration. There was a general feeling that 'collaboration does not get us anything'.

A system of dual-career ladders is used in some high-integration companies to reward R&D personnel so that they can enjoy the status, compensation and recognition of other functional specialists like marketing. The double career ladder can be combined with additional project funding or with stock options in new ventures.

Opportunities to communicate

We also found that the senior management in high-integration companies provided significantly greater opportunities for their R&D and marketing managers to communicate and understand one another's needs. Such opportunities helped R&D managers appreciate the pressures and perspectives of marketing, and assisted marketing managers in becoming more sensitive to the aspirations and limitations of R&D. These opportunities included informal interaction sessions, workshops, educational programs and rotating job assignments.

ORGANIZING NEW PRODUCT ACTIVITY

High-integration companies organized their new product activity differently than low-integration companies (Table 2). The most widely used methods among the high-integration companies were: temporary task forces; product, project or matrix managers; separate new product development departments; and venture teams.

In some cases the company president orchestrated the company's new product development process. We found that this approach was more likely to result in less integration between marketing and R&D. Other methods of organizing such as an R&D manager dominating the new product development effort, or a marketing manager being responsible for the development of new products, or a standing committee approach, were more or less equally distributed among high and low-integration companies.

Our findings regarding the use of venture teams for organizing new product activity are interesting. Venture teams are the least popular but most effective method of achieving R&D–marketing integration. Only five of the 167 companies in our study employed this as a dominant method of organizing new product activity. We suggest that venture teams can help achieve a high level of integration due to their reliance on and integration of multidisciplinary experts, e.g. marketing and R&D personnel. Team members thus become a conduit for the flow of information between a company's R&D and marketing groups.

SUMMING UP

The important lesson learned from the experiences of those companies that are able to achieve a high degree of R&D–marketing integration is that they make a deliberate effort to create and manage effective R&D–marketing relations. They treat integration as an organizational challenge and not just as a 'people' problem.

We found that high-integration companies had more productive and harmonious R&D–marketing relationships. The quality of the R&D–marketing relationship is both a result and cause of greater R&D–marketing integration efforts. These companies achieve integration by actively involving both R&D and marketing in the early phases of the new product development process and by resolving their conflicts quickly and at the lower organizational level.

Our research revealed that several organizational design issues contribute to improved R&D–marketing relations and greater integration. Clarity of roles; high degree of organizational involvement in the new product development process; decentralized decision-making; the physical proximity of R&D and marketing; and the methods for organizing new product activity were major factors in contributing to greater R&D–marketing integration.

Finally, senior management plays an important role in creating an effective interface. It is important for senior management to understand that innovation success often rests on the degree and quality of R&D–marketing integration. Moreover, senior management must take action to facilitate the integration process. We found that senior management in successful companies promote the need for R&D–marketing integration through memos and public statements; visiting customers with R&D and marketing teams; providing opportunities for managers from both departments to communicate with each other through seminars and information-sharing meetings; balancing short-term profit pressures with long-term growth prospects; and establishing joint reward systems. Finally, senior management can create a culture that rewards success as well as understands that failure is a part of the innovation process.

Building an integrative organization is a significant senior management responsibility. For high technology companies, where successful new product introduction is often equated with survival, building an effective R&D–marketing team is crucial.

ACKNOWLEDGEMENT

The authors thank Susan Thomas, research associate in the Syracuse University's Innovation Management Programme, for her helpful advice and editorial assistance.

28

Significance of Project Management Structure on Development Success

Erik W. Larson and David H. Gobeli

INTRODUCTION

'Innovate!' is one of the battle cries of business in the 1980s. In order to maintain and expand market share, companies must develop new products and services in the face of ever increasing global competition. According to Gobeli and Rudelius[1], to innovate is to successfully discover, decide and develop new products or services for delivery to the marketplace. Studies by Myers and Sweezy[2], Burgelmann[3] and Calatone and Cooper[4] reveal that most problems occur after the 'green light' has been given to develop the design and technologies necessary for producing the new product. Poor planning, breakdowns in coordination, power struggles and insufficient manpower are among the cited problems that plague this development phase.

There is considerable debate as to how to best manage the critical development phase. During the 1970s, matrix management was touted by many as the most effective means for developing new products and services (cf.[5–7]). More recently, Peters and Waterman[8] have criticized matrix management as being hopelessly bureaucratic and noncreative. They instead have championed the use of *ad hoc* task forces or project teams to develop new products. Others have argued that the matrix criticism applies only to specific forms of matrix, not matrix management in general[9]. To compound the question further, practitioners and academicians alike have questioned the importance of project management structure for project success. Several have argued that such factors as top management support, a clearly defined project mission and a cohesive project team are more critical for development success (cf.[10–13]).

The purpose of this study is to assess the relative importance of project management structure compared to other factors which are likely to contribute to project success. In addition, the relationship between alternative project management structures and project success will be examined for over 500 different development projects. This research is intended to shed light not only on the significance of project structure for development success, but also to explore the relative efficacy of different project management structures.

DESIGN OF THE STUDY

Project management structures

Galbraith[14] distinguished different types of project management systems on a continuum according to the relative influence of the project manager and functional managers involved. At one extreme is the traditional *functional organization*, whereby the development project is divided into segments and assigned to relevant functional groups with the heads of each functional group responsible for their segment of the project. The project is formally coordinated by functional and upper levels of management. At the other end of the spectrum is the project organization, or what we will refer to as a *project team*. Here a project manager is formally designated to manage a select group of specialists who work outside the normal boundaries of the organization to complete the project. Although the team members may defer to functional managers for advice and even sharing of some special resources, the project team itself has at least a core group of members that can get the bulk of the work done on their own. This approach has been popularized in the literature as 'new venture team', 'skunk works' and 'tiger team'.

Matrix is a 'mixed' organizational form in which the normal vertical hierarchy is 'overlaid' by some form of lateral authority, influence or communication. In a matrix there are usually two chains of command, one along functional lines and the other along project lines. Furthermore, participants are often assigned to multiple projects. Three different forms of matrix are commonly identified in the literature (cf.[15–17]).

A *functional matrix* occurs when the project manager's role is limited to coordinating the efforts of the functional groups involved. Functional managers are responsible for the design and completion of technical requirements within their discipline. The project manager basically acts as a staff assistant with indirect authority to expedite and monitor the project. Conversely, a *project matrix* refers to a situation in which the project manager has direct authority to make decisions about personnel and work flow activities. The functional manager's involvement is limited to providing resources and advisory support. Finally, the *balanced matrix*, is one in which the project manager and functional managers share roughly equal authority and responsibility for the project. Typically, the project manager defines what needs to be accomplished while the functional managers determine how it will be accomplished. The merger of 'what' and 'how' requires both parties to collaborate on establishing work schedules and resolving technical roadblocks.

Admittedly, this trifurcation of matrix is not as precise as the distinction between function, matrix and project team. Whether a matrix is a balanced or a project matrix is a question of degree, and there are likely to be shifts in responsibility and authority throughout the duration of a project. Still, researchers have found it meaningful to distinguish different forms of matrix in this manner (cf.[9, 18, 19]).

Research on the relative effectiveness of different project management structures is limited. Pro and con arguments for specific approaches are largely based on anecdotal evidence or armchair theorizing (cf.[20–22]). For example, Peters and Waterman[8] based their criticism of matrix on the fact that the 61 'excellent companies' they studied either did not use a matrix arrangement or had a bad experience with matrix management.

Systematic comparisons of different structures are rare and oftentimes fail to take into account other factors that contribute to success. Corey and Starr[23] surveyed 500 large manufacturing firms and reported that a project matrix or project team was more successful in developing and introducing new products. Marquis and Straight[24], in a study of 100 R&D projects, reported that a functional matrix is likely to produce better technical results while a project matrix is likely to reduce cost and schedule overruns. Another study that examined development projects in nine large firms reported that project structure influenced technical success but not necessarily economic success[25]. On the other hand, Murphy et al.[19] reported that no particular structure was associated with the success of over 600 construction and development projects. Perhaps the most rigorous study to date has been conducted by Katz and Allen[26]. Their study involving 86 R&D projects revealed that superior results were achieved with a balanced matrix in which the project manager had primary control over managing the project while the functional managers retained influence over technical details. Keller[13], however, was unable to replicate this finding and reported that group cohesiveness was a more important predictor of project performance for 32 R&D projects.

Contextual factors

In order to properly gauge the significance of project management structure for project success, other factors that are likely to contribute to success need to be accounted for. With this in mind, five variables, which represent factors external or predetermined for the specific project effort were considered. These contextual variables included project complexity, novelty of technology, clarity of objectives, priority, and resource availability. Although certainly not a complete list of all the factors that affect success, these variables are commonly cited as being among the most critical to success or failure[12].

Complexity refers to the number of different disciplines or departments involved on the project as well as the intricacy of the design itself. Novelty represents the extent to which new methods and procedures were necessary to complete the project. Complexity and novelty of technology provide an index of project difficulty, and presumably the more difficult the project the greater the likelihood of failure, independent of the project structure used.

Clarity of objectives has surfaced as a key factor contributing to success[19, 25, 27, 28]. Projects with clearly defined objectives to begin with have a clear advantage over those in which objectives are vague or undergo constant revision. This should be particularly true when considering cost and schedule criteria for success.

Another factor is the priority of the project to the parent organization. Several project managers have commented that important projects get done despite the project structure used. Furthermore, Rubin and Seelig[29] reported that the higher the level of priority the better the technical performance on R&D projects.

Finally, the degree to which sufficient resources have been made available to complete the project is likely to affect success[30]. Projects with inadequate resources are likely to be doomed to begin with regardless of the project structure used.

Project success

Currently, the project management literature is reassessing what constitutes a successful project. Some have advocated using customer satisfaction, market share and technological breakthrough (cf.[31, 32]). Since measures of these factors as well as other objective indicators of performance that are comparable across different projects have yet to be developed, previous research has relied on perceptual indicators of success (cf.[13, 26]). De Wit[33] has argued that the bottom-line indicator of success is whether key personnel associated with the project are satisfied with the overall results, and that such factors as controlling costs and meeting the schedule ultimately take a back seat to this global appraisal.

In this study, success was gauged according to the traditional criteria of cost, schedule and technical performance, as well as overall results. The interrelationship between these criteria varies. Often projects are termed a technical success despite being behind schedule and over budget. Conversely, projects may be ahead of schedule and under budget but still be a technical failure. This illustrates why assessment of performance is at least somewhat subjective. Project success will therefore be considered a multivariate variable in the attempt to approach a global view of success.

Summary

A schematic description of the study is presented in Figure 1. First, the relationship between project management structure and project success will be examined to determine whether success varies by structure used. This relatively simple analysis will be complemented by a more elaborate design in which external factors which are likely to affect success are controlled. Project success will be examined in terms of meeting schedule, controlling costs, technical performance and overall results.

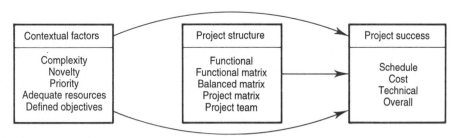

Figure 1. Research Framework.

METHOD

Sample

This study is part of a research programme sponsored by the Project Management

Institute (PMI). PMI is the professional association for practitioners of project management with over 5000 members worldwide. Data were collected by means of a questionnaire mailed to randomly selected PMI members in both Canada and the United States. Repeated mailings and reminders yielded a 64% response rate. This study is based on the 547 respondents who reported that they were primarily involved in development projects and who responded to a series of questions concerning a recently completed development project they were familiar with.

Over 30% of the respondents were either project managers or directors of project management programs within their firm. Sixteen percent were members of top management (i.e. president, vice president or division manager) while 26% were managers in functional areas such as marketing, operations and accounting. The remaining respondents were specialists working on the project. Eighty percent share the common experience of having been a project manager some time during their career. Collectively the sample averaged six years of project management experience.

The sample represents a wide variety of industries. For example, 14% were involved in developing pharmaceutical products, 10% were in aerospace, and 10% were involved in developing computer and data processing products. Among the other industries represented in lesser numbers were telecommunications, medical instruments, glass products, petrochemical products, software development and housewares goods.

Measures

The questionnaire was pretested on a group of eight project managers to check for consistency of comprehension. Respondents were also asked to indicate on the survey the extent to which they were confident they understood the questions. Only 1% of the respondents indicated that they were not confident and these responses were removed from the sample.

Project management structure

Respondents were provided with brief descriptions of each structure (see Appendix) and asked to choose the one which best described the primary structure used to complete the project. The distribution of projects according to structure was as follows: functional organization, $n = 71$; functional matrix, $n = 142$; balanced matrix, $n = 90$; project matrix, $n = 156$; and project team, $n = 87$.

Project success

Data collection procedures (mailed questionnaire) and the need to generate a large enough sample to draw meaningful comparisons prohibited the use of multirater evaluations of success which have been employed in other studies[13, 26]. Respondents were simply asked to evaluate their project according to (a) meeting schedule, (b) controlling cost, (c) technical performance and (d) overall performance with a response format of 'successful', 'marginal' and 'unsuccessful'. Although other researchers have relied on similar perceptual measures of success[18, 19, 33], individual appraisals do not provide a strong basis of measurement. The results of this study should therefore be considered exploratory.

Contextual factors

Information regarding clarity of project objectives, sufficient resources, complexity, novelty of technology, and project priority were obtained from Likert scaled single item questions. Respondents were asked to indicate the extent to which they agreed with each of the following statements: project objectives were clearly defined, funding and man-power were sufficient to complete the project, the project was complex, the project required no new technologies, and the project had high priority within the organization. Recognizing that not all of the respondents were likely to be in a position to assess each of these factors, they were given the option of responding 'don't know'. These responses were omitted from relevant analyses.

The means, standard deviations and intercorrelations of the success and contextual variables are presented in Table 1.

Table 1. Descriptive statistics

| Variables | $\overline{X}$ | SD | Intercorrelations | | | | | | | |
			1	2	3	4	5	6	7	8
Project success										
1. Meeting schedule	2.14	0.83	–							
2. Controlling cost	2.12	0.79	0.51	–						
3. Technical performance	2.53	0.66	0.34	0.30	–					
4. Overall results	2.38	0.70	0.56	0.46	0.62	–				
Contextual covariates										
5. Clearly defined objectives	3.43	1.38	0.32	0.30	0.27	0.34	–			
6. Sufficient resources	3.23	1.28	0.24	0.15	0.12	0.19	0.19	–		
7. Novelty of technologies	3.30	1.38	0.01	0.01	0.02	0.02	0.03	−0.03	–	
8. Complexity	3.92	1.08	0.05	0.06	0.07	0.10	0.05	0.02	0.33	–
9. Priority	3.92	1.17	0.23	0.07	0.15	0.22	0.14	0.20	0.08	0.28

RESULTS

Project structure and project success

Multivariate analysis of variance confirmed that project structure was significantly related to the measures of project success (Wilks Lambda 0.862, $F = 4.84, p < 0.001$). In order to examine this relationship further, individual analysis of variance was performed for each of the four criteria measures. The results of these analyses are reported in Table 2.

Table 2. ANOVA results for success criteria by project structure

Project structure	N	Controlling cost		Meeting schedule		Technical performance		Overall results	
		$\bar{X}$	SD	$\bar{X}$	SD	$\bar{X}$	SD	$\bar{X}$	SD
A. Functional organization	71	1.76	0.83	1.77	0.83	2.30	0.77	1.96	0.84
B. Functional matrix	142	1.91	0.77	2.00	0.85	2.37	0.73	2.21	0.75
C. Balanced matrix	90	2.39	0.73	2.15	0.82	2.64	0.61	2.52	0.61
D. Project matrix	156	2.64	0.76	2.30	0.79	2.67	0.57	2.54	0.66
E. Project team	87	2.22	0.82	2.32	0.80	2.64	0.61	2.52	0.70
Total sample	546	2.12	0.79	2.14	0.83	2.53	0.66	2.38	0.70
F statistics		10.38**		6.94**		7.42**		11.45**	
Scheffe results[a]		A,B < C,D,E, E < D		A,B < C < D,E		A,B < C,D,E		A,B < C,D,E	

[a] Significant differences between pairs of group means at the 0.05 level.
** $p < 0.01$.

Table 2 reveals that project structure was significantly related to each of the success measures. Examination of subgroup means indicates a consistent pattern across all four measures of success. New development projects which used the traditional functional organization had the lowest level of success in controlling cost, meeting schedule, achieving technical performance and overall results. This was followed by projects using the functional matrix which fared slightly better than the functional projects. On the other hand, projects which used the balanced matrix, project matrix or the project team appear to do equally well on all four measures of success.

Further information on the relative effectiveness of different project structures is provided by the Scheffe tests for significant differences between pairs of group means. Projects using either a functional organization or a functional matrix had a significantly lower success rate than the other three structures. No significant differences were found among the project matrix, balanced matrix and project team with the exception of meeting schedule and controlling cost. Projects using either a project matrix or a project team were more successful in meeting schedule than the balanced matrix. Conversely, projects using a project matrix were better able to control costs than those using a project team. Overall, the results indicate that project success does vary according to structure and that the most successful projects were ones that used a balanced matrix, project team, and especially a project matrix.

These results may have been tempered by self-interest since a significant portion of the sample was project managers. To examine this potential bias, a two-way analysis of variance was performed on each of the four success criteria with job title (top management, functional manager and project manager) and structure being the two factors. Neither job title nor the interaction were found to be significant, indicating that executives, functional managers and project managers shared similar perceptions of success according to project structure used.

Project structure, project success and contextual factors

Since the contextual factors are interval scales and project structure is a categorical variable, an analysis of covariance design was used to examine the significance of project structure for success, controlling for contextual factors. First, the multivariate analysis revealed that project structure was significantly related to project success even when the five contextual factors were controlled for (Wilks Lambda 0.859, $F = 4.22$, $p < 0.01$). The nature of this effect is revealed in the series of ANCOVA analyses conducted for each of the four success measures which are reported in Tables 3 and 4.

Table 3 reveals that project structure has a significant effect on all four success measures even when the portion of the variance explained by the contextual factors is controlled for. More specifically, the entire model explained 16% of the variance in controlling cost with the contextual factors accounting for 10% and project structure explaining 6%. Twenty-one percent of the variance in meeting schedule was explained with the contextual factors accounting for 16% of the variance and project structure explaining the remaining 5%. Only 13% of the variance in technical performance was explained by the model. Contextual factors explained 8% of the variance while project structure accounted for 5%. Twenty-two percent of the variance in overall results was explained with contextual factors accounting for 15% and project structure explaining an additional 7%.

Clearly defined objectives was the only contextual factor to be significantly related to each of the success criteria and this effect was by far the strongest of any of the variables. Sufficient resources was related to controlling cost, technical performance and overall results, but not meeting schedule. Project priority was related to meeting schedule, technical performance and overall results. Neither novelty of technology nor project complexity was related to any of the success measures. A skewed distribution ($\overline{X} = 3.92$, SD = 1.08, range 1–5) probably mitigated the effects of project complexity on project success with most projects being rated as very complex. Such an explanation cannot be provided for novelty of technology which displayed a more even distribution ($\overline{X} = 3.30$, SD = 1.38, range 1–5).

Table 4 reports the adjusted deviation from the grand mean for each of the success criteria. The data provide a means for assessing the relative effect of each project structure when the contextual factors are controlled for. The results tend to support the simpler analysis of variance results. Development projects using the functional organization suffered the most with regards to cost, schedule, technical performance and overall results. Projects which relied on a functional matrix experienced similar problems, but to a lesser extent. Projects using a balanced matrix were better able to control costs but tended to lag behind in meeting schedule. Projects using either a project matrix or project team were better able to meet schedule and to a lesser extent control cost. No clear differences were found between the balanced matrix, project matrix and project team on technical performance and overall results.

DISCUSSION

This research confirmed that the success of development projects does vary according to which project management structure is used and that project structure does have a

Table 3. Relationships between project structure and project success controlling for contextual factors

	DF	Controlling cost			Meeting schedule			Technical performance			Overall results		
		SS	F	R^2	SS	F	R^2	SS	F	R^2	SS	F	R^2
Contextual covariates	5	32.5	11.3**	0.10	55.9	19.1**	0.16	19	9.3**	0.08	39.1	7.8**	0.15
1. Objectives clearly defined	1	24.7	42.9**		26.1	44.6**		12.3	12.4**		21.5	48.6**	
2. Novelty of technology	1	0.2	0.2		0.1	0.1		0.1	0.1		0.5	1.1	
3. Complexity	1	0.1	0.1		0.1	0.1		0.1	0.1		0.3	0.8	
4. Sufficient resources	1	2.7	4.6*		7.8	13.3**		0.6	0.6		2.1	4.7*	
5. Priority	1	0.1	0.1		7.5	12.8**		2.3	2.3*		5.7	12.9**	
Factor													
Project structure	4	18.5	8.0**	0.06	16.1	6.9**	0.05	10.1	6.1**	0.05	18.4	10.4**	0.07
Total explained	9	50.8	9.8**	0.16	72.0	13.6**	0.21	29.2	7.9**	0.13	57.5	14.5**	0.22
Residual		266.7			271			190.8			204.8		

Table 4. Deviation from grand mean of success criteria adjusted for contextual covariates

Project structure	Controlling cost	Meeting schedule	Technical performance	Overall results
Functional organization	−0.36	−0.43	−0.26	−0.45
Functional matrix	−0.19	−0.08	−0.15	−0.13
Balanced matrix	0.24	−0.01	0.11	0.12
Project matrix	0.11	0.16	0.13	0.15
Project team	0.12	0.16	0.09	0.14
Grand mean	2.10	2.12	2.52	2.36

significant effect on success even when other determinants are considered. Still, the magnitude of the effect is not great, with 7% being the highest percentage of variance explained by structure. The combined model including structure and other contextual determinants of success was able to explain as much as 22% of the variance in success. These results testify to the complex nature of project success.

Among the contextual factors, clearly defined objectives was by far the strongest and most consistent predictor of project success. This supports previous research which has highlighted the importance of clearly defining the mission of a project before undertaking it. Sufficient resources and project priority were also related to a lesser extent to project success. The insignificance of project complexity may be attributable to insufficient variance to gauge its effect on success. The failure of novelty of technology is more puzzling; perhaps more rigorous measurement techniques would have revealed an effect on project success.

Comparisons of individual project structures revealed that the functional organization is clearly an inferior means for managing a development project. To a lesser extent, the same was true for projects using a functional matrix which were found to lag behind the other three project structures. The relative strengths and weaknesses of the balanced matrix, project matrix and project team were less discernible. The balanced matrix appears to have an advantage in controlling cost while the project matrix and project team were better able to meet schedule. All three structures achieved comparable results with regards to technical performance and overall results.

Before pursuing the implications of the findings it is important to note their limitations. First, this study was unable to capture the dynamic nature of product development. Oftentimes over the course of a large project, different project structures may be used at different phases of the project. Similarly, different structures may operate at different levels of a specific project. Project success was measured only according to project objectives; Allen[35] has warned that while specific project structures may lead to project success they may do so to the detriment of other organizational activities over the long run. Furthermore, a number of other contextual factors (i.e. competence of project manager, size of project) are also likely to affect project success, but were not included in the analyses. Finally, one should be reminded that individual perceptions of success do not provide a firm basis for evaluation and that the results of this study should be considered exploratory. Future research which combines multirater evaluations with objective indicators of project performance is needed to amplify the reported findings.

Recognizing these limitations, several conclusions can be drawn from this study of over 500 development projects. First, the findings confirm the notion that the traditional functional organization is ill equipped to foster development projects. The conventional hierarchical management organization is generally incapable of dealing with the added complexity and information demands of a development project. Delegating project segments according to functional expertise contributes to bottlenecks and suboptimization since there is a tendency for functional departments to become preoccupied with only their segment of the project.

Second, the results contradict previous research which reported that superior technical results are obtained with a functional matrix due to the heavy concentration of functional expertise[24]. The functional matrix was inferior to the balanced and project matrix with regards to technical performance as well as the other three measures of success. This suggests that technical quality does not necessarily have to be sacrificed when moving to a matrix structure which allocates greater control and responsibility to the project manager.

Third, the results do not support the recent criticism levelled by Peters and Waterman[8] at matrix management. Nor do the findings support their contention that task forces or project teams are the most effective vehicles for product development. Both the balanced matrix and project matrix were able to achieve comparable results as a project team. If anything, the data suggests that a project matrix is the superior form of project management since it outperformed the balanced matrix in meeting schedule and outperformed the project team in controlling cost.

Still, the fact that all three structures were found to be relatively equal in terms of technical and overall performance suggests a contingency perspective. That is, there is no one best way to manage a development project, but rather it depends upon the nature of the project and the requirements of the organization. For example, project teams have been recommended for high priority projects in which time is of the essence[17]. Both IBM and Apple used this approach to bring the PC and MacIntosh to the marketplace in record-breaking time. Alternatively, either a project or balanced matrix is advisable when an organization can not afford the luxury of tieing up manpower and resources on one project and need to share them across multiple projects[36]. Goggin[7] cited this as one of the principal reasons why matrix management is used at Dow-Corning.

Finally, previous discussions of the relative advantages and disadvantages of different project structures need to be put in a proper perspective given the overall results of this study. Although significant, project structure explained only a modest amount of success variance. This suggests that the importance of project management structure may be exaggerated in the literature, and that there might be more fundamental reasons for why some development projects fail while others succeed. Future research will need to look at the interrelationship between structural factors and project activities if effective models of project success are going to be developed.

APPENDIX. PROJECT MANAGEMENT STRUCTURES

Functional organization. The project is divided into segments and assigned to relevant functional areas and/or groups within functional areas. The project is coordinated by functional and upper levels of management.

Functional matrix. A person is formally designated to oversee the project across different functional areas. This person has limited authority over functional people involved and serves primarily to plan and coordinate the project. The functional managers retain primary responsibility for their specific segments of the project.

Balanced matrix. A person is assigned to oversee the project and interacts on an equal basis with functional managers. This person and the functional managers jointly direct workflow segments and approve technical and operational decisions.

Project matrix. A manager is assigned to oversee the project and is responsible for the completion of the project. The functional manager's involvement is limited to assigning personnel as needed and providing advisory expertise.

Project team. A manager is put in charge of a project team composed of a core group of personnel from several functional areas and/or groups, assigned on a full-time basis. The functional managers have no formal involvement.

REFERENCES

1. Gobeli, D.H. and Rudelius, W. R. (1985) 'Managing Innovation: Lessons from the Cardiac Pacing Industry', *Sloan Manag. Rev.* (Summer): 29–43.
2. Myers, S. and Sweezy, E. E. (1978) 'Why Innovations Fail', *Technol. Rev.* (Mar./Apr.): 40–46.
3. Burgelmann, R. A. (1984) 'Managing the Internal Corporate Venturing Process', *Sloan Manag. Rev.* (Winter): 33–48.
4. Calatone, R. and Cooper, R. G. (1981) 'New Product Scenarios: Prospects for Success', *J. Marketing* (Spring): 48–60.
5. Galbraith, J. (ed.) (1971a) *Matrix Organizations: Organization Design for High Technology*, Cambridge, MA: MIT Press.
6. Sayles, L. (1976) 'Matrix Management: The Structure with a Future', *Organizational Dynamics* (Autumn): 2–17.
7. Goggin, W. C. (1974) 'How the Multidimensional Structure Works at Dow-Corning', *Harvard Bus. Rev.* (Jan./Feb.): 54–65.
8. Peters, T. and Waterman, R. (1982) *In Search of Excellence*. New York: Harper & Row.
9. Larson, E. W. and Gobeli, D. H. (1987) 'Matrix Management: Contradictions and Insights', *Calif. Manag. Rev.* (Summer): 126–138.
10. Cooper, J. G. and Kleinschmidt, H. (1986) 'Factors Contributing to Project Success', *J. Product Innovation Manag.*, **3**: 173–182.
11. Gobeli, D. H. and Larson, E. W. (1986) 'Barriers to Project Success', in *Measuring Success*, Brunies, R. and Menard, P. (eds) Drexel Hill, PA: Project Management Institute: 85–94.
12. Pinto, J. K. and Slevin, D. P. (1987) 'Critical Factors in Successful Project Implementation', *IEEE Trans. Eng. Manag.*, **EM–34**: 22–27.
13. Keller, R. T. (1986) 'Predictors of the Performance of Projects Groups in R&D Organizations', *Acad. Manag. J.*, **29**: 715–726.
14. Galbraith, J. (1971) 'Matrix Organization Designs—How to Combine Functional and Project Forms', *Bus. Horizons*: 29–40.
15. Larson, E. W. and Gobeli, D. H. (1985) 'Project Management Structures: Is There a Common Language?', *Project Manag. J.*, **16**: 40–44.
16. Vasconcellos, E. and Hemsley, J. 'The Design of the Matrix Structure for R&D Organizations', presented at the 1981 PMI Conf., Boston, MA.
17. Youker, R. (1977) 'Organization Alternatives for Project Managers', *Manag. Rev.*: 46–53.
18. Might, R. J. (1984) 'An Evaluation of the Effectiveness of Project Control Systems', *IEEE Trans. Eng. Manag.*, **EM–31**: 127–137.
19. Murphy, D. C., Baker, B. N. and Fisher, D. (1974) 'Determinants of Project Success', Nat. Tech. Inform. Serv., Springfield, VA, tech. rep.

20. Avots, I. (1969) 'Why Does Project Management Fail', *Calif. Manag. Rev.*, **12**: 77–82.
21. Cleland, D. I. (1964) 'Why Project Management?' *Bus. Horizons*: 81–88.
22. Sinclair, J. M. (1984) 'Is the Matrix Really Necessary?' *Project Manag. J.*: 49–52.
23. Corey, E. R. and Starr, S. A. (1971) *Organization Strategy: A Marketing Approach*. Boston, MA: Harvard Univ.
24. Marquis, D. G. and Straight, D. M. (1965) *Organizational Factors in Project Performance*. Washington, DC: NASA.
25. Rubenstein, A. H., Chakrabarti, A. K., O'Keefe, R. D., Souder, W. E. and Young, H. C. (1976) 'Factors Influencing Innovation Success at the Project Level', *Res. Manag.*: 15–20.
26. Katz, R. and Allen, T. J. (1985) 'Project Performance and the Locus of Influence in the R&D Matrix', *Acad. Manag. J.*, **28**: 67–87.
27. Bergen, S. A. and Pearson, A. W. (1983) 'Project Management and Innovation in the Scientific Instrument Industry', *IEEE Trans. Eng. Manag.*, **EM–30**: 194–199.
28. Souder, W. E. and Chakrabarti, A. K. (1978) 'The R&D/Marketing Interface: Results from an Empirical Study of Innovation Projects', *IEEE Trans. Eng. Manag.*, **EM–25**: 88–93.
29. Rubin, I. M. and Seelig, W. (1967) 'Experience as a Factor in the Selection and Performance of Project Managers', *IEEE Trans. Eng. Manag.*, **EM–14**: 72–81.
30. Cleland, D. I. and King, W. R. (1983) *Systems Analysis and Project Management*. New York: McGraw-Hill.
31. Cleland, D. I. (1986) 'Measuring Success: The Owner's Viewpoint', in *Measuring Success*, Brunies, R. and Menard, P. (eds) Drexel Hill, PA: Project Management Institute: 6–13.
32. Stuckenbruck, L. C. (1986) 'Who Determines Project Success?', in *Measuring Success*, Brunies, R. and Menard, P. (eds) Drexel Hill, PA: Project Management Institute: 85–94.
33. de Wit, A. (1986) 'Measuring Project Success: An Illusion', in *Measuring Success*, Brunies, R. and Menard, P. (eds) Drexel Hill, PA: Project Management Institute: 13–21.
34. Might, R. J. and Fischer, W. A. (1985) 'The Role of Structural Factors in Determining Project Management Success', *IEEE Trans. Eng. Manag.*, **EM–32**: 71–77.
35. Allen, T. J. (1984) 'Organizational Structure, Information Technology, and R&D Productivity', *IEEE Trans. Eng. Manag.*, **EM–31**: 212–217.
36. Davies, S. M. and Lawrence, P. R. (1977) *Matrix*. Reading, MA: Addison-Wesley.

Index